EVOLUTIONARY TRENDS IN FORAMINIFERA

EVOLUTIONARY TRENDS IN FORAMINIFERA

A COLLECTION OF PAPERS DEDICATED TO

I. M. VAN DER VLERK

ON THE OCCASION OF HIS 70TH BIRTHDAY

edited by

G. H. R. VON KOENIGSWALD
J. D. EMEIS
W. L. BUNING
C. W. WAGNER

ELSEVIER PUBLISHING COMPANY
AMSTERDAM – LONDON – NEW YORK
1963

SOLE DISTRIBUTORS FOR THE UNITED STATES AND CANADA

AMERICAN ELSEVIER PUBLISHING COMPANY, INC.

52, VANDERBILT AVENUE, NEW YORK 17, N. Y.

SOLE DISTRIBUTORS FOR GREAT BRITAIN

ELSEVIER PUBLISHING COMPANY LIMITED

12B, RIPPLESIDE COMMERCIAL ESTATE

RIPPLE ROAD, BARKING, ESSEX

LIBRARY OF CONGRESS CATALOG CARD NUMBER 62–18142

WITH 101 ILLUSTRATIONS, 18 PLATES AND 11 TABLES

LIST OF CONTRIBUTORS

Dr. T. Barnard
University College Department of Geology
Gower Street
London, W. C. 1 (Great Britain)

Dr. F. Brotzen
Sveriges Geologiska Undersökning
Stockholm (Sweden)

Prof. Dr. Maria B. Città-Sironi
Instituto di Geologia della Università di Milano
Piazzale Gorini 15
Milan (Italy)

Dr. C. W. Drooger
Mineralogisch-Geologisch Instituut der Rijksuniversiteit
Oude Gracht 320
Utrecht (The Netherlands)

Prof. Dr. C. O. Dunbar
Director Emeritus Peabody Museum Yale University
New Haven, Conn. (U.S.A.)

Prof. Dr. M. F. Glaessner
University of Adelaide
Adelaide (Australia)

Dr. H. Hiltermann
Bundesanstalt für Bodenforschung
Wiesenstrasse 1
Hannover (Germany)

Dr. L. Hottinger
Service Carte Géologique Ministère du Commerce, de
l'Industrie, des Mines, de l'Artisinat et de la Marine
Marchande
Rabat (Morocco)

Dr. R. Lagaaij
Koninklijke/Shell Exploratie en Produktie Laboratorium
Volmerlaan 6
Rijswijk (The Netherlands)

Prof. Dr. H. J. Mac Gillavry
Geologisch Instituut der Gemeente Universiteit
Nieuwe Prinsengracht 130
Amsterdam (The Netherlands)

Prof. Dr. A. Papp
Paläontologisches Institut der Universität
Dr. Karl-Lueger Ring 1–3
Vienna I (Austria)

Dr. P. Rat
Université de Dijon Faculté des Sciences
Laboratoire de Géologie
Boulevard Gabriël
Dijon (France)

Dr. D. M. Rauzer-Chernousova
Geologicheskii Institut Akademii Nauk S.S.S.R.
Pyzhevskyi 7
Moscow (U.S.S.R.)

Prof. Dr. H. Schaub
Naturhistorisches Museum
Augustinergasse 2
Basel (Switzerland)

Dr. A. H. Smout
Exploration Division British Petroleum Research Centre
Chertsey Road
Sunbury-on-Thames, Middlesex (Great Britain)

B. F. M. COLLET, ad. phot. del.

PREFACE

G. H. R. VON KOENIGSWALD

Geological Institute of the State University of Utrecht,
Utrecht (The Netherlands)

The results of palaeontological investigations are published in so many different periodicals, yearbooks, reports, excursion guides and other forms of publicity, and moreover in so many different languages, that even the specialist has difficulty in keeping completely informed in his own field.

From time to time, it is necessary to survey a subject in order to clearly ascertain the state of affairs in it, and to point out ecological, stratigraphic and phylogenetic consequences.

In few groups has such an enormous body of material been collected and described as in that of the Foraminifera, because here scientific curiosity and economic interest coincide. With so many data available, we are arriving at the stage at which phylogeny and evolution can be studied in detail, which is of great importance to biologists, geneticists and the general reader interested in the fascinating problem of evolution. The present work discusses *Evolutionary Trends in Foraminifera,* in a collective volume.

This book has been published as an *Anniversary Volume* in honour of Professor I. M. VAN DER VLERK, to commemorate his 70th birthday, on the 31st of January 1962. He recently relinquished the chair of Palaeontology and Stratigraphy at the University of Leyden, which he had occupied for twenty-three years.

In the East Indies, together with his friend the late Professor J. H. F. UMBGROVE, he formulated a letter classification for the Tertiary, based on a careful study of the larger Foraminifera. This was a work of fundamental importance for the unravelling of the Tertiary stratigraphy in that part of the world, and ever since then, Professor VAN DER VLERK — who has shown a wide interest in other fields of palaeontology as well — has been an acknowledged leader in the field of micropalaeontology.

Among the gifts he will receive on his birthday, he will find this book as a token of personal friendship and scientific appreciation. On behalf of the committee I wish to thank colleagues from all over the world who have responded to our invitation to bring together a series of special papers concerning a sphere of research in which Professor VAN DER VLERK himself is still enthusiastically active.

CONTENTS

PROFESSOR VAN DER VLERK

AN APPRECIATION

R. LAGAAIJ

Koninklijke/Shell Exploratie en Produktie Laboratorium, Rijswijk (The Netherlands)

"The husky voice of the little grey professor sounded through the bright lecture-room. Gently satyrical, quietly incisive . . . Now and again, he interrupted his narrative to interject some anecdote or subtle witticism." It is tempting to wonder whether the author, DEN TEX, at that time one of his students, had the image of Professor VAN DER VLERK in his mind's eye when he wrote his description of a lecture on human palae- ontology[1], for surely, in these fragmentary impressions, there does lie a strong element of resemblance.

For the last thirty-three years, this little grey professor has played an important part in turning successive generations of geology students at Leyden University into geologists and, at the same time, in turning them into well-rounded human beings. The thought that Professor VAN DER VLERK's teaching career has now come to an end is thus one that must give us pause.

After six years with the Dienst van de Mijnbouw in Nederlandsch-Indië, a period during which he erected a monument to himself in the form of a stratigraphic subdivision of the Tertiary, based on Foraminifera (the famous Letter Classification of VAN DER VLERK and UMBGROVE, 1927), Dr. VAN DER VLERK was in 1928 appointed *privaat–docent* at Leyden University. This led to a readership, which was followed by his being appointed professor extraordinarius in 1938 and full professor in 1947.

There is good reason for offering our retrospective congratulations to those who were responsible for making this addition to the teaching staff of Leyden University. They had managed to procure someone who, on the one hand, was predestined to engage in scientific work by both training and inclination and who, on the other hand, had learned from his own experience to keep practical ends in view; someone, that is to say, who would be pre-eminently at home in our remarkably dualistic system of scientific education, which not only demands that the teacher should be capable of scientific achievements, but also lays emphasis on the task of teaching, of preparing others to take their place in the worlds of pure and applied science. Study or lecture- room? Microscope or slide projector? Both facets were to claim his attention.

VAN DER VLERK's lectures left a lasting impression on the mind. They were borne up by the force of the inspiration he gained from the subjects he taught, palaeontology

---

[1] DEN TEX, E., 1946. *Pithecanthropus erectus*. Kroonder, Bussum.

and historical geology[1]. Not a gifted speaker by nature, he succeeded in capturing and holding the attention of his audiences by his thorough preparation beforehand, his strict adherence to the ten commandments of good oratory and, perhaps more important than either of these, his exercise of that most human of gifts: humour. This was no studious hermit speaking, but a master of the telling anecdote and of the character-in-a-nutshell. How quick he has always been to see the humorous side of any situation. How few they must be who have not left his lecture-room with a smile on their lips, who have not left his study with a smile in their hearts.

Professor VAN DER VLERK often drew his students' attention to the dilemma that faces those starting out on a career of university teaching: one cannot give lectures adequately if one has not first embodied the material in a book, while, on the other hand, the writing of such a book can only be undertaken satisfactorily after several years' experience of lecturing. It is typical of VAN DER VLERK, the perfectionist, that he should unmistakably have chosen the latter alternative. The first edition of his best-seller, *Geheimschrift der Aarde* (The Earth's Secret Code), which was written in close co-operation with KUENEN, dates only from 1941, *i.e.*, thirteen years after the beginning of his teaching career.

While, then, his first book can be said to have been preceded by an attempt to compromise, his second major work, *Nederland in het IJstijdvak* (The Netherlands in the Ice Age), written in conjunction with FLORSCHÜTZ, was born precisely as a result of his unwillingness to compromise. The forcible closing of Leyden University by the occupying power in November 1940, and the threat of persecution as a reprisal for his active part in the stubborn resistance offered by that "Hornets Nest", compelled Professor VAN DER VLERK to go into hiding with his family in a forest hut on the Veluwe. Here, in the quiet countryside, and no doubt inspired by a landscape that had largely been given its present form by the great ice-sheets, there took shape that remarkable *profétie du Passé*, that brilliant synthesis of our country's Pleistocene history, with its many original illustrations of a fauna and flora that are now for the most part exotic or extinct. It is a pity that this book, which contains so many elements of general scientific interest, is only available in Dutch[2].

In addition to these two books, he has produced a large number of smaller publications, which, both chronologically and by subject, can be arranged in three categories. The first comprises publications that are the result of his studies in the Netherlands East Indies and deal with the stratigraphy (based on the larger Foraminifera) of that area. To the second belong papers concerning the Pleistocene stratigraphy of the Netherlands and adjacent countries, while into the third fall his studies of the evolution of the shell structure of the foraminiferal genus *Lepidocyclina*. Viewing his works as a whole, we may conclude that VAN DER VLERK the scientist must be numbered among the specialists, but, nevertheless, a specialist in a diversity of subjects.

---

[1] After 1938: historical geology and palaeontology, a subtle shift of emphasis.
[2] This drawback has only partially been remedied by the subsequent publication of VAN DER VLERK, I. M. and FLORSCHÜTZ, F., 1953. The palaeontological base of the subdivision of the Pleistocene in the Netherlands. *Koninkl. Ned. Akad. Wetenschap. Verhandel., Afdel. Nat.*, 20 : 1–58.

VAN DER VLERK's teaching has not been limited solely to the giving of lectures and the writing of books or articles, the field too, has been his lecture-room, and an important one at that. Once, and often twice, a year, he led groups of students on excursions to the classical exposures in England, Belgium, France and Germany. In this way, Professor VAN DER VLERK has, one might say, been "capped" thirty-nine times. Rather than conduct his students around the various exposures like so many sheep, he preferred to stimulate them to see and think for themselves and to gain in understanding by letting them do the work, by letting them take sections and by getting them to write excursion reports. Is it a wonder that the memory of these excursions remains so clearly in one's mind? Here, amid natural grandure, in a quarry or on the shore at the foot of a steep cliff, the student lost his natural feeling of shyness for the Professor and came to appreciate VAN DER VLERK the man.

Let there be no misunderstanding about this. If ever there was a man who made himself freely available to his students, showed them the warmth of his kindness and was aware of their situation with regard to their studies and their private lives, it was VAN DER VLERK. He knew all of them by name. It is only recently that he has broken with this custom, for as he himself has said, there was a danger that for every name of a student he would henceforth remember there would be the name of a fossil he would forget.

In 1955, Professor VAN DER VLERK was appointed Director of the National Museum of Geology and Mineralogy at Leyden. His task, already by no means light, was thereby made considerably more onerous. Here, too, he unhesitatingly applied his great energy and talent for organisation to the business of dressing this great shopwindow of geology in an attractive fashion and of making it what it should in the first place be, a medium of visual education for the public. His own words testify to the clarity with which he understood this need: "Any visitor who is used to viewing exhibitions in museums of art will feel somewhat strange in a natural history museum such as ours. For, in a museum of art, each separate exhibit is intended to attract the visitor's undivided attention. In a natural history museum, on the other hand, each section should be the embodiment of a guiding principle. In this respect, . . . we have had two aims in view. In the first place, we have tried to arrange the material in such a way that it can be easily viewed, and in the second, we have sought to make the descriptions short, while providing the maximum amount of information . . ."[1]. When the new director took up his post, a "wind of change" blew through the exhibition rooms. The dark, densely packed, wooden showcases, standing at waist height and dating from the previous century, were replaced by modern glass "aquariums" at eyelevel, and in them only a few outstanding exhibits were displayed. Explanations were in many cases brought up to date and improved. Under VAN DER VLERK's stimulating leadership, his staff of assistants became a close-knit team. He was constantly striving, by arranging film-shows and lectures, by buying collections, by encouraging exchanges

[1] VAN DER VLERK, I. M., 1957. Het Rijksmuseum van Geologie en Mineralogie. *Nieuws Bull. Koninkl. Ned. Oudheidk. Bond*, 10 (4) : 77–78.

with local museums, by making personal visits to excavations and dredgings, by arousing the enthusiasm of correspondents, etc., to make the Museum a living force in the community.

On the 31st of January 1961, Professor VAN DER VLERK relinquished his chair at the University of Leyden. The very next morning found him sitting at his desk in the Royal Dutch/Shell Exploration and Production Laboratory, Delft. On that morning began a new period of his life; not, as might have been expected, one of rest and relaxation, but a period of active scientific reserarch on a subject that he had already covered superficially at the very beginning of his career[1] and that he has returned to recently in order to give it fuller treatment: Evolutionary trends in the larger Foraminifera and their application in stratigraphy. It is, therefore, most appropriate that those who have undertaken to produce this anniversary volume should have chosen this subject as its theme.

[1] VAN DER VLERK, I. M., 1922. Studiën over Nummulinidae en Alveolinidae. *Verhandel. Ned. Geol. Mijnbouwk. Genoot. Ned. en Kol., Geol. Ser.*, 5: 329–464.
VAN DER VLERK, I. M., 1923. Een nieuwe *Cycloclypeus* soort van Oost-Borneo. *Samml. Geol. Reichs-Museums in Leiden*, 10: 137–140.

LIST OF SCIENTIFIC PUBLICATIONS BY PROFESSOR DR. I. M. VAN DER VLERK

1922

— . Studiën over Nummulinidae en Alveolinidae. *Verhandel. Ned. Geol. Mijnbouwk. Genoot. Ned. en Kol., Geol. Ser.*, 5 : 329–464. (Dissertatio Univ. Leyden).

1923

— . De stratigrafie van het Tertiair van Java. *De Ingr. in Ned. Indië*, 4 : 53–56.

— . Een overgangsvorm tusschen *Orthophragmina* en *Lepidocyclina* uit het Tertiair van Java. *Verhandel. Ned. Geol. Mijnbouwk. Genoot. Ned. en Kol., Geol. Ser.*, 7 : 91–98.

— . Een nieuwe *Cycloclypeus* soort van Oost-Borneo. *Samml. Geol. Reichs-Museums Leiden*, 10 : 137–140.

— . Een nieuwe vindplaats van fossiele werveldieren op Java. *De Ingr. in Ned. Indië*, 4 : 67–68.

1924

— . *Miogypsina Dehaartii* nov. spec. de Larat (Moluques). *Eclogae Geol. Helv.*, 13 : 429–432.

— . Foraminiferen uit het Tertiair van Java, I. *Wetenschap. Mededeel. Dienst Mijnbouw Ned. Indië*, 1 : 16–35.

— . De verspreiding van het foraminiferengeslacht *Lepidocyclina* en haar beteekenis voor de palaeo-geographie. *Handel. 3e Ned. Indisch Natuurwetenschap. Congr., Buitenzorg*, pp. 371–380.

1925

— . Voorlopig onderzoek van een aantal fossielhoudende gesteenten van Celebes. In: W. DIECKMANN en M. W. JULIUS, Algemeene geologie en ertsafzettingen van Zuidoost Celebes. *Jaarb. Mijnwezen Ned. Indië*, 13 (1924) : 64–65.

— . *Lepidocyclina mediocolumnata* nov. spec. de Pasir (SE-Bornéo). *Eclogae Geol. Helv.*, 19 : 267–269.

— . Het foraminiferen-genus *Spiroclypeus* en zijn beteekenis voor de stratigraphie van het Tertiair van den Indo-Australischen Archipel. *Verhandel. Ned. Geol. Mijnbouwk. Genoot. Ned. en Kol., Geol. Ser.*, 8 : 561–567.

— . A study of Tertiary foraminifera from the "Tidoengsche landen" (E. Borneo). *Wetenschap. Mededeel. Dienst Mijnbouw Ned. Indië*, 3 : 13–38.

1927

— en UMBGROVE, J. H. F. Tertiaire gidsforaminiferen van Nederlandsch-Oost-Indië. *Wetenschap. Mededeel. Dienst Mijnbouw Ned. Indië*, 6 : 1–35.

— and DICKERSON, R. E. Distinctions among certain genera of larger foraminifera for the field geologist of the East-Indies. *J. Paleontol.*, 1 : 185–192.

1928

— . Het genus *Lepidocyclina* in het Indopacifische gebied. *Wetenschap. Mededeel. Dienst Mijnbouw Ned. Indië*, 8 : 7–86.

— . The genus *Lepidocyclina* in the Far East. *Eclogae Geol. Helv.*, 21 : 182–211.

1929

— . Groote Foraminiferen van N.O. Borneo (with summary in English). *Wetenschap. Mededeel. Dienst Mijnbouw Ned. Indië*, 9 : 3–44.

— . De stratigrafie van het Indische Tertiair en de beteekenis der foraminiferen voor de stratigrafie. *Verslag. Geol. Sectie Geol. Mijnbouwk. Genoot. Ned. en Kol.*, 3 : 226–227.

— and WENNEKERS, J. H. L. Einige foraminiferenführende Kalksteine aus Süd-Palembang (Sumatra). *Eclogae Geol. Helv.*, 22 : 166–172.

1931

— . Caenozoic Amphineura, Gastropoda, Lamellibranchiata and Scaphopoda. *Leidsche Geol. Mededeel.*, 5 (Feestbundel Prof. Dr. K. Martin) : 206–296.

— . and LEUPOLD, W. The Tertiary. *Leidsche Geol. Mededeel.*, 5 (Feestbundel Prof. Dr. K. Martin) : 611–648.

1932

GORTER, N. E. and —. Larger Foraminifera from Central Falcon (Venezuela). *Leidsche Geol. Mededeel.*, 4 : 94–122.

— . Foraminiferenbepalingen uit gesteentemonsters van Zuid Rembang. In: H. SCHUPPLI, Kort verslag over de geologische situatie van het Zuidrembangsche heuvelland. *Jaarb. Mijnwezen Ned. Indië*, 59 (1930); *Verhandel. Ned. Geol. Mijnbouwk. Genoot. Ned. en Kol., Mijnbouwk. Ser.* 3 (1932) : 102–109.

— . Molluskenfauna uit het bovengedeelte van het Plioceen verzameld door Dr. H. SCHUPPLI in de vlakte ten N. van het Zuidrembangsche heuvelland (gebied Tondomoelo en gebied Ngambon-Toeri-Pelem). In H. SCHUPPLI, Kort verslag over de geologische situatie van het Zuidrembangsche heuvelland. *Jaarb. Mijnwezen Ned. Indië*, 59 (1930); *Verhandel. Ned. Geol. Mijnbouwk. Genoot. Ned. en Kol., Mijnbouwk. Ser.*, 3 : 110–112.

1933

— . The task of the Oil Paleontologist. *Geol. Mijnbouw*, 12 : 15–19.

— . De taak van den petroleum-palaeontoloog. *Verslag. Geol. Geogr. Sectie Ned. Natuurk. Geneesk. Congr. (Wageningen, 1933)*, vierde afd.: 261–262.

1934

— and DOZY, J. J. The tertiary rocks of the Celebes Expedition 1929. *Verhandel. Geol. Mijnbouwk. Genoot. Ned. en Kol., Geol. Ser.*, 10 : 183–217.

— . Verslag over een onderzoek van zeven gesteentemonsters van Noord Bengkoe. In: L. VON LÓCZY, Geologie van Noord Bengkoe en het Bongka-gebied tusschen de Golf van Tomini en de Golf van Tolo in Oost-Celebes. *Verhandel. Geol. Mijnbouwk. Genoot. Ned. en Kol., Geol. Ser.*, 10 : 290.

1935

— en VAN DEN BROEK, A. J. P. De pleistocene mensenschedel van Hengelo (Ov.). *Wetenschap in Vlaanderen*, 1 (1) : 9–11.

VAN DE GEYN, W. A. E. and — . A monograph on the Orbitoididae, occurring in the Tertiary of America. *Leidsche Geol. Mededeel.*, 7 : 221–272.

1936

FLORSCHÜTZ, F. and — . The Pleistocence human skull from Hengelo. I. Geological-palaeontological part. *Koninkl. Ned. Akad. Wetenschap., Proc.*, 39 : 76–80.

1937

FLORSCHÜTZ, F. and — . Fossiele cellenstructuur in jong-Pleistocene Oost-Nederlandsche afzettingen. *Koninkl. Ned. Akad. Wetenschap., Proc.*, 60 : 880–882.

1938

— . *Nederland in het IJstijdvak*. Inaugurele rede Univ. Leiden, Eduard Ydo, Leiden, 24 pp.

FLORSCHÜTZ, F. et — . Les phénomènes périglaciaires et leur rapport avec la stratigraphie de l'époque Weichselienne (Würmienne) en Twente. *Livre-guide Congr. Intern. Géogr. Amsterdam, Excursion B4* : 33–44.

BURSCH, F. C., FLORSCHÜTZ, F. and — . An early Palaeolithic site on the N. Veluwe. *Koninkl. Ned. Akad. Wetenschap., Proc.*, 41 : 909–920.

— . Uitgestorven dieren. In: H. C. REDEKE, *Het Dier in zijn Wereld. Overzicht der Levensverschijnselen in het Dierenrijk*. W. De Haan, Utrecht, pp. 323–370.

1939

FLORSCHÜTZ, F. en — . Duizend eeuwen geschiedenis van den bodem van Rotterdam. *De Maastunnel*, 2 (6) : 1–6.

1941

— en KUENEN, PH. H. *Geheimschrift der Aarde*. W. de Haan, Utrecht, 344 pp.

1942

— . Kwartaire Bovidae van Nederland. De schedels en hoornpitten, welke zich bevinden in het Rijksmuseum van Geologie te Leiden. *Leidsche Geol. Mededeel.*, 13 : 1–28.

1948

— . Palaeontologie. Stratigrafie. Historische Geologie. *Eerste Ned. Systematisch Ingerichte Encyclopedie (ENSIE)*, 5 : 126–144, 145–149, 149–154.

1949
— . Fylogenie der dieren. *Eerste Ned. Systematisch Ingerichte Encyclopedie (ENSIE)*, 6 : 197–200.

1950
— en FLORSCHÜTZ, F. *Nederland in het IJstijdvak*. W. de Haan, Utrecht, 287 pp.
— . Stratigraphy of the Caenozoic of the East Indies based on Foraminifera. *Repts. 18th. Sess. Intern. Geol. Congr. (Great Britain, 1948)*, 15 : 61–63.
— . Correlation between the Plio-Pleistocene deposits in East Anglia and in the Netherlands. *Repts. 18th. Sess. Intern. Geol. Congr. (Great Britain, 1948)*, 9 : 101–106.

1951
— . Zeeland in het IJstijdvak. *Koninkl. Ned. Akad. Wetenschap., Akademiedagen*, 4 : 110–124.
— . Tabulation of determinations of Larger Foraminifera. In: M. REINHARD and E. WENK. *Geol. Surv. Dept. British Territories in Borneo, Bull.*, 1 : 137–146.

1952
— . Pleistocene chronologie. *Koninkl. Ned. Akad. Wetenschap., Verslag Gewone Vergader., Afdel. Nat.*, 61 : 155–159.

1953
— . The stratigraphy of the Pleistocene of the Netherlands. *Koninkl. Ned. Akad. Wetenschap., Proc. Ser. B*, 56 : 34–44.
— and FLORSCHÜTZ, F. The palaeontological base of the subdivision of the Pleistocene in the Netherlands. *Koninkl. Ned. Akad. Wetenschap., Verhandel. Afdel. Nat.*, 20 : 1–58.
— . Een nieuwe methode voor de ouderdomsbepaling van fossiele beenderen. *Koninkl. Ned. Akad. Wetenschap., Verslag Gewone Vergader., Afdel. Nat.*, 62 : 112–114.
NIGGLI, E., OVERWEEL, C. J. and — . An X-ray crystallographical application of the fluorine-dating method of fossil bones. *Koninkl. Ned. Akad. Wetenschap., Proc. Ser. B*, 56 : 538–542.

1954
— . *Mosasaurus* en Rechtspraak. *Leids Universiteitsblad*, 19 (29) : 8–9.

1955
— . Correlation of the Tertiary of the Far East and Europe. *Micropaleontology*, 1 : 72–75.
— . The significance of Interglacials for the Stratigraphy of the Pleistocene. *Quaternaria*, 2 : 35–43.
— . Zijn er in Pleistocene lagen van Nederland skeletresten van de mens gevonden? *Leidse Geol. Mededel.*, 20 : 195–206.
— . Correlatie-problemen in de geologie. *Koninkl. Ned. Akad. Wetenschap., Verslag Gewone Vergader., Afdel. Nat.*, 64 : 129–132.

1956
— . The importance of the use of local subdivisions of the Pleistocene. *Actes 4e Congr. Intern. Quatern.*, pp. 1–4.
— . X-ray and chemical analysis of pleistocene mammalian remains. *Actes 4e Congr. Intern. Quatern.*, pp. 416–420.
— . Introduction (to "Subdivisions of the Pleistocene, etc."). *Quaternaria*, 3 : 205–206.

1957
— . Fluorine tests of Pleistocene mammalian skeletons. *Koninkl. Ned. Akad. Wetenschap., Proc. Ser. B*, 60 : 117–119.
— . Het Rijksmuseum van Geologie en Mineralogie. *Nieuws Bull. Koninkl. Ned. Oudheidk. Bond*, 10 (4) : 71–82.
— . De stratigrafische betekenis van het "genus" Lepidocyclina. *Koninkl. Ned. Akad. Wetenschap., Verslag Gewone Vergader., Afdel. Nat.*, 66 : 23–27.
— . Foreword; Conclusion (to "Pleistocene correlations between the Netherlands and adjacent areas: a symposium"). *Geol. en Mijnbouw*, 19 : 230, 310–312.
— . Rapport over de 20e zitting van het Internationaal Geologisch Congres, gehouden 4–11 Sept. 1956 te Mexico-City. *Koninkl. Ned. Akad. Wetenschap., Rapp.*, 9 : 11–14.
— . Rapport over het 5e Congres van de Internationale Associatie voor de Studie van het Quartair (Inqua) gehouden 2–16 September 1957 te Madrid en Barcelona. *Koninkl. Ned. Akad. Wetenschap., Rapp.*, 9 : 33–35.

1959

GRIMSDALE, T. F. and — . A review of some subgeneric nomenclature among the Lepidocyclinae (Tertiary Orbitoidal Foraminifera). *Koninkl. Ned. Akad. Wetenschap., Proc. Ser. B*, 62 : 1–7.

— . Orthogenese en orthoselectie. *Koninkl. Ned. Akad. Wetenschap., Verslag Gewone Vergader., Afdel. Nat.*, 68 : 116–119.

— . Problems and principles of Tertiary and Quaternary stratigraphy. (Fourteenth William Smith Lecture, delivered 7 January, 1959). *Quart. J. Geol. Soc. London*, 115 : 49–63.

— . Modification de l'ontogénèse pendant l'évolution des Lépidocyclines (Foraminifères). *Bull. Soc. géol. France, 7e sér.*, 1 : 669–673.

1960

— . Paleontologie en Evolutie. In: J. C. DORST *et al.*, *Evolutie. De Huidige Stand van het Vraagstuk.* Het Spectrum, Utrecht–Antwerpen, pp. 94–115.

— en KUENEN, PH. H. *Logboek der Aarde*. W. de Haan, Zeist, 195 pp. (Also published in the French language under the title "L'Histoire de la Terre").

1961

— . Printsipy stratigrafii pleistotsena zapadnoï Evropy. *Biûlleten' komissii po izucheniiû chet vertichnugo perioda*, 26 : 3–6.

— . *Lepidocyclina radiata* (K. MARTIN) 1880. *Koninkl. Ned. Akad. Wetenschap., Proc. Ser. B*, 64 : 620–626.

Professor VAN DER VLERK has also published numerous articles of a popular scientific nature in various newspapers and periodicals and has contributed to the Winkler Prins Encyclopaedia.

MAJOR TRENDS IN THE EVOLUTION OF THE FORAMINIFERA

M. F. GLAESSNER

University of Adelaide, Adelaide (Australia)

As the starting point for this discussion I take the seven propositions which had been previously considered (GLAESSNER, 1945, p. 87) as reasonably well established and suitable to form a basis for subdividing the order Foraminifera into seven super-families. At the same time it was noted that "there remains a number of much dis-cussed questions which cannot be settled by further discussion but only by a search for and discovery of new facts". The main lines on which this search has since pro-ceeded and relevant new facts together with some of the new and unforseen problems which they have raised will be mentioned.

1. *"The non-septate forms are more primitive than the septate."*

The basic difference between the non-septate and the septate forms appears to be that between continuous growth in one and discontinuous (periodic) growth in the other. The palaeontological evidence favours the quoted statement. The only definitely known Cambrian (and probably also Ordovician) Foraminifera belong to the non-septate families Astrorhizidae and Saccamminidae. As other Cambrian Foraminifera are questionable, obscure, or rare, a new observation may be mentioned here. The index fossil for one of the lowest zones of the Scandinavian–Baltic Lower Cambrian is known as *Platysolenites antiquissimus* EICHWALD. Thanks to the kind assistance of Prof. B. S. SOKOLOV and Dr. E. A. BALASHOVA specimens of this species from the Blue Clay of Revel on the Baltic Sea could be inspected in the collection of the Palae-ontological Institute of the Leningrad University in September 1960. They were found to be indistinguishable from *Bathysiphon* and are considered as the oldest known Foraminifera. A detailed account will be published elsewhere. Palaeontological evi-dence supports the statement quoted above also through the discovery of incompletely septate Palaeozoic Foraminifera in which septation occurs only in a late stage of the ontogeny, as in some Tournayellidae (LIPINA, 1955).

2. *"The higher, or septate, spirally coiled arenaceous Foraminifera form a well-defined group."*

The superfamily Lituolacea LAMARCK (1809) comprises septate Foraminifera with agglutinated arenaceous walls. LOEBLICH and TAPPAN (1961, p. 280) add to this description of the wall structure the words "with calcareous cement or microgranular calcite, ... epidermal layer imperforate". This raises the question of the recognition of agglutinated as distinct from secreted wall material, particularly when it appears in the form of microgranular calcite. This question is at present under extensive discussion in the literature and the cement in agglutinated tests is also being studied on living material. The results of this work will contribute much to our understanding of one of the most important steps in the evolution of Foraminifera.

As defined by LOEBLICH and TAPPAN (1961), the Lituolacea are represented in the Silurian and Devonian by the trochospirally coiled Trochamminidae, apparently the oldest septate Foraminifera, and only in the Carboniferous also by the straight uniserial Aschemonellidae (= Reophacidae), biserial Textulariidae, and the earliest Lituolidae (*Haplophragmoides, Ammobaculites*). Most of the Lituolacea, particularly the more complex Lituolidae and Ataxophragmiidae (including the Verneuilininae and Valvulininae) appear only in the Mesozoic time and evolve rapidly. This well-documented fact has to be considered in relation to the origin of the Devonian Fora-minifera of which much is now known, mainly as the result of work in the U.S.S.R. If the Lituolacea represent a link in foraminiferal evolution between the non-septate Ammodiscacea ("Astrorhizidea") and the more advanced septate Foraminifera with secreted walls, then this part could have been played only by Trochamminidae, as far as our present knowledge of pre-Devonian faunas goes. The early representatives of this family deserve more careful study.

3. *"The Fusulinidae are derived directly from Endothyridae."*

This statement remains uncontested. It indicates the only major evolutionary trend in Foraminifera which has led to extinction (at the end of the Palaeozoic). Much more is known now of the Endothyridae than in 1945. Their taxonomic status as a super-family is justified but the "Fusulinidae" are more conveniently separated from them as another distinct superfamily. Evolution within it has been considered recently in much detail (MIKLUKHO-MAKLAÏ *et al.*, 1958) and will not be discussed here. The Endothyracea deserve more de tailed consideration from the viewpoint of general evolutionary trends in Foraminifera. We can only outline the problems as they now appear to a non-specialist in the study of this group.

RAUZER-CHERNOUSOVA and FURSSENKO (1959) include in their "Order Endothy-rida" the families Endothyridae, Bradyinidae, Mesoendothyridae and Spirocyclinidae, the last two being Mesozoic forms included by LOEBLICH and TAPPAN (1961) in the Lituolidae. These authors define the superfamily Endothyracea as follows: "Tubular or with early trochospiral or irregular coil, biserial or uniserial; interior may be divided into chamberlets but not labyrinthic; wall calcareous, fibrous or granular, with some arenaceous material included in primitive forms, commonly with two layers in the wall, finely perforate; apertures simple to multiple, basal or terminal" (LOEBLICH and TAPPAN, 1961, p. 284). The progressive characters of the Endothyracea given here spaced seem to be the most important criteria for the inclusion of eleven families in this taxon. Four of five of these appear first in the Devonian and six or seven in the Carboniferous. The question of their ancestors and their descendants is a crucial one for the recognition of evolutionary trends in Foraminifera. Unfortunately, there is so far little evidence of their origins. FURSSENKO (in RAUZER-CHERNOUSOVA and FURSSENKO, 1959, p. 147) stated that septation developed from the non-septate condition of the Ammodiscacea more than once, as the Tournayellidae appear at the end of the Devonian, later than the first Endothyridae. Both develop fine-grained calcareous walls which are considered as secreted, though agglutinated grains still occur in them. In the Endothyridae the wall may consist of different layers (composite wall). Other Devonian families are the Colaniellidae, Semitextulariidae, and possibly the Palaeotextulariidae, while the following appear in the Carboniferous: Nodosinellidae, Tetrataxidae, Biseriamminidae, Archaediscidae, Lasiodiscidae, and Ptychocladiidae.

NØRVANG (1957, p. 23) has considered the Nodosinellidae as ancestors of the Nodosariidae (Nodosariacea). The Colaniellidae can hardly be far removed from them. The simplest assumption concerning the origin of those groups would be an evolutionary trend from agglutinate to calcareous granular (secreted ?), to composite, to hyaline wall structure combined with persistently straight uniserial chamber arrangement. In terms of families this would correspond to:

(Astrorhizidae) → Aschemonellidae → Nodosinellidae → Nodosariidae.

However, the same type of composite wall (with an inner fibrous layer) which characterizes the Nodosinellidae is also found in the Palaeotextulariidae (CUMMINGS, 1956, p. 203). This family, carefully analysed morphologically, stratigraphically and taxonomically by CUMMINGS, is assumed to be derived from a coiled endothyrid ancestor. One line leads (in the Permian) to *Monogenerina* which may be a synonym of *Nodosinella* (CUMMINGS, 1956, p. 234). Hence, another line of origination is possible:

Endothyrid ancestor → *Palaeotextularia* → *Palaeobigenerina* → *Nodosinella* → Nodosariidae.

No such detailed analysis has yet been carried out for the Tetrataxidae and Biseriamminidae. The wall of *Tetrataxis* consists typically of an inner granular calcareous and an outer hyaline radially fibrous wall. In *Globivalvulina* the wall is described as consisting of an inner granular and a thin outer hyaline perforate wall, with a third, "fibrous" or "canaliculate" layer covering only the inner surface of the last septa and resembling the keriotheca of the fusulinid wall (REICHEL, 1946, p. 550). It seems unlikely that these peculiar Foraminifera with their complex wall structure, chamber arrangement and aperture represent one of the major evolutionary trends. There is, however, little doubt, from the evidence of their wall structure and age, about their relationship with Endothyracea.

The Archaediscidae and Lasiodiscidae are of importance in this context mainly because they show the development of a finely granular calcareous wall with hyaline "pillars" in the second and a thick radially textured calcareous outer layer in the first of these families, without septation. This suggested to FURSSENKO (in RAUZER-

CHERNOUSOVA and FURSSENKO, 1959, p. 145, fig. 24) a derivation from "Ammodíscida", presumably parallel to the well-documented trend from Ammodiscidae to Tournayellidae.

The Semitextulariidae are now described as having a porous (?) hyaline wall (BYKOVA, 1952; also in RAUZER-CHERNOUSOVA and FURSSENKO, 1959, p. 264). They were placed in the Nodosariidae ("Lagenina") by FURSSENKO, on account of their wall structure, but they appear to precede them all while showing the chamber arrangement of much later representatives of this superfamily. POKORNÝ (1958) placed them near the Textulariidae but these groups differ fundamentally in their wall texture. LOEBLICH and TAPPAN (1961) include them in the Endothyracea and place them next to the Palaeotextulariidae, without mentioning in the definition their wall structure which is not composite. The appearance of such forms in Late or post–Palaeozoic strata would hardly call for comment but their presence in the Devonian is unexplained and demonstrates our lack of knowledge of the trends of evolution in early Foraminifera. The last group, the Ptychocladiidae are included in the Endothyracea on account of their granular calcareous wall. Their tests are attached and they are thus unlikely to represent a major trend in foraminiferal evolution. ELIAS (1950) has included with his Carboniferous forms the Lower Cambrian Chabakovia but there is no convincing evidence that this fossil belongs to the Foraminifera. The curious genus Stacheia which dates back to the Silurian has also been included in this family but its wall structure is described as arenaceous with calcareous cement.

What is considered by LOEBLICH and TAPPAN (1961) as a superfamily Endothyracea could represent a grade of evolution of the test wall and coiling through which some descendants of Ammodiscidae and possibly Trochamminidae passed independently. The possibility of a reversion to agglutinated wall structure along some of these trends cannot be ruled out. Three possibilities can be distinguished (see Table I) and should be investigated: (1) The Endothyracea all originated from Ammodiscidae and are a monophyletic group. (2) Some Endothyracea originated from Ammodiscidae and others from Trochamminidae. (3) Some Lituolacea originated from Endothyracea. The Fusulinidea are undoubtedly derived from Endothyridae. At the same time composite calcareous walls developed less successfully in other smaller groups. Their relationships are still largely conjectural.

4. "The different lines of the porcellaneous Foraminifera have a common origin in a coiled non-septate form."

A superfamily Miliolacea, recognized by LOEBLICH and TAPPAN (1961), includes these "different lines". The date of their origination would appear to be Devonian or Carboniferous. FURSSENKO (1959, p. 150, fig. 26) shows the range of the "Cornuspiridae" (now subfamily Cyclogyrinae LOEBLICH and TAPPAN) as beginning in the Devonian but the occurrence of other families in the Devonian and Carboniferous is uncertain. POKORNÝ (1958, p. 175) derives the "Ophthalmidiidae" (= Nubeculariidae JONES; LOEBLICH and TAPPAN, 1961) and the Miliolidae from Ammodiscidae. The

TABLE I

EVOLUTION OF FORAMINIFERA

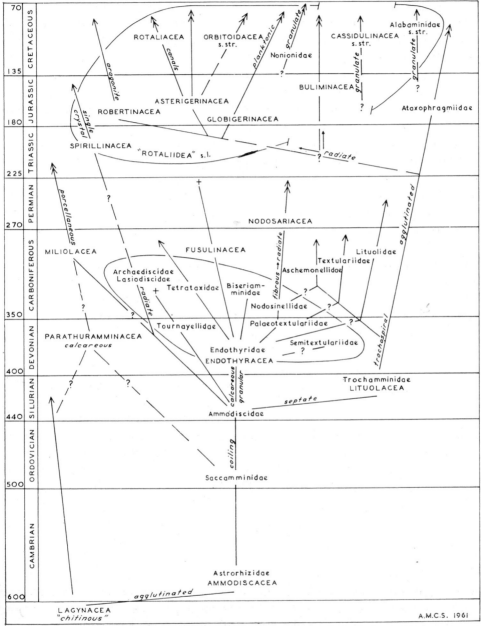

Time scale (in million years) after HOLMES, 1960. The superfamilies are those recognized by LOEBLICH and TAPPAN (1961), except where qualified by "s. str.". Some families discussed in the text are also included. Names of taxa are placed within limits of periods in which their first known occurrence falls but their placing within those limits does not indicate more precise dating. Their time ranges are not shown, but doubleheaded arrows indicate subsequent intense systematic differentiation and single-headed arrows indicate continued existence in later periods.

main new character is the distinctive porcellaneous (microgranular calcareous) wall. This has not been clearly demonstrated as the miliolid wall is not clearly recognizable in the diagenetically altered Palaeozoic and Triassic fossils. Another possibility has been considered, but not definitely accepted, by FURSSENKO (1959). In the Russian treatise (RAUZER-CHERNOUSOVA and FURSSENKO, 1959, p. 237) the genus *Moravammina* POKORNÝ, and others, from the Devonian, are considered as Miliolidea fam. incert., on account of their Ophthalmidiidae-like test. The wall is calcareous but "somewhat different from that of the Miliolida". The same group appears in LOEB-LICH and TAPPAN's taxonomy in the superfamily Parathuramminacea (Devonian to Permian) which has granular calcareous walls. There is nothing to connect this peculiar group with the agglutinated coiled Ammodiscacea. It is possible that it originated directly from chitinous Lagynacea. As an alternative to the more generally held view it could be suggested that the Miliolacea were derived in this way. The view that some of the calcareous Foraminifera evolved directly from chitinous forms (Lagynacea) has been expressed before. It needs to be reconsidered in the light of the more recent discovery of the Parathuramminacea.

The Miliolacea have an imperforate wall, the only exception being the perforate proloculus of the Peneroplidae. The physiological significance of both the rule and the exception is unknown. The Parathuramminacea are imperforate or coarsely perforate or form curious tubular stolons. In some Fusulinacea and Lituolacea, and in all hyaline calcareous Foraminifera the wall is perforate. This important character is almost certain to have evolved independently in different groups.

5. "The Polymorphinidae are derived from Lagenidae, but there is no clear evidence concerning the origin of this family."

The "Lagenidae" in the sense of this statement have been re-named Nodosariidae. Their descendants are the Polymorphinidae; no other major group of Foraminifera has been evolved from this stock which is now included in the superfamily Nodosariacea. The evidence concerning their origin is not yet entirely clear, but it has become certainly much clearer than it was in 1945. WOOD (1949) has shown that the wall texture of the Nodosariacea is uniformly radial, hyaline and perforate. NØRVANG (1957, p. 23) considers the Nodosinellidae as "the ancestral family within the superfamily of the Nodosariidea" and states that the tests of *Geinitzina* and *Spandelina* are calcareous, fibrous, and possibly finely perforate. He studied specimens from the Lias which other authors had assigned, and continue to assign, to such extant genera as *Lingulina* or *Frondicularia*. Some of these species occur also in the Triassic. BYKOVA (1952) described *Geinitzina* from the Upper Devonian. The walls of these forms have a thick fibrous hyaline outer and a thin, dark, fine-grained inner layer. This is said (p. 25) to contrast with the wall structure of *Frondilina* BYKOVA, another genus included by its author in the "Family Lagenidae". Here the outher layer is fine-grained, dark; the inner layer thicker, light but not hyaline (glassy), and radially fibrous. The septa are three-layered. This, apart from the difference in the relative thicknesses of the layers, appears to be the *Nodosinella*-wall structure as shown by CUMMINGS (1955)

If we accept the second line of reasoning outlined above for the evolution of *Nodosinella*, we can accept an endothyroid ancestor for the Nodosariidae. Not only straight and curved but also somewhat coiled (largely evolute) genera, with or without radiate apertures, represent this family in the Permian (CRESPIN, 1958). It is remarkable that trochospiral coiling is strictly excluded from the further range of test structures in the Nodosariidea. Accepting a Devonian endothyroid ancestor (as shown by the "prae-palaeotextularioid" "circular" chamber pattern with its curious *Globigerina*-like coil illustrated by CUMMINGS, 1956), it might be legitimate to invoke the irreversibility of evolution as the factor which has prevented the re-appearance of true trochospiral coiling, and of basal apertures which are structurally linked with it, in Nodosariacea.

This statement must be qualified by a reference to a group of Devonian to Permian planispirally coiled calcareous Foraminifera with basal to areal apertures. FURSSENKO (in RAUZER-CHERNOUSOVA and FURSSENKO, 1959) considered these forms as early Nodosariidea, together with the Colaniellinae and the *Lagena*-like Devonian "Umbellinae". This implies a very early differentiation of the three basic structural types of the Nodosariidea, the straight, coiled and single-chambered forms. On the other hand, LOEBLICH and TAPPAN (1961) include the Umbellininae in the Nodosinellidae and the "Nanicellinae" (as Loeblichiinae) in the Endothyridae. The phylogenetic significance of these early *Lagena*-like (see also WOOD, 1949) and *Lenticulina*-like Foraminifera is still uncertain.

6. *"The Cassidulinidae and Ellipsoidinidae (Pleurostomellidae) are related to the Buliminidae which can be traced back to a trochospiral ancestral form."*

On this assumption the superfamily Buliminidea was defined so as to include these families. Here we have to consider new evidence which finds its expression in the separation of a superfamily Cassidulinacea from the Buliminacea in LOEBLICH and TAPPAN's new classification. "Most of the other smaller calcareous perforate Foraminifera are clearly derived from rotaloid (trochospiral) ancestors."

With the exception of a few doubtful genera (and the complications in *Ehrenbergina* discussed by WOOD, 1949), all the Cassidulinidae, Pleurostomellidae and Chilostomellinae have been shown by WOOD (1949) and others to possess granulate calcareous tests instead of the radiate test of the Buliminidae. To the families with granulate tests we have to add some of the forms formerly known as *Virgulina* (and the genera *Virgulinella* and *Delosina*). Did the granulate wall texture evolve from the radiate wall, did this occur once (so that all granulate calcareous forms could be considered as "Cassidulinacea") or more than once, and what evolutionary trends can be recognized? Not all these questions can be answered now. It is relevant that most of these forms date back no further than to the Upper Cretaceous, and only *Pleurostomella* is known from the late Lower Cretaceous (Albian). *Virgulina jurassica* CUSH-

MAN and GLAZEWSKI may represent the genus formerly known under this name in the Upper Jurassic but its wall texture is unknown and its identification is doubtful. Another new fact to be considered is that the coiling of a biserial test which was considered as evidence of origination from Bolivininae (GLAESSNER 1945, p. 142) is no longer known only in Cassidulinidae. It is now also known in *Plectorecurvoides*, the Biseriamminidae and *Cassigerinella*. NØRVANG (1958) has shown that a *Cassidulina*-like form with radiate walls existed since the Eocene and that this genus *Islandiella* differs from the granulate-walled *Cassidulina* also in its apertural characters. The apertures in the Cassidulinidae and Pleurostomellidae are now known to be less similar to those of the Buliminidae than had been thought. The main argument for this family being the ancestor of the two others thus loses its force.

The only positive character common to all "Cassidulinacea" as defined by LOEBLICH and TAPPAN (1961) is the perforate granulate wall and therefore they cannot be considered as a necessarily genetically related group. The ancestors of the Cassidulinidae, Pleurostomellidae and Caucasinidae are not likely to be identical with those of the Nonionidae and even less likely to be also at the starting point of a lineage leading to the various genera with granulate walls which had thus far been included in the radiate "Discorbidea". The families Alabaminidae and Cibicididae were placed in the Cassidulinacea by LOEBLICH and TAPPAN (1961), but it is known (WOOD and HAYNES, 1957) that the type species of *Cibicides* has a radiate wall, and this is true also of other species of *Cibicides*, *Gavelinella*, *Stensioina* etc. The wall texture in Lower Cretaceous species of these genera is not known. The first appearance of the granulate wall in trochospirally coiled calcareous Foraminifera has not been established. What is known about granulate calcareous perforate forms can be summarized as follows:

In the Pleurostomellidae (and related "*Virgulina*"-like forms) this character is "fixed" and may have been present in the earliest (Albian) forms. On morphological grounds the Chilostomellidae (not including *Sphaeroidina* or *Pullenia*) could be related to this family. In the Cassidulinidae (from Upper Cretaceous) this character is also "fixed" but there may be exceptions. There is nothing to show any relation between this family and the other two, but it is not unlikely. The granulate wall also characterizes the Nonionidae which should include *Pullenia*, but I can see no convincing evidence why they should also include a subfamily Chilostomellinae as suggested by LOEBLICH and TAPPAN (1961). This family dates back to Lower Cretaceous. The same wall texture is found in *Alabamina*. It could be argued that *Alabamina* is derived from the early Cretaceous "barkerinid", *i.e.*, possibly lituolid, genus *Nezzazata* though "differences are greater than their similarities", and this could possibly also apply to *Globorotalites* and *Conorotalites* thus forming a separate monolamellid to bilamellid phyletic lineage (see REISS, 1960, p. 15). Of the Cibicididae, only few genera (*Gyroidinoides*, and the aberrant *Osangularia* and *Anomalinoides*), species (in *Karreria*, *Heronallenia*), or even parts of tests of some species (in *Cibicides*, *Anomalinoides*) have granulate wall texture and lack any other characters to distinguish them from Discorbidae. *Gavelinella* has radiate walls.

From this review we can conclude that the granulate wall originated in at least four different groups during the Cretaceous. We have no knowledge of the course of evolution which led to them either from Palaeozoic granular calcareous or from early Mesozoic forms.

There is no evidence for a derivation of the more common radiate from the granulate calcareous wall. The radiate wall texture is not identical with the "fibrous" texture of some Palaeozoic Foraminifera (CUMMINGS, 1956, p. 205) but may have evolved from it. The only truly radiate wall recognized by WOOD (1949) in Carboniferous Foraminifera is that of *Archaediscus*, a non-septate form.

What are the rotalioid (trochospiral) forms from which the Buliminidea and the "Discorbidea" originated? Some light may be thrown on this still very obscure field by further study of the recently discovered Triassic "Discorbidae" (KRISTAN-TOLLMANN, 1960). Details of the texture of their calcareous perforate wall are not known. The trochospiral coiling of the tests varies in one genus (*Variostoma*) from very high to very low-spired. The aperture is interio-marginal to umbilical and curiously lobulate. It may be significant that another author in the same publication described what may be one of these forms as "*Valvulina* (?) nov. sp." In two other genera (*Diplotremina* and *Duostomina*) the aperture consists of two openings separated by an umbilical flap as in *Discorbis*.

It is remarkable to find a complex rather than a simple aperture in such early forms and it is tempting to derive from them tentatively both the Buliminidae and the Discorbidae. *Discorbis*-like forms occur in the Jurassic. *Bulimina* and *Turrilina* are doubtfully recorded from the Jurassic and occur in the Lower Cretaceous. HOFKER (1956, p. 23) has suggested a derivation of the Buliminidea ("Protoforaminata") and the Rotaliidea *s.l.* from Valvulinidae. This group, now considered a subfamily of the Ataxophragmiidae, is known from Jurassic and later Periods. The same applies to all other subfamilies and genera now placed within this family, with the exception of *Digitina* CRESPIN and PARR (Permian), a coarsely agglutinated form which is irregularly trochospiral and biserial. The alternatives seem to be either a hypothetical downward extension of the time range of the Valvulininae which resemble Discorbidae only in late Jurassic time, or a common origin of both these groups from Palaeozoic Trochamminidae, since among the many known granular calcareous Palaeozoic forms none resembles Discorbidae.

REISS (1958) indicates accordingly the "Lituolidea" as an ancestral group from which he derives all "Rotaliidea" *s.l.*

Among these the Epistominidae and Ceratobuliminidae stand out because of their aragonitic wall composition and their very great and well-known septal and apertural complexity. They have finely perforate radiate walls and simple (monolamellid) septa. In LOEBLICH and TAPPAN's classification (1961) they are considered as a superfamily Robertinacea. Their structural complexity makes it unlikely that any other group is descended from them, but it should be considered whether the Nonionidae could have originated from them by simplification of structure and change to granulate walls. In connection with the origin of the Robertinacea and Asterigerinacea the Lower and Middle Jurassic genus *Reinholdella* is of special interest. It was re-examined by HOF-

KER (1952) and his main morphological observations were confirmed by a re-study of *R. macfadyeni* (TEN DAM), from the Lias of Northampton, England. This species is rather indistinctly bilamellid and has radiate wall texture. HOFKER concluded that it is related to the monolamellid *Conorboides* (Jurassic – Lower Cretaceous) and that the Epistominidae are derived from it (HOFKER 1957, p. 376). REISS (1958) makes use of distinctions in septal layering and considers forms with "simple" (monolamellid) septa to be the ancestors of those with "primarily double" (bilamellid) and others (Rotaliidae *s. str.*) with "secondarily double" (rotalioid) septa. The superfamily Rotaliacea (*s. str.*) can be based on additional characters, as noted by SMOUT (1955) and DROOGER (1960) and nothing can be added usefully to their studies of the evolution of this group.

Among the descendants of early Discorbidae which develop bilamellid septa are the Globigerinacea, the main planktonic branch of the Foraminifera. Their phylogeny is being discussed by many authors (BANNER and BLOW; BRÖNNIMANN and BROWN; HOFKER; LOEBLICH and TAPPAN; MOROZOVA; and others), but there is still much disagreement and, here again, origins are hidden among poorly known Triassic to Lower Cretaceous forms, probably of *Globigerina*-like appearance and *Conorboides*-like ancestry, though the "*Anomalina*"-like structure of early Globotruncanidae – Rotaliporidae – Planomalinidae has been observed and is not easily reconciled with a monophyletic origin of this important group.

The inter-relationships of the benthonic "Discorbidea" are complex and cannot yet be adequately documented. However, what is known about them does not support in any way their splitting up among the three superfamilies Asterigerinacea (a name substituted on grounds of priority for Discorbidea), Orbitoidacea, and Cassidulinacea (LOEBLICH and TAPPAN, 1961). According to the published diagnoses, the first of these has a radiate wall texture and "single walls and septa"; the second has also radiate wall texture but "primarily formed double septa, walls of two layers, outer lamella covering all previously deposited parts of test as well as forming new chambers, inner lining confined to each chamber and wedging out of the margins, present on the distal face of the chamber interior, on its roof and lateral walls." The third superfamily is distinguished by granulate walls. In it are placed the Alabaminidae and Cibicididae (including also the Gavelinellinae and Almaeninae) which are currently considered as closely related to the Discorbidae. Apart from the primitive "Conorboididae" (which are included by LOEBLICH and TAPPAN (1961) in the Discorbidae), only the Asterigerinidae, Baggininae and Siphoninidae have monolamellid septa while many other Discorbidae including the "*Eponides repandus*" group and also the Epistomariidae, Planorbulinidae and Acervulinidae are bilamellid, according to the work of REISS and to unpublished data kindly supplied by DR. MARY WADE. While evolutionary trends from mono- to bilamellid and from monolamellid to "rotalioid" septal layering as postulated by REISS (1958) are highly probable, there is at present no good reason to assume that each of these developments occurred only once. There is no evidence that the earliest "Discorbidea" (in the sense of SMOUT, 1955) had monolamellid septa. The great differences in apertural characters and test shapes in groups in which a particular type of septal layering occurs make this single character an unsatisfactory basis for major classification. It follows that the "Orbitoidacea" cannot comprise those bilamellid "Discorbidea" which share all important characters with such genera as the bilamellid *Discorbis* or the monolamellid *Conorboides*.

This brings us to a consideration of the final point on major grouping based on evolution as known before 1945.

7. "*Most of the larger calcareous perforate Foraminifera including Siderolites, Orbitoides, Lepidocyclina, Miogypsina, and probably the nummulites, developed from a number of different but closely interrelated small rotalioid (trochospiral) ancestors.*"

This statement is partly supported by later work. SMOUT (1954, 1955) has given a reclassification of the Rotaliidea, in which he separated the canaliculate Rotaliidea *s. str.* from the non-canaliculate "Discorbidea". The possible derivation of the Miogypsinidae and the Nummulitidae (through Miscellaneidae) from Rotaliidae is accepted. DROOGER (1960) has tentatively included *Lepidorbitoides* in the "Rotaliidea *s. str.*". In an earlier study, DROOGER (1956) came to the important conclusion that the main trend along several parallel lines of evolution in larger Foraminifera including Miogypsinidae, Orbitoididae, Lepidocyclinidae, and others, tends to produce greater radial symmetry of the test. He ascribes to this a selective value. Another well-known concomitant trend is that towards size increase and strengthening of the test. The origin of the Miogypsinidae from the *Pararotalia*-lineage is as clearly established as any phylogeny in fossil Foraminifera. That of the various Pellatispiridae and Nummulitidae is shown, as clearly as possible on the basis of our present knowledge, in DROOGER's table (DROOGER, 1960, p. 325). The ancestry of the Orbitoididae is still in doubt. KÜPPER (1954), whose untimely death cut short much valuable research, suggested a "*Gümbelina*"-like planktonic ancestor for *Orbitoides* and *Omphalocyclus*, on the basis of his observation on the nepionic stages of microspheric individuals. He described this as biserial but as the four "periembryonic" spirals are shown arising from different parts of the "embryo", including in each of the three figured tests chambers not showing apertures in the plane of section, its supposed "biserial" structure must be questioned. The first chambers were irregularly or trochospirally arranged so that not all apertures can appear in the median section. Alternatively, the central portions of the figured specimens may be fragments from which regeneration proceeded in its usual way. The pre-Campanian ancestor of the Orbitoididae is still unknown.

The Lepidocyclinidae are thought to have their origin in the Amphisteginidae as demonstrated by BARKER and GRIMSDALE (1936). This means that some of the "higher calcareous perforate Foraminifera" originated from Rotaliidea *s. str.* and others from "Discorbidea" ("Asterigerinacea", LOEBLICH and TAPPAN, 1961). Only "orbitoidal" larger Foraminifera with large embryonic gamonts and complex structure could conceivably be combined as a superfamily Orbitoidacea, provided that it can be reasonably assumed that the origin of the Orbitoididae was not too far removed from that of the Amphisteginidae. For this assumption there is yet no proof.

GENERAL REMARKS

The Foraminifera as a highly differentiated group of Protozoa are not ancient but of geologically relatively recent origin. Their differentiation occurred in two major bursts of evolution, one in Devonian and the other in Triassic – early Jurassic time. In each instance it took about 50 million years before major taxonomic diversification was achieved. The first major evolutionary novelties were septation (periodic growth) and calcareous wall secretion. Both express changes in basic physiological processes which can be reasonably thought of as advantageous, though non-septate, chitinous and agglutinated tests are still produced in living forms. The novelties, however, provided the basis of intense further structural differentiation of the test and textural differentiation of the shell wall during Late Palaeozoic times. While the Miliolacea, Nodosariacea and Lituolacea proved permanently successful, the structurally most advanced (and presumably most specialized) Fusulinidea failed to survive, and others were superseded by their descendants. The second great burst of evolution began in Late Triassic – Early Jurassic time and gathered momentum throughout the Cretaceous. Characteristically, it does not appear to have originated directly from or built on the results of the earlier differentiation but to have begun from a new starting point. It was achieved by a new departure in the direction of perfection of wall texture (as granulate or radiate), independently, as far as can be seen, of the earlier parallel trend to radiate wall texture in the Nodosariacea. It evolved now on the basis of trochospiral coiling of the test. Only rare departures to planispiral coiling occurred later. For reasons which are largely unknown, this combination of basic characters proved most successful. Among the new "achievements" were "bigger and better" (in bulk of the sarcode and strength and complexity of the test) larger Foraminifera, and for the first time successful adaptation to planktonic life in Foraminifera. Complications of the apertures reach extremes in the development of tooth-plates and other obstructions, for reasons which are unknown as we know very little about the function of apertures. The building of the wall from aragonite instead of the more common calcite seems to have been persistent in a group which has decreased in numbers but increased in structural complexity since its first appearance. Another side branch builds single-crystal tests which remain entirely or largely non-septate (Spirillinacea). The initiation of this trend is uncertain as Late Palaeozoic tests with similar structure have different textures. An important trend is towards increased morphological expression of the alternation of sexual and asexual generations, which is all we know of the evolution of sexuality in Foraminifera. In other (apogamic) lines the sexual generation may have been suppressed. A trend which manifests itself within the major lineages, often on the level of evolving species, is the increase in pore size. This again must be related to an unknown selective value in physiological efficiency.

This review could be continued at length by enumerating many other trends in morphology, often well documented in phylomorphogenetic series. This would go beyond its object which is to review present knowledge (and lack of knowledge) in foraminiferal phylogeny and to show the main lines of their intense morphological and systematic differentiation, during the last 400 million years. This fact, together with their abundance and the enormous scale of stratigraphically well controlled sampling, would make them uniquely valuable objects in the study of evolution in Protozoa. The value of further work on these lines will, however, depend on greater knowledge of not merely their morphology, but also their physiology and ecology.

ACKNOWLEDGEMENTS

I wish to thank Dr. MARY WADE and Mr. BRIAN McGOWRAN, University of Adelaide, who willingly supplied information from their current research work and who have read the manuscript of this contribution. My thanks are due also to numerous colleagues in many countries who are generously supplying me with copies of their publications. Particular reference should be made here to J. HOFKER, The Netherlands, and to the micropalaeontologists of the Academy of Science and other institutions of the U.S.S.R., whose work has been more stimulating for this study than the number of publications included in the list of references indicates.

SUMMARY

The validity of statements made by the author in 1945 concerning phylogenetic relationships of Foraminifera is investigated, in the light of work published in the intervening years or in progress. Major trends in the evolution of test and wall structure and wall layering during the first major phase of morphological differentiation in the Late Palaeozoic are described. Trends in the evolution of wall composition and texture and septal differentiation are characteristic of the second major phase in the history of Foraminifera in the Middle and Late Mesozoic. This investigation leads to a criticism of some aspects of a recently proposed classification of the Foraminifera which do not adequately represent phylogenetic relationships. The need for further work on functional morphology and ecology is stated. A glossary of proposed morphological terms is presented.

APPENDIX

Glossary of some morphological terms applied to calcareous foraminiferal tests

A complex terminology has come into use in connection with modern detailed studies of foraminiferal morphology. The following glossary includes a number of terms which are currently applied, though not all are used in the preceding text. Most of the terms are defined and used as proposed by other authors. Some modifications are suggested.

Test

Structure: non-septate
                    septate (test structure is here used also as a general term for chamber arrangement)

Wall

Layering: composite = consisting of several layers of different texture
                   lamellar = consisting of layers added with each additional chamber
                   non-lamellar = consisting of a single layer

Composition: calcite
                   aragonite

Structure: agglutinated
                   fibrous
                   micro-granular

Texture: (see WOOD, 1949)
                   porcellaneous
                   granulate
                   radiate
                   single-crystal
                   spicular

Perforation: imperforate
                   perforate

Septa

Layering: (see REISS, 1957, 1958)
                   simple = monolamellid
                   primarily double = bilamellid
                   secondarily double = rotalid

Structures: (see REISS, 1960)
                   septal shelf = murus reflectus
                   infra-marginal sulcus = scrobis septalis (may evolve into infundibulum)

Apertures

Structures: toothplate (internal plate, often contorted, typically extending from
                   adaxial side of aperture to peripheral side of preceding foramen, and often
                   adaxially attached to chamber wall)
                   lip (an external rim or plate extending from the margin of the aperture)

Position: umbilical (within the umbilicus)
                   areal (within the apertural face, not extending to margins)
                   interio-marginal = extra-umbilical (on the adaxial margin of the apertural
                   face)
                   exterio-marginal (on the peripheral margin of the apertural face)
                   (Note: other positions of the aperture may be designated)

Homology: (see HOFKER, 1951)
                   protoforamina
                   deuteroforamina

Other openings

Umbilicus: open space between whorls which do not touch along axis of coiling

Pseudoumbilicus: open space formed by chambers projecting around axis of coiling

Umbilical depression: shallow depression formed by axial endings of chambers

Interlocular spaces: openings in test where later chamber walls do not touch earlier-formed
                        chambers

Canals: septal, marginal, umbilical, etc.

General terms

Proximal:	nearer to proloculus in direction of growth
Distal:	further from proloculus in direction of growth
Adaxial:	nearer to axis (in coiled tests)
Peripheral:	nearer to periphery (in coiled tests)

REFERENCES

BARKER, R. W. and GRIMSDALE, T. F., 1936. A contribution to the phylogeny of the orbitoidal Foraminifera. *J. Paleontol.*, 10 : 231–247.

BYKOVA, E. V., 1952. Foraminifery Devona Russkoi Platformy i Priuralya. *Mikrofauna S.S.S.R.*,
5 : 5–64.

CRESPIN, I., 1958. Permian Foraminifera of Australia. *Bull. Bur. Mineral Resources Australia*, 48 :
7–207.

CUMMINGS, R. H., 1955. *Nodosinella* BRADY, 1876, and associated Upper Palaeozoic genera. *Micropaleontol.*, 1 : 221–238.

CUMMINGS, R. H., 1956. Revision of the Upper Palaeozoic textulariid Foraminifera. *Micropaleontol.*
2 : 201–242.

DROOGER, C. W., 1956. Parallel evolutionary trends in larger Foraminifera. *Proc. Koninkl. Ned.
Akad. Wetenschap.*, Ser. B, 59 : 458–469.

DROOGER, C. W., 1960. Some early rotaliid Foraminifera. *Proc. Koninkl. Ned. Akad. Wetenschap.*,
Ser. B, 63 : 287–334.

ELIAS, M. K., 1950. Paleozoic Ptychocladia and related Foraminifera. *J. Paleontol.*, 24: 287–306

GLAESSNER, M. F., 1945. *Principles of Micropalaeontology*. Melbourne University Press, Melbourne,
296 pp.

HOFKER, J., 1951. Foraminifera, Ordo Dentata, Subordines Protoforaminata, Biforaminata, Deutero-
foraminata. *Siboga Expedition Monograph*, 4a (3) : 1–513.

HOFKER, J., 1952. The Jurassic genus *Reinholdella* BROTZEN (1948) (Foram.). *Paläontol. Z.*, 26 : 15–29

HOFKER, J., 1956. Foraminifera dentata. Foraminifera of Santa Cruz and Thatch Island, Virginia–
Archipelago, West–Indies. *Spolia Zool. Museum Hauniensis*, 15 : 1–237.

HOFKER, J., 1957. Foraminiferen der Oberkreide von Nordwestdeutschland und Holland. *Beih. Geol.
Jahrb.*, 27 : 1–464.

KRISTAN-TOLLMANN, E., 1960. Rotaliidea (Foraminifera) aus der Trias der Ostalpen. *Jahrb. Geol.
Bundesanstalt* Sonderbd., 5 : 47–78.

KÜPPER, K., 1954. Notes on Upper Cretaceous larger Foraminifera. II. Genera of the subfamily
Orbitoidinae with remarks on the microspheric generation of *Orbitoides* and *Omphalocyclus*.
Contrib. Cushman Found. Foraminiferal Research, 5 : 179–184.

LIPINA, O. A., 1955. Foraminifery turneyskogo yarusa i verkhney chasti Devona. *Trudy geol. Inst.
Akad. Nauk S.S.S.R.*, 163 : 1–96.

LOEBLICH, A. R. AND TAPPAN, H., 1961. Suprageneric classification of the Rhizopodea. *J. Paleontol.*,
35 : 245–330.

MIKLUKHO-MAKLAI, A. D., RAUZER-CHERNOUSOVA, D. M. i ROZOVSKAYA, S. E., 1958. Siste-
matika i filogeniya fusulinidei. *Voprosy Mikropaleontol.*, 2 : 5–21.

NØRVANG, A., 1957. The Foraminifera of the Lias Series in Jutland, Denmark. *Medd. Dansk Geol.
Foren.*, 13 : 279–414.

NØRVANG, A., 1958. *Islandiella* n.g. and *Cassidulina* D'ORBIGNY. *Vidensk. Mededd. Dansk naturh.
Foren.*, 120 : 25–41.

POKORNÝ, V., 1958. *Grundzüge der zoologischen Mikropaläontologie*. VEB Deutsch. Verlag der
Wissenschaften, Berlin, 582 pp.

RAUZER-CHERNOUSOVA, D. M. i FURSSENKO, A. V., 1959. *Osnovy Paleontologii, Obshchaya Chast.
Prosteishie.* Akad. Nauk S.S.S.R., Moscow, 482 pp.

REICHEL, M., 1946. Sur quelques foraminifères nouveaux du Permien méditerranéen. *Eclogae Geol.
Helv.*, 38 : 524–560.

REISS, Z., 1957. The Bilamellidea, nov. superfam., and remarks on Cretaceous Globorotaliids. *Contrib. Cushman Found. Foraminiferal Research*, 8 : 127–145.

REISS, Z., 1958. Classification of lamellar Foraminifera. *Micropaleontol.*, 4 : 51–70.

REISS, Z., 1960. Structure of so-called *Eponides* and some other rotaliiform Foraminifera. *Bull. Geol. Surv. Israel*, 29 : 1–28.

SMOUT, A. H., 1954. *Lower Tertiary Foraminifera of the Qatar Peninsula*. Brit. Museum (Nat. Hist.), 96 pp.

SMOUT, A. H., 1955. Reclassification of the Rotaliidea (Foraminifera) and two new Cretaceous forms resembling *Elphidium. J. Washington Acad. Sci.*, 45 : 201–210.

WOOD, A., 1949. The structure of the wall of the test in the Foraminifera; its value in classification. *Quart. J. Geol. Soc. London*, 104 : 229–255.

WOOD, A. and HAYNES, J., 1957. Certain smaller British Paleocene Foraminifera. *Contrib. Cushman Found. Foraminiferal Research*, 8 : 45–53.

TRENDS OF EVOLUTION IN AMERICAN FUSULINES

CARL O. DUNBAR

Peabody Museum of Natural History, Yale University, New Haven, Conn. (U.S.A.)

INTRODUCTION

The Fusulinidae constitute the most prolific family of Paleozoic Foraminifera, and amongst their contemporaries they were relative giants. A few rare species of minute size appeared before the end of Mississippian time and their descendants increased in size as they ranged upward until their extinction late in Permian time. Meanwhile they deployed into at least four subfamilies, perhaps 100 genera, and some 2000 species. Where the environment was suitable they thrived in such abundance as to be important rock makers in all the continents except Australia and Antarctica. Their shells are thus readily observed, either in outcrop or in well samples and the gradual and progressive specialization of several shell structures permits the recognition of many steps in their evolution and makes the fusulines almost uniquely useful for zonation and correlation of the Late Paleozoic formations. For the morphology of typical fusuline shells reference is made to DUNBAR and HENBEST (1943).

The evolution of the fusulines is too complex to discuss in detail in the space allotted to this article and emphasis will therefore be placed on the major trends in the two largest and most prolific subfamilies, the Fusulininae and the Schwagerininae. First, however, a brief account must be given of the probable origin of the fusulines and of the character of the earliest genera, all of which the present author includes in the subfamily Staffellinae.

Criteria for generic differentiation among these minute forms are difficult to assess and although several genera have been proposed there is still confusion as to their relations and several may be synonyms. Because of the limits of this paper only the best known American genera will be discussed and most of the nomenclatorial problems must be bypassed. Unfortunately, however, the important genus *Staffella*, the type of this primitive subfamily, has been the subject of so much confusion that it requires further discussion.

Staffella was the first of these primitive genera to be named and, when proposed by OZAWA (1925), was intended to include all subspheroidal species. He chose as generotype a form from the Permian of Armenia illustrated by VON MÖLLER (1878) under the name *Fusulinella sphaerica*. OZAWA overlooked the fact that this was a redescription of the species *Fusulina sphaerica* ABICH (1858). Unfortunately ABICH's types were silicified and poorly preserved and the original description and illustrations were so poor as to leave room for doubt whether the species is really a fusuline. VON MÖLLER's illustrations also left much to be desired but proved that the specimens he studied, at least, were fusulines. THOMPSON (1942) decided that ABICH's types were probably not fusulines and in any event were specifically distinct from the specimens figured by VON MÖLLER. He therefore proposed the name *Staffella moellerana* for the shells described by VON MÖLLER, which by original designation stand as the generotype.

In 1939, however, LICKHAREV restudied ABICH's types which are preserved in Moscow and were almost certainly accessible to VON MÖLLER; and since the specimens described by VON MÖLLER (1878) came from the same remote area it appears highly probable that they were ABICH's type material and that *S. moellerana* is a synonym of *S. sphaerica*. Because the types were silicified and badly preserved, LICKHAREV's illustrations left much to be desired but he showed beyond doubt that they are fusulines and he stated that their spiral wall consists of four layers and that chomata are well developed.

By 1942, numerous species of small subspheroidal fusulines had been described and THOMPSON then decided to recognize two distinct genera, *Staffella* and *Pseudostaffella*. The latter he proposed to include Lower Pennsylvanian species in which the juvenile whorls were broadly rounded and subspheroidal like the adult whorls, the spiral wall consisted of only three layers and the shells were well preserved in calcite. The original types of *Staffella*, he noted, attained a size about twice as great as these primitive species, the juvenile whorls were nautiliform and higher than wide so that the young shells were more widely umbilicate than in *Pseudostaffella*, and the shells were silicified. In 1948 he discussed the relations of these genera further and stated that although both ranged through most of the Pennsylvanian System all known species of *Staffella* were silicified and poorly preserved and therefore had probably differed in chemical composition from the shells he referred to *Pseudostaffella*.

To the present writer these distinctions are highly questionable. Certainly the difference in size (± 2 mm against a maximum of 3–4 mm) is not a generic character. Second, the change from a three-layered to a four-layered wall (discussed below) was a gradual one and in many of the small early forms the distinction is difficult to make. Furthermore, in many of the early forms that are well preserved in calcite and have broad, spheroidal juvenile walls (*e.g., Staffella paradoxa, S. subquadrata* and *S. cuboides*) the wall consists of four layers. Third, among the subspheroidal fusulines there is great variation in the breadth of the juvenile whorls and the size of the umbilici. The fact that many species otherwise referable, according to THOMPSON (1942), to *Pseudostaffella*, are well preserved in calcite throws grave doubts on silicification as a generic character.

Therefore, while admitting that a distinction may eventually be made on wall structure, the present writer feels that such distinction is at present not useful, and, in this paper he therefore places all these minute spheroidal species in the genus *Staffella*.

The four primitive genera characteristic of pre–Atokan rocks in America are represented by axial sections a – d in Fig. 1.

Millerella THOMPSON 1942 has a very short axis, rarely attains an equatorial diameter of more than 0.5 mm, and consists of five to seven volutions all of which are higher than wide. The early whorls are involute but the last two are slightly evolute, leaving wide and very shallow umbilici. Of numerous closely similar species, only *M*.

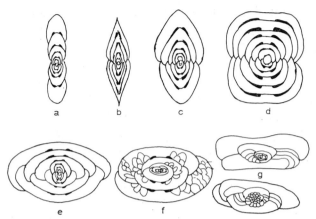

Fig. 1. Diagram to show the range of shape in the subfamily Staffellinae, as represented by axial sections. a – d, four primitive genera; e – g, Late Permian forms. a. *Millerella*; b. *Ozawainella*; c. *Parastaffella*; d. *Staffella*; e. *Leëlla*; f. *Dunbarula*; g. two specimens of *Rauserella*.

marblensis, the generotype, has evolute outer whorls and for the rest THOMPSON proposed the genus *Paramillerella*. This distinction appears to the writer to be of doubtful value.

Parastaffella RAUZER-CHERNOUSOVA 1948 has a somewhat longer axis and the sides of the volutions converge to a narrowly rounded periphery. In most, but not all, species the shells are completely involute and the greatest width is at the axis.

Staffella OZAWA 1925, in contrast, is subspheroidal and broadly rounded or even slightly flattened across the equator.

These three genera appear to represent steps in the elongation of the axis leading to the first fusiform genus, *Profusulinella* (of the subfamily Fusulinellinae), in which the juvenile whorls are always staffelloid.

Ozawainella THOMPSON 1935, on the contrary, specialized in the opposite direction as its volutions became very high and narrow with concave slopes leading up to an acutely angular periphery. It had one descendant in the Permian, the genus *Reichelina*, which became evolute as it approached maturity, and in which the periphery was extended into a thin keel.

Staffella persisted with little change up through the Pennsylvanian and into the high Permian where it gave rise to three quite remarkable minute genera: *Leëlla*, *Dunbarula*, and *Rauserella* (sections e–g of Fig. 1).

Leëlla DUNBAR and SKINNER 1937 is staffelloid in its early whorls and then rapidly elongates into a minute melon-shaped shell that is bilaterally symmetrical throughout. Its septa remain perfectly plane. *Dunbarula* CIRY 1948 starts with an endothyroid juvenarium (described below) and after passing through a brief spheroidal stage becomes elongated and melon-shaped like *Leëlla*, from which it differs in having strongly folded septa. *Rauserella* DUNBAR 1944 likewise starts with an endothyroid juvenarium and then rapidly elongates, but its whorls are so irregularly coiled that the shell has no plane of symmetry.

In spite of their minute size and shape, these genera are recognized as fusulines because of their planispiral coiling, the presence of a median tunnel with bordering chomata, the wall structure, and the early ontogeny of subsequent fusiform genera.

Millerella appears to be slightly the oldest of the pre–Atokan genera, ranging through at least the upper half of the Chesterian Series of the Mississippian System in its type area (D. E. ZELLER, 1953), and in the Cordilleran region (E. J. ZELLER, 1957). It reaches its acme in the Morrowan Series at the base of the Pennsylvanian System and ranges higher. *Parastaffella* also appears in the Late Mississippian but the other genera start in the Morrowan Series and range far up into the high Permian.

It appears probable that *Millerella* developed out of the genus *Endothyra* (family Endothyridae) which is extremely abundant in the Mississippian System (SCOTT *et al.*, 1947). *Endothyra* consists of two or three volutions of bead-like chambers coiled in a nearly flat spiral. Some species approach planispiral coiling. The endothyroid juvenarium of the microspheric forms of all later fusulines also suggests their ancestry in *Endothyra*.

TRENDS OF FUSULINE EVOLUTION

The time and tempo of specialization varied among the several shell structures and in some instances a trend was repeated more than once, or occurred independently in different branches of the family. It will be convenient, therefore, to examine each evolutionary trend individually before attempting a general synthesis.

The spiral wall

Among the fusulinids there are two basic types of wall structure (Fig. 2); the more primitive is non-alveolar and thin, the more specialized much thicker and alveolar. The first is commonly known as a fusulinellid wall because it was first recognized in the genus *Fusulinella*; the second type is known as the schwagerinid wall because of its typical development in the genus *Schwagerina*.

In both *Fusulinella* and *Fusulina* the spiral wall consists of four distinct layers differing in opacity: a thin dark rind, the tectum, underlain by a thicker and more transparent layer, the diaphanotheca, and outer and inner layers of intermediate opacity, the epitheca which forms the tectoria. All these layers are penetrated by extremely abundant mural pores that have the form of simple capillary tubes not over 2–3 μ in diameter. They are easily overlooked except in well-preserved shells. The origin of the several layers of the wall is well shown in sagittal sections of complete shells (Fig. 2). In the last several chambers the wall consists of only two layers, the

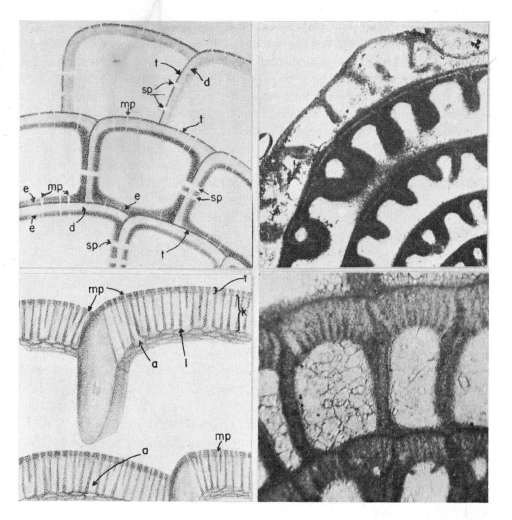

Fig. 2. Upper left, diagram to show the structure of a non-alveolar (fusulinellid) wall; upper right, photograph of part of a corresponding sagittal section of *Fusulina rockymontana*; lower left, diagram to show the structure of the alveolar (schwagerinid) wall; lower right, photograph of part of a corresponding sagittal section of *Triticites ventricosus*. *a* = alveoli; *d* = diaphanotheca; *e* = epitheca; *k* = keriotheca; *l* = lamella; *mp* = mural pore; *sp* = septal pore; *t* = tectum.

tectum and the diaphanotheca. These constitute the primary wall or protheca. In the penultimate and earlier whorls each chamber is lined by the tectoria. The epitheca laid down on the roof of the chambers forms the inner tectorium, and that laid down on the floor forms the outer tectorium. Thus, the wall in the inner volutions appears four-layered.

The reason for the difference in opacity of these layers was an enigma until GUBLER (1935) etched thin sections with very dilute acid to remove the calcite and found a residue of organic matter (tectine) where the darker layers had been, whereas the diaphanotheca completely disappeared. From this it is inferred that the pigment in the wall is organic matter and the opacity varies inversely with its concentration. It seems evident that, as in modern Foraminifera, when a new chamber was to be added, the foram first excreted a thin film of tectine that formed a base upon which nearly pure calcite was deposited. If our reasoning is correct the epitheca laid down later, as a lining of the chambers, contained an appreciable amount of organic matter admixed within the calcite but less than the first layer which formed the tectum.

In *Profusulinella* which preceded *Fusulinella*, the wall displays only three layers. These have commonly been interpreted to be the tectum and outer and inner tectoria, the diaphanotheca being absent. However, a sagittal section of a complete shell shows that the protheca consists of two layers precisely as in *Fusulinella*. The inner layer should thus be the homologue of the diaphanotheca. Furthermore in the preceding whorls it can be seen that the epitheca spreads over the floor of the chambers, but not the roof, thus forming the outer tectorium of the three-layered wall. For some unknown reason there was no appreciable difference in the amount of organic matter in the inner layer of the protheca and in the epitheca of this genus, and the outer and inner layers thus a p p e a r to be tectoria. In some of the later species of *Profusulinella* (*e.g.*, *P. pulchella*) the inner layer appears somewhat more transparent than the outer, especially across the middle of the outer volutions where the wall is thickest, and there is a tendency for a thin film of epitheca to form on the roof of the chambers where it appears in thin sections as a thin dark selvage along the inner margin of the wall. In such shells it is difficult to decide whether to regard the wall as three- or four-layered.

Wherever the change in the concentration of organic matter was marked and abrupt the wall layers are distinct, but in the most primitive genera, from *Millerella* to *Profusulinella*, it is commonly difficult to recognize distinct layers in the early whorls and toward the end zones where the wall is very thin. In the primitive genera *Millerella*, *Ozawainella*, *Parastaffella*, and *Profusulinella*, as in the older species of *Staffella*, the wall generally displays no more than three layers, but in the more advanced species of *Staffella* there are four well-defined layers. We conclude that in the three-layered wall the layers must be regarded as outer tectorium, tectum and diaphanotheca. About the beginning of Atokan time a greater differentiation between the organic concentration in the diaphanotheca and the epitheca set in, as the epitheca gradually spread up over the roof of the chambers, and thereafter the diaphanotheca was clearly differentiated in a four-layered wall that persisted through the range of the genera *Fusulinella* and *Fusulina*. In the youngest species of *Fusulina*, however, near the top of the Desmoinesian Series, a counter trend developed as the epitheca gradually thinned almost to disappearance and in these the wall secondarily approached a two-layered condition, consisting of tectum and diaphanotheca.

A striking structural change in the wall occurred about the end of Desmoinesian time leading to the alveolar wall of *Triticites* and subsequent genera. This, the schwagerinid type of wall (Fig. 2) consists of tectum and k e r i o t h e c a. The keriotheca is clearly a homologue of the diaphanotheca and the transition from one to the other involved a remarkable specialization of the mural pores.

As the fusulines increased in size they faced the problem of secreting a shell strong enough for protection but light enough to be transported by their feeble pseudopodia. In the Desmoinesian and older genera the mural pores remained as exceedingly slender capillary tubules, but in *Triticites* these rapidly became coarser (except in the tectum) as the intervening shell material was reduced to thin lamellae bounding alveoli and the wall came to resemble a piece of wasps nest or of honeycomb. In a thin section the fine dark lines crossing the keriothecal layers are the edges of the lamellae and the clear spaces are the alveoli (Fig. 2). As the alveoli developed, the intervening shell lamellae grew thinner and longer, and thus the wall increased in thickness without the addition of weight until the maximum strength was attained. That this was of selective value is indicated by the fact that none of the species attained a size much larger than a grain of wheat until the alveolar wall was developed and thereafter they soon attained much larger size. The fusulinellid wall rarely exceeded 35 μ in thickness even in the adult whorls, but the schwagerinid walls are commonly at least twice as thick and rarely as much as 150 μ thick.

The alveolar condition was gradually attained by the early species of *Triticites*. In the most primitive species, such as *T. irregularis* and *T. ohioensis*, the pores in the keriothecal layers are coarser than in *Fusulina* but are still tubular. In slightly younger species they are coarser and tend to unite in groups of two or three as the intervening lamellae of shell become thinner toward the inner margin. At this stage the pores commonly appear to branch outward toward the tectum. Still later, as bundles of pores fused, the alveoli were reduced in number but increased in size through the full thickness of the keriotheca. On the basis of this trend the genus *Triticites* has been subdivided into four subgenera (Rozovskaia, 1948).

During this change the mural pores remained fine in the tectum which served as a fine protective sieve Girty (1904) at one time believed that the tectum was imperforate,

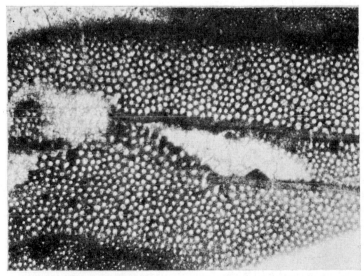

Fig. 3. Tangential slice of a bit of the wall of *Parafusulina guatemalaensis* showing alveoli in the keriotheca and fine pores in the tectum.

but at high magnification the pores are clearly evident in tangential slices of well-preserved shells (Fig. 3).

Once fully developed in *Triticites*, the schwagerinid type of wall persisted with no appreciable change throughout the Permian genera *Schwagerina*, *Parafusulina* and *Polydiexodina* and the collateral genera *Pseudoschwagerina* and *Paraschwagerina*.

The septa

In primitive fusulines having short axes, such as *Staffella* and *Parastaffella*, the septa were perfectly plane; but as later genera became elongate the septa gradually became ruffled, especially along their lower (inner) margin. Such septal folds appeared first in the outer whorls and in the polar extremities, and in the course of time spread gradually to the middle of the shell and were crowded back in ontogeny until they became well developed in all volutions.

Throughout fusuline history the forward folds of one septum faced the backward folds of the next. In the early genera, *Profusulinella* and *Fusulinella*, the folds remained mostly in the end zones of the shell, were somewhat irregular, and were shallow (fore and aft) in comparison with the width of the chambers, so that opposed folds did not meet except in the end zones where the septa converge. In *Fusulina*, however, the folds had spread all along the septa and had become so strong that the tips of opposed folds met to subdivide the lower part of each meridional chamber into a series of chamberlets; but change from *Fusulinella* to *Fusulina* was gradual and some intermediate species are difficult to place.

Septal folding has reached its acme of intensity in the late species of *Fusulina* high in the Desmoinesian Series. Early species of *Triticites*, which appear at the base of the Missourian Series, have gently and weakly folded septa and the folds are concentrated chiefly in the end zones and in the outer volutions. The ancestry of *Triticites* is, therefore, still a problem. It cannot be in any of the late species of *Fusulina* which are altogether too specialized. It may be in persistent species of *Fusulinella* or possibly in late species of *Wedekindellina* (which is discussed below). At any rate *Triticites* starts with relatively simple septa and their specialization begins all over again as the folds spread across the middle of the shell, rise higher on each septum, and appear earlier and earlier in the ontogeny. During the Upper Pennsylvanian there is considerable variation in the degree of septal folding in different species of *Triticites* but in a few (*e.g.*, *T. plummeri*) the folds were almost as strong as they were in late species of *Fusulina*. One branch of this tribe began to develop strong septal folds during Missourian time and were characterized by slender juvenile whorls and notable axial deposits (discussed below). THOMPSON (1942) proposed the distinct genus *Dunbarinella* for this early offshoot from *Triticites*.

By Early Permian time the folds in some species had become high and strong all across the shell, even in the early whorls. Meanwhile the chomata (discussed below) had become obsolete, and with this advance we pass to the genus *Schwagerina* which dominated the Wolfcampian faunas (Fig. 4).

There remained one final stage of septal specialization which began early in Leonardian time. Here the tips of advancing folds were not calcified, or were resorbed before a new chamber was added, and the tips of backward folds on the new septum joined the margin of the opposed folds to form saddle-like arches between chambers. This left a series of open passages running spirally around the shell. These passage-

Fig. 4. Photographs to contrast *Schwagerina* (left) with *Triticites* (right). At the top, whole shells showing the antetheca; middle, tangential cuts to show the septa in plan and the presence of chomata in *Triticites* and their absence in *Schwagerina*; at the bottom, axial thin sections showing septal loops where folds were intersected, and the presence of chomata in *Triticites*.

ways are the cuniculi that distinguish the genus *Parafusulina* from *Schwagerina* (Fig. 5). They can be observed either in silicified shells etched free of matrix, or in tangential slices cut near the floor of a volution. Like the septal folds, the cuniculi made their appearance first in the outer whorls only, but in younger species they were crowded back in the ontogeny until finally they were present even in the early whorls; but, unlike the septal folds they appeared first at the middle of the shell and gradually spread poleward.

In view of this gradual change, the earliest species having cuniculi are strictly transitional between *Schwagerina* and *Parafusulina*. Furthermore, in these early species the cuniculi are low and narrow and can be detected only in parts of tangential slices that lie very close to the floor of a volution. As a result, some species near the Wolfcampian–Leonardian boundary are difficult to place and have been referred by one specialist to *Schwagerina* and by another to *Parafusulina*.

As the cuniculi were crowded back in ontogeny, *Parafusulina* became clearly differentiated early in Leonardian time, and by Early Guadalupian time the cuniculi were present even in the earliest whorls and so enlarged as to be conspicuous in any tangential slice. Thus, in a general way, it is possible to distinguish Leonardian from Guada-

Fig. 5. Upper, part of a shell of *Parafusulina kingorum* in which the outer wall is broken away, showing the septal folds in full relief at the center right, and the basal sutures on the floor of the volution where the septa have been broken away across the center. These spiral sutures separate the cuniculi lower Tangential cut into the outer volution of *P. kattaensis* showing the appearance of cuniculi in tangential sections. *cu* = cuniculi.

lupian species of *Parafusulina* by the stage of septal specialization, but since the trend was gradual, no sharp boundary can be drawn on this basis.

It appears probable that cuniculi were of selective value in providing for adequate communication between chambers in very much elongated shells, and that they were developed independently in two branches of the *Parafusulina* complex, first about the end of Wolfcampian time in *Monodiexodina* (e.g., *M. linearis*) and somewhat later in other species with higher septal folds that gave rise to true *Parafusulina*. They also developed quite independently in one genus of the subfamily Boultoniinae as noted below.

The final, Late Permian genus *Polydiexodina* agrees in all respects with *Parafusulina* except for the addition of auxiliary tunnels which are discussed below (Fig. 7).

The tunnel

One of the most distinctive features of the fusuline shell is the tunnel, a passageway through the chambers formed by the resorption of the basal margin of each septum at the middle of the shell (Fig. 6). These slit-like openings were supposed to record the

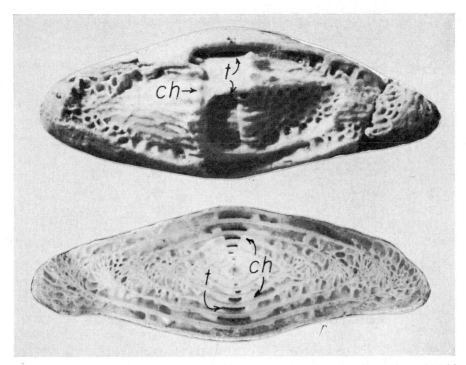

Fig. 6. Tunnel and chomata in *Triticites ventricosus*. Upper, a whole shell, empty of matrix, with the front broken away. Lower, an axial slice of another specimen showing the appearance of the tunnel and chomata in section. *ch* = chomata; *t* = tunnel.

external aperture until WHITE (1932) observed that perfectly preserved shells have no aperture and DUNBAR and HENBEST (1943) showed that at all stages of growth the tunnel falls short of the last formed chamber by about half a volution. It is therefore clearly a secondary feature formed by resorption. DUNBAR and HENBEST (1943, pl. 16, fig. 17) figured a section cut so as to intercept a septum in which the resorption was only partly accomplished before the animal died. See also the last volution at the bottom of Fig. 6.

It is inferred that the function of the tunnel was to provide a passageway through which the nucleus could migrate forward as new chambers were added and thus keep near the center of mass of the living protoplasm.

Auxiliary tunnels

In the large elongate species of *Parafusulina* the median tunnel is invariably well developed but commonly is relatively narrow. In the genus *Polydiexodina* which appeared as an outgrowth from *Parafusulina* at the base of the upper division of the Guadalupian, the Bell Canyon formation, additional tunnels appeared in series as the shells grew longer (Fig. 7). The first pair of these auxiliary tunnels appears some

Fig. 7. Auxiliary tunnels in *Polydiexodina capitanensis*. Upper, tangential thin section showing, across the center, the median tunnel and four auxiliary tunnels and intervening cuniculi. Lower, median slice of the center of a specimen. t = median tunnel; t_1–t_4 = auxiliary tunnels.

distance from the median tunnel when the shell is partly grown. Soon another pair develops farther out, and eventually a third and fourth, and in large shells a fifth pair appears. Like the median tunnel these are secondarily produced by resorption of parts of the basal margins of the septa. This marks the final and ultimate specialization effecting the septa.

In the standard section of West Texas *Parafusulina* disappears just below the appearance of *Polydiexodina* but it is to be expected that in other provinces *Parafusulina* persisted somewhat longer and may be found associated with *Polydiexodina*.

The chomata

In all the Pennsylvanian fusulines the tunnel was bordered by a pair of ridges like the natural levees of an aggrading stream (Fig. 6). These ridges, the chomata, are secondary deposits following the tunnel as it grows forward but tapering down at their terminus and falling slightly short of the end of the tunnel. Furthermore, in thin sections they appear laminated, and the inner laminae have contours corresponding in profile to the forward tips of the chomata.

Their association with the tunnel suggests that the material resorbed to form the latter was redeposited to form the chomata. The ridges are generally higher where they intercept a septum than between septa. In some species the deposited material spreads up alongside the tunnel to thicken the margin of each septum, and in some species the deposits are so concentrated at the septa as to appear as a string of beads rather than a ridge.

As seen in axial sections, the height and massiveness of the chomata may depend on whether the slice lies near a septum or midway between septa. Thus in a single section the chomata may appear to be more massive in some volutions than in others, or even on one side rather than the opposite side of a single volution.

Although chomata are present in all Pennsylvanian fusulines they became obsolete at the base of the Permian in the line leading into *Schwagerina* (Fig. 4) and are lacking in the succeeding genera, *Parafusulina* and *Polydiexodina*.

Axial fillings

In as much as the tectoria had become obsolete and the keriothecal wall had been developed by upper Pennsylvanian time, apparently as a means of keeping the large shells light, it is the more surprising that a considerable number of Permian species weighted their shells by deposits termed a x i a l f i l l i n g s. These deposits line some or

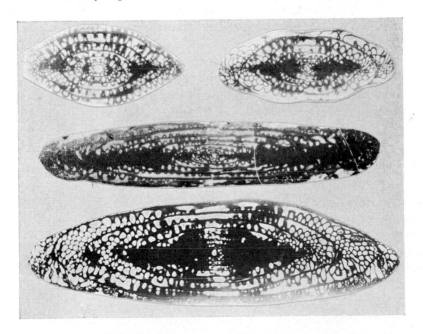

Fig. 8. Axial fillings as seen in thin sections of three species. Above, *Schwagerina gümbeli*; center *Monodiexodina linearis*; below, *Parafusulina schucherti*.

all of the chambers of the inner whorls. In parts of the shell, and in some species, these deposits thicken until they completely fill the chambers and form an almost solid axis of the shell (Fig. 8). Such deposits assume a distinctive pattern of distribution in some species. They appear in certain species of several different genera and evidently were independently developed several times. They probably represent a special adaptation to some distinctive mode of bottom life.

Dimorphism and gigantism

Dimorphism is common if not universal among the fusulines. The microspheric shells, being the sexually formed generation, are readily identified by the presence of a distinctive j u v e n a r i u m, beginning with a very minute proloculus, rarely as much as 50 μ in diameter, followed by two to four volutions of minute, beadlike, spheroidal chambers arranged in a nearly flat spiral. Following this the shell begins to elongate and quickly assumes its typical fusiform or subcylindrical shape. The axis of coiling of the juvenarium is normally at a large angle to that of the rest of the shell, commonly almost at right angles to it. The juvenarium so strikingly resembles an adult shell of the genus *Endothyra* as to suggest that the fusulines descended from that genus.

The megalospheric shells, on the contrary, begin with a much larger proloculus and are planispirally coiled and bilaterally symmetrical from the start. In many species, however, the proloculi of the megalospheric shells show a considerable range in size. In some short species, moreover, occasional individuals show the first volution to be somewhat askew, and early workers have sometimes considered such shells to be microspheric. We believe, however, that microspheric shells are always marked by a distinct endothyroid juvenarium.

In all of the Pennsylvanian forms, as well as those of the Wolfcampian and Leonardian Series in the Permian, the microspheric and megalospheric shells are alike in size and shape and the distinction can only be seen when the shells are sectioned. In some genera microspheric shells are quite common and they may predominate, but in most genera the microspheric forms are rare, occurring one to hundreds or even one to a thousand or more megalospheric shells, and in a few genera, notably *Triticites*, they are almost never seen.

An extraordinary change occurred about the base of the Guadalupian Series of the Permian (DUNBAR *et al.*, 1936) when the microspheric shells suddenly developed into giants several times as large as the megalospheric shells (Fig. 9). In these the proloculus is not over 50 μ in diameter and the juvenarium is typically endothyroid, but the shell grew to have at least twice as many volutions as the megalospheric form and to be fully twice as long. Such gigantism reached its acme in *Parafusulina antimonioensis* of the Word horizon in Mexico, in which the microspheric shells attained a length up to 10 cm and a diameter of almost 10 mm.

It is remarkable that no such microspheric shells have been seen in the Leonardian Series where *Parafusulina* is represented by numerous well-defined species, and that they occur in most if not all of the Guadalupian species of the same genus, and in its

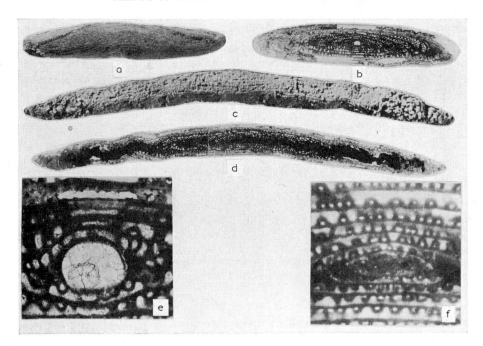

Fig. 9. Dimorphism in *Parafusulina deliciasensis*. a and b, whole specimen and axial section of a megalospheric shell; c and d, corresponding views of a microspheric shell; e, greatly enlarged view of the center of b; f, equivalent enlargement of the center of d.

descendant, *Polydiexodina*, and that in some of the species, *e.g.*, *P. antimonioensis* and *P. rothi*, they are fairly common. It is also remarkable that of all fusulines only these giant microspheric forms lack a median tunnel. The reason for this is unknown but it is suggested that probably they were multinucleate and the many small nuclei could readily migrate through the well-developed cuniculi of these Late Permian giants.

The reason for the sudden appearance of gigantism in the microspheric forms in the midst of the range of the genus *Parafusulina* is another unsolved problem. It is suggested that they may have been polyploids.

It cannot be assumed that these giants represent a separate generic branch of the fusulines, since they invariably occur along with much more abundant megalospheric shells, usually of a single species, and the giants of each such species have a distinctive size and shape. This extreme dimorphism finds a remarkable parallel in the living species, *Alveolinella quoyii*.

COLLATERAL TRENDS OF EVOLUTION

Thusfar we have concentrated on the main line of fusuline evolution from *Staffella* to *Polydiexodina*. Several collateral specializations also occurred, but for lack of space only a few of these can be discussed.

Wedekindellina. This genus represents an early and rather extreme specialization during Desmoinesian time. Whereas *Fusulinella* remained rather thickly fusiform and developed conspicuous septal folds, *Wedekindellina* became extremely elongate, slender, and tightly coiled, retained almost plane septa, and developed massive axial fillings (Fig. 10). It has a well developed four-layered wall as in *Fusulinella*, and appears

Fig. 10. Axial section of *Wedekindellina euthysepta* showing extreme flatness of the septa, and massive axial filling.

to have descended from early species of that genus, or possibly to have undergone a parallel specialization of the wall as a descendant of *Staffella*. In the Mississippi Valley Province it made its appearance about the middle of the Desmoinesian Series and, although widely distributed, had a very short range and then disappeared. The genus probably persisted elsewhere, however, since a single species, *W.ultimata*, reappeared in a very thin zone at the base of the Missourian Series. This species has greatly reduced axial deposits and its outer volutions have a considerable amount of septal folding in the end zones of the outer whorls. It seems to be transitional to a form found in the Salem School limestone at the base of the Cisco (= Virgil) Series in Texas that THOMPSON (1942) made the type of a new genus, *Waeringella*. That form resembles *Wedekindellina* in general appearance, but axial deposits are slightly developed and the spiral wall consists of only two layers, the tectoria having become obsolete. The loss of tectoria in this line parallels the trend in the latest species of the genus *Fusulina* but occurred later. It seems possible that *Triticites* may have evolved from this line at about the stage of *W. ultimata*.

   Pseudoschwagerina and Paraschwagerina. These genera (Fig. 11) evolved at the very base of the Permian, the first from *Triticites* and the second from *Schwagerina* (DUNBAR and SKINNER, 1936). Each underwent a rapid evolution during Wolfcampian time and is confined to the Wolfcampian with the exception of one known species, *Pseudoschwagerina stanislavi*, very near the base of the Leonardian Series in Texas, and possibly a few foreign species such as *Paraschwagerina staffi* of the Permian of Sicily.

   The young shells of *Pseudoschwagerina* are in every respect like *Triticites* until they have attained two to four volutions. Then a sudden and rapid inflation takes place and within about half a whorl the volution has doubled in height. Subsequent whorls are very high and loosely coiled and the shell approaches a spheroidal shape. The final volution, however, decreases appreciably in height. Meanwhile, in the inflated whorls the spiral wall and the long septa are very thin. As a result the shell has a tightly coiled, triticitid juvenarium that contrasts strikingly with the later, inflated whorls (Fig. 11).

Paraschwagerina begins with more slender juvenile whorls in which all the septa are intensely folded, young shells of three or four volutions agreeing in all respects with

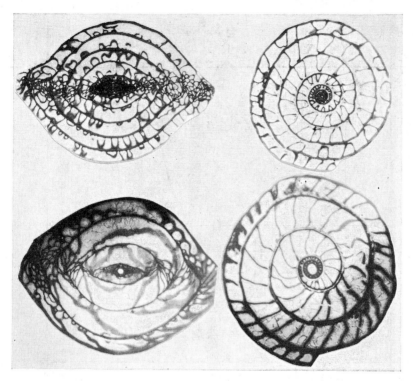

Fig. 11. Above, axial and sagittal sections of *Paraschwagerina kansasensis*; below, axial and sagittal sections of *Pseudoschwagerina uddeni*.

Schwagerina. Following this the shell becomes highly inflated with high adult whorls, thus paralleling the evolution in *Pseudoschwagerina* but differing in that the septa are intensely folded in all volutions.

The reason for the sudden inflation in these two Lower Permian genera is problematical, but since both are very widely distributed in the world it seems possible that it was an adaptation to a floating habit, the protoplasm in the inflated part of the shell having been distended by gaseous vacuoles.

Subfamily Boultoniinae. This subfamily (SKINNER and WILDE, 1954), embraces several genera of minute shells having a very thin spiral wall that commonly appears resinous or waxy in thin sections and seems to have had a composition somewhat different from that in the other fusulines. Although this family ranged from low in the Pennsylvanian to high in the Permian its wall structure showed little change and all species remained extremely small. Their relation to the other fusulines is rather obscure.

Eoschubertella THOMPSON (1937) appears to be the stem from which other genera descended. It occurs in rocks equivalent in age to our Lower Pennsylvanian and its septa are almost plane. *Schubertella* VON STAFF and WEDEKIND 1910 appeared about the beginning of Permian time with gentle folds in the end zones of the outer

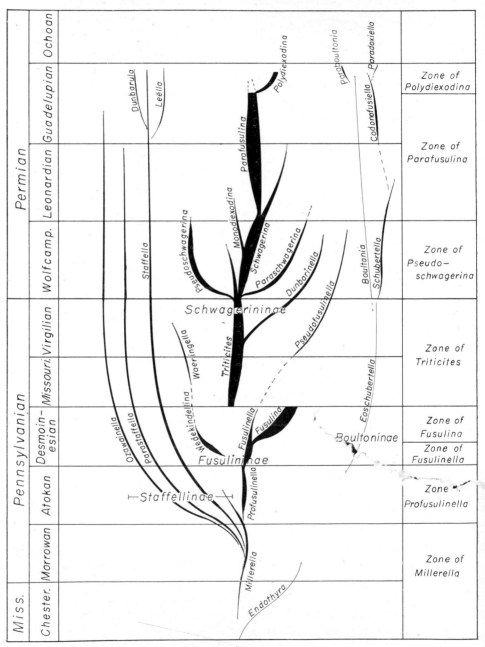

Fig. 12. Diagram to summarize the evolutionary history of the Fusulinidae.

whorls. *Boultonia* LEE 1927 is closely similar and may be a synonym of *Schubertella*. *Paraboultonia* SKINNER and WILDE 1954 has strongly and regularly folded septa in which cuniculi have developed, and its last volution is high and slightly evolute. *Codonofusiella* DUNBAR and SKINNER 1937 resembles *Paraboultonia* until nearly mature but its final volution is evolute and flares out to become larger than all the rest of the shell so that in sagittal section it flares out like the bell of a trumpet. *Parado-xiella* SKINNER and WILDE 1955 carries this specialization to a fantastic extreme in which the last volution expands into a subcircular, hat-shaped layer of cyst-like chamberlets with a tiny coiled juvenarium at its crown. This is the latest fusuline in the Permian section of the Guadalupe region, and is known only from the Lamar limestone a little above the highest range of *Polydiexodina*.

Family Neoschwagerinidae. This great family, which in many ways mimics the Fusulinidae and in other ways contrasts with them, almost certainly arose from *Staffella* during Permian time. Its evolution thereafter was entirely independent of the Fusulinidae and took place chiefly in the Orient. No attempt will be made to discuss it here.

SYNTHESIS

We may now summarize the evolutionary history of the Fusulinidae in the form of a diagram showing the taxonomic relations and stratigraphic ranges of the more important genera (Fig. 12). For lack of space many of the lesser genera have been omitted.

SUMMARY

The evolutionary trends in American Fusulininae and Schwagerininae are discussed. Emphasis is placed on the morphological changes in the spiral wall, septa, tunnel, chomata and axial fillings during Upper Paleozoic time.

REFERENCES

ABICH, H., 1858. Vergleichende Grundzüge der Geologie des Kaukasus wie der armenischen und nordpersischen Gebirge. *Acad. Imp. Sci., St. Petersbourg, 6th ser.*, 7.

CIRY, R., 1948. Un nouveau fusulinide permien, *Dunbarula mathieui. Bull. Sci. Bourgogne*, 11 : 403–410.

DUNBAR, C. O., 1944. Fusulinidae. In: R. E. KING, C. O. DUNBAR, P. E. CLOUD and A. K. MILLER, 1944. Geology and Paleontology of the Permian area northwest of Las Delicias, southwestern Coahuila, Mexico. *Geol. Soc. Am., Spec. Paper*, 52 : 35–48.

DUNBAR, C. O. and CONDRA, G. E., 1927. The Fusulinidae of the Pennsylvanian System in Nebraska. *Nebraska Geol. Surv., Bull., 2nd Ser.*, 2 : 1–130.

DUNBAR, C. O. and HENBEST, L. G., 1943. Pennsylvanian Fusulinidae of Illinois. *Illinois State Geol. Surv., Bull.*, 67 : 1–218.

DUNBAR, C. O. and SKINNER, J. W., 1936. *Schwagerina* versus *Pseudoschwagerina* and *Paraschwagerina. J. Paleontol.*, 10 : 83–91.

DUNBAR, C. O. and SKINNER, J. W., 1937. Permian Fusulinidae of Texas. *Univ. of Texas, Bull.*, 3701 : 517–825.

DUNBAR, C. O., SKINNER, J. W., and KING, R. E., 1936. Dimorphism in Permian Fusulines. *Univ. Texas, Bull.*, 3501 : 173–190.

GIRTY, G. H., 1904. *Triticites*, a new genus of Carboniferous foraminifera. *Am. J. Sci.* (4), 17 : 234–240.

GUBLER, J., 1935 (1936). Les Fusulinidés du Permien de l'Indochine. *Mém. Soc. géol. France, N.S.*, 11 (4) : 1–171.

LEE, J. S., 1927. Fusulinidae of North China. *China Geol. Surv., Paleontologica Sinica*, B, 4, (1): 1–172.

LICKHAREV, B., 1939. *The Atlas of the Leading Forms of the Fossil Fauna, U.S.S.R.* Moscow, Vol. 6.

OZAWA, Y., 1925. On the classification of Fusulinidae. *J. Coll. Sci., Imp. Univ. Tokyo*, 45.

RAUZER-CHERNOUSOVA, D., 1948. Contributions to the foraminiferal fauna of the Carboniferous deposits of central Kazakhstan. *Geol. Inst. Nauk, Trudy, Akad. Nauk, S.S.S.R.*, 66.

ROZOVSKAIA, S. E., 1948. Classification and systematic characteristics of the genus *Triticites*. *Doklady, Akad. Nauk, S.S.S.R., N.S.*, 59 : 1635–1638.

SCOTT, H. W., ZELLER, E. J. and ZELLER, D. E., 1947. The genus *Endothyra*. *J. Paleontol.*, 21 : 557–562.

SKINNER, J. W. and WILDE, G. L., 1954. The fusulinid subfamily Boultoniinae. *J. Paleontol.*, 28 : 434–444.

SKINNER, J. W. and WILDE, G. L., 1955. New fusulinids from the Permian of West Texas. *J. Paleontol.*, 29 : 927–940.

THOMPSON, M. L., 1935. The fusulinid genus *Staffella* in America. *J. Paleontol.*, 9 : 111–120.

THOMPSON, M. L., 1937. Fusulinids of the subfamily Schubertellinae. *J. Paleontol.*, 11 : 118–125.

THOMPSON, M. L., 1942. New genera of Pennsylvanian fusulinids. *Am. J. Sci.*, 240 : 403–420.

VON MÖLLER, V., 1878. Die spiralgewundenen Foraminiferen des russischen Kohlenkalks. *Acad. Imp. Sci., St. Petersbourg*, 7th Ser., 27.

VON STAFF, H. und WEDEKIND, R., 1910. Der Oberkarbone Foraminiferensapropelit Spitzbergens. *Bull. Geol. Inst. Univ. Upsala*, 10 : 81–123.

WHITE, M. P., 1932. Some Texas Fusulinidae. *Univ. of Texas, Bull.*, 3211 : 1–105.

ZELLER, D. E., 1953. Endothyroid Foraminifera and ancestral fusulinids from the type Chesterian (Upper Mississippian). *J. Paleontol.*, 27 : 183–199.

ZELLER, E. J., 1957. Mississippian Endothyroid Foraminifera from the Cordilleran geosyncline. *J. Paleontol.*, 31 : 679–704.

EINIGE FRAGEN ZUR EVOLUTION DER FUSULINIDEEN

D. M. RAUZER-CHERNOUSOVA

Geologisches Institut der Akademie der Wissenschaften der U.S.S.R., Moskau (U.S.S.R.)

EINLEITUNG

Das Problem der Entwicklung der Foraminiferen ist von besonderer Aktualität, da die Evolution dieser Organismen die sicherste Grundlage der Stratigraphie ist. In dieser Hinsicht sind die Ergebnisse der Evolutionsforschung an Fusulinideen interessant, da diese Gruppe nicht allein gut studiert, sondern auch sehr weit verbreitet ist. Ausserdem existierte diese Gruppe in ununterbrochener Folge praktisch während des ganzen Jungpaläozoikum, wobei sie eine rasch ablaufende Entwicklung zeigte. Deshalb haben sich viele Forscher mit der Entwicklung der in Frage stehenden Gruppe im speziellen befasst.

Schon DOUVILLÉ (1906), DEPRAT (1912, 1913) und andere haben die Hauptrichtungen der Evolution der Fusulinideen hervorgehoben. Diese äussert sich in der starken allgemeinen Vergrösserung und der Zunahme der Kompliziertheit des Baues, und zwar der Schalenwände, der Septen und der Mundöffnungen. Diese wesentlich erscheinenden morphologischen Merkmale werden auch in den neuesten Zusammenstellungen der Fusulinideenevolution beigezogen. Dabei glauben verschiedene Autoren, wie z.B. CIRY (1942) oder THOMPSON (1945) in dieser Entwicklung einen Ausdruck der Orthogenese erkennen zu können, während andere, z.B. DUNBAR und HENBEST (1942) darin den Einfluss innerer und äusserer Kräfte sehen wollen, wieder andere, so MIKLUKHO-MAKLAI (1959a), führen Tatsachen an, welche den Einfluss der Umwelt auf den Gang der Evolution der Fusulinideen bestätigen.

Im folgenden sollen einige Fragen der Evolution der Fusulinideen betrachtet werden, wobei besonders die Ergebnisse der Untersuchungen in den U.S.S.R. verwertet werden, ohne dass jedoch die Resultate, welche man in anderen Ländern erarbeitet hat, ausser Acht gelassen werden, da die Evolution eines grossen Stammes im Rahmen eines begrenzten Raumes kaum untersucht werden kann. Dabei haben die sovjetischen Forscher den grossen Vorteil, dass in den U.S.S.R. die jungpaläozoischen Ablagerungen weit verbreitet und vollständig sind. Es ist bekannt, dass die Fusulinideen nur in Gewässern mit gleichbleibender karbonatischer Sedimentation sich gut entwickeln konnten. Demzufolge kann die Evolution der in Frage stehenden Gruppe allein dort ausführlich untersucht werden, wo praktisch lückenlose karbonische und permische Ablagerungen in Form mariner Karbonatgesteine auftreten. Gerade solche Ablagerungen finden sich zahlreich in den U.S.S.R., während in Amerika, im südwestlichen

Europa, in Nordchina und in Japan im Karbon und Perm karbonatisch-terrigene Sedimentation mit grossen stratigraphischen Lücken vorherrschte.

Da die Evolution der Organismen im allgemeinen aus der Evolution der Arten folgt, soll im folgenden die Entwicklung der Fusulinideen gemäss systematischer Kategorien betrachtet werden. Der Rahmen der vorliegenden Studie erlaubt es lediglich, auf die Arten und Gattungen einzugehen, welche bereits gut bekannt und weit verbreitet, d.h. wenigstens zwei Kontinenten gemeinsam sind.

DER CHARAKTER DER EVOLUTION DER FUSULINIDEENARTEN

Das moderne System der Fusulinideen nähert sich immer mehr einer natürlichen, phylogenetischen Systematik, in erster Linie dank des Umstandes, dass die Ergebnisse der Evolutionsuntersuchungen an Arten — und nicht an Gattungen — herangezogen werden. Alle Forscher stimmen darin überein, dass morphologische Aehnlichkeit und geologisches Alter die Grundlagen der Entwicklungsinterpretation abgeben.

Es ist wohl ohne Zweifel, dass DEPRAT (1913) einem Irrtum verfiel, als er seine *Schwagerina prisca* [= *Profusulina prisca* (DEPRAT)] als Ahnenform der Schwagerinen und seine *Palaeofusulina prisca* als Ausgangsart der Fusulinen annahm, da ihm damals die geologischen Tatsachen noch nicht genügend bekannt waren. Demgegenüber nähert sich das von LEE (1933) vorgeschlagene Schema der Phylogenie der Fusulinideen bereits den heute als richtig angenommenen Vorstellungen, da dessen Angaben über die phylogenetischen Beziehungen auf geologisch-stratigraphischen Grundlagen aufgebaut sind. Heute kann die stratigraphische Verbreitung der Grosszahl der Fusulinideengattungen, mit Ausnahme einiger mittel- und spät-permischer Genera, als gut bekannt gelten.

Da in den älteren Arbeiten die noch ungenügenden Kenntnisse der Morphologie der Fusulinideenschale oft zu falschen Schlüssen führte, sollen in dieser Studie allein solche Kriterien benützt werden, welche in modernen Arbeiten beigezogen wurden.

In der umfangreichen Fusulinideenliteratur sind bis heute über tausend Arten beschrieben worden. Demgegenüber sind der Evolution der Arten allein ungefähr zehn Publikationen gewidmet, wenn man die nicht argumentierten oder nebenbei gemachten Bemerkungen ausser Betracht lässt.

Ausführlich ist die Evolution der Arten aus der Gattung *Triticites* GIRTY durch ROZOVSKAIA (1950) untersucht. Diese Autorin begründet die Evolution auf den folgenden morphologischen Gegebenheiten: Variabilität der Fusulinideenarten und ihrer Uebergangsformen[1]; Tatsachen der Ontogenese und der konkreten Phylogenese; Richtungen der Umgestaltung während der Phylogenese hinsichtlich der Grösse der Initialkammer und der Schale im Ganzen, der Intensivierung der Septenfaltung, der Verdickung der Schale, zusammen mit der Verstärkung ihres Baues und der Verände-

---

[1] Die Uebergangsformen zwischen nahe verwandten Gattungen sollen an späterer Stelle behandelt werden.

rung der Schalenform. Diese Veränderung der Schalen entwickelt sich anfangs von gebläht-spindelförmigen zu länglich-spindelförmigen Formen und divergiert später in zwei Richtungen, nämlich nach langgezogen-zylindrischen Formen einerseits, nach abgekürzt-geblähten, bis runden anderseits. Die wesentlichen Richtungen hinsichtlich der Triticiten-Evolution finden sich bereits in der Arbeit von BURMA (1942), wurden später durch THOMPSON (1957) bestätigt und in neuester Zeit durch MYERS (1958) noch ausführlicher dargelegt. Der letztgenannte Autor hebt vor allem die allmähliche Umgestaltung hinsichtlich der Form sowie das Auftreten von Uebergangsformen hervor.

Die Ontogenese der Triticiten wurde durch ROZOVSKAIA (1950) anhand von 25 Arten studiert. Dabei gruppierte diese Autorin die Arten aufgrund der Aehnlichkeit und der Beständigkeit hinsichtlich der Ontogenese morphologisch nahe verwandter Arten von gleichem geologischem Alter und weist sie vier Untergattungen zu.

Auf das ontogenetische Kriterium legt auch RAUZER-CHERNOUSOVA in ihren verschiedenen Arbeiten grossen Wert. Auf die Ontogenese und die Evolution der Gruppe *Profusulinella librovitchi* (DUTKEVICH) und der Reihe *Verella* DALMATSKAIA – *Eofusulina* RAUZER-CHERNOUSOVA wurde im speziellen in einer rezenten Publikation eingegangen (RAUZER-CHERNOUSOVA 1960a). Die Entwicklung der Pseudostaffellen aus der Reihe *Pseudostaffella antiqua* DUTKEVICH – *Pseudostaffella sphaeroidea* (EHRENBERG) wurde durch die genannte Autorin ausführlich in mehreren Publikationen behandelt (RAUZER-CHERNOUSOVA, 1949, 1960) sowie in einer im Druck befindlichen Arbeit. In der genannten Reihe ist die gerichtete Evolution sehr bemerkenswert, wobei sie sich speziell in der Variabilität der Populationen und in der Ontogenese der Arten äussert (Fig. 1). Im Verlaufe des Mittelkarbon lässt sich eine Verstärkung der Chomaten (sekundäre Ablagerungen der Wandsubstanz im Gebiete der Mundöffnung zur Verstärkung der Schale) bei der ganzen Gruppe beobachten, wobei gleichzeitig auch eine Vergrösserung der Schale festzustellen ist. Die Chomaten der ersten Umgänge aller Arten dieser Reihe sind primitiv ausgestaltet und rekapitulieren die Merkmale ihrer Ahnenformen. Die neuen Eigenschaften der Arten werden allein auf den letzten Umgängen sichtbar. Demzufolge lässt sich die Evolution anhand der Anlage eines neuen Stadiums und der Verschiebung neuer Merkmale auf eine ontogenetisch jüngere Stufe feststellen (Fig. 1).

Weniger ausführlich und hauptsächlich nur aufgrund der gegenseitigen Aehnlichkeit und Steigerung der Septenfaltung haben DUNBAR und HENBEST (1942) die Evolution einiger Arten von Fusulinellen und *Fusulina* FISCHER DE WALDHEIM aus Nordamerika beschrieben. Hinsichtlich der Entwicklung von *Pseudofusulina gümbeli* (DUNBAR und SKINNER) und *P. crassitectoria* (DUNBAR und SKINNER) sind die Angaben von ROSS (1960), welcher Autor die beiden in Rede stehenden Arten zur Gattung *Schwagerina* MOELLER rechnet, ausserordentlich interessant. Nach ROSS sind in den älteren Ablagerungen, wo *Schwagerina gümbeli* DUNBAR und SKINNER und *S. crassitectoria* DUNBAR und SKINNER zusammen auftreten, die beiden Arten nur sehr schwer zu unterscheiden. Demgegenüber sind in stratigraphisch höheren Lagen, wo die beiden Arten in verschiedenen Fazies vorkommen, die unterscheidenden diagnostischen Merkmale viel deutlicher.

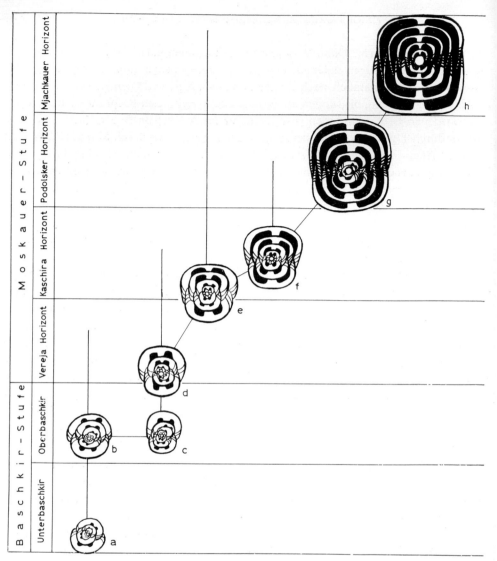

Fig. 1. Schematische Darstellung der Evolution innerhalb der Artenreihe *Pseudostaffella antiqua* (Dutkevich) – *Pseudostaffella sphaeroidea* (Ehrenberg).

(a) *Pseudostaffella antiqua* (Dutkevich) ⎫ (Beide Formen besitzen schwache, halbkreis-
(b) *Pseudostaffella antiqua grandis* Shlykova ⎭ förmige Chomaten).

(c) *Pseudostaffella praegorskyi* Rauzer-Chernousova (In den inneren Windungen wird das Stadium der *Pseudostaffella antiqua* (Dutkevich) rekapituliert; auf den äusseren Windungen erscheinen höhere, eckige Chomaten).

(d) *Pseudostaffella gorskyi* (Dutkevich) forma *primitiva* (Zu den bereits vorhandenen Stadien der *Pseudostaffella antiqua* (Dutkevich) und *Pseudostaffella praegorskyi* Rauzer-Chernousova wird ein neues Stadium mit starken, rechteckigen Chomaten angelegt).

(e) *Pseudostaffella gorskyi* (Dutkevich) (Eine Form mit mässig breiten Chomaten).

(f) *Pseudostaffella gorskyi* (Dutkevich) (Eine Form mit breiten Chomaten; die Ontogenese vollzieht sich in langsamer Morphogenese).

(g) *Pseudostaffella sphaeroidea* (Ehrenberg) (Die Ontogenese zeigt noch immer die Rekapitulation der Ahnenmerkmale).

(h) *Pseudostaffella sphaeroidea* (Ehrenberg) (Die bei der vorigen Form noch vorhandenen Rekapitulationsstadien sind verdrängt).

In diesem Zusammenhang erscheint die Frage nach der Ablaufsgeschwindigkeit der gerichteten Evolution für die Stratigraphie von besonderer Bedeutung. Nach der Auffassung von MYERS (1958) können die Evolutionsstadien der *Triticites*-Arten für die Korrelation der Ablagerungen benützt werden. Demgegenüber hat ROZOVSKAIA (1950) überzeugend nachgewiesen, dass die Hauptrichtungen der Evolution innerhalb dieser Gattung sich bei den Artengruppen wiederholen. Dies lässt sich auch innerhalb der von MYERS (1958) speziell studierten Gruppe von *Triticites plummeri* DUNBAR und CONDRA feststellen. Dass sich der Evolutionsvorgang in seinen Hauptzügen innerhalb grosser stratigraphischer Einheiten ziemlich gleichzeitig vollzieht, haben vor allem auch die durch RAUZER-CHERNOUSOVA an Pseudostaffellen durchgeführten Untersuchungen gezeigt. Allerdings können an konkreten Beispielen wesentliche Unterschiede auftreten. So erscheinen beispielsweise abweichende Exemplare vom Typus der *Pseudostaffella sphaeroidea* (EHRENBERG) in den Populationen von *P. gorskyi* (DUTKEVICH) bereits im Baschkirien in den Gebieten der Wolga und Kama. Allerdings scheinen diese abweichenden Exemplare keine Weiterentwicklung erfahren zu haben und sind genetisch auch nicht fixiert (RAUZER-CHERNOUSOVA, 1960b). Nach DUNBAR und HENBEST (1942) wiederholt sich die Weiterentwicklung der Septenfaltung bei einigen Gruppen innerhalb der Gattungen *Fusulina* FISCHER DE WALDHEIM und *Fusulinella* MOELLER auf verschiedenen Evolutionshöhen, wobei auf die sehr häufige Homoeomorphie innerhalb der Fusuliniden hingewiesen wird, welche zur Wiederholung der Evolutionsstufen führt. Allerdings muss nach VISSARIONOVA (1959), BRAZHNIKOVA (1956), ROZOVSKAIA (1952) und SEMIKHATOVA (1956) auch der Unterschied des geologischen Alters einiger Arten unter verschiedenen geotektonischen Bedingungen in Betracht gezogen werden.

Aus dem im Vorstehenden Gesagten wird es deutlich, dass die Evolution der Fusulinideenarten sich nicht immer überall gleichzeitig und in einer Richtung vollzieht. Somit können die Evolutionsstadien einzelner Arten auch nur mit grosser Vorsicht und unter Vorbehalt für stratigraphische Zwecke benutzt werden.

Die oben erwähnten Tatsachen hinsichtlich der Evolution der Fusulinideenarten bestätigen durchaus die Ansicht von BURMA (1942, 1948), wonach statistische Untersuchungen der Variabilität der Fusulinideen unentbehrlich sind. Die Variationsbreite innerhalb dieser Gruppe wird in den U.S.S.R. mit Hilfe zahlreicher Reihenfotos untersucht und ausgewertet (RAUZER-CHERNOUSOVA, 1953). Dieselbe Methode wird nach MERCHANT und KEROCHER (1939) sowie nach ROSS (1960) auch in den U.S.A. verwendet, doch hat es sich gezeigt, dass sie für diese Studien nicht vollauf genügt.

Die unzureichende Bearbeitung der Fusulinideenvariabilität hat in erster Linie ihre Ursache darin, dass die Evolutionsfaktoren bis heute noch zuwenig untersucht wurden, und die Fragen der Artbildung nicht die ihnen zukommende Beachtung gefunden haben, wenngleich die unmittelbare Abhängigkeit der Morphogenese von den Umweltfaktoren durch verschiedene Autoren speziell erwähnt wird. So weisen unter anderen DUNBAR und HENBEST (1942), THOMPSON (1948) sowie MIKLUKHO-MAKLAI (1959) auf den adaptiven Charakter einiger Artmerkmale hin, im besonderen auf jene, welche korrelativ bedingt sind, z.B. das Auftreten sekundärer Axialablagerungen bei den langen Formen, Verminderung der Chomaten bei Steigerung der Septenfaltung, u.s.w. In diesem Zusammenhang weist RAUZER-CHERNOUSOVA (1950) im speziellen auf die Unterschiede der Schalenform innerhalb einer Art oder innerhalb nahe verwandter Arten in verschiedenen Fazien hin: In den Riffazien erscheinen die Schalen kürzer und die Septenfaltung ist stärker ausgebildet, in den geschichteten Sedimenten der Riffumgebung jedoch finden sich mehr längliche und schwach gefaltete Formen derselben oder nahe verwandter Arten. BENSH (1955) hat gleichartige morphologische Veränderungen bei verschiedenen Arten aus ein und demselben Horizont beobachtet. Danach sind viele Arten aus den Gattungen *Pseudofusulina* DUNBAR und SKINNER und *Schwagerina* MOELLER im Ungartauer Horizont durch dickere Septen und stärkere Septenfaltung gekennzeichnet. Anderseits findet man bei allen im Ulukaer Horizont auftretenden Formen deutlich engere Windungen, während die kurzschaligen Triticiten hinsichtlich der Septen eine stärkere Faltung, die langschaligen jedoch eine Verstärkung an den Polen erkennen lassen. Die hier offenbare Einwirkung äusserer Umstände auf die Morphogenese von Unterarten muss bereits genetisch fixiert sein, da die morphologisch eindeutigen Merkmalsveränderungen sich einheitlich in mehreren aufeinanderfolgenden Generationen und in Ablagerungen beträchtlicher Mächtigkeit äusserten. Auch das Beispiel der Verstärkung der Chomaten bei den Pseudostaffellen im Verlaufe der Evolution kann als Beweis dafür angeführt werden, dass die Umweltseinflüsse auf die Selektion und auf die Richtung des Evolutionsprozesses einwirken. So sind die primitiven Pseudostaffellen noch aus ganz verschiedenen Fazien bekannt, während die späteren Formen deutlich eine Anpassung an ein Milieu erkennen lassen, welches zur Ablagerung von gröberen und zugleich seichteren sandigen Sedimenten führte.

Leider ist bis heute über die Palaeo-Oekologie der Fusulinideen nur sehr wenig bekannt geworden. Die letzte zusammenfassende Darstellung der Kenntnisse auf diesem Gebiete stammt von DUNBAR (1957). Leider sind jedoch in dieser Zusammenfassung die Arbeiten der sovjetischen Forscher, wie ROZOVSKAIA (1952) oder MANUKALOVA (1956) unberücksichtigt geblieben. In späterer Zeit wurde über die Palaeo-Oekologie der in Rede stehenden Gruppe auch von ROZOVSKAIA (1958), G. D. KIREEVA und MAKSIMOVA (1959), E. A. KIREEVA (1959), u.a. gearbeitet.

Für die Frage der Artbildung sind Untersuchungen der Faziesverhältnisse und der Periodizität in der Entwicklung der Fusulinideen in Beziehung zu den Sedimentationszyklen von besonderer Wichtigkeit (RAUZER-CHERNOUSOVA und KULIK, 1949; RAUZER-CHERNOUSOVA, 1953; LUN'IAK, 1953; SEMIKHATOVA, 1954, 1956; VOLOZHANINA, 1961). Aus diesen Untersuchungen kann ein wesentlicher Schluss gezogen werden: Bei den Fusulinideen fällt die Art- bzw. Gattungs-bildung nicht an den Anfang eines Sedimentationszyklus, sondern offensichtlich in eine etwas spätere Periode, d.h. in die Zeit der tektonisch ruhigeren Phasen.

Die letzte Frage, welche in diesem Zusammenhang noch Erwähnung finden muss, ist diejenige nach der Migration der Fusulinideen, im speziellen nach den Wanderwegen und den Wandergeschwindigkeiten. In diesem Zusammenhang glauben verschiedene Forscher, so z.B. DUNBAR (1933), dass die Evolution der Arten auf in sich geschlossene Meeresbecken begrenzt sei. Unter diesem Gesichtspunkt könnten dann die Arten an für sich interkontinentale Korrelationen kaum beigezogen werden, sondern lediglich die vergleichbaren Evolutionsstadien der Gattungen: Gattungszonen der Fusulinideen. Demgegenüber nehmen andere Forscher Wanderungen ganzer Artenkomplexe über grosse Räume an, wobei dann die Zonengliederung über grosse Strecken auf Arten basiert werden (KAHLER, 1939, 1952, etc.).

Es kann wohl als unbestritten angesehen werden, dass die Ausbreitung der Fusulinideen entlang der Küstenlinien oder Inselketten sehr rasch vor sich ging. Dies geht vor allem aus der Tatsache hervor, dass innerhalb der permischen Fusulinideen identische Arten oder nahe Rassenformen innerhalb eines relativ kurzen Zeitintervalles an voneinander sehr weit entfernten Fundorten aufgefunden werden. Gleichermassen beweist auch die weitgehende Identität der mittelkarbonischen Fusulinideen aus China und der Russischen Platte (bis 25 % der Typen einer Artengemeinschaft) die grosse Geschwindigkeit der Migration, indem diese Arten auch in den geographisch dazwischen liegenden Gebieten und in denselben stratigraphischen Lagen bekannt sind (RAUZER-CHERNOUSOVA, 1960). Gleichermassen kann das Uebereinstimmen der Fusulinideen-Arten im Asselien über weite Strecken (Schwagerinen Horizont, Wolfcamp Formation, Rattendorfer Schichten) allein mit Wanderungen über weite Räume erklärt werden (RAUZER-CHERNOUSOVA, 1961).

Von ausserordentlichem Interesse ist die von der Autorin in Zusammenarbeit mit S. SHERBOVICH (diesbezügliche Arbeit im Druck) festgestellte Identität der Fusulinden aus unterpermischen Ablagerungen Armeniens und Mittelamerikas. Dabei sind *Pseudofusulina grupperaënsis* (THOMPSON und MILLER), *Parafusulina australis* THOMPSON und MILLER und *P. guatemalensis* DUNBAR sowie *Staffella sphaerica* (ABICH) und Eoverbeekinen-Arten für die beiden geographisch sehr weit auseinanderliegenden Gebiete charakteristisch. Diese Feststellungen lassen die Vermutung aufkommen, dass die Wanderung der Fusulinideen nicht allein im Gebiet der seichten epikontinentalen Meere sich vollzog, wie dies DUNBAR (1957) angenommen hatte, sondern auch entlang der Schelfe der offenen Ozeane. Dabei ist die Möglichkeit, dass die Fusulinideen in sehr frühen Jugendstadien durch Strömungen auf weite Strecken hin verfrachtet wurden, nicht ganz von der Hand zu weisen.

Aus den im vorstehenden aufgezeigten wenigen Beispielen können für die Evolution der Fusulinideen die folgenden Schlüsse gezogen werden:

(a) Die grosse Variabilität innerhalb der Fusulinideen ist als Hauptfaktor der Evolution der Arten zu betrachten. Dabei ist ein gewisses Gerichtetsein hinsichtlich der allmählichen Umwandlung der Artmerkmale feststellbar. Dabei verhindern jedoch die Uebergangsformen zwischen den einzelnen Arten das klare Diagnostizieren der Arten nicht.

(b) Einige morphologische Artmerkmale sind durch Adaptation entstanden und durch Umwelteinflüsse und entsprechende Selektion bedingt.

(c) Die Evolution der Arten vollzieht sich in erster Linie durch die Rekapitulation der Merkmale ihrer Ahnenformen. Die neu erworbenen Artmerkmale erscheinen erst nach dem Jugendstadium und nicht selten tritt der Ansatz eines neuen Stadiums erst in der letzten Schalenwindung auf.

(*d*) Im allgemeinen werden die Gattungen, Artengruppen und einzelne Arten durch dieselbe Evolutionsrichtung charakterisiert. Der Evolutionsablauf verschiedener Artengruppen kann demzufolge ohne weiteres asynchron vor sich gehen, sodass die Evolutionsstadien einzelner Arten als Korrelationsgrundlage ungeeignet erscheinen.

(*e*) Die weiträumige geographische Verbreitung in sich identischer Arten führt zu der Annahme, dass man es mit einer monophyletischen Entwicklung gepaart mit rascher Migration aus dem Artbildungszentrum zu tun hat. Demzufolge können auch identische Artengemeinschaften für interkontinentale Zonengliederung ausgewertet werden.

DER CHARAKTER DER EVOLUTION DER FUSULINIDEENGATTUNGEN

In der einschlägigen Literatur sind bis heute rund hundert Fusulinideengattungen beschrieben, doch steigt die Zahl der neu beschriebenen Gattungen laufend. Nichtsdestotrotz ist jedoch über das geologische Alter und die Phylogenie dieser neu beschriebenen Gattungen nur sehr wenig bekannt. Es sollen demzufolge an dieser Stelle allein die Hauptgattungen (Fig. 2) und im speziellen diejenigen der von der Autorin besonders eingehend bearbeiteten aus der Superfamilie der Fusulinidea hinsichtlich ihrer Evolution betrachtet werden.

In den letzten Jahren wurde die Evolution der Fusulinideengattungen durch THOMPSON (1948, 1954), MIKLUKHO-MAKLAI (1953) sowie MIKLUKHO-MAKLAI et al. (1958) speziell erörtert. Eine grosse Zahl von Publikationen sind vor allem der Evolution einzelner Gattungen und Familien gewidmet, wobei diese Studien hauptsächlich die Hauptrichtungen innerhalb der Entwicklung aufgezeigt und die häufig auftretende Konvergenz und Parallelität einerseits, die Divergenz der Merkmale sowie andere Eigenarten hinsichtlich der Fusulinideenevolution anderseits beleuchtet haben. Im speziellen mit der Homoeomorphie haben sich besonders DUNBAR (1945) und neuestens MIKLUKHO-MAKLAI (1957, 1959a) beschäftigt. Im Gegensatz dazu sollen im folgenden in erster Linie diejenigen Fragen beleuchtet werden, welche bis heute in der Literatur weniger eingehend behandelt worden sind.

Nach der Ansicht von ISHII (1957) sind als Grundkriterien für die Deutung der Evolution und der systematischen Stellung der Fusulinideen allein die Ontogenese und das geologische Alter zu betrachten. Im Rahmen der von ihm durchgeführten Revision der Gattungen *Fusulina* FISCHER DE WALDHEIM und *Fusulinella* MOELLER wies ISHII im speziellen auf die Aehnlichkeit der Jugendstadien innerhalb der Fusuliniden vom Typus der *Fusulina girtyi* (DUNBAR und CONDRA) einerseits, auf die wesentlichen Unterschiede im Verlaufe der Ontogenese beim Generotyp *Fusulina cylindrica* FISCHER DE WALDHEIM anderseits hin. Während für die erste Artengruppe eine Abstammung von Fusulinellen wahrscheinlich gemacht wird, muss die Herkunft des zweiten Typus in einer anderen Richtung gesucht werden. Dabei kommt ISHII zum Schluss dass die Ausgangsform der ersten Gruppe in der Gattung *Beedeina* GALLOWAY zu finden ist, und diese Gattung demzufolge in ihrer taxonomischen Wertigkeit durchaus berechtigt ist.

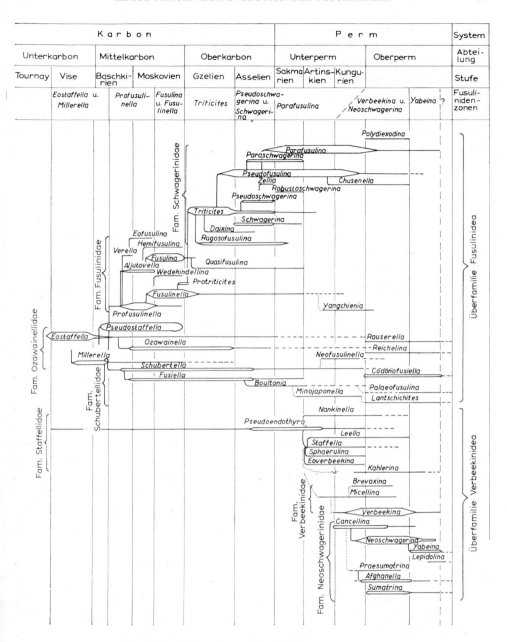

Fig. 2. Phylogenie der Fusuliniden.
Einfache Linie = geringe Artenzahl
Enge Doppellinie = ziemlich grosse Artenzahl
Breite Doppellinie = grosse Artenzahl

Auf die Tatsache, dass durch die Ontogenese die Ahnenmerkmale rekapituliert werden, haben eine grössere Zahl von sovjetischen Forschern hingewiesen, so vor allem im Rahmen mehrerer Studien MIKLUKHO-MAKLAI (1949, 1953, 1959a und

1959b). Als illustrierende Beispiele mögen dabei die folgenden Tatsachen speziell genannt sein: Die Ontogenese der Eofusulinen wiederholt die Merkmale der Ahnengattung *Verella* DALMATSKAIA; Die Primärwindungen der Fusulinellen gleichen sehr stark den bei den Profusulinellen auftretenden Windungen; Die bei den schwach gefalteten Triciten auftretenden morphologischen Merkmale finden sich auch in den Jugendstadien der Schwagerinen, diejenigen der stärker gefalteten Triticiten bei den Initialstadien der Pseudoschwagerinen; Die Ontogenese der Pseudofusulinen wiederholt bis zu einem gewissen Grade diejenige der Triticiten; Die Reichelinen und Rauserellen rekapitulieren die Merkmale der Ozawainellen. Innerhalb der Neoschwageriniden wurde die Systematik und die Phylogenie durch praktisch alle Forscher aufgrund der durch die Ontogenese ermittelten Zusammenhänge ermittelt. Für die Richtigkeit einer Anwendung des biogenetischen Grundgesetzes von HAECKEL zur Interpretation der Fusulinideenentwicklung kann noch eine ganze Reihe weiterer Beispiele angeführt werden. Selbst die amerikanischen Fusulinideenspezialisten, welche sich im Prinzip dem HAECKEL'schen Grundgesetz gegenüber eher skeptisch verhalten, mussten eingestehen, dass sehr oft eine Rekapitulation der Ahnenmerkmale innerhalb der Ontogenese feststellbar ist (vgl. DUNBAR und HENBEST, 1942, p. 53). In diesem Zusammenhang mag es von besonderem Interesse sein, zu erwähnen, dass ISHII (1957) sowie auch MIKLUKHO-MAKLAI (1959b) aufgrund der besonderen Ontogenese die Gattung *Kansanella*, welche von THOMPSON (1957) als neu beschrieben worden war, erkannten, obwohl der ursprüngliche Autor auf die besondere Ontogenese nicht speziell hingewiesen hatte.

Neue Gattungsmerkmale treten meistens im Erwachsenenstadium der Schale oder in den äussersten Windungen auf. Dabei verschieben sich im Verlaufe der Evolution die neu erworbenen Merkmale nach und nach auf jüngere Windungen. Dieses Phänomen ist von vielen Autoren beschrieben worden und findet sich besonders deutlich bei den Neoschwageriniden. Eine Reihe besonderer Fälle, bei denen innerhalb von Fusulinideengattungen die Rekapitulationsstadien während der Ontogenese vollkommen verdrängt werden und die neu erworbenen Gattungsmerkmale bereits in den ersten Windungen auftreten, sind von RAUZER-CHERNOUSOVA (1949) im speziellen erwähnt worden.

Auf die Bedeutung der Entwicklung der Wandstruktur der Schalen wurde in der Interpretation der Fusulinideenevolution durch WHITE (1932) zu grosses Gewicht gelegt, indem dieser Autor dieses Merkmal als das weitaus wichtigste betrachtete. Dass dem Merkmal der Wandstruktur als leitendem Prinzip zu grosse Bedeutung beigemessen worden war, wurde vor allem durch die Untersuchungen von MIKLUKHO-MAKLAI (1953), SKINNER und WILDE (1954), SOLOV'EVA (1955), u.a. deutlich, welche nachwiesen, dass die Entwicklungstendenz hinsichtlich der Schalenwände nicht geradlinig verläuft, sondern viele Abweichungen aufweist.

Es erscheint durchaus wahrscheinlich, dass jede Gattungsgruppe bzw. Familie ihre eigenen leitenden Merkmale hatte. So ist für die Familie der Ozawainellidae THOMPSON und FOSTER die Form der Schale als leitendes Hauptmerkmal anzusehen, während die Struktur der Wand innerhalb dieser Familie nicht von Wichtigkeit ist. So muss die Diaphanothek bei verschiedenen Formen der Pseudostaffellen, von der primitiven *Pseudostaffella antiqua* (DUTKEVICH) bis zu den spätesten Arten, als unbeständig betrachtet werden, und es können innerhalb der Gruppe der Pseudostaffellen kaum neue Gattungen aufgestellt werden, welche auf dem besonderen Bau der Schalenwände basieren.

Auch für die kleinen Gattungen der Familie der Schubertellidae SKINNER kann die Wandstruktur nicht als leitendes Merkmal betrachtet werden, da die Evolution offensichtlich in Richtung einer Umgestaltung der Schalenform und der Septenfaltung tendierte, was auch von SKINNER und WILDE (1954) anerkannt wurde. Demgegenüber kann die Wandstruktur innerhalb der Familie der Fusulinidae MOELLER als gutes gattungsdefinierendes Merkmal gewertet werden, indem innerhalb dieser Familie die Wandstruktur sich sehr rasch entwickelte. Andere generische Charaktermerkmale innerhalb der Fusuliniden ergeben die Septenfaltung, die Schalenform und die Chomaten. Innerhalb der Familie der Schwagerinidae DUNBAR und HENBEST wiederum verliert die Wandstruktur ihren leitenden Wert und an deren Stelle treten andere Merkmale.

Als gutes illustrierendes Beispiel für eine gerichtete Evolution mögen die beiden Entwicklungsäste innerhalb der Neoschwageriniden angeführt sein, welche von mehreren Autoren untersucht wurden, so von THOMPSON (1948), TUMANSKAIA (1953), MIKLUKHO-MAKLAI (1953) und KANMERA (1957). Zunahme der Schalengrösse sowie der Zahl der Umgänge zusammen mit der Kompliziertheit des Wandbaues und der Septen sind für die mehr kugeligen Formen der Reihe *Cancellina* HAYDEN – *Neoschwagerina* YABE – *Yabeina* DEPRAT charakteristisch, während innerhalb der Reihe *Praesumatrina* TUMANSKAIA – *Afghanella* THOMPSON – *Sumatrina* VOLZ den hohen und engen Parachomaten sowie der Verlängerung der Schale besondere diagnostische Wertigkeit zukommt.

Die Uebergangsformen zwischen den einzelnen Gattungen wurden von praktisch allen Forschern im Zusammenhang mit phylogenetischen Erläuterungen in Betracht gezogen. Da solche Uebergangsformen immer wieder erwähnt werden und eine Aufzählung einzelner Beispiele den Rahmen dieser Arbeit sprengen würde, sollen im folgenden lediglich einige allgemeine Bemerkungen angefügt werden.

Gattungsbildung und Uebergangsformen können zu verschiedenen Zeiten festgestellt werden, teils am Anfang der Gattungsentwicklung, teils während der Blütezeit, teils endlich am Ende des Vorkommens einer Gattung. Ein Auftreten von Uebergangsformen am Anfang der Gattungsentwicklung lässt sich innerhalb der Gattung *Pseudostaffella* THOMPSON feststellen, in welcher in der Gruppe *Pseudostaffella minor* RAUZER-CHERNOUSOVA Uebergangsformen zu den Gattungen *Schubertella* STAFF und WEDEKIND und *Profusulinella* RAUZER-CHERNOUSOVA und BEL'AEV auftreten. Oefters erscheinen Uebergangsformen während der Blütezeit einer Gattung, so u.a. in der Gruppe *Eostaffella protvae* RAUZER-CHERNOUSOVA, wo Ahnenformen von *Pseudostaffella* THOMPSON auftreten, oder in der Gruppe *Eostaffella ikensis* VISSARIONOVA, in welcher sich Ahnenformen der Ozawainelliden erkennen lassen. Bei den Schubertellen vollzieht sich während des Baschkirien innerhalb der Gruppe *Schubertella acuta* RAUZER-CHERNOUSOVA der Uebergang zu der Gattung *Fusiella* LEE und CHEN. Nach KANMERA (1957) findet auch innerhalb der Familie der Neoschwagerinidae DUNBAR und CONDRA eine Gattungsneubildung nicht in Form einer direkten Gattungsablösung statt, sondern während der Blütezeit einer Gattung aus einer Reihe von Uebergangsformen. Als Beispiele für eine Gattungsneubildung zur Zeit des Aussterbens einer Gattung seien aus der grossen Reihe hieher zu rechnender Typen die Gruppen *Profusulinella* RAUZER-CHERNOUSOVA und BEL'AEV – *Fusulinella* MOELLER, *Aljutovella* RAUZER-CHERNOUSOVA – *Fusulina* FISCHER DE WALDHEIM, *Fusulina* FISCHER DE WALDHEIM – *Quasifusulina* CHEN sowie *Protriticites* PUTRIA (? *Obsoletes* KIREEVA) – *Triticites* GIRTY speziell genannt, wobei angenommen werden kann, dass sich die an zweiter Stelle genannten Gattungen aus den höchstentwickelten Formen der an erster Stelle aufgeführten Genera herausentwickelt haben.

Innerhalb der Besprechung der Gattungsevolution kann man der Frage nach der Adaptation morphologischer Gattungsmerkmale kaum ausweichen. Es sollen deshalb auch dazu zwei Beispiele namhaft gemacht werden, nämlich die gerunzelte Wand bei den Rugosofusulinen und die schwagerinoide Aufrollung innerhalb der Gattungen, welche durch geblähte Formen charakterisiert sind.

Die durch die gerunzelte und gewellte Wand charakterisierte Gattung *Rugosofusulina* RAUZER-CHERNOUSOVA ist nicht allgemein anerkannt, vor allem deshalb, weil, wie MIKLUKHO-MAKLAI (1949) deutlich machte, die gerunzelte und gewellte Wand auch innerhalb mehrerer anderer Gattungen zu beobachten ist und deshalb diesem als Anpassungserscheinung zu interpretierenden Merkmal nach dem genannten Autor kaum gattungstypischer Wert beigemessen werden kann. Tatsächlich tritt die gerunzelte und gewellte Wand bei einigen Arten aus der Gattung *Triticites* GIRTY auf, doch ist dieses Merkmal bei diesen Arten unbeständig und ausserdem oft nur in den äussersten Windungen ausgebildet. Andere Autoren, wie beispielsweise ROZOVSKAIA (1958) oder BENSH (1955) wollen in der gerunzelten und gewellten Wand lediglich eine infraspezifische Variabilität sehen, welche als Folgeerscheinung von Einwirkungen äusserer Umstände zustande kommt. Das Auftreten von gewellten Wänden bei Exemplaren von *Fusulinella bocki* MOELLER wurde in neuester Zeit von NIKITINA (1961) beschrieben, wobei es wohl als bewiesen gelten kann, dass bei dieser Art das genannte Merkmal oekologisch-adaptiven Charakter besitzt. Demgegenüber ist das Vorkommen der gewellten Wand innerhalb der Gruppe *Fusulina aspera* CHERNOVA bereits genetisch fixiert, indem das in Diskussion stehende Merkmal hier bei mehreren Arten konstant auftritt. Während in den genannten, die gattungstypischen Merkmale von *Rugosofusulina* scheinbar entkräftenden Beispielen eine weitere Evolution der gewellten und gerunzelten Wand, eine dauernde Fixierung dieses Merkmales in der Reihe der sich weiter entwickelnden Formen, eine Zunahme der Artenzahl mit demselben Merkmal und eine Ausbreitung auf weitere Räume nicht festgestellt werden kann, können für alle in der Gattung *Rugosofusulina* zusammengefassten Arten diese Kriterien als erfüllt angesehen werden, sodass die Berechtigung dieser Gattung als durchaus genügend begründet zu betrachten ist.

Die durch Arten mit geblähten, kugeligen Schalen charakterisierten Gattungen mit schwach gefalteten oder geraden Septen und eng gewundenen Initialstadien (Schwagerinen, Pseudoschwagerinen, Zellien und Paraschwagerinen) wurden von vielen Forschern, so z.B. von DUNBAR (1945) als Planktonformen betrachtet. MIKLUKHO-MAKLAI (1959b) seinerseits anerkannte mit Recht den adaptiven Charakter des Auftretens schwagerinoider Windungen innerhalb der genannten Gattungen. Als Beweise für den adaptiven Charakter des genannten Merkmales führt der sovjetische Wissenschafter an, dass die Gattungen mit schwagerinoiden Windungen während des Asselien, wo die oekologischen Bedingungen durch die Transgression eines warmen und nährstoffreichen Meeres besonders günstig lagen, eine sehr weite Verbreitung aufweisen, während die genannten Gattungen ziemlich plötzlich ausstarben infolge veränderter Umweltsbedingungen. Es sind diese Gattungen blind endigende Aeste innerhalb der Entwicklungsreihe (Fig. 2).

Abschliessend kann bezüglich der mit der Gattungsbildung zusammenhängenden Problemen das folgende gesagt werden: Die Momente intensiver Gattungsbildung fallen immer mit bestimmten Phasen der geologischen Geschichte zusammen. Einen ersten Aufschwung der Gattungen beobachtet man am Ende des Baschkirien (Fig. 2). Während des Moskovien treten neue Gattungen nicht schon am Anfang dieser Stufe auf, sondern entwickeln sich erst etwas später, wobei ein Maximalauftreten in der zweiten Hälfte des Moskovien zu beobachten ist. Ein weiterer Aufschwung der Gattungen ist während des Asselien festzustellen, wobei an dieser Stelle erwähnt sein mag, dass diese letztere Stufe nach der Ansicht der Autorin nicht ins Untere Perm, sondern noch zum Karbon gehört. Die Frühpermzeit war für die Fusulinideen besonders ungünstig, was sich daran erkennen lässt, dass die Staffelliden, welche immer dann die Lebensräume der Vertreter der Superfamilie der Fusulinidea (MOELLER) CIRY einnahmen, wenn die Lebensbedingungen für die Fusulinidea ungünstig wurden, in dieser Zeit eine ausgesprochene Blüte erreichten. Später, zu Ende des Artinskien bzw. Kungurien (?) findet eine explosive Gattungsbildung bei den Staffelliden, Verbeekiniden, Schubertelliden u.a. statt, während die Fusuliniden eine der hervorragendsten Blütezeiten zu Ende des Perm erlebten.

Aus dem im vorstehenden gegebenen kurzen Ueberblick ergibt sich eindeutig, dass sowohl die Umwelteinflüsse als auch die geologische Geschichte die Gattungsbildung beeinflussten. Die Blütezeit der Fusulinideen fällt immer mit den ruhigen Phasen weiter Transgressionen in der zweiten Hälfte der Stufen bzw. Abteilungen oder mit dem Ende der Systeme zusammen. Es erscheint wesentlich und ausserordentlich interessant, dass dieses Ereignis weltweit verbreitet ist. Man muss vielleicht dafür nicht allein die Ursache in dem zyklischen Gang der geologischen Geschichte suchen, sondern auch in der Einwirkung kosmischer Faktoren. Sollte diese letztere Vermutung bewiesen werden können, so würden die stratigraphischen Grenzen auf mehr natürlichen Grundlagen basieren.

In Zusammenfassung des im Vorstehenden gesagten können die folgenden Schlussfolgerungen gezogen werden:

(a) Ein prinzipieller Unterschied zwischen der Evolution der Arten und der Evolution der Gattungen besteht nicht. Die Mehrzahl der Gattungen entwickelte sich allmählich aus Uebergangsformen und rekapituliert in den Jugendstadien die Merkmale der Ahnenformen, während die neu erworbenen Merkmale in den späteren Stadien auftreten. Adaptive Merkmale können genetisch fixiert werden und dann den Wert eines Gattungsmerkmales erhalten.

(b) Die Evolution der Gattungen wird mehr von leitenden Merkmalen beeinflusst. Diese Merkmale wechseln ihren Wert im Verlaufe der Gattungsentwicklung, doch sind sie meist typisch und konstant für die Gattungen ein und derselben Familie bzw. Unterfamilie. Dies bezeugt ihre gemeinsame Abstammung.

(c) Das Aufblühen neuer Gattungen und das Auftreten von Uebergangsformen kann zu verschiedenen Zeiten beobachtet werden, doch ist dieses Phänomen für jede Gattung bzw. Gattungsgruppe charakteristisch.

(d) Die weltweit verbreiteten Blütezeiten der verschiedenen Fusulinideenfamilien fallen mit den thalattokratischen Phasen des zyklischen Ablaufes der geologischen Geschichte zusammen und sind vielleicht durch kosmische Einflüsse bedingt.

DER CHARAKTER DER EVOLUTION DER FUSULINIDEENFAMILIEN

Auf die Eigenart der Evolution einiger Familien wurde bereits im Rahmen der Besprechung der Gattungsentwicklung hingewiesen. Ebenfalls wurde bereits im vorstehenden hervorgehoben, dass jede Familie durch die ihr eigenen Leitmerkmale charakterisiert wird. Es muss an dieser Stelle darauf hingewiesen werden, dass einige Familien (Fusulinidae MOELLER, Schwagerinidae DUNBAR und HENBEST) eine oder zwei progressive Hauptgattungen aufweisen, welche auch für das Auftreten neuer Elemente innerhalb der direkt folgenden Familien verantwortlich sind. Die bereits aufgeführten Beispiele haben aufgezeigt, wie wichtig es für die phylogenetische Systematik ist, die richtigen Leitmerkmale sowie die Evolutionsrichtung der Familien zu unterscheiden, doch erlaubt es der Rahmen der vorliegenden Veröffentlichung leider nicht, näher auf diese Fragen einzutreten.

Die Evolutionsgeschwindigkeit sowie der Charakter der Evolution ist bei den einzelnen Familien sehr verschieden. So zeigt die phylogenetisch älteste Familie der Ozawainellidae THOMPSON und FOSTER eine sehr langsame Evolutionsgeschwindigkeit und die hieher gehörigen Gattungen zeigen eine lange stratigraphische Verbreitung (Fig. 2). Deshalb steht auch die Gattung *Pseudostaffella* THOMPSON der Familie der Ozawainellidae noch näher als der Familie der Fusulinidae MOELLER, zu welcher sie lange Zeit wegen ihrer Wandstruktur gerechnet wurde. Denselben Evolutionstypus findet man auch bei den älteren Schubertelliden und Staffelliden, während die Entwicklung der Familien der Fusulinidae MOELLER und der Schwagerinidae DUNBAR und HENBEST einen vollkommen anderen Evolutionstypus repräsentieren. Dieser ist durch das Auftreten rasch sich verzweigender und schnell sich entwickelnder Gattungen, welche jedoch auch rasch wieder aussterben, gekennzeichnet und findet sich in erster Linie bei den beiden genannten mittel- und ober-karbonischen Familien. Einen ähnlichen Evolutionstypus zeigen wahrscheinlich auch die spätpermischen Familien der Verbeekiniden und der Neoschwageriniden, doch sind diese bis heute noch zu wenig eingehend untersucht, um eine endgültige Entscheidung zuzulassen (RAUZER-CHERNOUSOVA und ROZOVSKAIA, 1955).

Auffallend ist der Umstand, dass die ältesten und sich nur langsam weiter entwickelnden Gattungen der Ozawainellidae THOMPSON und FOSTER, der Schubertellidae SKINNER und der Staffellidae (MIKLUKHO-MAKLAI) THOMPSON plötzlich am Ende ihrer Entwicklung einen raschen evolutionären Aufschwung erreichten und zur Entwicklung von aberranten, planktischen Gattungen führten (MIKLUKHO-MAKLAI, et al., 1958). Die kleinere Gestalt der zu den drei genannten Familien gehörenden Arten sowie die primitivere Schalenstruktur haben höchstwahrscheinlich eine rasche Anpassung an die veränderten Lebensumstände im planktischen Milieu erleichtert und eine Besiedlung der durch das Aussterben der grösseren und weiter entwickelten Fusulinideen leer gewordenen Lebensräume stark begünstigt.

Es bleibt am Schluss dieses Abschnittes noch darauf hinzuweisen, dass die älteren, sich langsam entwickelnden Gattungen verhältnismässig artenarmer waren, sich langsamer ausbreiteten, ein relativ enger begrenztes Areal einnahmen und meist an bestimmte Fazies gebunden waren, während die sich rasch entwickelnden Vertreter der jüngeren Familien der Fusulinidae, der Schwagerinidae und der Neoschwagerinidae verhältnismässig die höchste Zahl an Gattungen und Arten aufweisen, sehr weit verbreitet waren und in verschiedenen Fazies angetroffen werden. Die letzteren Arten und Gattungen sind denn auch für stratigraphische Belange besonders wertvoll (RAUZER-CHERNOUSOVA und REITLINGER, 1957).

DIE AHNENFORMEN DER FUSULINIDEEN

Unser Ueberblick über die Evolution der Fusulinideen wäre unvollständig, würden wir nicht auch der Frage nach ihren mutmasslichen Vorfahren einige Worte gönnen. Allgemein betrachtet man die Endothyren als die Ahnenform der Fusulinideen. Diese Annahme gründet sich auf dem Bau der ersten Schalenwindungen der Fusulinideen. Die Jugendwindungen der Angehörigen der Ozawainelliden sowie vieler Schubertelliden und der primitiven Gattungen der Fusuliniden sind durch die Verschiebung der Achsenrichtung sowie durch die nautiloide oder linsenförmige Schalenform gekennzeichnet. Diese Merkmale treten bei den Schwageriniden nur selten auf, während sie sich wieder bei einigen Vertretern aus den Familien der Verbeekiniden und der Neoschwageriniden feststellen lassen. Die Konstanz dieser Eigenschaften bei gewissen Familien einerseits, das Verschwinden derselben Merkmale im Verlaufe der Evolution innerhalb anderer Familien anderseits, kann schwerlich allein durch die Einwirkung physikalischer, speziell mechanischer Kräfte während des Wachstums der ersten Kammern erklärt werden, wie dies DUNBAR und HENBEST (1934, 1942) befürworten. Nach der Meinung der Autorin der vorliegenden Zusammenstellung handelt es sich dabei vielmehr um eine Rekapitulation der Merkmale der Ahnenformen. So machen vor allem die zu beobachtenden Uebergangsformen der Eostaffellen und der Endothyren (*Endothyra staffelliformis* CHERNYSHEVA und *Endothyra transita* LIPINA) eine Herkunft der Eostaffellen von den Endothyren sehr wahrscheinlich.

Etwas schwieriger gestaltet sich die Frage der Herkunft bei den Staffelliden. Bereits THOMPSON (1954) hat mit Recht die Aufmerksamkeit auf die besondere Beschaffenheit der Wandstruktur der Staffelliden gelenkt, welche in der Folge auch den Anlass zur Aufstellung der Gattungen *Eostaffella* und *Parastaffella* durch RAUZER-CHERNOUSOVA (1948) bot. Die besondere Wandstruktur der Staffellen und der ihr ähnlichen Gattungen genügt nach der Ansicht von THOMPSON (1954) durchaus, die Unterfamilie der Staffellinae MIKLUKHO-MAKLAI als eigene Familie abzutrennen und ihre besondere Herkunft zu beweisen, wobei wir uns ohne weiteres in dieser Hinsicht mit THOMPSON einverstanden erklären können. Ergänzend kann hier noch beigefügt werden, dass die Eostaffellen in den ersten Windungen immer eine gerundete Peripherie aufweisen, während alle Staffelliden die linsenförmige Gestalt des ersten Stadiums der Ontogenese beibehalten haben, wobei ihre Achsenlage praktisch kaum schwankt. Es ist sehr wahrscheinlich, dass die Ahnenformen der Staffelliden eine linsenförmige Schale aufwiesen, wobei die Windungsachsen ziemlich beständig waren.

Die verschiedene Herkunft der Eostaffellen einer-, der Staffelliden anderseits führt zu den folgenden Schlussfolgerungen:

Die Staffelliden müssen der Superfamilie der Verbeekinidea STAFF und WEDEKIND und nicht derjenigen der Fusulinidea (MOELLER) CIRY untergeordnet werden, da das Hauptmerkmal der Verbeekinideen, die Parachomaten, bereits bei zwei Gattungen der Staffelliden vorhanden ist. Dabei sind die Eoverbeekinen und *Staffella sphaerica* (ABICH) einander derart ähnlich, dass nur ein sehr guter Erhaltungszustand der Parachomaten (was bei diesen Formen leider nur sehr selten angetroffen wird) diese zwei Gruppen zu unterscheiden erlaubt. Es ist deshalb nicht weiter verwunderlich, dass bereits THOMPSON (1948) die Berechtigung der Selbständigkeit der beiden Gattungen in Frage gestellt hat, doch haben Untersuchungen an Exemplaren von *Staffella sphaerica* (ABICH) aus Armenien eindeutig erwiesen, dass bei dieser Form die Parachomaten vollkommen fehlen. Immerhin ist die sehr nahe Verwandtschaft zwischen den Staffellen und den Eoverbeekinen unbestritten, sodass die Gattung *Eoverbeekina* LEE zweifelsohne zu den Staffelliden gestellt werden muss. Bei der den Staffellen ebenfalls nahestehenden Gattung *Kahlerina* KOCHANSKY-DEVIDÉ und RAMOVŠ sind die Parachomaten ebenfalls gut ausgebildet. Es scheint, dass die Stammform der Verbeekiniden und der Neoschwageriniden unter den Staffelliden zu suchen ist, doch ist dies eine der noch immer ungelösten Fragen innerhalb der Fusulinideenevolution.

Es mag zum Schluss der vorliegenden Zusammenstellung nochmals auf die Tatsache hingewiesen sein, dass noch viele der im vorigen berührten Fragen noch lange nicht eindeutig und allgemein befriedigend gelöst erscheinen und demzufolge sicherlich bis zu einem gewissen Grade diskutabel bleiben. Nicht allein die Variabilität innerhalb der Fusulinideen bedarf noch einer ausführlichen und gründlichen Untersuchung, sondern auch die allgemeineren Fragen der Artbildung sowie die Einwirkungen der oekologischen Faktoren auf die Morphogenese bleiben noch ein weites und immer noch weitgehend unbearbeitetes Untersuchungsgebiet. Wenn die vorliegende Zusammenstellung die Aufmerksamkeit auf diese interessanten und aktuellen Fragen zu richten vermochte, so erachtet die Autorin dieser Zeilen ihre Aufgabe als durchaus erfüllt.

SUMMARY

In the above article, "Some Problems of the Evolution of Fusulinids", the general trends of evolution in this group are outlined. The subject is treated in three parts, viz. (*a*) evolutionary trends in species, (*b*) evolutionary trends in genera, and (*c*) evolutionary trends in families.

(*a*) The great variability within the species is considered to be the main factor in evolution. Some specific morphological characters have originated through adaptation to environment and selection. The evolution of species is characterized by the recapitulation of morphological features of the ancestral forms. The newly gained specific characters develop only after the initial stages. Evolution within different groups of species may well develop asynchronously, since the same evolutionary trends are followed in different taxonomic groups. Evolutionary stages of the species are therefore not suitable as a basis for stratigraphic correlation. The wide geographical range of identical species leads to the conclusion that they originated monophyletically and migrated within a short period. Accordingly, specific associations may well be used as a basis for intercontinental correlation.

(*b*) The trends of evolution in genera do not differ essentially from those recognized in species. Most genera originated gradually from transitional forms, and recapitulate in the initial stage the characters of the ancestral forms. Adaptive characters may become genetically fixed, and may then be of generic value. The development of new genera and the occurrence of transitional forms may take place at different times. However, it must be emphasized that this phenomenon is characteristic of each genus or generic group. The worldwide optima for the fusulinid families coincide with thalattocratic phases and is possibly due to cosmic influences.

(*c*) The phylogenetically most ancient families show a very slow evolution, and their genera and species are stratigraphically very long-ranging. At the end of this slow evolution, however, they exhibit a sudden outburst which led to a number of aberrant planktonic genera. It is pointed out that the genus *Pseudostaffella* most probably belongs to the family Ozawainellidae. The more advanced families, on the other hand, show an entirely different type of evolution, characterized by a sudden and multibranching outburst of genera with a short stratigraphic range.

The final chapter suggests that the ancestors of the fusulinids might have been the endothyrids. Most evolutionary trends are illustrated by pertinent examples. Much work still remains to be done, and the author considers her summarizing paper merely a basis for discussion, not a statement of final conclusions.

LITERATUR[1])

BENSH, F. R.; Бенш, Ф. Р., 1955. Стратиграфия и фузулиниды верхнепалеозойских отложений Северной Ферганы (автореферат диссертации), Ташкент, 1955. (Stratigraphie und Fusuliniden der oberpaläozoischen Ablagerungen im nördlichen Teiles des Bezirkes Fergana). Autorreferat der Dissertation, *Akad. Wiss. Usbek. S.S.R., Tashkent,* 1955: 1–16.

BRAZHNIKOVA, N. E.; Бражникова, Н. Е., 1956. „Фораминиферы" в сборнике „Фауна и флора каменноугольных отложений Галицийско-Волынской впадины" ("Foraminiferen" in "Fauna und Flora der Karbon-Ablagerungen des galizischen und volhynischen Beckens"). Тр. Инст. геол. наук АН УССР, сер. стратигр. палеонт. *Trudy Inst. geol. Nauk, Akad. Nauk Ukr.SSR, Ser. Stratigr. Paleontol.,* 10 : 16–103.

BURMA, B. H., 1942. Missourian *Triticites* of the northern mid-Continent. *J. Paleontol.,* 16 : 739–755.

BURMA, B. H., 1948. Studies in quantitative paleontology: I. Some aspects of the theory and practice of quantitative invertebrate paleontology. *J. Paleontol.,* 22 : 725–761.

CIRY, R., 1942. Les fusulinidés de Turquie. *Ann. Paléontol.,* 29 : 51–78.

DEPRAT, J., 1912. Étude des fusulinidés de Chine et d'Indochine et classification des Calcaires à fusulines. *Mem. serv. géol. Indochine,* 1 : 1–63.

DEPRAT, J., 1913. Les fusulinidés des calcaires Carboniferiens et Permiens du Tonkin, du Laos et du Nord-Annam. *Mem. serv. géol. Indochine,* 2 : 1–76.

DOUVILLE, H., 1906. Les Calcaires à fusulines de l'Indo-Chine. *Bull. Soc. géol. France, 4e sér.,* 6 : 576–587.

DUNBAR, C. O., 1945. The geologic and biologic significance of the evolution of the Fusulinidae, *Trans. N. Y. Acad. Sci., Ser. 2,* 7 (8) : 57–60.

DUNBAR, C. O., 1957. Fusuline Foraminifera. In: J. W. HEDGPETH *(Editor),* Treatise on marine ecology and paleoecology. 2. *Geol. Soc. Am. Mem.,* 67 : 753–754.

DUNBAR, C. O. and HENBEST, L. G., 1934. Comparative anatomy and evolutionary trends of Pennsylvanian Fusulinidae. *Proc. Geol. Soc. Am.,* 1933 : 352–353.

DUNBAR, C. O. and HENBEST, L. G., 1942. Pennsylvanian Fusulinidae of Illinois. *Illinois State Geol. Survey, Bull.,* 67 : 1–218.

ISHII, K., 1957. On the so-called *Fusulina. Proc. Japan Acad.,* 33 : 652–656.

KAHLER, F., 1939. Verbreitung und Lebensdauer der Fusulinen-Gattungen *Pseudoschwagerina* und *Paraschwagerina* und deren Bedeutung für die Grenze Karbon – Perm. *Senkenbergiana,* 21 : 169–215.

KAHLER, F., 1952. Entwicklungsräume und Wanderwege der Fusuliniden am Eurasiatischen Kontinent. *Geologie,* 4 : 178–188.

KAHLER, F. und KAHLER, G., 1937. Stratigraphische und fazielle Untersuchungen im Oberkarbon und Perm der Karnischen Alpen. *Compt. rend., 2e Congrès stratigr. Carbonifère, Heerlen,* 1 : 445–487.

KAHLER, F. und KAHLER, G., 1938. Beobachtungen an Fusuliniden der Karnischen Alpen. *Zentr. Geol. u. Palaeontol., Ser. B,* 4 : 101–116.

KANMERA, K., 1957. Revised classification of *Cancellina* and *Neoschwagerina,* and evolution of Sumatrininae and Neoschwagerininae. *Mem. Fac. Sci. Kyushu Univ., Ser. D (Geol.),* 6 : 47–64.

KIREEVA, E. A.; Киреева, Е. А., 1959. Опыт использования данных экогении для детального стратиграфического подразделения осадочных отложений. (Versuch der Auswertung oekologischer Daten für detailstratigraphische Untersuchungen von Sedimentgesteinen). Учен. зап. Саратовск. Гос. Унив., вып. геол. *Uchen. zap. Saratovsk. Gos. Univ., vyp. Geol.,* 65 : 13–19.

KIREEVA, G. D.; Киреева, Г. Д., 1949. Некоторые новые виды фузулинид из каменноугольных известняков центрального района Донбасса. (Einige neue Fusuliniden aus den Karbon-Kalken des zentralen Teiles des Donez-Becken). Тр. геол. исслед. бюро Главуглеразведки. *Trudy geol. issled. Biuro Glavuglerazvedki,* 6 : 25–55.

---

[1] Transkriptionen der russischen Autornamen und der Titel russischer Zeitschriften nach dem "Library of Congress System".

KIREEVA, G. D. und MAKSIMOVA, S.; Киреева, Г. Д., Максимова, С. 1959 Фациальные изменения известняков Донецкого бассейна. (Fazielle Veränderungen der Kalkstein-lagen des Donez-Becken). Тр. Всес. научно-исслед. инст. прир. газов. *Trudy Vses. nauchno-issled. Inst. prirod. gazov*, 4 : 3–127.

LEE, J. S., 1933. Taxonomic criteria of Fusulinidae with notes on seven new Permian genera. *Mem. Nat. Research Inst. Geol.*, 314 : 1–32.

LUN'IAK, I. A.; Луньяк, И. А., 1953. Учет фациальной зависимости фауны фораминифер при корреляции разрезов верхнего карбона. (Analyse der faziellen Abhängigkeit der Fusuliniden bei der Korrelation der Oberkarbon-Ablagerungen). Материалы Палеонтологического совещания по палеозою,1951г. Акад. наук СССР. *Materialy paleontologicheskogo soveshchaniia po paleozoiu, Akad. Nauk. S.S.S.R.*, (1951) : 161–171.

MANUKALOVA, M.; Манукалова, М., 1956. Стратиграфическое подразделение среднего карбона Донецкого бассейна по фораминиферам. (Stratigraphische Gliederung des Mittelkarbons des Donez-Becken auf Grund von Foraminiferen). Бюлл. Моск. Общ. испыт. прир., отд. геол. *Biull. Mosk. Obshch. Ispyt. prir., otd. Geol.*, 31 (6) : 79–102.

MERCHANT, F. E. and KEROCHER, R. P., 1939. Some fusulinids from the Missouri Series of Kansas. *J. Paleontol.*, 13 : 594–614.

MIKLUKHO-MAKLAI, A. D.; Миклухо-Маклай, А. Д., 1949. Верхнепалеозойские фузулиниды Средней Азии. Ленинград. (*Oberpalaeozoische Fusuliniden von Zentral-Asien*). Leningrader Univ., Leningrad, 110 pp.

MIKLUKHO-MAKLAI, A. D.; Миклухо-Маклай, А. Д., 1953. К систематике семейства Fusulinidae. (Zur Systematik der Familie Fusulinidae). Уч. зап. енинг адск. Гос. У ив. *Uchen. zap. Leningradsk. Gos. Univ.*, 159 (3) : 12–24.

MIKLUKHO-MAKLAI, A. D.; Миклухо-Маклай, А. Д., 1957. О гомеоморфии фузулинид. (Ueber die Homoeomorphie der Fusuliniden). Ежегодн. Всес. палеонт. общ. *Ezhegodn. Vses. Paleontol. obshch.*, 26 : 48–56.

MIKLUKHO-MAKLAI, A. D.; Миклухо-Маклай, А. Д., 1959. Значение гомеоморфии для систематики фузулинид. (Der Wert der Homoeomorphie für die Systematik der Fusu-liniden). Учен. зап. Ленинградск. Гос. Унив., сер. геолог. наук, *Uchen. zap. Leningradsk. Gos. Univ. 268, Ser. Geol. Nauk*, 10 : 155–172.

MIKLUKHO-MAKLAI, A. D.; Миклухо-Маклай, А. Д., 1959b. Систематика и филогения фузулинид(род *Triticites* и близкие к нему роды). (Systematik und Phylogenie der Fusuliniden (Gattung *Triticites* und dieser nahestehende Gattungen)). Вестн. Ленинградск. Унив. сер. геол. и геогр. *Vestn. Leningradsk. Univ. 6, Ser. Geol. Geogr.*, 1 : 5–23.

MIKLUKHO-MAKLAI, A. D., RAUZER-CHERNOUSOVA, D. M. und ROZOVSKAIA, S. E.; Миклухо-Маклай, А. Д., Раузер-Черноусова, Д. М., Розовская, С. Е., 1958. Филогения и систематика фузулинид. (Phylogenie und Systematik der Fusuliniden). Вопр. микропалеонт., сборн. *Vopr. Micropaleontol. Sborn.*, 2 : 5–21.

MYERS, D., 1958. Stratigraphic distribution of some Fusulinids from the Thrifty Formation, Upper Pennsylvanian, Central Texas. *J. Paleontol.*, 32 : 677–681.

NIKITINA, G. P.; Никитина, Г. П., 1961. О волнистой стенке у некоторых фузулинелл. (Ueber die wellige Wand bei einigen Fusulinellen). Вопр. микропалеонт., сборн. *Vopr. mikropaleontol. Sborn.*, 5 : 143–146.

RAUZER-CHERNOUSOVA, D. M.; Раузер-Черноусова, Д. М., 1948. Материалы к фауне фораминифер каменноугольных отложений Центрального Казахстана. (Materialien zur Foraminiferenfauna der Karbonablagerungen Zentral-Kazakhstans). Тр. Инст. геол. наук АН СССР. *Trudy Inst. geol. Nauk, Akad. Nauk. S.S.S.R.*, 66 : 1–27.

RAUZER-CHERNOUSOVA, D. M.; Раузер-Черноусова, Д. М., 1949. Об онтогенезе не-которых палеозойских фораминифер. (Ueber die Ontogenese einiger paläozoischer Foraminiferen). Тр. Палеонт. инст. АН СССР. *Trudy paleontol. Inst. Akad. Nauk. S.S.S.R.*, 20 : 339–353.

RAUZER-CHERNOUSOVA, D. M.; Раузер-Черноусова, Д. М., 1950. Фации верхнекамен-
ноугольных и артинских отложений Стерлитамакско-Ишимбайского
Приуралья (на основе изучения фузулинид), (Die Fazien des Oberkarbons und der
Artinsker Stufe des Uralvorlandes im Raume von Sterlitamak-Ishimbaisk — nach den Untersuch-
ungen der Fusuliniden). Тр. Инст. геол. наук АН СССР. *Trudy Inst. geol. Nauk, Akad.
Nauk. S.S.S.R.*, 119 : 1–109.

RAUZER-CHERNOUSOVA, D. M.; Раузер-Черноусова, Д. М., 1953a. Опыт и форма кол-
лективных работ в области изучения верхнепалеозойских фораминифер.
(Organisation und Ergebnisse der Gemeinschafts-Arbeiten zum Studium der oberpaläozoischen
Foraminiferen). Материалы палеонтологического совещания по палеозою,
АН СССР 1951. *Materialy paleontologicheskogo soveshchaniia po paleozoiu, Akad. Nauk.
S.S.S.R.*, 1951 : 71–80.

RAUZER-CHERNOUSOVA, D. M.; Раузер-Черноусова, Д. М., 1953b. Периодичность в
развитии фораминифер верхнего палеозоя и ее значение для расчленения
и сопоставления разрезов. (Die Periodizität in der Entwicklung der Foraminiferen des
Oberpaläozoikum und ihre Bedeutung für die Gliederung und Korrelation der Ablagerungen).
Материалы палеонтологического совещания по палеозою, АН СССР 1951.
Materialy paleontologicheskogo soveshchaniia po paleozoiu, Akad. Nauk. S.S.S.R., 1951 : 139–160.

RAUZER-CHERNOUSOVA, D. M., 1960a. Sur l'ontogénèse chez les fusulinidés. *Bull. Soc. géol. France*,
7e sér., 1 (7) : 658–661.

RAUZER-CHERNOUSOVA, D. M.; Раузер-Черноусова. Д. М., 1960b. Критерии географи-
ческого ареала в систематике фораминифер. (Die Kriterien des geographischen
Areales in der Systematik der Foraminiferen). Сборн. ,,Дочетвертичная микропалеон-
тология''. Докл. советск. геол. Междун. Геол. Конгр., XXI. сессия. Москва.
*Sborn. "Dochetvertichnaia mikropaleontologiia", Dokl. sovetsk. geol. mezhdyn. Geol. Kongr. 21
Sessiia, Moskva*, pp. 23–31.

RAUZER-CHERNOUSOVA, D. M.; Раузер-Черноусова, Д. М., 1961. Ревизия швагерин
с близкими родами и граница карбона и перми. (Revision der Schwagerinen nebst
nahestehender Gattungen und die Karbon-Perm-Grenze). Вопр. микропалеонт., сборн.
Vopr. mikropaleontol. Sborn., 4 : 3–32.

RAUZER-CHERNOUSOVA, D. M. und KULIK, E. L.; Раузер-Черноусова, Д. М., Кулик, Е. Л.,
1949. Об отношении фузулинид к фациям и периодичность в их развитии.
(Ueber die Wechselbeziehungen zwischen Fusuliniden und Fazien und über die Periodizität in ihrer
Entwicklung). Изв. АН СССР, сер. геол. *Izv. Akad. Nauk. S.S.S.R., Ser. Geol.*, 6 : 131–148.

RAUZER-CHERNOUSOVA, D. M. und REITLINGER, E. A.; Раузер-Черноусова, Д. М., Рейт-
лингер, Е. А., 1957. Развитие фораминифер в палеозойское время и их
стратиграфическое значение. (Die Entwicklung der Foraminiferen während des Paläo-
zoikum und ihr stratigraphischer Wert). Изв. АН СССР, сер. геол.- *Izv. Akad. Nauk.
S.S.S.R., Ser. Geol.*, 11 : 103–124.

RAUZER-CHERNOUSOVA, D. M. und REITLINGER, E. A.; Раузер-Черноусова, Д. М., Рейт-
лингер, Е. А. (im Druck). О формообразовании у фораминифер. (Ueber die Form-
bildung der Foraminiferen). Вопр. микропалеонт., сборн. *Vopr. mikropaleontol., Sborn.*,
6 : im Druck.

RAUZER-CHERNOUSOVA, D. M. und ROZOVSKAIA, S. E.; Раузер-Черноусова, Д. М., Розовская С. Е., 1955. Систематика и филогения фузулинид (автореферат доклада)
(Die Systematik und Phylogenie der Fusuliniden; Sitzungs-Autorreferat). Бюлл. Моск. общ.
испыт. прир., отд. геол. *Biull. Mosk. obshch.ispyt.prir., otd. geol.*, 3 (6) : 99–100.

ROZOVSKAIA, S. E.; Розовская, С. Е., 1950. Род *Triticites*, его развитие и стратиграфическое значение. (Die Gattung *Triticites*, ihre Entwicklung und ihr stratigraphischer
Wert). Тр. Палеонт. инст. АН СССР, *Trudy paleontol. Inst. Akad. Nauk. S.S.S.R.*, 26 :
1–78.

Rozovskaia, S. E.; Розовская, С. Е., 1952. Фузулиниды верхнего карбона и нижней перми Южного Урала. (Die Fusuliniden des Oberkarbons und Unterperms des Süd-Ural). Тр. Палеонт. инст. АН СССР. *Trudy paleontol. Inst. Akad. Nauk. S.S.S.R.*, 40 : 5–50.

Rozovskaia, S. E.; Розовская, С. Е., 1958. Фузулиниды и биостратиграфическое расчленение верхнекаменноугольных отложений Самарской Луки. (Die Fusuliniden und die biostratigraphische Gliederung der Oberkarbon-Ablagerungen der Samara-Biegung). Тр. Геол. инст. АН СССР. *Trudy geol. Inst. Akad. Nauk. S.S.S.R.*, 13 : 57–120.

Ross, Ch. A., 1960. Fusulinids from the Hess Member of the Leonard Formation, Leonard Series (Permian), Glass Mountains, Texas. *Contr. Cushman Found. Foraminiferal Research*, 11 : 117–133.

Semikhatova, E.; Семихатова, Е., 1954. К вопросу о выяснении взаимоотношений фауны фузулинид и фаций каменноугольных отложений в северо-восточной части Большого Донбасса. (Zur Frage der Aufklärung der Beziehungen der Fusulinidenfaunen und der Fazien der Karbonablagerungen des nord-östlichen Teiles des Grossen Donez-Becken) Учен. зап. Ростовск./Дон. Гос. Унив. *Uchen. zap. Rostovsk./ Don. Gos. Univ.*, 23 (5) : 61–76.

Semikhatova, E.; Семихатова Е., 1956. К вопросу о периодичности в развитии фауны фузулинид в верхней части среднего карбона Сталинградской области. (Zur Frage der Periodizität in der Entwicklung der Fusulinidenfauna der oberen Abteilung des Mittel-Karbons im Gebiet von Stalingrad). Учен. зап. Ростовск./Дон. Гос. Унив. *Uchen. zap. Rostovsk./Don. Gos. Univ.*, 24 (7) : 39–46.

Skinner, J. W. and Wilde, G. L., 1954. Fusulinid wall structure. *J. Paleontol.*, 28 : 445–451.

Solov'eva, M. N.; Соловьева, М. Н., 1955. К вопросу о строении стенки фузулинид и систематическом значении этого признака. (Zur Frage der Wandstruktur der Fusuliniden und des systematischen Wertes dieses Merkmales). Докл. Акад. Наук СССР. *Dokl. Akad. Nauk. S.S.S.R.*, 101 (1) : 163–164.

Thomson, M. L., 1945. Evolutionary trends of the Fusulinids and their application to correlation and zonation of Pennsylvanian rocks. *Bull. Geol. Soc. Am.*, 56 : 1207–1208.

Thomson, M. L., 1948. Studies of American Fusulinids. *Univ. Kansas Publ. Paleontol. Contr. "Protozoa"*, 4 (1) : 1–184.

Thomson, M. L., 1954. American Wolfcampian Fusulinids. *Univ. Kansas Publ. Paleontol. Contr. "Protozoa"*. 14 (5) : 1–226.

Thomson, M. L., 1957. Northern Midcontinent Missourian Fusulinids. *J. Paleontol.*, 31 : 289–328.

Tumanskaia, O.; Туманская, О., 1953. О верхнепермских фузулинидах Южно-Уссурийского края. (Ueber die oberpermischen Fusuliniden des Gebietes von Süd-Ussuri). Тр. Всес. научно-исслед. геол. инст. (ВСЕГЕИ) *Trudy Vses. nauchno-issled. geol. Inst. (VSEGEI)*, pp. : 1–56.

Vissarionova, A. IA.; Виссарионова, А. Я., 1959. Стратиграфия и фации средне- и нижнекаменноугольных отложений Башкирии и их нефтеносность. (Die Stratigraphie und Fazien der unter- und mittel-karbonischen Ablagerungen von Bashkirien und ihre Erdölführung). Тр. Уфимск. нефт. научно-исслед. инст. *Trudy Ufimsk. neft. nauchno issled. Inst.*, 5 : 1–230.

Volozhanina, P.; Воложанина, П., 1961. Взаимоотношения фузулинид и фаций в разрезе среднего карбона Южного Тимана. (Die Wechselbeziehungen zwischen Fusuliniden und Fazien im Mittel-Karbon des südlichen Timan-Rückens). Вопр. микропалеонт. сборн. *Vopr. mikropaleontol. Sborn.*, 4 : 71–82.

White, M., 1932. Some Texas Fusulinidae. *Univ. Texas Bull.*, 3211 : 1–104.

EVOLUTIONARY TRENDS IN CERTAIN CALCAREOUS FORAMINIFERA ON THE PALAEOZOIC – MESOZOIC BOUNDARY

F. BROTZEN

Sveriges Geologiska Undersökning, Stockholm (Sweden)

The most characteristic difference between the foraminiferal fauna in the Palaeozoic and in the Mesozoic is the lack of rotalioid genera in the former supersystem and their appearance in the latter. The nodosarioid Foraminifera show a similar stratigraphic distribution: they rarely occur in the upper part of the Palaeozoic but are already prominent in the fauna of small Foraminifera in the Triassic. In the Jurassic the nodosarioid Foraminifera have the richest number of genera and species, and their variations and species diminish progressively upwards in the geological succession.

In 1936, when knowledge of the stratigraphic distribution of Foraminifera in general, and his own knowledge in particular, were very incomplete, the author published a table (Fig. 1) which gave his view of the foraminiferal associations during post-Triassic times. In this table the range of distribution assumed for nodosarioid and

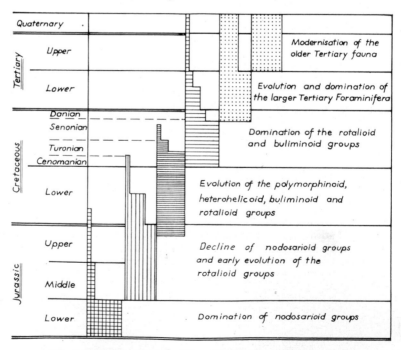

Fig. 1. Time associations of Foraminifera younger than Triassic.

rotalioid groups was more or less what it is now; the difference lies in the richness of additional details which to-day fill out the early, more rudimentary scheme.

The nodosarioid group seems to begin in the Devonian, but it is essential first to decide which forms belong to the Nodosariidea before the problem of their stratigraphic range can be discussed.

Taxonomists have used very different units for this group of Foraminifera. The first well-defined unit for the group was established in 1854 by SCHULTZE, who classified it as a family and named it Nodosarida. In 1861 the same family was called Lagenidea by REUSS. Since each author based the unit on one of two different genera, *Nodosaria* and *Lagena*, the name of the family has varied. In the same way, the taxonomic status of this unit has changed from a family to a superfamily and to an order. Following the law of priority, the present author will speak below of Nodosariidea as a group of families. The diagnosis of this superfamily is that of the Lagenidea as given by GLAESSNER (1945): "Foraminifera with finely perforate calcareous (hyaline) outer chamber wall, chambers arranged in a planispirally coiled or straight series, or regularly coiled about a longitudinal axis. Aperture peripheral or terminal, typically radiate, but simple in earlier forms".

According to this clear and concise definition all such forms which do not have a calcareous, hyaline and perforate wall do not belong to the Nodosariidea, and must be separated from it even if they have many other characters in common. This makes the stratigraphic distribution of the superfamily simple: no genus of the group is known before the Upper Permian.

The diagnosis "finely perforate calcareous (hyaline) outer chamber wall" is a very broad definition, and needs elaboration. CUMMINGS (1955) emended the family Nodosinellidae and found that it possessed a compound wall structure. The wall of *Nodosinella* has an inner layer of finely perforate, fibrous calcite and an outer layer of microgranular calcite. According to CUMMINGS the taxonomic position of the Nodosinellidae "is not fully understood as yet. The unique wall-structure, which has not been observed in a completely unaltered state in *Nodosinella*, seems to indicate a position between the Endothyridea of the Upper Palaeozoic and the Lagenidea of the Mesozoic".

The formulation of GLAESSNER (1945) does not allow tubular or uniserial tests such as those of Earlandiidae to be included in the Endothyridea, as has been done by CUMMINGS (1955). But it seems that the Earlandiidae, with their wall of equidimensional granules of calcite bound by calcareous cement, can be very closely related to the Nodosinellidae. Research on wall structures of many Recent and fossil Foraminifera demonstrates that both calcite and other mineral granules can be used for wall-building in the same genus, or often even in the same species. An evolutionary trend may exist from the Earlandiidae via the Reophacidae to the Nodosinellidae. The inner fibrous layer of Nodosinellidae can be regarded as one of the characters which the Mesozoic Nodosariidea retained after a reduction of the other layer or layers of the compound wall of the Palaeozoic groups. It is interesting to follow such an evolution from a compound wall structure to a lamellar-fibrous and perforate wall.

A direct transition between Nodosinellidae and Nodosariidae is not known. From the Devonian, Bykova (1952) described the genus *Multiseptina* (Fig. 2b). This genus has a compound wall structure with a transparent hyaline and radial outer layer and a finely granular, non-transparent inner part. No relationships can be found between *Multiseptina* and *Nodosinella* (Fig. 2a). In the first form a system of radial septae is directed from the wall towards each chamber. The system of interior septae is preserved and developed in the Permian genus *Colaniella* Licharev (redescribed and revised

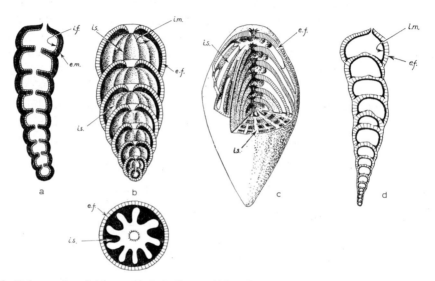

Fig. 2. Palaeonodosarioids. a. *Nodosinella* sp. (After Cummings, 1955); b. *Multiseptina corallina* Bykova (After Bykova, 1952); c. *Colaniella parva* (Colani) (After Reichel, 1946); d. "*Nodosaria*" *tereta* Crespin (After Crespin, 1958). e.f. = exterior fibrous layer; e.m. = exterior massive layer; i.f. = interior fibrous layer; i.m. = interior massive layer; i.s. = interior septum.

by Reichel, 1946) (Fig. 2c). Its wall is already reduced to one main, hyaline, calcareous layer, and pores seem to occur, but they are very indistinct and difficult to observe. A black interior layer, described by Reichel (1946) as "secondary haematite", covers the inside of the wall. The possession of a radial hyaline calcareous wall in this genus represents a big evolutionary step by comparison with the compound wall structure of the older forms. The aperture of *Multiseptina* is radiate; this feature is also present in *Colaniella* and can be considered a part of the interior septation of the chambers. As a result of a long-term reduction in general shape the interior septae disappear, and eventually the only persistent character is the radiate aperture.

The present author therefore thinks that two evolutionary lines existed, one in which the chambers were simple and without septations, and a second in which the chambers were originally septate. In the first evolutionary line, the general shape was unchanged, and the apertures were simple and not radiate. In the second line the primitive and geologically older genera had septate chambers and radiate apertures. The radiate apertures of all younger genera become the only character which demonstrates their relation to their ancestors. Reduction of the wall structure during evolution of the nodosarioid group can be considered as a general trend.

PAALZOW (1935) published a revision of the foraminiferal fauna of the Permian from central Germany. The present author has specimens of the species concerned in his collection, and could study the details of their wall structure. None of PAALZOW's "*Nodosaria*" and "*Dentalina*" species have a real "Nodosariidea" wall structure. All transitions occur, from finely granular and agglutinated calcareous walls to completely calcareous radiate walls and preserved compound calcareous walls. But all these structures differ in character from the wall of the Mesozoic Nodosariidae. Specimens of "*Nodosaria*" *geinitzi* REUSS show a thin, finely granular calcareous wall, without any pores at all. Types of PAALZOW's *Dentalina permiana* (his pl. 4, fig. 32) possess a thick, indistinctly radiate wall with extremely fine pore canals which are irregularly curved and distributed. No radiation of the wall can be clearly observed, and it may be that the pores give the impression that the wall is radiate. The pores are extremely fine and only visible under the high magnification of a phase-contrast microscope. A lamellation of the wall is lacking, and the wall itself seems to be built of only one massive layer.

In the Triassic a new type of "Nodosariidea" begins, with a radiate, partly calcareous wall, which is thin and transparent, often similar to milk glass or clear glass. WEDEKIND (1937) called this calcareous material "Glasschmelz" (glass melt) and "Milchglass" (milk glass). The structure of these glassy and milky walls has not been studied in detail, but it is different from the wall material of younger Mesozoic and Cenozoic genera. The radiation is visible only under high magnification and special illumination. The pore canals are extremely fine, curved (never straight) and irregularly distributed.

The majority of "*Nodosaria*", "*Dentalina*" and related genera from the Lower Jurassic have the same wall structure as above. The wall structures which characterized the Permian groups have entirely disappeared in the Triassic. Here, as an aid towards understanding the evolution of the nodosarioid groups, the author will call the genera with the thick massive wall structure of the Upper Palaeozoic the p a l a e o - n o d o s a r i o i d s , and the Triassic and Lower Jurassic groups with a glassy, indistinct wall structure, the m e s o n o d o s a r i o i d s . These two names have been adopted only to demonstrate the author's opinion regarding the evolution of the groups; a more detailed analysis will be required in order to prove their value in the taxonomy of the Nodosariidea.

The youngest group of Nodosariidea shows a wall structure of lamellate, radiate, well-perforated calcite. The pore canals are easy to observe under magnifications of 20–40 times. They are finely curved or straight, regularly distributed over the entire wall, or collected in bundles. This type of wall structure was extremely well figured by BEISSEL (1891). This group of nodosarioid genera seems to occur rarely in the Middle Jurassic, and becomes dominant from the Upper Cretaceous to Recent. Meanwhile, the mesonodosarioids disappear at the end of the Lower Cretaceous.

The long evolution of *Nodosaria*-like forms is characterized by the change in the wall structure. From agglutinating calcareous walls, the course of evolution was towards compound structures; reduction of the different layers to simple massive ones which were granular in some cases, radiate in others; the glassy Early Mesozoic forms; and finally the lamellate, perforate forms preserved in living groups.

During the Mesozoic, genera which are characterized by a compressed section occur together with other nodosarioid forms. Such groups of compressed uniserial nodosarioid genera are abundant in the Jurassic and have been assigned to *Lingulina* and *Frondicularia*. In the Liassic their species are excellent guide fossils. In 1957 Nørvang assigned these Lingulinae and Frondiculariae from the Liassic to the genera *Geinitzina* and *Spandelina* respectively. His investigations showed that the wall of these Liassic forms is partly calcareous, fibrous, and imperforate, and therefore they must belong to the family Nodosinellidae and not to the family Nodosariidae, which have a calcareous, fibrous, perforate wall. Nørvang united both families in the superfamily Nodosariidea. In the course of detailed discussion of the matter he found that the wall of *Spandelina*, *Geinitzina* and *Monogenerina* is calcareous, possibly granular or fibrous, but always imperforate. Cummings (1956) described the wall structure of *Monogenerina* as calcareous compound, consisting of a granular calcareous main layer and an inner layer of fibrous imperforate calcite. Cummings left open the question of which wall structure *Spandelina* and *Geinitzina* exhibit. The present author's studies on Triassic and Liassic "*Frondicularia*" and "*Lingulina*" showed that they have the same structure as already found in the "*Nodosaria*" and "*Dentalina*" groups of the same age. Their wall is thin, indistinctly fibrous, often also granular. The pore canals are very indistinct or lacking; when they occur they are curved, never straight. As Nørvang (1957) found, the compressed genera from the Triassic and Liassic are closely related to the Permian ones and also to the younger Mesozoic ones, even if they are distinguished by a very varied wall structure.

It would hamper further studies to name the Liassic genera *Geinitzina* and *Spandelina*. According to the author's material from the Permian, these two genera have compound walls or are agglutinated. It is impossible to unite them with the younger genera *Frondicularia* and *Lingulina*, with the perforate and radiate walls, and therefore it is proposed here that they should be called *Neogeinitzina* and *Neospandelina*.

Diagnoses·
   Neogeinitzina nov. gen.: Shape as in *Geinitzina*, distinguished by its wall structure. Wall calcareous, transparent, indistinctly perforate or imperforate, fibrous.
   Type species: *Marginulina tenera* Bornemann 1854.

   Neospandelina nov. gen.: Shape as in *Spandelina*, distinguished by its wall structure, which is the same as in *Neogeinitzina*.
   Type species: *Frondicularia bicostata* d'Orbigny 1849.

Just as the nodosarioid group of straight or fairly curved genera had a long evolutionary history before their Recent genera were formed, the Mesozoic *Lingulina*, *Frondicularia* and related genera also had a long evolutionary history, beginning in the Palaeozoic. These genera, which all have the same shape, had a more or less compound calcareous wall structure during the Palaeozoic, which reduced to a simple fibrous or granular wall during the Late Permian and Early Trias. In the Jurassic, the first genera with a calcareous perforate and lamellate wall occur. This structure has persisted down to Recent time.

It is difficult to follow the history of the Nodosariidea with a planispiral arrangement of chambers from the Palaeozoic to the Mesozoic. The first *Lenticulina*-shaped Foraminifera seem to have been described by CRESPIN (1958) from the Permian. She noted that *Lenticulina (Astacolus) initialis* CRESPIN should have a calcareous, finely perforate wall. The shape of the radiate aperture makes it possible that this can be the oldest known *Lenticulina*, but some remarks are necessary.

In the same paper, CRESPIN figured *Nodosaria tereta* CRESPIN on pl. 26, fig. 1–4, and some sections of the same species on pl. 31, fig. 9 and 12. These sections show the typical compound wall structure, described by REICHEL (1946) for *Colaniella parva* and by BYKOVA (1952) for *Multiseptina*. The wall possesses an outer fibrous calcareous layer and a dark inner layer. REICHEL noted that the inner layer could be of secondary matter, but its presence in the same group of Foraminifera, in different genera, makes it possible that this second layer is inherent in the test. Accordingly, the possibility exists that the Permian *Lenticulina* species are different from the species of *Lenticulina* s.str. The Permian *Lenticulina* can possess another wall structure, and therefore it would be of great interest to restudy the Permian Lenticulinae very carefully.

The wall structure of the *Lenticulina*-shaped Permian genus *Robuloides* REICHEL is described in great detail by that author (REICHEL, 1946). The fibres of the calcareous test are not arranged radially, but are orientated parallel to the surface; pores are indistinct, and it is uncertain whether they are even present. Lamellation of the wall is not observed. The genus *Robuloides* undoubtedly has a wall structure other than that of the genus *Lenticulina* from the younger Mesozoic and Cenozoic. In the Triassic and Jurassic many *Lenticulina*-shaped genera (or subgenera) occur. Their wall is highly transparent, and glass-like as in the "*Nodosaria*"-shaped genera of the same age. The parallel evolution of all these closely related genera has reached the same stage, and it will be necessary to distinguish them from younger ones.

The history of the different groups of Nodosariidea, such as the nodosarioid, lingulinoid and lenticulinoid-shaped genera, does not allow construction of phylogenetic lines in which one of the living forms can be the descendant of the others. It is impossible to derive *Nodosaria* from *Cristellaria*, or *Frondicularia* from *Nodosaria*. The differentiation already began in the Lower Palaeozoic, and at least three different groups occur in their ancestral shape in the Permian: a group of straight genera like *Nodosaria*, a second with the same straight shape and compressed sections as *Frondicularia*, and a third group with planispiral arrangement of chambers as in *Lenticulina*. Their wall history seems to have developed contemporaneously from calcareous agglutinated in earliest Palaeozoic to the calcareous radiate and lamellate design of the Recent species.

The abundance of descriptions of genera and species of the nodosarioid groups from the Permian, Triassic and Jurassic enables their evolution to be reviewed. But such descriptions of a second large group of small Foraminifera — the rotalioid-shaped — are very rare. Up to some years ago all that was known of the occurrence of this group in the Permian, Triassic and Liassic related only to a few incompletely described and figured species. However, in 1960 the papers by OBERHAUSER and KRISTAN-TOLLMANN on the Triassic Foraminifera lifted a curtain which had hitherto covered part of the history of these Foraminifera.

The few known rotalioid Foraminifera of the Lower Jurassic are so highly specialized that a long and complicated evolution must have taken place before the Jurassic. One of the first rotalioid genera from the Liassic to be studied in detail was *Reinholdella*. The wall was originally composed of aragonite, in contrast to that of the younger and closely related genera of the Epistominidae. The walls of the former should be monolamellar calcareous and radiate, according to REISS (1958). There is a partition in the interior of the chambers. The chambers communicate by septal areal openings, and the aperture is directed to the umbilical side over the partition of the last and often also of the preceding chambers, according to HOFKER (1952).

Derivation of this highly specialized *Reinholdella* from the more simply organized genera of the Upper Jurassic and Cretaceous is, of course, impossible, and ancestral genera were not known before KRISTAN-TOLLMANN (1960) published a rich foraminiferal fauna from the Triassic of Austria which she determined as belonging to the Rotaliidea. No general limitation of this superfamily exists, and hence it is extremely doubtful whether the new genera of KRISTAN-TOLLMANN can be included in it.

The widely differing diagnoses of the Rotaliidea by various authors agree on one point: the wall should be perforate calcareous. But KRISTAN-TOLLMANN noted (1960, p. 51): "Interessant und noch genauer zu untersuchen ist auch die Fähigkeit der triadischen Rotaliideen, in ihre bisweilen aus Kalkkörnern in kalkigem Zement bestehende Schale je nach Milieu prozentuell verschieden auch Sandkörnchen einzubauen. Diese Erscheinung tritt innerhalb einer Gattung uneinheitlich nur bei einzelnen Arten auf und innerhalb einer Art wieder nur in einzelnen Fundpunkten".

In the description of the species, the character of the wall structure is commonly only briefly indicated, as: "Schale zart und glatt, kalkig perforat" (see exception below). These notes on the wall structure can only be used for some very theoretical conclusions regarding the evolution of the wall. It seems that the rotalioid-shaped group of Foraminifera has also undergone an evolution from calcareous agglutinated walls to perforate, lamellar ones. The content of sand grains in the walls of some of the Triassic rotalioid genera can be an ancestral character of value in tracing their evolutionary history (see below). But more important is the fact that most of the genera and species described from the Triassic have multiple or lobate apertures, characters which only some of the Jurassic Epistominidae and Ceratobuliminidae have retained and passed on to their younger successors. No mention is made of an interior structure in the chambers of the Triassic genera, and the shape of the septal apertures between the chambers has not been studied. Theoretically it is not difficult to reconstruct an evolution between apertures of the genera *Duostomina* or *Diplotremina* and the apertures and septal openings of the Jurassic Epistominidae and Ceratobuliminidae. No important differences exist between the shape and apertures of *Duostomina* (e.g., *D. biconvexa* KRISTAN-TOLLMANN and *D. alta* KRISTAN-TOLLMANN) and *Reinholdella* (Fig. 3). Both genera are more or less biconvex, with closed umbilicus. *Reinholdella*

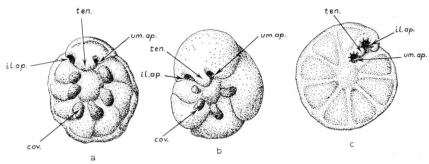

Fig. 3. Comparison between *Reinholdella* (Jurassic) and *Duostomina* (Triassic). a. *Reinholdella macfadyeni* (TEN DAM) (After HOFKER, 1952); b. *Reinholdella brandi* HOFKER (After HOFKER, 1952); c. *Duostomina turboidea* KRISTAN-TOLLMANN (After KRISTAN-TOLLMANN, 1960). *cov.* = secondary covers of umbilical apertures; *il. ap.* = interior lateral aperture; *ten.* = tenon; *um. ap.* = umbilical aperture.

from the Liassic and Dogger always has an umbilical foramen from the partition of the last chamber out of the test (the protoforamen of HOFKER, 1952), and an interior lateral foramen (possibly the deuteroforamen of HOFKER). For simplification of the nomenclature of the openings, the former is called here the umbilical and the latter the interior lateral aperture. During the growth of the individuals of *Reinholdella* the umbilical foramen of all preceding chambers is plugged or covered with a porous cover. The interior lateral opening does not exist in all *Reinholdella* specimens, and seems to occur at a certain stage of growth. Later it becomes the septal foramen between two chambers. When both foramina occur in the last chamber a part of the frontal umbilical wall forms a tenon between the two openings. This is not a toothplate in the nomenclature of HOFKER as stated by KRISTAN-TOLLMANN, but is the tenon of the present author (1948), which characterizes many Cretaceous and younger genera, *e.g.*, *Rosalina*, and in this and related genera both the separated apertures communicate below the tenon. Nothing is yet known about the interior of the chambers of *Duostomina*, and the plugging of the umbilical aperture of the preceding chambers is not discussed or figured by KRISTAN-TOLLMANN. According to KRISTAN-TOLLMANN's figures, in the genus *Diplotremina* secondary masses seem to occur in umbilical parts of the sutures, which can be covers of the umbilical apertures of the preceding chambers and correspond to the apertural covers of *Reinholdella*. The general shape and the occurrence of two apertures in the last chambers emphasize the fact that the Triassic genus *Duostomina* and the Jurassic *Reinholdella* are closely related. The first genus can be an ancestor of *Reinholdella* or must belong to the Triassic groups which were the ancestors of the Jurassic genus. Besides modifications to minor characters, the following changes took place from the Triassic to the Jurassic: in the older group the calcareous, possibly aragonitic, wall contains sandy grains, which are lacking in younger genera; the two apertures of the last chamber are a constant feature of the older genus whereas in *Reinholdella* the lateral opening is only occasionally preserved and usually performs another function. The history of the long line of evolution from *Reinholdella* to *Höglundina* was given by HOFKER (1954).

Just as in the case of *Duostomina* and *Reinholdella*, an attempt can be made to homologize the details of the Triassic and Early Mesozoic Ceratobuliminae. Both genera have a deep umbilicus, and both possess the same system of two apertures, one directed to the umbilicus and the other into the septum. Until the interior of *Diplotremina* has been studied, a detailed correlation will be difficult; *Ceratobulimina* species from the Liassic have been mentioned but not described. On the other hand, it is easy to perceive that a species such as *Diplotremina astrofimbriata* KRISTAN-TOLLMANN is ancestral to *Ceratobulimina* on account of its apertures and possibly also its interior structure.

The Triassic rotalioid species are ranged in few new genera by KRISTAN-TOLLMANN. The main characters are the double apertures and the shape of the umbilicus. The general shape of species in one and the same genus varies so strongly that a separation into some new genera is justified. The various species demonstrate that as early as the Triassic a differentation took place which resulted in different lines of evolution. Such species as *Duostomina turboidea* KRISTAN-TOLLMANN can be closely related to those genera of the Mesozoic which have a flat spiral and a high umbilical side. The two apertures or apertural branches found in many younger Mesozoic genera can have developed from such double apertures as are described for the genera *Duostomina* and *Diplotremina*. The umbilical apertural opening and interior marginal aperture present in *Osangularia*, *Gyroidinoides*, *Gavelinella* and *Cibicides*, to mention only the common ones, must be homologous with the two clearly separated apertures of the oldest "Rotaliidea" hitherto described. It is the author's opinion that the broad differentiation of the structure of the wall represents only a stage in different lines of evolution of rotalioid Foraminifera. The same structure of the wall in different genera does not always demonstrate a close relationship between them. An early pre-Triassic stage of wall structure of the entire group was a simple or compound calcareous wall, generally agglutinated from foreign grains with organic calcareous cement. This wall structure changed during geological time through the development of pores at some stage of evolution; changes are likewise to be seen in the lamellation of the wall, and the wall also becomes fibrous, granular and radiate. Hence, structural evolution of the wall can have occurred along different evolutionary lines in "Rotaliidea". The crystallization of the calcareous masses as aragonite or the more stable calcite must be considered as a character of evolution rather than as a character of relationship. The two ancestral groups of genera, the *Ceratobulimina* and *Epistomina* groups ("group" will be used here to avoid the taxonomic unit of "family"), retain a monolamellar granular and aragonitic wall, but many of their related genera have left this stage of evolution and reached a stage of calcitic, lamellar and radiate walls.

No ancestors of the Triassic "Rotaliidea" of KRISTAN-TOLLMANN are known from the Palaeozoic. Such ancestors possibly occur in different groups among the Endothyridae, Tetrataxidae or Trochamminidae. This theory may be an unexpected one. To demonstrate and discuss it, I wish to recall that our knowledge of the history of the Globigerinae can give some evidence for such a theory. OBERHAUSER (1960) described two *Globigerina* species from the Triassic. These fossils are indeterminable and nothing can be learned of their taxonomic position; their wall structure is unknown, their apertures not studied, and only in general shape do they resemble *Globigerina* s.str. *Globigerina* species described from the Jurassic were examined by the author, who found that they must belong to a group with a calcareous agglutinated wall without distinct perforations and much nearer to *Ammoglobigerina* than to *Globigerina*. The first Globigerinae, with perforated and entirely calcareous radiate and perforate walls, known to occur for certain are found in the Lower Cretaceous. Such "*Globigerina*" species may already have existed earlier, and possibly they occur together with "*Globigerina*" species possessing an agglutinated calcareous test. It is impossible to derive the living "*Globigerina*" genera from calcareous rotalioid groups of the Mesozoic, because evidence for such a phylogenesis is not yet available.

In this connection a secondary problem should be mentioned. In many papers in recent years on planktonic Foraminifera, *Globigerina* and related genera have been expressly called "planktonic". Naturally, in the present-day oceans they are planktonic. But their long geological history shows the ancestors of the Recent genera to have had imperforate or very finely perforate, thick and heavy walls. This would never have allowed the genera to lead a planktonic life. The association in which such fossil "Globigerinae" occur is very different from the Recent *Globigerina* oozes. Accordingly, even if the descendants of fossil Foraminifera are still present as planktonic organisms in Recent seas, it is advisable to be very cautious before considering the fossil forms as planktonic.

Many authors have already mentioned a relationship between Buliminidea and Rotaliidea. But ancestral forms which could demonstrate such relations have not yet been found. The paper of KRISTAN-TOLLMANN gave an important clue to the history of the Buliminidea. Her genus *Variostoma* contains species which have the characte-

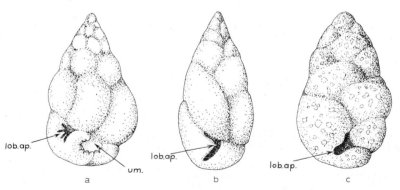

Fig. 4. Comparison between *Variostoma* (Triassic), *Buliminella* (Cretaceous) and *Arenobulimina* (Cretaceous). a. *Variostoma pralongense* KRISTAN-TOLLMANN (After KRISTAN-TOLLMANN, 1960); b. *Buliminella laevis* (BEISSEL); c. *Arenobulimina d'orbignyi* (REUSS); *lob. ap.* = lobate aperture; *um.* = umbilical aperture or covered umbilical aperture.

ristic shape of Buliminidae, and whose apertures are only slightly different in their main features from those of the Buliminidae. The lobate or divided aperture of *Variostoma* species is simplified in the Buliminidae, which can have an aperture with branches and lobes (see Fig. 4 and 5). The internal structure behind the aperture occurring in the Buliminidae is as yet unknown in the Triassic *Variostoma*. It seems to be difficult to study such detail on the Alpine specimens. The umbilicus of *Variostoma* is well figured and described, but cannot be followed in its evolution to the Buliminidae. It may be that a second aperture existed which developed into an inner structure during the Mesozoic. It is interesting that the structure of the wall varies. *V. pralongense* KRISTAN-TOLLMANN from the Middle Triassic should have a wall which is "glatt, kalkig, perforiert, zart", and the Rhaetian *V. cochlea* KRISTAN-TOLLMANN was described as follows: "Die Schale ist feinkörnig kalkig bis grobkörnig kalkig mit kalkigem Zement und ziemlich dick. Eingelagerte Sandkörnchen schwanken in der Häufigkeit je nach Individuum." This variation of the wall structure leads the author to the conclusion that Ataxophragmiidae and Buliminidea can only be sharply distinguished in Late Mesozoic and Cenozoic faunas. Their evolution must have begun with an initial group with an agglutinated calcareous wall, as in, for example, such high-conical species of *Variostoma*. Even the Ataxophragmiidae often have lobate apertures in the Cretaceous (see Fig. 5) as an ancestral character.

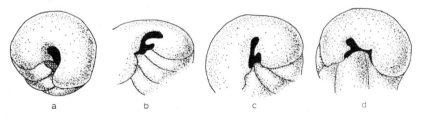

a   b   c   d

Fig. 5. Lobate apertures in Cretaceous Arenobuliminidae. a. *Arenobulimina obliqua* (D'ORBIGNY); b. *Ataxogyroidina variabilis* (D'ORBIGNY); c. *Ataxogyroidina concava* MARIE; d. *Ataxogyroidina globosa* (V. HAGENOW); (All figures after MARIE, 1941).

Imperfect knowledge of the history of the Foraminifera from the uppermost Palaeozoic and Lower Mesozoic only allows of an attempt at a vague synthesis of the evolutionary trends of the small calcareous Foraminifera. Even in the Palaeozoic, some highly specialized genera with calcareous agglutinated walls evolved into different ancestral genera of Nodosariidea, Rotaliidea and Buliminidea with calcareous walls. Ancestors should be found in the families of Reophacidae, Endothyridae and Trochamminidae. During the Mesozoic, different evolutionary lines of different families and subfamilies already existed. On the basis of the characteristics previously mentioned the author unites the three genera *Variostoma*, *Diplotremina* and *Duostomina* in the new family D u o s t o m i n i d a e nov. fam.; and the genera *Plagiostomella*, *Asymmetrina* and *Involana* in the new family A s y m m e t r i n i d a e nov. fam. These two central groups clearly demonstrate both ancestral and modern features.

The term p r a e r o t a l i o i d s is here proposed as a collective name for forms now included in such families as the Duostominidae and Asymmetrinidae, which are, in general, similar to the Rotaliidea but are easily distinguished from the latter by their wall structure.

It is to be expected that more genera of the new families will be discovered in the future, and that they will enable detailed studies to be made of the evolutionary history of the Foraminifera.

Fig. 6 gives a review of the present author's theory of evolution in certain foraminiferal groups.

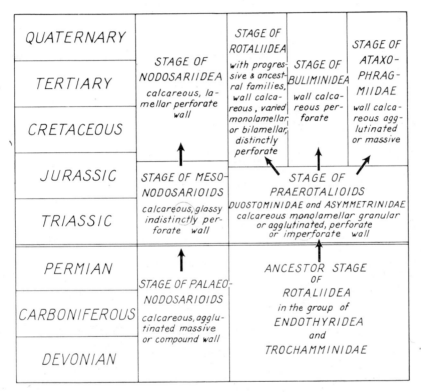

Fig. 6. Table showing the main evolutionary trends in nodosarioid and rotalioid Foraminifera.

SUMMARY

An attempt is made to trace the ancestors of the Nodosariidea and Rotaliidea. In both groups of Foraminifera, a similar evolution of the wall structure took place from agglutinated or compound calcareous imperforate to calcareous perforate. The general change of wall structure occurred in the beginning of the Mesozoic. On the basis of their wall structure, Palaeozoic and Early Mesozoic nodosarioid and rotalioid genera must be taxonomically separated from the Nodosariidea and Rotaliidea s. str. The general evolutionary trend in these Foraminifera is shown in Fig. 6.

REFERENCES

ADAMS, G. C., 1957. A study of the morphology and variation of some Upper Lias Foraminifera. *Micropaleontol.*, 3 : 205–226.

BARTENSTEIN, H., 1948. Entwicklung der Gattung *Lenticulina (Lenticulina)* LAMARCK 1804 mit ihren Untergattungen. (For.). *Senkenbergiana*, 29 : 41–67.

BEISSEL, I., 1891. Die Foraminiferen der Aachener Kreide. Herausgegeben durch E. HOLZAPFEL. *Abhandl. K. preuss. geol. Landesanstalt*, N. F., 3 : 1–78 pp.

BROTZEN, F., 1936. Einige Bemerkungen zur Stratigraphie Schonens. *Geol. Fören. i Stockholm Förh.*, 58 : 116–121.

BROTZEN, F., 1953. Problems in the nomenclature of the Foraminifera. *Micropaleontol.*, 7 : 35–38.

BYKOVA, E. V., 1952. Foraminifery devona russkoj platformy i Priuralja. *Trudy Vsesoyuz. Neftyan. Nauch. Issledovatel. Geologorazvedoch Inst.*, 60 : 5–64.

CRESPIN, I., 1958. Permian Foraminifera of Australia. *Commonwealth Australia Bur. Mineral Resources, Geol. Geophys. Bull.*, 48 : 1–207.

CUMMINGS, R. H., 1955. *Nodosinella* BRADY 1876 and associated Upper Palaeozoic genera. *Micropaleontol.*, 1 : 221–238.

CUMMINGS, R. H., 1956. Revision of the Upper Palaeozoic textulariid Foraminifera. *Micropaleontol.*, 2 : 201–242.

FURSENKO, A. W. *et al.*, 1959. Subclasse Foraminifera. In: J. A. ORLOV *et al. Osnovy paleontologii*, pp. 115–367.

GALLOWAY, J. J., 1933. *A Manual of Foraminifera.* James Furman Kemp Memor. Series Publ. No. 1. Bloomington, Indiana, 483 pp.

GLAESSNER, M. F., 1945. *Principles of Micropaleontology.* Melbourne University Press. Melbourne, 296 pp.

HOFKER, J., 1952. The Jurassic genus *Reinholdella* BROTZEN (1948). *Paläontol. Z.*, 26 : 15–29.

HOFKER, J., 1954. Über die Familie Epistomariidae. *Palaeontographica*, 105 (A) : 166–206.

KRISTAN, E., 1957. Ophthalmidiidae und Tetrataxinae (Foraminifera) aus dem Rhät der Hohen Wand in Nieder-Österreich. *Jahrb. geol. Bundesanstalt*, 100 : 269–298.

KRISTAN-TOLLMANN, E., 1960. Rotaliidea (Foraminifera) aus der Trias der Ostalpen. *Jahrb. geol. Bundesanstalt, Sonderband*, 5 : 47–78.

MARIE, P., 1941. Les foraminifères de la craie à *Beleminitella mucronata* du bassin de Paris. *Mém. Musée Natl. d'histoire naturelle, n. sér.*, 12.

NØRVANG, A., 1957. The Foraminifera of the Lias Series in Jutland, Denmark. *Medd. Dansk Geol. Foren.*, 13 : 279–414.

OBERHAUSER, R., 1960. Foraminiferen und Mikrofossilien "incertae sedis" der landinischen und karnischen Stufe der Trias aus den Ostalpen und aus Persien. *Jahrb. geol. Bundesanstalt, Sonderband*, 5 : 5–46.

PAALZOW, R., 1935. Die Foraminiferen im Zechstein des östlichen Thüringen. *Jahrb. preuss. geol. Landesanstalt*, 56 : 26–45.

POKORNÝ, V., 1958. *Grundzüge der zoologischen Mikropaläontologie.* Bd. 1. Deutsch. Verl. Wiss. Berlin, 582 pp.

REICHEL, M., 1945. Sur quelques foraminifères nouveaux du Permien méditerranéen. *Eclogae Geol. Helv.*, 38 : 524–560.

REICHEL, M., 1946. A propos de *Pyramis parva* COLANI. Bericht der schweizerischen Paläontologischen Gesellschaft. *Eclogae Geol. Helv.*, 39 : 371–373.

REISS, Z.,1957. The Bilamellidea, nov. superfam., and remarks on Cretaceous globorotaliids. *Contrib. Cushman Found. Foraminiferal Research*, 8 : 127–145.

REISS, Z., 1958. Classification of lamellar Foraminifera. *Micropaleontol.*, 4 : 51–70.

REISS, Z., 1959. The wall-structure of *Cibicides, Planulina, Gyroidinoides*, and *Globorotalites*. *Micropaleontol.*, 5 : 355–357.

SIGAL, J., 1952. Ordre des Foraminifera. In: J. PIVETEAU, *Traité de Paléontologie.* Masson et Cie, Paris, 1 : 133–301.

TODD, R. and BLACKMON, P., 1956. Calcite and aragonite in Foraminifera. *J. Paleontol.*, 30 : 217–219.

TROELSEN, J. C., 1955. On the value of aragonite tests in the classification of the Rotaliidea. *Contrib. Cushman Found. Foraminiferal Research*, 6 : 50–51

WEDEKIND, R., 1937. *Einführung in die Grundlagen der historischen Geologie.* Enke, Stuttgart, 2 : 136 pp.

EVOLUTION IN CERTAIN BIOCHARACTERS OF SELECTED JURASSIC LAGENIDAE

TOM BARNARD

University College, London (Great Britain)

INTRODUCTION

In a series of papers (BARNARD, 1947–1960) the author has already pointed out that the Lagenidae represent a difficult group for study. This is owing to the extreme variation which takes place, and a general lack of definite, stable, generic and specific characters. Furthermore, earlier classifications of the family were based for the most part on studies of Recent or Tertiary genera, where the generic characters had become reasonably stable by successive sorting due to natural selection.

Such factors as the effect of environment, both internal (genes) and external, present the usual difficulties, for little is known of the ecology, living habits and — what is perhaps more important — the physiology of the cell of these animals.

Coupled with the lack of knowledge of the living animal, problems arise through collecting bias; differences in state of preservation of individuals, when dealing with successive populations; and many unknown factors which may or may not be mirrored in the extremely variable facies occurring in the Jurassic.

Basically, the present paper deals with examples of the Lagenidae taken from British Jurassic facies, with only a brief mention of other localities. It would be beyond the paper's scope to deal fully with the changes which take place in biocharacters of the Jurassic lagenid genera, and hence the author has selected a few to illustrate the various problems of taxonomy and stratigraphy presented by this so-called evolutionary change. It is also important that the Lagenidae comprise most of the Foraminifera to be found in the Jurassic, and were also at an early stage in their evolution, for, although they occur in the Trias, it was not until the widespread marine environments arose in the Lias of northwestern Europe that they became firmly established.

To anyone studying the group, it soon becomes apparent that an "explosive burst" of evolution took place in the Lower Jurassic, where, although the forms are generally smaller than those from later periods, a wider range of morphology and variation exists. In the Lower Jurassic, variation is confined for the most part to biocharacters which influence the general morphology of the test, whereas minor characters, such as ornament, are emphasized later. It often appears that even within one species a gradation exists between different genera. This is due to the fact that many genera were described and set up on the basis of a description of the type specimen only, without reference to any variation that might exist.

Such unknown factors as hybridization may affect the morphology and, at certain horizons produce peculiar aberrant forms, which would not be included in the general evolution of the family but form abortive offshoots (BARNARD, 1960).

For the present paper, examples have been chosen to illustrate variation in one or more biocharacters which may affect classification and taxonomy, as well as in those which may be used as aids to stratigraphy.

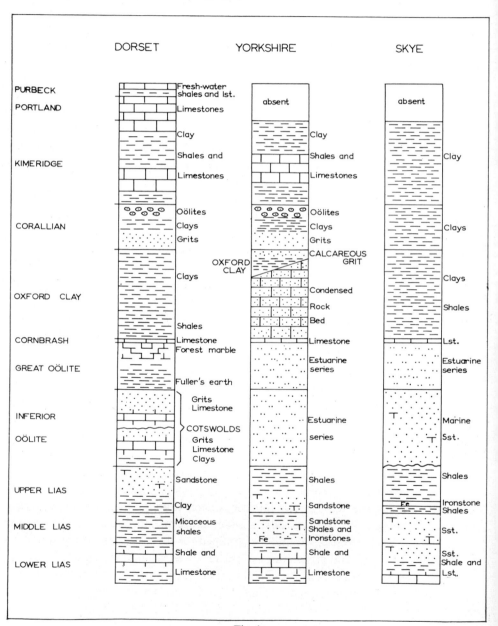

Fig. 1.

STRATIGRAPHY

Before an account is given of the changes that take place in the Lagenidae, it is necessary to briefly discuss the broad changes in facies which took place in Britain during Jurassic times.

The main outcrops of Jurassic rocks occur in two areas in Britain. One, in England, runs from Dorset in the southwest to Yorkshire in the northeast. Here the Jurassic rocks form an almost continuous outcrop across the country, except where they are affected by east-west axes, which produced shallow-water facies and divided the area up into a number of basins of deposition.

The second main outcrop lies in the northwest, in the island of Skye. This has only partially been studied, but presents a large outcrop of rocks ranging from Lower Lias to Kimeridge Clay. This outcrop exhibits many differences from that of England, and no work on the microfauna has yet been published.

As shown on the simplified diagram (Fig. 1), many changes of lithology and facies occur, but it is perhaps the main clay formations of the Lias, Oxford Clay and Kimeridge Clay which give the most continuous record of evolution of the Jurassic Lagenidae. However, many environmental changes take place within these formations, but for the most part these will be ignored in the present paper. Major variations from the marine clays to the shallow-water grits and limestones of the Middle Jurassic (Bathonian) and the Corallian are of interest, and the general changes taking place will be noted. Over most of the outcrop the Lias is a clay formation, with localized sand and ironstone facies occurring. The Lias of the island of Skye is sandy, and as yet has yielded few or no microfossils.

A remarkable change takes place in the lithologies from the clays of the Lias to the extremely varied rocks of the Middle Jurassic, where, in both the Inferior and Great Oölites, a series of grits, limestones, clays, and Fuller's earth occur in the southern part of England. These facies are replaced further north in North Lincolnshire and Yorkshire by beds of the Estuarine series.

In Skye the Inferior Oölite is a massive marine sandstone, but the Great Oölite is estuarine.

The successions throughout the Oxford Clay, Corallian, and Kimeridge Clay are generally similar in Dorset and Yorkshire, except for details. The two clay lithologies of the Oxford Clay and the Kimeridge Clay are separated by variable lithologies, mostly marine oölites, thin sandy clays, marls and grits. In Skye, however, the clay formation appears to be continuous, although no work on the Upper Jurassic microfossils from Skye has yet been published.

DISCUSSION OF CERTAIN GENERA

Rectoglandulina (Fig. 2 a–s)

The author (BARNARD, 1950b, pp. 24–28) has described the variation of some speci-

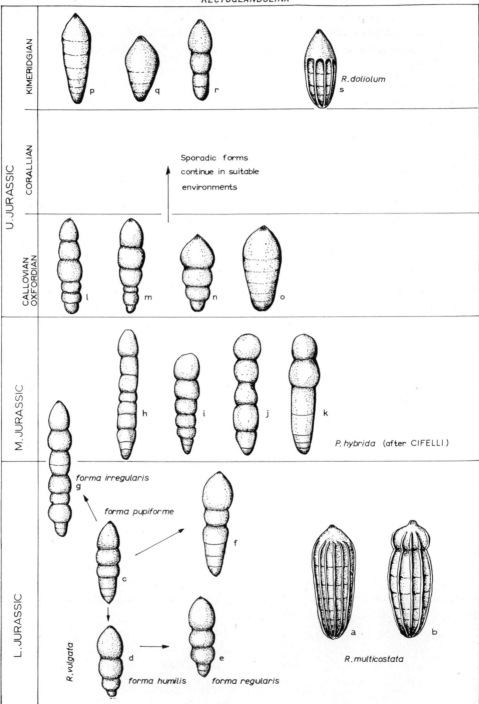

Fig. 2.

mens from the Upper Lias belonging to *Pseudoglandulina vulgata* (BORNEMANN). It was pointed out that many of the forms which had been assigned to a number of different species by earlier authors fell within the normal range of variation of the species. It was stated that slight variation in the growth rate, the biocharacter controlling the size and shape of the chambers, would result in a wide range of variants in the final shape of the test.

LOEBLICH and TAPPAN (1955) reconsidered the genus *Pseudoglandulina*, and placed the Jurassic forms in a new genus *Rectoglandulina*. However, they did not study the variation of the type species *Pseudoglandulina comatus* BATSCH. Specimens from the Challenger Collection show a range of variation similar to that shown by forms from the Lias. But for the purpose of this paper the genus *Rectoglandulina* has been accepted.

Some of the variation occurring in Jurassic species of *Rectoglandulina* is illustrated in Fig. 2a–s. However, it has been impossible to illustrate the wide range of the size of the test which occurs from horizon to horizon, a character which has affected identification and taxonomy. The author does not consider the size of the test to be a diagnostic specific character.

On account of the sporadic occurrence of the species of Jurassic and Cretaceous Rectoglandulinae, the author suggested (BARNARD, 1950b) that, as somewhat similar variation occurs at widely scattered horizons, the appearance of trends should not be ascribed to one slowly evolving group, with occasional bursts of excessive variation, but to a number of closely similar though perhaps not closely related species. These gave rise to similar patterns of variation with heterochronous homoeomorphy.

This suggestion (BARNARD, 1950b, p. 26) has been followed up by CIFELLI (1960, p. 564) and LUTZE (1960, p. 478). Both give examples of species from higher levels than the Lias but with a closely similar pattern of variation.

Two main forms appear in all the Jurassic species of *Rectoglandulina*. The first is a pupiform or fusiform test, and the second a nodosarine test. In both forms the early chambers usually increase in size to become a conical initial stage to the test, which varies in length according to the size and number of the chambers. Furthermore, the sutures between the chambers are usually flush with the surface of the test in the initial stages, and show little or no constriction.

In the pupiform test (Fig. 2c) the initial cone is followed by a series of chambers gradually decreasing in diameter so that the test becomes pupiform. Most of the sutures are flush with the surface, and only occasional constrictions occur.

In the nodosarine test (Fig. 2d) the early conical portion is followed by a series of chambers which usually increase in height as well as diameter, and this is accompanied by strong constrictions occurring at the sutures.

The diameter of the final chambers may either increase or decrease fairly regularly. Occasionally the growth rate changes abruptly with either a rapid increase or decrease in the diameter of the chambers. This usually occurs for one to three chambers before the normal steady rate of growth is attained. Such a rapid change in growth rate may occur more than once in a specimen and, although the general shape of the chambers is fairly constant, an overall irregular appearance may then be observed in the test.

The amount of constriction of the sutures does not bear a strict relationship to the amount of overlap of the chambers. For both in forms with deep constrictions and in those in which the sutures are almost flush with the surface, the chambers are overlapped by about one sixth to one third of their volumes.

Two chief species occur in the Lias, and both show an almost identical pattern of variation in the shape of the test.

Rectoglandulina vulgata (BORNEMANN) is unornamented and has many heterochronous homoeomorphs at later horizons, whereas *Rectoglandulina multicostata* (BORNEMANN) is ornamented by a series of coarse longitudinal costae. The two fundamental shapes occurring in *Rectoglandulina multicostata* (BORNEMANN) are illustrated in Fig. 2; Fig. 2a is the pupiform test, and Fig. 2b is basically pupiform but with the end chamber deeply constricted. In this species the tendency towards the nodosarine habit is not so strongly developed as in the smooth species of *Rectoglandulina*.

This is also the case in the ribbed *Rectoglandulina doliolum* (TERQUEM and BERTHELIN) (Fig. 2s), which occurs in the Kimeridge Clay, where no form with the deeply constricted sutures has yet been recorded, and even the ordinary pupiform variety occurs only rarely.

The smooth form *Rectoglandulina vulgata* (BORNEMANN) is illustrated in Fig. 2c–g. The pupiform test is shown in Fig. 2c, and the test is seen to be composed of six chambers, with an initial widening cone followed by three drum-shaped chambers with flush sutures, so that the early part of the test is bullet-shaped. After this initial stage the height of the chambers increases, and they sometimes become constricted, presenting a faintly nodosarine appearance. All the variation in the shape of the test appears after the initial conical portion is formed. Fig. 2d, where the initial cone is small and the three following chambers are deeply constricted, is similar to the form recorded as *Pseudoglandulina humilis* (ROEMER) by many authors.

In forma *regularis* (Fig. 2e) the test is similar to Fig. 2d but the conical part consists of more chambers. Forma *pupiforme* (Fig. 2c) is similar to Fig. 2f, except that in the latter the conical portion is bigger and the penultimate chamber is smaller than the end chamber.

Forma *irregularis* (Fig. 2g) shows a large variable portion of the test after a small initial cone is formed. In the variable end stage the chambers vary in size and shape, being either globular, ellipsoidal or drum-shaped, and it is in this test that "rejuvenation" appears to have taken place.

CIFELLI (1960) deals with the variation in *Pseudonodosaria hybrida* (TERQUEM and BERTHELIN). Although CIFELLI has placed his forms from the Middle Jurassic in a different genus, they are the same as those from the Upper Lias. All his figured specimens (p. 564), together with those studied by the present author from similar beds in England, show the usual conical early stage followed by a nodosarine stage in which there is considerable variation in the constrictions between the chambers.

The nodosarine part of the test is generally longer than in the earlier forms from the Lias, which, on account of other different characters, should be referred to another species.

LUTZE (1960, p. 478) figures a wide range of variants from the Lias, Callovian and Lower Cretaceous. Some of his illustrations of Lias forms have been shaded to show the close similarity to other authors' species. A large number of forms are figured from the Callovian in northwest Germany and are similar to those from the Calovian and Oxfordian rocks of Britain.

Four variants are shown in Fig.2 l–o from the Oxfordian of England. Fig.2 o, the pupiform variety, has often been assigned to *Rectoglandulina oviformis* (TERQUEM), whereas Fig.2n is the nodosarine form similar to *Rectoglandulina vulgata* forma *humilis* from the Lias.

Both Fig.2 l and m are similar to *Rectoglandulina vulgata* forma *irregularis* and show a variable nodosarine habit with differing size and shapes of the chambers. These variants are continued into the Corallian, but here the rapid changes in environment obviously affected the Foraminifera, for the recurrence is both sporadic and sparse. This factor must have also affected the Rectoglandulinae from the Kimeridge Clay for, although the somewhat similar variations occur, specimens are generally rare. At some horizons the pupiform variety outnumbers the nodosarine.

Summarizing the history of the species of *Rectoglandulina*, it can be said that the two morphs occur throughout, the nodosarine being more variable, and that similar forms are produced from time to time in different species. Most of the variation occurs in the size and shape of the chambers.

Lingulina and Frondicularia (Fig. 3a–y)

The history of the genera *Lingulina* and *Frondicularia* throughout the Jurassic is important because the various species illustrate several major aspects of evolution. The author has already given a few examples of this (BARNARD, 1956, 1957), and shown the stratigraphic importance of some of the species.

Both genera provide examples of evolution of a single biocharacter, chiefly the biocharacter controlling the ornament. Often the ornament shows a "progressive evolution", which is of importance in stratigraphy.

It is, however, necessary to deal with successive populations of the Foraminifera so that the extreme variation of the forms can be taken into account. *Lingulina* and *Frondicularia* are so closely related that it is often only a matter of degree which separates them. The degree of slope of the sutures is the biocharacter used to separate the two genera. In *Lingulina* the sutures are convex, in *Frondicularia* inverted V-shaped. This character not only varies from individual to individual, but also in the ontogeny of the specimens, and difficulty sometimes arises in assigning the specimens to a definite genus. In order to avoid confusion, the author has used the name applied by most micropalaeontologists working on the group, although for other reasons he may not always agree with their determinations. Groups of smooth forms have been described under the species *Lingulina brizaeformis* (BORNEMANN) and *Frondicularia franconica* GÜMBEL, occurring in the Lower and Upper Jurassic respectively. These groups show somewhat similar variation at scattered horizons.

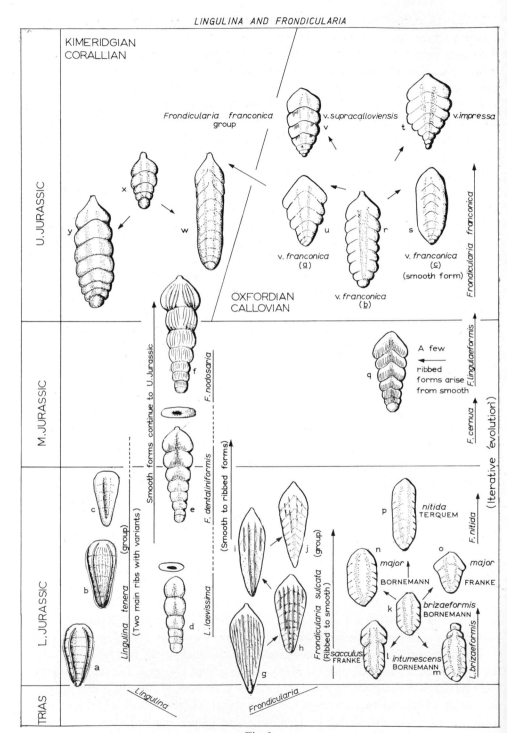

Fig. 3.

In the Lias, *Lingulina brizaeformis* (BORNEMANN) is well represented, with numerous variants which show several well-marked trends in growth and variation. Fig. 3k shows the most abundant form, assigned by BORNEMANN to *Lingulina brizaeformis* (BORNEMANN). This form commences with a few slightly chevron-shaped chambers, which increase in size so that the initial part of the test has widely divergent sides. The growth rate is then established and the next chambers are almost equal in size, so that the edges of the test are parallel.

This type of test may give rise to several major variants. A general increase in the overall size produces *Lingulina major* (BORNEMANN) (Fig. 3n). If, subsequent to the initial stage, the chambers go on slowly and regularly increasing until the whole of the test has broadly triangular edges, then *Lingulina major* FRANKE (non BORNEMANN), (Fig.3o) is produced.

If Fig. 3k is increased until the final stage, the parallelsided portion, becomes elongated, then *Frondicularia nitida* TERQUEM (Fig. 3p), results, a form which becomes common in higher beds of the Lias.

Irregularities in the growth rate produce two other forms. *Frondicularia sacculus* TERQUEM consists of the regular growth of Fig. 3k, together with a few chambers which, although maintaining the parallel sides to the test, increase so much in width that there is an apparent break in the growth rate. This character is shown better in FRANKE's interpretation of *Frondicularia sacculus* TERQUEM than in TERQUEM's original figures; see our Fig.3 l.

Lingulina intumescens (BORNEMANN) (Fig. 3m) also has the regular early growth stage, but later chambers are greatly reduced in size, producing the opposite effect to *Frondicularia sacculus* TERQUEM *sensu* FRANKE (Fig.3 l).

These variants occur abundantly in the Lower Lias *angulatum* to *semicostatum* zones. Forms from the Upper Lias described as *Frondicularia nitida* TERQUEM occur frequently and show similar trends of variation; and they are almost certainly the same species. Much rarer, but still showing the same general trends in variation, are forms from the Middle Jurassic.

In the Middle Jurassic, however, a new element is introduced. On forms with usually smooth tests striations appear at sporadic horizons. These forms occur among those which have been described as *Frondicularia lingulaeformis* SCHWAGER (Fig. 3q). The striations appear on morphological variants of this species which are similar to those occurring in the *Frondicularia sulcata* group.

LUTZE (1960) has already drawn attention to several smooth forms occurring in the Callovian and belonging to the *Frondicularia franconica* GÜMBEL group.

Although *Lingulina brizaeformis* (BORNEMANN) and *Frondicularia franconica* GÜMBEL are two separate species, with somewhat different characters, both have trends in variation which are closely comparable. LUTZE (1960) has given some of the variants subspecific or varietal names, which seems to be unnecessary as these forms appear to be of no stratigraphic significance and are only heterochronous homoeomorphs of earlier variants. In fact, this procedure would complicate taxonomy.

The central variant (Fig. 3r) is *Frondicularia franconica* GÜMBEL form *b* of LUTZE, which can be seen to be closely comparable with Fig. 3n or k, except that, although the sides of the test are parallel, they are slightly lobulate, indented at the sutures. *Frondicularia franconica* GÜMBEL form *c* LUTZE is similar in many respects to *Frondicularia nitida* TERQUEM (Fig. 3p); moreover, *Frondicularia franconica* GÜMBEL form *a* of LUTZE (Fig. 3u) has a test with divergent sides closely comparable with *Lingulina major* FRANKE (non BORNEMANN) (Fig.3 o). It is soon apparent that, whereas many forms occur in the Callovian to Kimeridgian with smooth sides to the test, there is a further biocharacter, interacting in some forms, which produces indentation at the sutures and hence a lobulate periphery to the test.

Two further modifications arise on *Frondicularia franconica* GÜMBEL: in var. *supracalloviensis* LUTZE, striations also appear, weakly developed near the sutures (Fig. 3v); and in *Frondicularia franconica* GÜMBEL var. *impressa* LUTZE (Fig. 3t), and several other variants, the test has a slightly biconcave cross-section instead of being convex or even trilobed, as in *Lingulina brizaeformis* BORNEMANN.

The author considers this to be variation which occurs in the Callovian; but when the Kimeridgian is reached the test has lost or reduced this tendency. When the tendency to biconvexity is very pronounced, specimens appear on casual examination to belong to different species. If sufficient specimens are available, a gradation between the forms is seen to exist.

The overall variation in the shape of the test is similar from the Lias to the Kimeridge Clay. However, the total variation may not be present at every horizon. Only a few specimens are generally available for examination from the Middle Jurassic and Corallian, with their differing environments. The full variation width of the species may not be entirely present for study.

Ornamented groups of species which show "progressive evolution" in the ornament often appear to have shorter ranges than the smooth species, and consequently are more important stratigraphically.

One group, comprising the species *Lingulina laevissima* (TERQUEM), *Frondicularia dentaliformis* TERQUEM, and *Frondicularia nodosaria* TERQUEM, range through the Upper Lias, and Middle Jurassic into the early part of the Upper Jurassic. *Lingulina laevissima* (TERQUEM) (Fig. 3d) appears first, and is smooth with slightly convex sutures, although these may be almost straight in early stages of ontogeny. This smooth form continues throughout the whole range of the species group, but becomes rarer towards the end of the range. However, in the Middle Jurassic, forms referred to *Frondicularia dentaliniformis* TERQUEM (Fig. 3e) arise, gradually increasing in numbers. In this species the sutures are slightly more chevron-shaped than in *Lingulina laevissima* (TERQUEM), but what is of more importance are fine striations at and near the sutures, usually on the lower parts of the later chambers in the ontogeny of the specimens.

The amount and degree of striation increases in *Frondicularia nodosaria* TERQUEM (Fig. 3f), and hence in this species the ribs continue over the whole chambers. Furthermore, the striations occur in earlier chambers in the ontogeny until striae cover the surface of all chambers.

The author (BARNARD, 1957) has already dealt with the details of the *Frondicularia sulcata* Bornemann species group, which exhibits a "progressive evolution" in the ornament of the test throughout the Lower Lias. Early forms of this group (Fig. 3g) have eight to twelve longitudinal costae, and are replaced by forms with six to eight ribs. Degeneration of the peripheral ribs takes place first, and slowly spreads to the inner central costae (Fig. 3h). The number is then reduced to four (Fig. 3i) and then to two. Forms often show remnants of the early ribs, either discontinuous or badly developed. Finally, variants are formed which have only slight traces of the ribs or are completely smooth, and are assigned to *Frondicularia terquemi* d'Orbigny (Fig. 3j).

It must be emphasized that the change from one form to another is gradual, and the evolution is detected when one is dealing with successive populations. These later appear to show "progressive evolution".

Another group of species (Fig.3 o–c) showing a change in ornament is *Lingulina tenera* Bornemann, from the Lias, which has already been dealt with in detail by the author (Barnard, 1957). On each side of the *Lingulina* (Fig.3a) are two main longitudinal well-developed costae, which show little or no variation in development. At some horizons, however, there is a tendency for these ribs to degenerate towards a smooth form (Fig. 3c) whilst at other levels the ribs in later stages of ontogeny bifurcate, so that four costae occur on each side of the test. The chief change, however, is in the secondary ornament, which is made up of striations occurring on various parts of the test. Several patterns of striation are seen. First, fine longitudinal striae occur between the two main ribs (Fig. 3b) and the number varies considerably. Sometimes the striations also arise between the periphery and the main ribs, and furthermore striations can appear over the whole test. This change in ornamentation though useful in stratigraphy, is more complicated than that in the *Frondicularia sulcata* Bornemann group, and does not show the same simplified "progressive evolution".

Dentalina (Fig. 4a–k)

This is perhaps the most difficult of all the groups of the Lagenidae to study, because at certain horizons the differences between the genus *Nodosaria* and *Dentalina* become so much reduced that the genera appear to grade into each other, with accompanying difficulties in taxonomy.

Most of the Jurassic species of *Dentalina* are smooth forms; and, although they have been separated by various authors into a number of separate species, when sufficient specimens are obtained, some are seen to grade into one another. For the purposes of the present paper only a few of the species are mentioned, and taxonomy is applied in its most general sense.

Differentiation into species is usually based on one or more of the following characters: size and shape of chambers, slope of sutures, degree of curvature of the longitudinal axis, and position and shape of the aperture. All these biocharacters are extremely variable, and therefore the smooth forms are represented as being one species plexus. The various genomorphs may arise at many different horizons.

Generally speaking, the smooth arcuate specimens of *Dentalina subsiliqua* Franke

DENTALINA

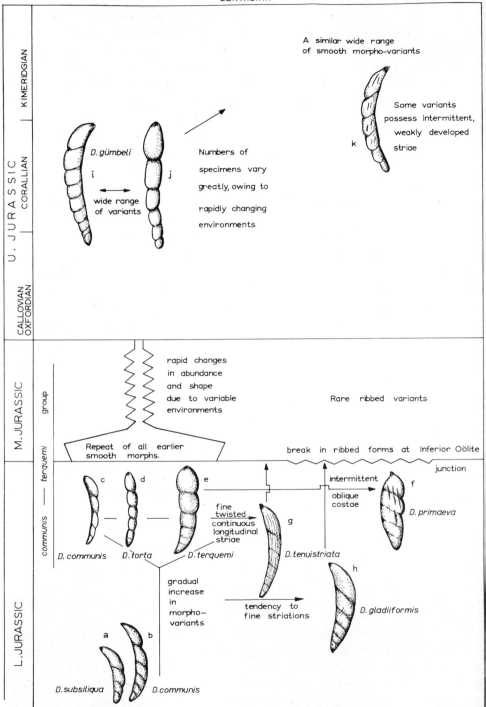

Fig. 4.

and *Dentalina communis* D'ORBIGNY (Fig. 4a, b) are extremely similar, and juvenile specimens are often referred to different species. This group, which occurs early in the Lias, gradually increases in numbers through the Lias, and the variation in the test also becomes more pronounced.

At scattered horizons throughout the Lias, ornament in the form of intermittent striations or costations arises periodically in a few specimens. Sometimes the ornament is stabilized for a brief period and a "new species" arises.

In the Lias a species very similar in general shape to *Dentalina communis* D'ORBIGNY is *Dentalina gladiiformis* FRANKE (Fig. 4h). This latter has fine striations, which usually appear at the sutures and are not continuous over the whole surface of the test but are confined to small areas on either side of the chamber sutures. The type of striation is often seen in various otherwise smooth species of uncoiling *Lenticulina*.

The ornament is usually not developed strongly enough and only appears for a short while, as a variant, and is not considered to be a specific character. Another species arising at about the same time in the Lias as *Dentalina gladiiformis* FRANKE is *Dentalina tenuistriata* TERQUEM (Fig. 4g) which has fine, twisted, longitudinal striations. In shape this species closely resembles *Dentalina communis* D'ORBIGNY, and may have arisen from it by the addition of striae. It is unlikely that *Dentalina gladiiformis* FRANKE has given rise to *Dentalina tenuistriata* TERQUEM, for the ornament in the latter starts at the proloculum and continues for the whole length of the test, and does not appear either intermittently or late in ontogeny.

Similar in general appearance to, but occurring much later than *Dentalina gladiiformis* FRANKE is *Dentalina primaeva* D'ORBIGNY (Fig. 4f). The latter, instead of having oblique, intermittent, fine striations, has oblique, intermittent costae, which are again confined to the areas immediately around the sutures.

The *Dentalina communis* D'ORBIGNY – *terquemi* D'ORBIGNY group of smooth species continues from the Lower into the Middle Jurassic, with repeats occurring of all the major genomorphs. Changes in the number of individuals from horizon to horizon are now extremely rapid, probably due to the rapid alternations of environments. The full range of variation may not be represented at every horizon.

Between the Upper Lias and the Inferior Oölite there is a definite break in the ribbed forms. These do not appear to cross the junction, and variants of *Dentalina* with ornament are extremely rare in the Middle Jurassic as a whole.

It is perhaps only when the environment is stable over a considerable length of time that the striate and costate variants of the smooth Dentalinae occur.

In the Upper Jurassic the smooth forms are very similar to those occurring much lower down in the sequence, but now they have been grouped around *Dentalina gümbeli* SCHWAGER (Fig. 4i–j).

A very wide range of morpho-variants occurs through the Callovian, Oxfordian, Corallian, and Kimeridgian, but only occasionally do ornamented variants occur. As before, the ornament can appear on any type of smooth morpho-variant, and cannot be taken as indicative of a specific character. In the Kimeridgian some variants possess intermittent weakly developed striae, similar to specimens from earlier horizons.

CONCLUSION

Only a few of the biocharacters affecting the evolution of selected Lagenidae from the Jurassic have been discussed. Some biocharacters are responsible for producing grades between forms often described as separate genera, others affect superficial features such as ornament, and the changes relating to the latter may be of stratigraphic importance.

SUMMARY

Species from four genera, *Rectoglandulina*, *Lingulina*, *Frondicularia* and *Dentalina*, have been selected to show variation or "progressive evolution" in one or more biocharacters. In some forms of *Rectoglandulina* and *Dentalina*, the basic shape of the test occurs in disconnected species groups and the production of heterochronous homoeomorphs limits stratigraphic value, whereas in certain species of *Lingulina* and *Frondicularia* "progressive evolution" of ornament is of extreme value.

REFERENCES

ADAMS, G. C., 1957. A study of the morphology and variation of some Upper Lias Foraminifera. *Micropaleontology*, 3 : 205–226.

BARNARD, T., 1950a. Foraminifera from the Lower Lias of the Dorset Coast. *Quart. J. Geol. Soc. London*, 105 : 347–391.

BARNARD, T., 1950b. Foraminifera from the Upper Lias of Byfield, Northamptonshire. *Quart. J. Geol. Soc. London*, 106 : 1–36.

BARNARD, T., 1952. Foraminifera from the Upper Oxford Clay (Jurassic) of Warboys, Huntingdonshire. *Proc. Geol. Assoc.*, 63 : 336–350.

BARNARD, T., 1953. Foraminifera from the Upper Oxford Clay (Jurassic) of Redcliff Point, near Weymouth, England. *Proc. Geol. Assoc.*, 64 : 183–197.

BARNARD, T., 1956. Some Lingulinae from the Lias of England. *Micropaleontology*, 2 : 271–282.

BARNARD, T., 1957. *Frondicularia* from the Lower Lias of England. *Micropaleontology*, 3 : 171–181.

BARNARD, T., 1960. Some species of *Lenticulina* and associated genera from the Lias of England. *Micropaleontology*, 6 : 41–55.

BARTENSTEIN, H. und BRAND, E., 1937. Mikropaläontologische Untersuchungen zur Stratigraphie des nordwestdeutschen Lias und Doggers. *Abhandl. Senckenberg, naturforsch. Ges.*, 439 : 1–224.

CIFELLI, R., 1960. Variation of English Bathonian Lagenidae and its phylogenetic significance. *J. Paleontol.*, 34 : 556–569.

FRANKE, A., 1936. Die Foraminiferen des deutschen Lias. *Abhandl. Preuss. Geol. Landesanstalt*, 169 : 1–138.

LOEBLICH, A. R. and TAPPAN, H., 1955. A revision of some glanduline Nodosariidae (Foraminifera). *Smith. Misc. Collections*, 126 (3) : 1–9.

LUTZE, G. F., 1960. Zur Stratigraphie und Paläontologie des Callovien und Oxfordien in Nordwest-Deutschland. *Geol. Jahrb.*, 77 : 391–532.

NØRVANG, A., 1957. The Foraminifera of the Lias Series in Jutland, Denmark. *Medd. Dansk. Geol. Foren.*, 13 : 279–414.

L'ACCROISSEMENT DE TAILLE
ET LES MODIFICATIONS ARCHITECTURALES CORRÉLATIVES
CHEZ LES ORBITOLINES

PIERRE RAT

Laboratoire de Géologie, Université de Dijon, Dijon (France)

C'est avec le plus grand plaisir que je m'associe à l'hommage international qui est rendu au Professeur VAN DER VLERK sur l'initiative de ses disciples, et que je lui dédie cette suite de réflexions qui me paraissent rejoindre certaines préoccupations exprimées dans ses travaux sur le concept même et sur la valeur pratique de l'espèce dans le monde fossile.

Dans une note récente, j'ai attiré l'attention sur l'influence que pouvait exercer le milieu de vie sur la sélection ainsi que sur certains traits de l'organisation des orbitolines et par là même sur leur évolution (RAT, 1960). Presque en même temps DOUGLASS (1960 a, b) a publié une importante monographie qui apporte une documentation nouvelle, extrêmement riche, sur le genre *Orbitolina* en Amérique du Nord, puis un examen critique de l'ensemble des orbitolinidés. D'un autre côté le travail de MOULLADE (1960), qui veut tirer le genre *Orbitolinopsis* du flou dans lequel il demeurait, représente un autre effort pour ordonner et hiérarchiser les divers caractères des orbitolinidés. L'intérêt que suscite actuellement ce groupe n'est donc pas à démontrer.

C'est dans un esprit un peu différent de celui des grandes monographies de SILVESTRI (1931), HENSON (1948) et DOUGLASS (1960a) que sont conduites pour le moment mes recherches sur les orbitolines. Avant de tenter de redécrire des espèces classiques en les caractérisant mieux que n'ont pu le faire les créateurs, ou avant de décrire des espèces nouvelles que suggèrent les matériaux rassemblés, plusieurs pierres d'achoppement me retiennent.

Quelle est la signification biologique des populations recueillies? Peut-on vraiment y reconnaître des espèces définissables par un certain nombre de caractères constants que l'on puisse clairement retrouver d'un gisement à un autre? Ou bien ne correspondent-elles qu'à des variétés locales en nombre pratiquement infini, plus ou moins dépendantes du milieu et ne se retrouvant pas identiques en des gisements un peu éloignés quoique contemporains? Nous rencontrons ici les difficultés soulevées à la fois par le problème de l'espèce en paléontologie et par celui de l'espèce chez les unicellulaires. HENSON (1948, p. 71) a exprimé des inquiétudes analogues à propos des orbitolines de l'Asie du Sud-Ouest.

Une autre question, intimement liée aux précédentes, concerne la recherche et la délimitation de critères morphologiques ou structuraux qui puissent servir pour la description rigoureuse et la reconnaissance des variantes; qui puissent servir ensuite pour caractériser des espèces paléontologiques utilisables par les stratigraphes. Il s'agirait donc de trouver des fils directeurs solides à travers cette irritante ressemblance entre les innombrables orbitolines: elle cache une diversité sous-jacente que les diverses diagnoses ou figurations, malgré leur précision croissante, n'ont encore jamais réussi à cerner et ordonner de façon pleinement satisfaisante ou pratique. Une solution est-elle possible ? Nous devons le croire avant de nous décourager.

Enfin quelle est l'ampleur de la variabilité chez les orbitolines et comment la cerner ? Orienté par ces préoccupations, je me suis attaché à l'analyse d'un fait banal d'observation: l'accroissement de taille des orbitolines au cours du Crétacé inférieur.

CARACTÈRES STABLES, ÉVOLUTIFS ET ADAPTATIFS

Unités taxonomiques étudiées

Sous le nom commun d'orbitolines, je place les orbitolinidés dont les loges présentent intérieurement une zone radiale clairement apparente. Cette zone se situe entre la zone marginale dont le compartimentage à tendance alvéolaire est dû à de minces lames horizontales ou verticales, et la zone centrale dont la structure variable tend à devenir confuse. Elle est caractérisée par la présence de cloisons radiales épaissies par rapport à celles de la zone marginale qu'elles prolongent, sinueuses ou zig-zagantes, de section habituellement trapézoïdale ou triangulaire à pointe tournée vers le bas sur les coupes subaxiales ou obliques.

Ainsi définis, les orbitolinidés (Orbitolinidae) à cloisons sinueuses correspondent aux genres *Orbitolina* et *Simplorbitolina* et se séparent des orbitolinidés à piliers, tels que les *Dictyoconus*. Cependant, l'opposition n'est peut-être pas aussi radicale que le souhaiterait notre logique cartésienne. Réexaminant des échantillons de *Simplorbitolina*, DOUGLASS (1960b) a attiré l'attention sur le fait que la partie basse des cloisons radiales se scindait plus ou moins en discrets piliers. Il fait alors de ce trait l'un des caractères du genre dans la diagnose qu'il redonne. J'ajouterai qu'il existe aussi des *Orbitolina* dont les cloisons radiales présentent une certaine tendance à se résoudre en piliers vers le centre: d'où une certaine distinction, qui méritera d'être discutée, entre les orbitolines avec disposition radiale claire et les orbitolines à structure plus ou moins pilaroïde. Je laisserai aujourd'hui ce point, me proposant d'y revenir plus tard de façon détaillée.

Retenons donc que le matériel que nous allons examiner est groupé pour l'instant dans les genres *Simplorbitolina* et *Orbitolina*. Stratigraphiquement, nous sommes situés dans le Crétacé inférieur et moyen: du Barrémien au Cénomanien inclus.

Caractères évolutifs

Ayant circonscrit l'objet de notre examen, nous allons pouvoir rechercher quels sont chez les orbitolines les caractères qui se modifient au cours du temps. Deux tendances évolutives ont été retenues (voir DOUGLASS, 1960b):

(a) Complication de la zone marginale par compartimentage dû au recoupement de cloisonnettes radiales et de lames horizontales.

(b) Accroissement de taille.

Or ces deux tendances semblent communes à tous les orbitolinidés; elles sont bien exprimées chez *Orbitolina* pour les formes à cloisons radiales, chez *Dictyoconus* pour les formes à piliers. En ce qui concerne la zone marginale, une discussion aussi serait nécessaire. En effet, on admet volontiers que l'évolution est allée dans le sens de la complication car les zones marginales sans divisions secondaires ou à subdivisions simples se rencontrent chez des formes petites qui présentent d'autres signes de simplicité estimés primitifs: *Simplorbitolina* par exemple. Cependant un fait doit frapper: le maximum de complication apparaît très tôt au Crétacé inférieur avec *Dictyoconus* et *Orbitolina* alors que l'on voit bien plus tard des zones marginales non compartimentées. Il y a donc là encore une question dont la réponse précise est à laisser en suspens jusqu'à plus ample information.

Nous pouvons encore ajouter les transformations suivantes:

(c) Ouverture de l'angle apical.

(d) Oblitération de la structure dans la zone centrale.

(e) Formation de loges annulaires (tendance qui paraît propre, ainsi que la précédente, aux orbitolinidés à cloisons radiales).

(f) Passage de la structure à piliers à la structure radiale.

Je pense actuellement, sans que les observations faites en apportent une vraie démonstration, que la transformation s'est faite dans le sens piliers → cloisons radiales.

En réalité, tous ces caractères, que nous isolons pour mieux les étudier, ne sont pas totalement indépendants les uns des autres; certains sont plus ou moins liés et se modifient corrélativement. En particulier, les transformations chaotiques de la zone centrale semblent sous la dépendance des mêmes facteurs que la genèse des loges annulaires. Nous pourrions grouper les trois traits (c), (d) et (e) sous le même titre: tendance à la réalisation de l'orbitoline plate.

Caractères adaptatifs

Enfin certaines modifications méritent d'être classées sous une troisième rubrique: adaptation. Il est évident que la frontière n'est pas toujours nette entre caractères adaptatifs et caractères évolutifs mais la distinction, une fois de plus, est pratique pour l'étude. Nous retiendrons essentiellement:

(a) La capacité d'utilisation d'un matériel étranger pour la construction du test.

(b) Peut-être la prolifération des formes A macrosphériques, issues de la sporulation asexuée, dans la colonisation d'un milieu.

(c) Peut-être l'aplatissement facilitant la tenue sur le fond dans un milieu un peu agité. Nous avons noté que les orbitolines plates étaient en effet plus fréquentes dans les milieux plus ou moins sableux c'est-à-dire quand existaient des mouvements de l'eau suffisants pour amener le matériel terrigène (RAT, 1960).

L'accroissement de taille

L'accroissement progressif de taille au cours du Crétacé inférieur a été noté depuis longtemps chez les orbitolines. Il est particulièrement frappant avec les très grandes *O. concava* et *O. aperta* du Cénomanien qui représentent les termes ultimes de cette évolution avec des diamètres dépassant 3 ou 4 et même 5 cm. On a bien remarqué aussi qu'aux époques où les grandes orbitolines étaient florissantes, au Cénomanien tout spécialement, les petites continuaient à être nombreuses: petites orbitolines assez coniques à côté de grandes orbitolines plates. Dès lors, si l'on considère les orbitolines

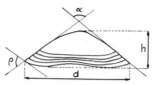

Fig. 1. Définition des grandeurs mesurables utilisées. α = angle apical ou angle au sommet; ρ = angle de raccordement; d = diamètre; h = hauteur; pour l'épaisseur voir Fig. 3e.

dans leur ensemble, on est conduit à se rallier à la conclusion formulée par DOUGLASS (1960b, p. 254): chez les orbitolines, "there is an overall tendency toward greater size with time, but the trend is not persistent".

Par contre, si l'on admet que, suivant toute vraisemblance, il y a dans l'ensemble des orbitolines des lignées de durée plus ou moins longue qui se sont séparées les unes des autres à divers moments et ont évolué indépendamment, le phénomène n'est plus surprenant. On peut concevoir dans chaque lignée un accroissement de taille assez régulier qui soit allé plus ou moins loin pour chacune d'entre elles, le Cénomanien ayant vu une réalisation extrême du processus. Il faudrait donc se garder de mettre toutes les grandes orbitolines soit en filiation les unes par rapport aux autres soit dans un même rameau buissonnant: elles constitueraient un ensemble artificiel polyphylétique. Les faits donnent-ils des arguments en faveur de cette interprétation?

D'autre part, le passage des petites aux grandes orbitolines se fait avec un changement dans l'organisation: aux orbitolines coniques, petites, se substituent de grandes espèces plates dont le diamètre a pu, dans certains cas, s'accroître de façon presque illimitée. Un tel changement ne semble jamais être intervenu dans le genre parallèle *Dictyoconus*. Comment saisir et décrire cette transformation pour pouvoir l'interpréter?

L'ARCHITECTURE DU TEST: DÉFINITION, DIVERS MODES

Pour étudier les modifications liées à l'accroissement de taille et à la réalisation de l'orbitoline plate, il est nécessaire de faire une hiérarchie dans les caractères observés. C'est pourquoi je distinguerai dans l'organisation interne des orbitolines:
(1) L'architecture, c'est-à-dire l'agencement d'ensemble: concrètement, il s'agit de la disposition et de la forme des loges (voir Tableau I).

TABLEAU I

LES DIVERS TYPES ARCHITECTURAUX NOTÉS CHEZ LES ORBITOLINES ET LEURS RAPPORTS AVEC LA FORME DU TEST

Types architecturaux	Formes extérieures	Taille
A . *Architectures à loges entières*		
— *planiseptale:* les septes interloculaires sont plans	coniques	1 – 2 mm
— *sphériseptale:* les septes interloculaires sont des calottes sphériques	conico-convexes ou biconvexes	
— *scutiseptale:* les septes interloculaires sont en forme d'écuelles		
— *sigmoseptale:* les septes interloculaires ont une courbure en S	conico-concaves ou convexo-concaves	
B . *Architectures à loges annulaires* (caractérisées par leur partie annulaire)		
(a) Imparfaites		
— dispositif annulaire accidentel	conico-concaves hautes	
— dispositif annulaire réduit à *quelques loges* — stades séniles	conico-concaves ou convexo-concaves	
— anneau *d'épaisseur décroissante*		
(b) Parfaites (orbitolines "plates")		
— anneau *d'épaisseur constante*	conico-concaves et convexo-concaves, basses ou réfléchies; discoïdales	10 mm et plus
— anneau *d'épaisseur croissante*		

La nomenclature concernant la forme est empruntée à HENSON (1948, p. 49).

(2) La structure qui nous fait considérer le test à une échelle plus fine: organisation interne des loges, communications, structure des parois, etc.

Le nombre des architectures n'est pas infini. Deux catégories majeures seront faites d'après l'extension des loges: continues ou entières si elles s'étalent sans interruption sur toute la face inférieure de la coquille, annulaires s'il leur manque la partie centrale; dans ce cas, elles créent une sorte de bourrelet sur le pourtour du test.

Architectures à loges entières ou continues (Fig. 2)

L'allure générale des loges ou, ce qui revient au même, le dessin des septes interloculaires sur une coupe verticale, permet aisément de définir 4 styles:

(1) *L'architecture planiseptale*

L'architecture planiseptale (à loges en disques de taille croissante régulièrement empilées) est réalisée chez les orbitolinidés coniques dont *Simplorbitolina manasi* donne un très bon exemple. Elle ne semble pas pouvoir s'accommoder d'une grande ouverture de l'angle au sommet (de l'ordre de 60° au maximum). En dehors des *Simplorbitolina* nous la trouvons chez *Coskinolina* et divers *Dictyoconus*. Elle est plus rare chez les formes qui ont été rapportées jusqu'à maintenant au genre *Orbitolina*.

Par sa simplicité géométrique, par le fait qu'elle existe chez les petits orbitolinidés, nous aurions volontiers tendance à considérer que l'architecture planiseptale est primitive. C'est possible, mais la prudence conseille de tempérer ce jugement.

(2) *L'architecture sphériseptale*

L'architecture sphériseptale (à loges en calottes) donne des tests constitués par des calottes sphériques de taille croissante, régulièrement emboîtées les unes dans les autres. Elle est particulièrement nette sur les figurations qu'a données SILVESTRI (1931, pl. 13, fig. 5–6) pour *Orbitolina trochus*. Ce mode admet un angle apical assez variable, éventuellement bien supérieur à celui du type planiseptal (de l'ordre de 120° par exemple). Corrélativement, il admet aussi de plus grands diamètres. D'importants écarts se notent d'ailleurs dans la valeur des rayons de courbure; pour un même individu, elle est susceptible aussi de changer pendant la croissance. En même temps, le centre de courbure, qui ne coïncide pas habituellement avec le sommet de l'orbitoline, se déplace parfois progressivement.

Extérieurement les coquilles sphériseptales ont une face inférieure convexe. Elles se distinguent par leur aspect plus ou moins ventru et par la forme de la face supérieure: séries des biconvexes et des conico-convexes de HENSON (1948).

L'architecture sphériseptale peut être estimée tout aussi primitive que l'architecture planiseptale à laquelle elle se relie par des individus à septes très peu courbes. Elle se rencontre, hors des genres *Orbitolina* et *Dictyoconus*, dans des organismes très simples tels qu'*Iraqia*, *Simplorbitolina* ou *Orbitolinopsis*.

(3) L'architecture scutiseptale

L'architecture scutiseptale (à loges en écuelles) est géométriquement intermédiaire entre les deux précédentes: les septes ressemblent à des écuelles à fond plat relevé par une courbe régulière vers les bords. Cependant rien n'implique que le mode scutiseptal soit un terme de passage entre plani et sphériseptal. On peut le concevoir aussi comme

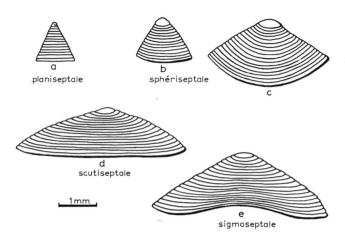

Fig. 2. Architectures à loges entières. Pour la disposition des loges et la taille du test, les schémas sont inspirés de figurations ou de coupes réelles; cependant, afin que les dessins soient clairs, le nombre des loges a été réduit. *a.* Planiseptale: *Simplorbitolina manasi* CIRY et RAT. *b.* Sphériseptale à faible rayon de courbure: *Orbitolina* sp. *c.* Sphériseptale à angle apical ouvert et fort rayon de courbure: *O. trochus* (FRITSCH), d'après SILVESTRI (1931). *d.* Scutiseptale: *O.* cf. *lenticularis* (BLUMENBACH). Vallée de Soba. *e.* Sigmoseptale idem.

une adaptation de l'architecture planiseptale à l'ouverture de l'angle apical: la courbure de la partie marginale des loges permet en effet de maintenir une valeur normale égale ou supérieure à 60° pour l'angle de raccordement des septes avec la face supérieure du test quand l'angle apical croît de façon démesurée. On peut le situer aussi entre l'arrangement sphériseptal et le sigmoseptal.

(4) L'architecture sigmoseptale

L'architecture sigmoseptale (à loges en cul-de-bouteille) réalise une transition vers les constructions annulaires. Elle représente surtout un stade final ou transitoire dans le développement de certaines orbitolines. Les loges sont encore entières mais l'amincissement de leur zone centrale, légèrement marqué dans l'architecture scutiseptale, s'accentue. Tout se passe comme si elles s'étiraient avant de se rompre. En coupe axiale, elles acquièrent ainsi un aspect flexueux, sigmoïde. Extérieurement, la face inférieure se déprime: les silhouettes conico-concaves et convexo-concaves de HENSON (1948) commencent discrètement.

Architectures annulaires (Fig. 3)

Elles sont réalisées, à partir d'un stade de développement variable suivant les espèces ou les individus intéressés, quand les loges ne s'étendent plus de la périphérie jusqu'au centre du test et se restreignent à une sorte de bourrelet annulaire. Elles s'amincissent vers le centre, de sorte que leur section a normalement l'aspect d'une virgule.

D'un point de vue purement descriptif, les orbitolines à loges annulaires diffèrent entre elles:

(*a*) Par l'architecture de la partie initiale: sphériseptale ou en écuelles avec passage au type annulaire soit directement soit par l'intermédiaire d'un stade sigmoseptal.

(*b*) Par l'importance relative de cette partie initiale qui peut être extrêmement réduite (voir les figurations d'*O. concava* données par DOUGLASS, 1960a, pl. 2, et 1960b) ou au contraire constituer le test presque en entier. Dans le deuxième cas, à la limite, la disposition annulaire n'apparaît que comme une sorte d'accident terminal de la croissance.

(*c*) Par la valeur de l'angle apical, susceptible elle-même de varier au cours du dével-

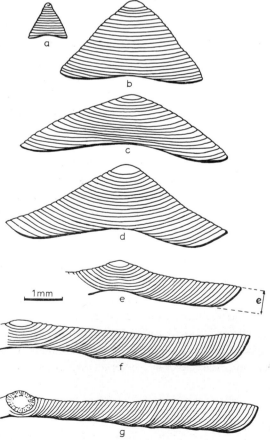

Fig. 3. Architectures à loges annulaires. (Même remarque que pour Fig. 2)

a. Une loge annulaire sénile sur test planiseptal: *S. manasi* CIRY et RAT (topotype).

b. Quelques loges annulaires sur une orbitoline sphériseptale à très faible courbure. *Orbitolina sp.* La Clape.

c. Loges annulaires apparaissant comme une exagération de la disposition sigmoseptale: *O.* cf. *lenticularis* (BLUM.) Vallée de Soba.

d. Anneau d'épaisseur décroissante sur une architecture sphériseptale: *O. crassa* DOUGLASS (DOUGLASS, 1960a, pl. 13).

e. Anneau d'épaisseur constante succédant à un stade sigmoseptal transitoire: *O. trochus* (FRITSCH), d'après SILVESTRI (1931).

f. Anneau d'épaisseur sensiblement constante, avec quelques irrégularités de croissance: *O.*cf. *subconcava* LEYMERIE. Cimetière d'Izurdiaga.

g. Anneau d'épaisseur croissante: *O. concava* (LAMARCK).

oppement individuel. En particulier, l'angle au sommet peut s'ouvrir rapidement au moment où se fait la substitution des loges annulaires aux loges continues.

(*d*) Par l'organisation même de la partie annulaire.

Nous allons essayer un classement dans un ordre qui nous paraît être aussi bien ontogénique que phylogénétique.

(1) *Types annulaires imparfaits*

Ici le nombre des loges incomplètes est limité. C'est donc la partie à loges entières qui donne son allure au test. La disposition annulaire semble bien ne correspondre qu'à un stade ultime du développement, stade sénile qui ne pouvait se maintenir long-temps et qui aurait résulté uniquement de l'incapacité de l'organisme à édifier des loges complètes dans la partie centrale. Il ne s'agirait donc pas nécessairement encore d'un caractère marquant un nouveau degré dans l'évolution mais simplement d'une parti-cularité ontogénique. Les loges annulaires se moulent sur les loges entières sans vrai-ment introduire un nouvel arrangement dans le plan d'organisation. Cependant des degrés se reconnaissent:

Formation exceptionnelle de loges annulaires chez des individus âgés. C'est tout parti-culièrement dans le cas de l'architecture planiseptale que la production de loges annu-laires paraît une véritable anomalie de la vieillesse. En section axiale, on voit ces loges s'effiler en biseau vers le centre et leur nombre est des plus restreint: éventuellement une seule.

Dispositif annulaire apparaissant comme une exagération du mode sigmoseptal. D'une façon imagée, nous pouvons dire que l'étirement des loges qui se manifeste dans le mode sigmoseptal est allé jusqu'à la rupture. Le nombre des loges annulaires est encore relativement réduit mais, en moyenne, moins que dans le cas précédent. La variabilité est d'ailleurs beaucoup plus grande que chez les formes planiseptales: au sein d'une population, le mode annulaire semble pouvoir persister plus longuement, s'installer même, pourrait-on dire, chez certains exemplaires. Les figurations que donne DOUGLASS (1960a, pl. 13) pour *Orbitolina crassa* montrent que l'apparition des loges annulaires sonne le glas pour de nombreux individus tandis que, sur d'autres, un nombre déjà important d'anneaux réussit à se construire.

A partir d'ici on peut vraiment parler de tendance évolutive. La loge annulaire n'est plus, ou tout au moins n'est plus pour tous les individus d'une population, le résul-tat d'une incapacité du protoplasme à édifier la zone centrale.

Dispositif annulaire à épaisseur décroissante. Il s'agit encore d'un type architectural théoriquement limité dans ses possibilités de développement. Souvent, au fur et à mesure que les loges se dilatent, la grandeur des lanières annulaires qu'elles consti-tuent se restreint. En conséquence, le test s'amincit en biseau du centre vers la péri-phérie. Cependant les loges terminales forment déjà un véritable anneau, parfois très important.

(2) *Types annulaires parfaits*

Chez les orbitolines que l'on peut qualifier du nom d'orbitolines plates, la partie annulaire constitue l'essentiel du test. La partie jeune à loges entières peut cependant être nettement apparente (1er type) ou au contraire être extrêmement réduite (2ème type). Pratiquement, nous fonderons la distinction sur un caractère externe: l'épaisseur de l'anneau aux différentes époques de la croissance.

Le dispositif annulaire à épaisseur sensiblement constante est assez répandu chez les orbitolines plates. On y reconnaît nettement deux parties:

La première, celle de jeunesse, est à loges entières bien développées. Quoique d'importance relativement réduite par rapport à l'ensemble du test chez les grandes orbitolines, ce stade jeune qui correspond à la partie centrale est bien individualisé: le nombre des loges peut être d'une quinzaine par exemple. Son architecture paraît normalement sphériseptale avec éventuellement passage, dans la partie terminale, au mode sigmoseptal. Cette première étape du développement permet au bord du test d'atteindre approximativement l'épaisseur adulte.

La partie adulte est constituée de loges annulaires régulières. L'épaisseur du test étant pratiquement atteinte dès que les premières apparaissent, la croissance ne porte donc que sur le diamètre des loges et du test. En réalité, si certaines orbitolines se conforment rigoureusement à ce plan, d'autres montrent certains changements traduisant des incidents de leur histoire individuelle: un léger épaississement progressif qui peut être suivi, aux approches du bord, d'un amincissement où l'on pourrait voir un indice de sénilité. D'autre part, quelques fluctuations peuvent être notées, en fonction des conditions du milieu vraisemblablement. Le passage du jeune à l'adulte se manifeste parfois par une ouverture de l'angle apical.

Le dispositif annulaire d'épaisseur nettement croissante est représenté typiquement chez *Orbitolina concava*. Sa première originalité réside dans l'extrême réduction du stade à loges entières qui mérite pratiquement le nom de stade embryonnaire. Le test est donc presque entièrement formé de loges annulaires dont les premières ne donnent encore à son bord qu'une épaisseur relativement faible; les suivantes les débordent et atteignent progressivement la taille définitive.

Ce dernier arrangement dérive en quelque sorte du précédent, par une accélération du développement qui franchirait rapidement les stades à loges entières que nous considérons comme ancestraux.

ACCROISSEMENT DE TAILLE, ARCHITECTURE ET ÉVOLUTION

Corrélations entre l'accroissement de taille et certains changements architecturaux

L'augmentation de la taille que l'on évalue pratiquement par celle du diamètre est d'abord, chez tous les orbitolinidés, le résultat de deux processus souvent associés:

(1) *L'augmentation du nombre des loges*

L'augmentation du nombre des loges n'offre cependant que des possibilités limitées chez les orbitolinidés à loges entières. On peut voir dans cette limitation une conséquence de la forme conique ou évasée du test: elle exige de la dernière loge édifiée un diamètre toujours supérieur à celui de la précédente; finalement, elle aboutirait à des dimensions de loges incompatibles avec les capacités de construction du protoplasme.

(2) *L'ouverture de l'angle apical*

Ce processus est, lui aussi, restreint dans ses possibilités lorsqu'il s'agit de coquilles planiseptales. Une explication a été avancée tout à l'heure par la nécessité de maintenir un angle de raccordement suffisant entre les septes et la face supérieure du test.

Augmentation du nombre des loges et ouverture de l'angle au sommet se manifestent chez tous les orbitolinidés: *Dictyoconus* aussi bien qu'orbitolines. Or chez ces dernières, des transformations architecturales plus profondes interviennent. Elles apportent une nouvelle formule et permettent de dépasser largement les tailles obtenues par la conjonction des deux premiers processus. Il s'agit de la f a c u l t é d e s a c r i - f i e r l a p a r t i e c e n t r a l e d e s l o g e s au profit, en quelque sorte, de l'auréole périphérique. La fraction vraiment active du protoplasme semble alors s'être localisée dans la zone radiale et surtout la zone marginale. Tout se passe comme si, dans les grandes orbitolines plates, le protoplasme avait vécu essentiellement en surface juste au-dessous de la face supérieure et sur la marge annulaire du test. Cette faculté de sacrifier la zone centrale que ne semblent pas avoir possédé les orbitolinidés à piliers, se traduit par la gradation théorique suivante:

(*a*) Oblitération plus ou moins poussée de la zone centrale qui peut être grossièrement construite à l'aide de matériel détritique étranger au foraminifère.

(*b*) Amincissement de cette zone.

(*c*) Enfin sa disparition et le passage à l'architecture nettement annulaire.

Débarrassés, si l'on peut dire, de cette partie, gênante à construire par la démesure qui finit par la frapper, les orbitolines annulaires auraient acquis une capacité nouvelle et considérable d'accroissement.

Modalités de l'évolution

La superposition stratigraphique ne nous apprend guère autre chose que l'antériorité des coquilles petites et hautes, ainsi que la persistance des petites formes tandis que les orbitolines géantes proliféraient. L'é t u d e d e l'o n t o g é n è s e est en accord avec ce fait car les architectures annulaires viennent se greffer sur des constructions à loges entières auxquelles nous attribuons la priorité dans la phylogénèse. Le développement individuel montre aussi que l'organisation sigmoseptale peut constituer une étape intermédiaire — qui n'est pas indispensable — entre loges entières et loges annulaires, ce que nous résumerons ainsi:

$$\text{sphéri- ou scutiseptal} \xrightarrow{\nearrow \text{ sigmoseptal} \searrow} \text{loges annulaires.}$$

Pour les mêmes raisons, l'architecture scutiseptale se situerait normalement après le mode sphériseptal, formant un passage (non obligatoire) entre sphéri et sigmo ou annulaire. Enfin, les orbitolines à anneau d'épaisseur croissante dériveraient soit d'orbitolines à épaisseur constante soit d'orbitolines à stade annulaire imparfait, par accélération, condensation, du début du développement (tachygénèse). Ces interprétations relatives aux enchaînements entre les principaux types architecturaux sont exprimés dans la partie supérieure de la Fig. 5.

L'examen de la variation apporte d'autres éléments d'appréciation. Une population déterminée correspond rarement, et vraisemblablement même ne correspond jamais, à un type architectural unique. Cependant, il semble que l'on puisse toujours reconnaître un type plus fréquent, normal si l'on veut, avec une variation plus ou moins ample de part et d'autre. Ainsi, chez *Simplorbitolina manasi*, dans les plaques minces où des comptages ont été faits, 60% environ des coquilles sont nettement planiseptales. Chez d'autres (20% environ), les cloisons interloculaires s'infléchissent légèrement acheminant vers l'architecture sphériseptale nette que l'on rencontre dans 20% environ de l'ensemble. Dans ce cas, la courbure reste assez faible et l'angle apical n'apparaît pas sensiblement modifié. Enfin, exceptionnellement, les dernières loges peuvent s'amincir dans la partie centrale jusqu'à prendre une disposition annulaire (voir Tableau II et Planche I).

Le milieu de vie a-t-il eu une influence sur ces fluctuations? Vraisemblablement oui, mais il est difficile d'apprécier les modalités et la portée de son action, de distinguer clairement une variation phénotypique d'une variation génotypique.

L'étude des populations montre aussi que certains types architecturaux sont très fréquemment sinon toujours associés. Leurs affinités sont donc étroites, le passage de l'un à l'autre facile. On peut concevoir qu'il en a été de même au cours de l'évolution. Ainsi les formes planiseptales vont normalement avec des sphériseptales à faible rayon de courbure, soit qu'elles constituent le type moyen, soit qu'elles représentent au contraire un cas extrême de variation à partir d'un type moyen sphériseptal (Tableau II). Le mode sigmoseptal est associé au sphéri ou au scutiseptal ainsi qu'à des tests pourvus de quelques loges annulaires.

Dans ces séries, l'évolution nous apparaît comme la fixation dans le patrimoine héréditaire d'un caractère qui était à la limite de la variation chez certaines populations: par exemple, le mode sigmoseptal qui est atteint occasionnellement dans un gisement, deviendrait plus tard le type moyen normal chez des ensembles issus du premier. L'évolution se produirait par une sorte de glissement progressif de la variation, régulier ou non, irréversible ou non: déplacement du centre de gravité de l'espèce sans qu'il y ait nécessairement création d'une architecture vraiment nouvelle (Fig. 4).

Cependant, tous les faits connus ne se laissent pas aisément inclure dans ce schéma. En particulier, il semble difficile de trouver une série continue entre les orbitolines pourvues de quelques anneaux dans leur vieil âge et les orbitolines vraiment annulaires. Une sorte de bond évolutif se situerait à ce niveau. Sans insister plus, je soulignerai l'analogie entre ces faits pressentis chez les orbitolines et les deux modalités de l'évolution distinguées par SIMPSON (1944): évolution phylétique et évolution quantique.

TABLEAU II

VARIATION DE L'ARCHITECTURE AU SEIN DE DIVERSES POPULATIONS D'ORBITOLINIDÉS

Nombre de tests comptés	Architectures à loges entières				Quelques loges annulaires			Architectures à nombreuses loges annulaires			Provenance	Affinités	Renvoi à la planche photographique
	Planiseptales	Sphériseptales	Scutiseptales	Sigmoseptales	Sur plani- ou sphériseptales	Sur scutiseptales	Sur sigmoseptales	Epaisseur décroissante	E. constante	E. croissante			
78	47	30	·	·	1	·	·	·	·	·	Gulina	Simplorbitolina manasi	3
50	30	19	·	·	1	·	·	·	·	·	Las Alisas	(Simplorbitolina manasi)	1–2
41	4	35	·	·	1	·	1	·	·	·	Durango	Orbitolina sp. à structure pilaroïde	
37	6	20	3	4	2	1	·	1	·	·	Castro de Valnera	Orbitolina sp. avec matériel arénacé	4
107	·	2	22	21	·	17	45	·	·	·	Soba	O. cf. lenticularis	6
60	·	1	14	7	·	8	29	1	·	·	La Clape	O. cf. lenticularis	
37	·	4	7	4	·	3	19	·	·	·	La Clape	O. cf. lenticularis	
69	2	18	10	6	5	1	6	12	9	·	Montagne de Tauch	Orbitolina sp.	

L'évolution phylétique qui "implique le glissement soutenu, orienté (mais pas nécessairement rectilinéaire) des caractères moyens des populations", s'applique bien aux modifications survenues chez les petites orbitolines. "Elle conduit vers des espèces nouvelles moins par scission d'une population que par changement d'une population en bloc" (traduction SAINT-SEINE, 1950, p. 311).

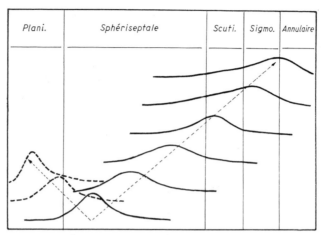

Fig. 4. Schéma théorique d'une évolution phylétique chez les orbitolines. Les populations considérées sont représentées par leur courbe de variabilité. A partir d'une population initiale supposée sphérisep-tale, deux directions possibles d'évolution sont indiquées: l'une à droite, vers des tests dont la courbure des septes s'accentue avant que commence une réduction de la zone centrale (scuti- puis sigmoseptale) et qu'apparaissent des loges annulaires; l'autre à gauche, vers des populations ou domineront les formes planiseptales.

SIMPSON a créé le terme d'évolution quantique pour un "glissement rapide d'une population vivante en déséquilibre, vers un équilibre distinctement différent de la condition ancestrale". Des types d'adaptation nettement nouveaux apparaissent. C'est le cas, me semble-t-il, pour les architectures annulaires parfaites.

SIMPSON ajoute encore (traduction SAINT-SEINE, 1950, p. 318): "Dans l'évolution phylétique, l'équilibre du système organisme–milieu est continu ou presque tel, quoique que le point d'équilibre puisse glisser et le fasse généralement. Dans l'évolution quan-tique, l'équilibre est perdu et un nouvel équilibre est atteint". Une fois de plus, je mettrais volontiers en relation de cause à effet l'apparition des architectures annulaires parfaites et la diffusion des orbitolines dans des milieux de sédimentation terrigènes (RAT, 1960).

Superposition de l'évolution architecturale à celle de diverses structures

Ayant fixé notre attention sur l'architecture du test, nous avons négligé jusqu'à maintenant les détails plus fins, sauf pour souligner la véritable dégénérescence sus-ceptible de toucher la zone centrale. Il est temps d'y revenir. En effet l'évolution archi-tecturale mise en évidence n'est pas réservée à un type unique de structure. Par exemple, le mode sphériseptal parfait se rencontre chez des orbitolines pilaroïdes et chez des orbitolines avec matériel clastique agglutiné abondant. Il en est de même pour l'architecture sigmoseptale. Sans pousser loin cette investigation, nous pouvons

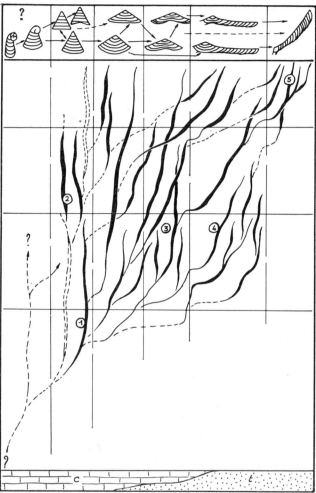

Fig. 5. Schéma théorique d'un enchaînement possible des orbitolines en fonction de l'architecture. Le point de départ hypothétique a été supposé sphériseptal. Chaque ligné est figurée d'après la position de son type architectural moyen. Certains rameaux, sensiblement verticaux, n'auraient pratiquement pas subi de changements architecturaux au cours du temps; mais il n'en a pas nécessairement été de même pour les autres caractères, la structure en particulier. D'autres rameaux, de direction oblique, figurent une évolution phylétique avec glissement plus ou moins régulier, rectiligne, de la variabilité. D'autres encore présentent sur le schéma un coude brusque avec acquisition rapide d'un nouveau type d'architecture (évolution quantique); une discontinuité majeure est probable à l'origine des architectures annulaires parfaites. Au bas du schéma est indiqué un changement de milieu auquel un rôle peut être attribué dans cette transformation: à gauche milieux de sédimentation essentiellement calcaires (c), à droite milieux avec apports terrigènes notables (t). Situation approximative de quelques types classiques: 1. *Orbitolina conulus* Douvillé (avec incertitude sur l'âge); 2. *Simplorbitolina manasi* Ciry et Rat; 3. *O.* groupe *lenticularis* (Blum.); 4. *O.* groupe *discoidea* Gras; 5. *O.* groupe *concava* (Lamarck) *aperta* (Erman).

affirmer qu'un même type architectural a pu se réaliser sur des orbitolines de structure différente, donc dans des lignées séparées.

De plus, un même arrangement architectural peut apparaître au cours de l'ontogénèse suivant des modalités différentes: une disposition annulaire se greffant directement sur un test sphériseptal ou au contraire lui succédant par l'intermédiaire d'un stade sigmoseptal. Nous avons toute latitude pour penser qu'il en a été de même au cours de l'évolution. Ces faits me paraissent suffisants pour confirmer l'hypothèse avancée dans la première partie suivant laquelle les grandes orbitolines, disons maintenant les orbitolines d'architecture annulaire, ont des origines diverses et ne forment qu'un groupe polyphylétique dû à une convergence. Un même type architectural a dû s'établir de façon indépendante sur des lignées distinctes, caractérisées par exemple par des structures différentes, et à plusieurs époques. Nous connaissons des grandes orbitolines parfaitement annulaires de diamètre supérieur à un centimètre aussi bien dans l'Aptien que dans l'Albien et le Cénomanien cantabriques, alors qu'une permanence de grands individus pendant la durée des deux premiers de ces étages est douteuse.

Fluide et multiple, la vie répugne à se couler dans les catégories que nous lui traçons pour essayer de la saisir. Tout particulièrement le monde des Protozoaires avec ses générations sexuées ou asexuées. Tout particulièrement celui des orbitolines, protéiforme, ancien conquérant de milieux changeants auxquels il a su s'adapter, qui nous laisse comme témoin de son importance la masse de ses accumulations devenues roches. Petit à petit on y pénètre comme dans une forêt serrée où tous les troncs se ressemblent, où l'on n'est pas sûr que les directions essayées ne s'achèveront pas en impasse.

Dans cette progression par efforts successifs, sans insister sur les interprétations dont certaines demanderaient une confrontation avec un plus grand nombre de faits, je retiendrai plutôt un résultat pratique: la distinction entre architecture et structure, l'introduction d'une nomenclature précise, donneront j'espère un langage commode pour aider à décrire les populations ou les espèces et faciliter l'analyse de leurs variations et de leurs rapports.

SUMMARY

In order to ascertain some modes of the increase in size among orbitolines, a distinction is made between architecture and fine structure of test. The various architectural types observed are described and classified. A new feature of variation in a population may then be measured. Hence an attempt is made to interpret architectural evolution among all the orbitolines.

BIBLIOGRAPHIE

CIRY, R. et RAT, P., 1953. Description d'un nouveau genre de Foraminifère: *Simplorbitolina manasi*. *Bull. sci. Bourgogne*, 14 : 85–100.

DOUGLASS, R. C., 1960a. The foraminiferal genus *Orbitolina* in America. *U.S. Geol. Surv.*, *Profess. Paper*, 333 : 1–55.

DOUGLASS, R. C., 1960b. Revision of the family Orbitolinidae. *Micropaleontology*, 6 : 249–270.

DOUVILLÉ, H., 1904. Sur la structure des orbitolines. *Bull. Soc. géol. France*, 4e sér., 4 : 653–661.

HENSON, F. R. S., 1948. *Larger imperforate Foraminifera of South-Western Asia*. British Museum London, 127 pp.

MOULLADE, M., 1960. Les Orbitolinidae des microfaciès barrémiens de la Drôme. *Rev. Micropaléontol.*, 3 : 188–198.

SILVESTRI, A., 1931. Foraminiferi del Cretaceo della Somalia. *Paleontographia italica*, 32 (n. ser. 2) : 143–204.

RAT, P., 1959. Les Pays crétacés basco-cantabriques. *Publ. Univ. Dijon*, 18 : 520 pp.

RAT, P., 1960. Le milieu et le développement des Orbitolines. *Bull. Soc. géol. France*, 7e sér., 1 : 651–657.

SIMPSON, G. G., 1944. *Tempo and mode in evolution*. Columbia University Press New-York, 237 pp. (traduction française par P. DE SAINT-SEINE, 1950. *Rythme et modalités de l'évolution*. Albin Michel, Paris, 354 pp.)

PLANCHE I

1. Architecture planiseptale (avec légère tendance au relèvement de la partie marginale des septes). *Simplorbitolina manasi* CIRY et RAT: Las Alisas. Aptien sup. ou Albien inf.; × 15.

2. Présence exceptionnelle de plusieurs loges annulaires sur une architecture scutiseptale chez *Simplorbitolina manasi*: même provenance; × 15.

3. Une loge sénile incomplète dans sa partie centrale chez *Simplorbitolina manasi*. Holotype. Aptien sup. ou Albien inf. (Agrandissement partiel de l'exemplaire figuré par CIRY et RAT, 1953, pl. 1, fig. 5); × 72.

4. Architecture planiseptale représentant un cas limite de la variation dans une population d'*Orbitolina* sp. qui comprend essentiellement des coquilles sphériseptales (voir Tableau II). Castro de Valnera. Aptien; × 15.

5. Architecture sphériseptale. *Orbitolina* sp. Aulestia. Aptien ou Albien inf.; × 10.

6. Architecture scuti- puis sigmoseptale. Structure caractérisée par l'abondance des grains de quartz et leur ordonnance très régulière. L'individu figuré s'est trouvé légèrement usé avant fossilisation de sorte qu'il lui manque une partie au moins de la zone marginale. *Orbitolina* aff. *lenticularis* (BLUM.). Soba. Aptien sup. ou Albien inf.; × 15.

7. Architecture sphéri- puis sigmoseptale avec apparition de quelques loges annulaires par exagération de la disposition sigmoseptale. La structure diffère de celle de l'échantillon précédent, en particulier par une disposition nettement plus anarchique des grains de quartz. *Orbitolina* sp. La Cilape. Aptien; × 15.

8. Architecture annulaire d'épaisseur constante. Photographie en lumière réfléchie d'un individu isolé sectionné et poli, puis attaqué doucement à l'acide dilué. *Orbitolina* cf. *subconcava* LEYMERIE. Izurdiaga. Albien sup.; × 25.

9. Architecture annulaire d'épaisseur croissante avec quelques irrégularités dans la vigueur du développement. Structure caractérisée en particulier par la présence d'yeux de calcite. *Orbitolina* cf. *aperta* (ERMAN). Route de Vitoria à Amurrio. Cénomanien inf.; × 15.

GISEMENTS CITÉS

Aptien

Calcaires dits du Castro de Valnera (extrême Nord de la province de Burgos, Espagne)

Aptien supérieur ou base de l'Albien

La Clape	: "Calcaires supérieurs à Rudistes" au-dessus de St-Obre (Aude, France).
Aulestia	: Calcaires urgoniens sombres (Biscaye, Espagne).
Durango	: Calcaires urgoniens de l'Aitz-Txiki (Biscaye, Espagne).
Vallée de Soba	: Calcaires gréseux, route du col de la Sia (province de Santander, Espagne).
Gulina	: Gisement type de *Simplorbitolina manasi* (Navarre, Espagne).
Las Alisas	: Route de Solares à Arredondo, vers le km 13 dans la montée au col de Las Alisas (province de Santander, Espagne).

Albien supérieur

Cimetière d'Izurdiaga	: Près d'Irurzun (Navarre espagnole).

Cénomanien

Route de Vitoria à Amurrio:	Lentille calcaire près du km 25 (Alava, Espagne). Cénomanien inférieur.
Montagne de Tauch	: (Aude, France). Echantillon recueilli et communiqué par P.-CH. DE GRACIANSKY. (Pour la situation des gisements cités dans le Nord de l'Espagne, voir RAT, 1959).

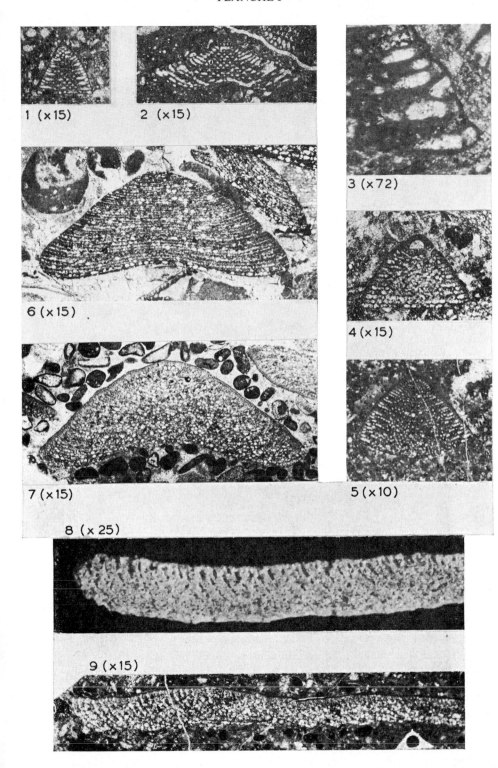

1 (×15)

2 (×15)

3 (×72)

4 (×15)

5 (×10)

6 (×15)

7 (×15)

8 (×25)

9 (×15)

TENDANCES ÉVOLUTIVES DES FORAMINIFÈRES PLANCTIQUES (GLOBOTRUNCANAE) DU CRÉTACÉ SUPÉRIEUR

MARIA BIANCA CITA-SIRONI

Istitut de Géologie, Université de Milan, Milan (Italie)

On traitera dans les pages suivantes les foraminifères planctiques[1] du Crétacé supérieur appartenant au genre *Globotruncana*[2].

La diffusion géographique des Globotruncanae, qui comprend les deux hémisphères et s'étend à tous les continents ainsi que leur importance stratigraphique qui devient de plus en plus grande et qui fait de ces formes-là d'excellents marqueurs, ont emmené la parution de nombreuses études et monographies spécialisées, aussi bien que des tentatives de classification et d'interprétations phylogénétiques.

Il s'ensuit que le genre, défini par CUSHMAN en 1927, est actuellement interprété d'une façon beaucoup plus restreinte, tandis que des formes très nombreuses, liées plus ou moins strictement aux Globotruncanae, sont rangées parmi des genres différents.

Il s'agit d'un groupe de foraminifères qui comprend plus de cent espèces, groupées dans une vingtaine de genres qui appartiennent, selon les classifications les plus récentes et les plus spécialisées, à trois familles différentes: les Hantkeninidae, les Globotruncanidae et les Globorotaliidae.

L'ÉVOLUTION DES CONNAISSANCES

L'histoire des Globotruncanae est plus que centenaire: elle débute dès 1839, année dans laquelle D'ORBIGNY décrivait *Rosalina linneiana* dans les sédiments récents de Cuba (Fig. 1). On sait bien que l'espèce était remaniée, et que la description fort incomplète de D'ORBIGNY a donné lieu à une grande confusion à propos de l'interprétation de cette espèce. Puis, d'après BROTZEN (1936), les formes voisines ou identiques à celles décrites par D'ORBIGNY étaient rangées parmi la *Globotruncana lapparenti*, opinion acceptée pendant un certain temps. Cependant, récemment BRÖNNIMANN et BROWN (1955) ont décrit des topotypes de *Globotruncana linneiana* et démontré que

---

[1] Voir la note éditoriale à la p. 138.

[2] C'est un plaisir pour moi que de remercier ici M. M. DI NAPOLI ALLIATA et ZEEV REISS, qui ont lu critiquement ce manuscrit, et particulièrement le dernier auteur pour ses observations et discussions amicales.

cette espèce était valable mais différente de *Globotruncana lapparenti* créée par
BROTZEN (1936)[1].

Les nouvelles que l'on trouve ensuite dans la littérature géologique sont très rares:
il faut mentionner REUSS (1845, 1854) et QUEREAU (1893) qui ont défini des espèces
nouvelles et enfin DE LAPPARENT (1918), qui a fait des observations extrêmement
intéressantes, soit strictement paléontologiques, soit pour la stratigraphie des "rosalines"; un nom qui, quoiqu' incorrect du point de vue de la nomenclature, est encore
utilisé couramment par les paléontologistes français.

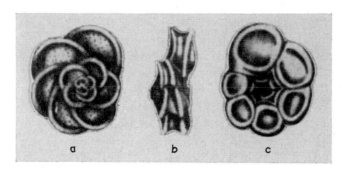

Fig. 1. *Rosalina linneiana* D'ORBIGNY, la première *Globotruncana* de l'histoire. (d'Après D'ORBIGNY,
1839).

Après, c'est aux États-Unis que se déplace le centre d'intérêt pour ces foraminifères
du Crétacé. Les chercheurs sont plus ou moins liés à la recherche pétrolière: doréna-
vant, pourrait-on dire, les études sur les Globotruncanae sont souvent, même si
c'est indirectement, en connexion avec la recherche du pétrole, et s'étendent aux divers
continents au fur et à mesure que ladite recherche y est intéressée.

Une autre date importante dans l'histoire des Globotruncanae est l'année 1927: la
date de la création du genre par CUSHMAN.

Une étude approfondie par AYALA CASTAÑARES, publiée en 1955 par l'Asociación
Mexicana de Geológos Petroleros, dans laquelle on trouve toutes les données histori-
ques à propos de ce genre, nous évite de passer en revue les publications, même les
plus importantes, parues avant 1954. Il faut seulement ajouter un ouvrage important,
qui a échappé à l'attention du paléontologiste mexicain: celui de RENZ (1936) sur la
"Scaglia" de l'Apennin. Bien que l'étude ait été faite seulement sur des coupes
minces, il faut souligner la publication de RENZ puisque pour la première fois on a
suivi l'évolution des Globotruncanae dans une coupe stratigraphique assez puissante,
en faisant des tentatives de zonation, et encore pour la création de l'espèce *Globotruncana appenninica*, marqueur très important pour le Cénomanien.

Outre la monographie d'AYALA CASTAÑARES, trois ouvrages de première importance
pour la taxonomie des Globotruncanae furent publiés en 1955: celui de GANDOLFI

---

[1] BANNER et BLOW (1960), qui ont examiné la collection de D'ORBIGNY à Paris, affirment que le seul
syntype de *Rosalina linneiana* qui reste, est morphologiquement très proche et pratiquement impossible à distinguer de *Pulvinulina tricarinata* QUEREAU (1893), qui tomberait donc en synonymie.

(1955), "The genus *Globotruncana* in northeastern Colombia", celui de BRÖNNIMANN et BROWN (1955), "Taxonomy of the Globotruncanidae" et celui de DALBIEZ (1955), "The genus *Globotruncana* in Tunisia". Dans les deux premièrs on trouve des clefs pour la détermination des genres; AYALA CASTAÑARES et GANDOLFI arrivent à mettre "en clef", en se basant sur des couples de caractères contrastants, la détermination des espèces, mais les résultats sont parfois contradictoires.

À la fin de 1955 la situation était donc très compliquée et confuse: GANDOLFI considérait comme sous-genres d'un seul genre (*Globotruncana*): *Rotalipora*, *Thalmanninella*, *Ticinella* et *Rugoglobigerina*, reconnus par AYALA CASTAÑARES (qui suivait BERMÚDEZ) comme véritables genres. BRÖNNIMANN et BROWN (1955), non seulement les reconnaissaient comme des genres, mais en outre créaient quatre genres nouveaux: *Hedbergina*[1], *Rugotruncana*, *Kuglerina* et *Bucherina:* ils étaient donc douze, les genres de la famille Globotruncanidae BROTZEN 1942, y compris *Rugoglobigerina*, *Plummerita* et *Trinitella*, trois genres créés précédemment par BRÖNNIMANN (1952), dont *Plummerita* avait été considéré comme un sous-genre de *Rugoglobigerina*.

Un autre travail important, publié en 1953, mais qui n'est arrivé en ouest que quelques années plus tard, est celui de SUBBOTINA sur les foraminifères planctiques du Crétacé et du Tertiaire de l'U.R.S.S. On y trouve défini le genre *Rotundina* (espèce-type *Globotruncana stephani*), qui tombe en synonymie avec *Praeglobotruncana* BERMÚDEZ 1952[2].

Pendant les années suivantes d'autres publications très importantes ont paru, qui traitent la question non seulement du point de vue descriptif, mais qui souvent s'efforcent d'éclaircir la taxonomie extrêmement complexe et d'interpréter la phylogénèse des Globotruncanae. Nous rappelons particulièrement les ouvrages de REISS (1957), EDGELL (1957), BOLLI *et al.* (1957), BOLLI (1957, 1959), KLAUS (1959), BANNER et BLOW (1959) et LOEBLICH et TAPPAN (1961 a, b).

Dans ces publications on trouve décrites beaucoup d'espèces nouvelles, et de nombreux genres, surtout par REISS: le groupement des genres dans les sous-familles existantes, ou dans d'autres proposées comme nouvelles, varie beaucoup d'un auteur à l'autre.

Il serait fort intéressant de comparer de près les classifications des Globotruncanae parues au cours de ces dix dernières années, en analysant critiquement la valeur des différents groupements proposés, mais cela nous porterait beaucoup trop loin du thème proposé, et hors des limites de l'espace donné.

Pour conclure, on peut dire que les traités, même les plus récents, ne sont jamais à jour, à cause de l'évolution extrêmement rapide des connaissances.

C'est un cas rare dans le domaine de la paléontologie — peut-être un cas unique — qu'un tel nombre de spécialistes s'occupent en même temps, mais de façon indépendante, dans les cinq continents, du même problème.

---

[1] Changé ensuite en *Hedbergella*, voir BRÖNNIMANN et BROWN (1958).

[2] L'espèce-type de *Rotundina* est *Globotruncana stephani* GANDOLFI, qui est considérée par BRÖNNIMANN et BROWN (1955), comme synonyme de *Globorotalia delrioensis* PLUMMER, espèce-type du genre *Praeglobotruncana* BERMÚDEZ 1952. Selon KLAUS (1959) les deux espèces peuvent être distinguées. Néanmoins elles sont sans doute congénères.

On a passé très rapidement (peut-être trop rapidement) des espèces peu nombreuses connues jusqu'à 1940 aux plus de 100 espèces d'aujourd'hui. Du seul genre connu jusqu'en 1941 (*Globotruncana* CUSHMAN 1927) aux 23 genres actuels.

Il y a des espèces et des genres synonymes, ce qui est inévitable quand plusieurs chercheurs travaillent en même temps à un sujet si spécialisé.

Une révision complète est souhaitable, et elle a été entreprise pour quelques groupes limités (KLAUS, 1959; LOEBLICH et TAPPAN, 1961b). Il s'agit évidemment d'un travail énorme, et peut-être encore prématuré.

À l'heure actuelle, malgré l'abondance de la littérature spécialisée, la classification de cet important groupe de foraminifères reste extrêmement confuse.

LE CONCEPT D'ESPÈCE ET DE GENRE CHEZ LES GLOBOTRUNCANAE

Avant d'illustrer les caractères que l'on observe chez les Globotruncanae et leur évolution, il faut établir une prémisse.

Le concept d'espèce tel qu'il est appliqué par les spécialistes aux foraminifères planctiques, et en particulier aux formes crétacées, est extrêmement restreint. Au cours de ces dernières années on a assisté à un "splitting" très poussé: chacune des vieilles espèces a été subdivisée en d'autres espèces plus limitées morphologiquement et stratigraphiquement. Les différences entre l'une et l'autre des nombreuses espèces décrites au cours de ces dernières dix années sont tellement difficiles à voir que seuls les spécialistes peuvent posséder la sensibilité nécessaire pour apercevoir les nuances qui les différencient.

Il faut ajouter que souvent on a illustré seulement l'holotype de ces espèces nouvelles et qu'on ne trouve pas grand'chose, dans les descriptions, à propos de la variabilité spécifique et d'éventuelles formes de passage entre une "espèce" et l'autre.

D'autre côté on doit avouer que les illustrations — documents d'importance fondamentale — sont presque toujours excellentes, et permettent ainsi de se rendre au moins très clairement compte des caractères observés chez l'holotype.

L'application des méthodes statistiques employées à présent ne semble pas apporter une aide considérable à la solution du problème. Chaque chercheur — on peut le croire — qui a vu sous le microscope des associations à *Globotruncana*, constituées par des milliers d'exemplaires, a été tenté par la statistique, puisque dans une population suffisamment riche on voit des formes bien différenciées, typiques, qu'on arrive facilement à identifier avec des espèces connues. Mais on voit aussi un grand nombre de formes non-typiques, qui présentent des caractères intermédiaires entre une espèce et l'autre, et que l'on n'arrive pas, par conséquent, à classifier.

Le problème de fond subsiste, malgré la récente multiplication (il s'agit d'une vraie "pulvérisation") des espèces.

Les méthodes statistiques, chez les petits foraminifères comme les Globotruncanae, ne peuvent se baser que sur le mesurage de caractères concernants la morphologie externe, tels que le nombre des loges, le rapport entre diamètre et hauteur de la spire, etc. Et les résultats sont souvent décevants. Il semble, par exemple, que les rapports entre le diamètre et la hauteur de la spire ne suffisent pas pour établir l'attribution à l'une plutôt qu'à l'autre espèce.

Cependant, les tentatives d'application des méthodes statistiques de KLAUS (1960b) sont fort intéressantes. Mais nous ne partageons pas ses conclusions optimistes et bien pour trois raisons: la première est que les erreurs que l'on peut faire, suivant ses indications, pour mesurer la hauteur de la courbure ventrale sont à notre avis du même ordre de grandeur — sinon plus grandes — que les différences que l'on cherche à mettre en évidence. La deuxième est que les points correspondant aux holotypes des trois espèces considérées (*Praeglobotruncana stephani*, *P.marginaculeata*, *P.* cf. *delrioensis*) se trouvent aux bords extrêmes ou en dehors des surfaces de dispersion relatives aux mêmes espèces. Le diagramme de dispersion, enfin, est tellement homogène et régulier qu'il nous semble discutable de le diviser en trois parties, comme l'a fait KLAUS, pour les trois espèces, d'autant plus que les surfaces de dispersion relatives aux différentes espèces se recouvrent en partie.

Ces considérations nous portent à un point d'interrogation: qu'est-ce que c'est qu'une espèce chez les Globotruncanae? Nous sommes très loin d'une interprétation biologique d'espèce paléontologique: nos connaissances mêmes sur la reproduction des foraminifères planctiques sont jusqu'à présent très limitées[1].

Un des rares auteurs qui se soit occupé de ce problème-là est HOFKER, qui a publié en 1951 des analyses de dimension du proloculus des espèces vivantes aussi bien que des espèces fossiles; entre elles il y a *Globotruncana linnei*. Les conclusions de HOFKER sont que l'apogamie (reproduction agamique qui comporte une seule génération, de type B) prévaut chez les foraminifères planctiques. À côté de l'apogamie on observe du trimorphisme, du paratrimorphisme et du dimorphisme. Les espèces géologiquement plus anciennes présentent du trimorphisme.

Des observations sur les dimensions des proloculi chez *Globotruncana linnei* se trouvent aussi dans la monographie de GANDOLFI (1942), qui admet l'existence éventuelle d'une forme microsphérique se distinguant de la forme macrosphérique uniquement par les dimensions de la loge initiale.

Cependant, le problème n'est pas encore résolu: ce sont surtout les expériences *in vivo* qui font défaut, en partie aussi à cause des grandes difficultés d'observation sur des formes qui vivent à la surface de l'eau.

Dans des conditions pareilles, il est bien possible que ce qu'on appelle espèces, surtout dans le cas ou il y a des formes transitionnelles entre l'une et l'autre, ne soient que des variétés ou bien des variantes d'une seule population. Rappelons du reste ce que disait en 1956 RAUZER-CHERNOUSOVA (p. 18), dans un article sur les unités taxonomiques élémentaires dans la systématique des foraminifères: "Chez les foraminifères les différences spécifiques et intraspécifiques ne sont pas toujours nettement exprimées et leur interprétation peut être subjective".

[1] Nous remercions vivement M. M. ORVILLE L. BANDY de l'Université de la Californie du Sud, ALLAN W. H. BÉ du Lamont Geological Observatory de New York et ENRICO F. DI NAPOLI ALLIATA de Rome, pour les renseignements qu'ils nous ont fournis à cet égard.

Mais si les espèces sont discutables, les genres, entités taxonomiques toujours abstraites et artificielles, le seront d'autant plus.

En effet, les caractères génériques des "Globotruncanae" *s. l.*, concernent essentiellement les ouvertures et les carènes. Les études approfondies concernant ces caractères sont tout-à-fait récentes (voir surtout SIGAL, 1948; REICHEL, 1949; REISS, 1957; BOLLI *et al.*, 1957; BANNER et BLOW, 1959; KLAUS, 1959), et ont amené, comme conséquence, la multiplication des genres. Jusqu'à 1948, on ne posait pas le problème des ouvertures. Personne n'avait jamais approfondi la question sauf BROTZEN (1942), mais l'importance de ses observations ne fut relevée que plus tard: attitude bien justifiée du reste, surtout puisqu'en général les ouvertures ne se voient qu'avec peine (Fig. 2).

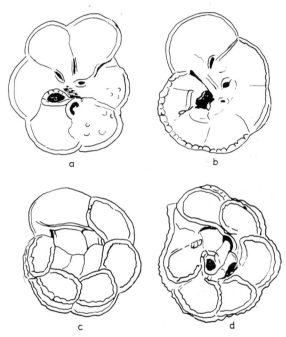

Fig. 2. Ouvertures visibles dans des exemplaires très bien conservés de *Rotalipora* (a, b) et *Globotruncana* (c,d). Chez les Rotaliporae on voit clairement les ouvertures supplémentaires suturales. Dans l'exemplaire de *Globotruncana arca*, représenté dans la Fig. 2d, les tegillae sont cassées et l'on peut observer l'ouverture primaire, qui était toujours cachée pendant la vie de l'animal. Dans l'exemplaire de la même espèce représenté dans la Fig. 2c au contraire les tegillae sont entières, ce qui est extrêmement rare: on ne voit que les ouvertures accessoires infralaminales. a. *Rotalipora turonica* BROTZEN; b. *Rotalipora* cf. *appenninica* (RENZ); c, d. *Globotruncana arca* (CUSHMAN). (Dessins d'après BOLLI *et al.*, 1957).

Voici donc une des plus grandes difficultés de reconnaître les genres: la possibilité d'une bonne observation des caractères aperturaux, qui ne sont visibles qu'après un traitement spécial chez des individus bien conservés et, naturellement, isolés. En coupes minces — même bien orientées — ou bien avec des faunes dégagées mais mal conservées, on ne peut, dans la majorité des cas, être sûr de la position générique des exemplaires.

En ce qui concerne les carènes, les études récentes de REISS (1957) et de BANNER et BLOW (1959) ont démontré que leur structure interne est différenciée chez certains groupes. Même dans ce cas, l'observation des caractères génériques est très difficile; puisque, pour observer la structure des carènes, il faut disposer d'exemplaires isolés, sectionnés ensuite dans des directions préfixées, et dans lesquels ladite structure est bien conservée.

Mais ce n'est pas seulement la difficulté d'appliquer des critères sur lesquels est basée la définition des genres qui rend extrêmement confuse actuellement la classification (mieux, les classifications) des Globotruncanae. Bien d'autres raisons, telles que l'élévation au rang de "caractère générique" d'un caractère généralement considéré comme spécifique (il y a aussi des morphogenres reconnus comme tels), l'inclusion de caractères accessoires dans les premiers, etc., font que la même espèce soit placée dans des genres différents par les divers auteurs.

LES CARACTÈRES TAXONOMIQUES

Les caractères taxonomiques sont traités d'une façon schématique et on a utilisé ici pour l'exposé la terminologie adoptée par BOLLI et al. (1957).

Ils sont indiqués par ordre d'importance décroissante, c'est-à-dire on va des plus généraux aux plus particuliers. Cela n'implique pas une vraie hiérarchie des caractères: hiérarchie extrêmement difficile à reconnaître chez les foraminifères planctiques, de la même façon que chez les foraminifères rotaliformes (DROOGER, 1960, p. 319).

(1) Constitution et structure du test

(2) Mode d'enroulement

(3) Ouvertures

(4) Carènes

(5) Ombilic et "plaques ombilicales"

(6) Forme des loges

(7) Sutures

(8) Ornementation

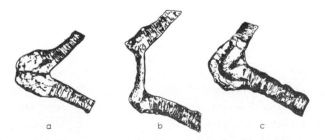

Fig. 3. Structure des carènes chez *Globotruncana arca* (a), *G. lapparenti tricarinata* (b) et *G.elevata stuartiformis* (c). Les photographies à fort grossissement montrent comment soit les bourrelets carénaux, soit le bandeau carénal sont imperforés. (d'Après BANNER et BLOW, 1959).

(*1*) Constitution et structure du test. Le test des Globotruncanae est calcitique radié et perforé. Les perforations sont nombreuses et relativement grandes, mais leur fréquence par unité de surface est variable. Les parties imperforées du test sont: les carènes (Fig. 3), le bandeau carénal, les septa et les sutures, les tegillae. Les études de Reichel (1949) et Reiss (1957) ont démontré que la paroi est composée de deux couches, dont la plus interne est plus obscure. La couche externe primaire est simple dans les loges, mais elle est plus épaisse dans les premiers tours du fait d'un grossissement constitué par de nombreuses lamelles et qui est plus accentué surtout du côté spiral (Fig. 4).

Fig. 4. Coupe axiale d'une globorotalid, schématisée. (d'Après Reiss, 1957).

(*2*) Mode d'enroulement. Toutes les formes considérées ici sont trochospiralées. Une tendance évolutive se manifeste dans l'élévation progressive de la spire (Fig. 5).

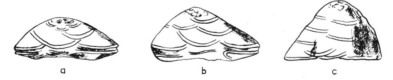

a   b   c

Fig. 5. Élévation progressive de la spire dans la suite évolutive *Globotruncana fornicata – G.caliciformis – G.contusa*. a. *Globotruncana fornicata* Plummer; b. *Globotruncana caliciformis* (De Lapparent); c. *Globotruncana contusa* (Cushman). (Dessins d'après Cita, 1948).

(*3*) Ouvertures. Ouverture primaire ombilicale. Les loges du dernier tour qui précèdent la dernière, sont munies d'ouvertures accessoires ombilicales ("labial apertures" d'après Reiss, 1957) dont la forme est déterminée par celle des lèvres, qui sont "en cornet" et étirées dans le sens de l'enroulement chez quelques espèces (Klaus, 1959).

Les études sur les ouvertures chez le genre *Globotruncana* s.str. n'ont pas encore éclairci complètement leur structure (Fig. 6). Les expansions lamelleuses imperforées

Fig. 6. Schéma structural de la disposition des ouvertures chez le genre *Globotruncana*. Ouverture primaire ombilicale, à lèvre étroite. Le cornet de l'ouverture accessoire se prolonge en expansion lamelleuse (tegillum) dans l'ombilic. (d'Après Klaus, 1959).

(tegillae) très développées, que l'on observe chez quelques espèces comme *G.arca* et qui peuvent recouvrir entièrement l'ombilic (Fig. 2c) sont munies d'ouvertures accessoires infralaminales.

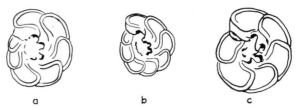

Fig. 7. Ouvertures ombilicales ("labial apertures" dans la signification de REISS, 1957) chez trois espèces de *Globotruncana*. Les lèvres sont toujours arquées et forment un cornet qui est particulièrement évident chez *G.stuarti*. a. *Globotruncana lapparenti coronata* BOLLI; b. *Globotruncana lapparenti lapparenti*. BROTZEN; c. *Globotruncana stuarti* (DE LAPPARENT). (Dessins d'après SIGAL, 1952).

(*4*) Carènes. Toutes les Globotruncanae possèdent un bandeau carénal avec une ou deux carènes. Soit le bandeau carénal, soit les bourrelets carénaux sont imperforés. Les carènes périphériques se prolongent du côté spiral dans les sutures septales dorsales, du côté ombilical dans les sutures septales ventrales. Souvent on observe un pro-

Fig. 8. Coupes axiales de Globotruncanae bicarénées, à bandeau carénal parallèle à l'axe d'enroulement (a–d), ou bien évasé vers le haut (e). (d'Après BOLLI, 1951). a. *Globotruncana lapparenti lapparenti* BROTZEN; b. *Globotruncana lapparenti tricarinata* (QUEREAU); c. *Globotruncana globigerinoides* BROTZEN; d. *Globotruncana ventricosa* WHITE; e. *Globotruncana contusa* (CUSHMAN).

longement périombilical de la carène (voir en particulier *Globotruncana lapparenti tricarinata*). La carène dorsale est en général plus proéminente que la carène ventrale, mais les deux peuvent être également développées, comme chez *G. lapparenti*

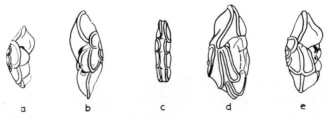

Fig. 9. Vues latérales de *Rotalipora* spp. (a, b) et de *Globotruncana* spp. (c–e). Chez les formes unicarénées de *Globotruncana* (e) la carène se dichotomise, ce qui ne se vérifie jamais chez le genre *Rotalipora*. a. *Rotalipora ticinensis* (GANDOLFI); b. *Rotalipora appenninica* (RENZ); e. *Globotruncana lapparenti* BROTZEN; d. *Globotruncana fornicata* PLUMMER; e. *Globotruncana stuarti* (DE LAPPARENT). (Dessins d'après SIGAL, 1952).

lapparenti. Les deux carènes peuvent se rapprocher jusqu'à se confondre (voir *G. rosetta*) ou bien se présenter vraiment confondues dès les premiers stades de développement (voir *G. stuarti*). Même dans ce cas, elles sont toujours dichotomiques.

Chez de rares espèces telles que *Globotruncana imbricata* et *Abathomphalus mayaroensis*, on observe des carènes imbriquées fort caractéristiques (Fig. 10).

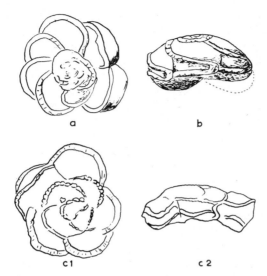

Fig. 10. Carènes imbriquées chez *Globotruncana imbricata* (a, b) et *Abathomphalus mayaroensis* (c). a. *Globotruncana imbricata* MORNOD: vue spirale d'un paratype; b. *Globotruncana imbricata* MORNOD: vue latérale de l'holotype (d'Après MORNOD, 1949); c 1, 2. *Abathomphalus mayaroensis* (BOLLI): vues spirale et latérale de l'holotype (d'Après BOLLI, 1951).

(5) Ombilic et ''plaques ombilicales''. L'ombilic est étroit et déprimé dans les formes les plus primitives: il devient de plus en plus grand et superficiel au cours de l'évolution (Fig. 11). Souvent il est en partie ou complètement oblitéré par les structures relatives aux ouvertures: celles-ci consistent en des lèvres et expansions lamelleuses, qui peuvent être très développées. Les lèvres ont une section en U et sont

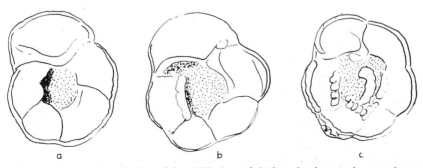

Fig. 11. Variation progressive de la cavité ombilicale, qui devient de plus en plus grande et superficielle. Suite évolutive *Globotruncana renzi* (a) – *G.concavata* (b) – *G. ventricosa* (c). (Dessins d'après BOLLI *et al.*, 1957).

toujours arquées vers la cavité ombilicale. Quand ces lèvres sont très accentuées, elles donnent parfois lieu à des expansions lamelleuses en cornet. Les expansions lamelleuses, appelées tegillae, se chevauchent l'une sur l'autre: elles sont dérivées des expansions en cornet et recouvrent complètement l'ombilic.

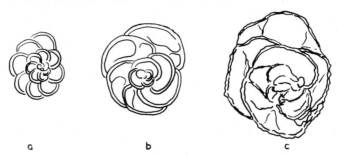

Fig. 12. Forme des loges (en vue spirale). a. *Globotruncana lapparenti* BROTZEN: loges pétaloïdes; b. *Globotruncana fornicata* PLUMMER: loges allongées; c. *Globotruncana contusa* (CUSHMAN): loges allongées et pliées. (Dessins d'après SIGAL, 1952, et BOLLI, 1951).

(6) Forme des loges. Elle détermine, en partie, la forme du test. En vue spirale, les formes les plus caractéristiques sont: pétaloïde (voir *Globotruncana arca*), trapézoïdale (voir *G.stuarti*), allongée (voir *G.fornicata*) (Fig. 12). En vue ombilicale, la forme des loges est moins variable: plus ou moins pointue, triangulaire dans les formes à ombilic étroit, elle devient réniforme chez les *Globotruncana* du groupe *lapparenti* (Fig. 13).

Quant au nombre des loges, on considère d'habitude celui du dernier tour: il varie entre un minimum de quatre et un maximum de neuf à dix et n'est pas nécessairement en rapport avec la grandeur du test. Il est un caractère spécifique d'une certaine valeur.

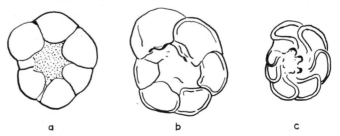

Fig. 13. Rapports entre les sutures et la forme des loges (vues ombilicales). a. *Globotruncana helvetica* BOLLI: sutures radiales, loges renflées; b. *Globotruncana schneegansi* SIGAL: sutures arquées, loges pétaloïdes (en partie) c. *Globotruncana lapparenti coronata* BOLLI: sutures sigmoïdales, loges réniformes. (Dessins d'après SIGAL, 1952).

(7) Sutures. Les caractères concernant les sutures sont déterminés par la forme des loges. On distingue une suture spirale entre les tours, qui peut être déprimée ou plus souvent en relief, et les sutures septales. Elles sont déprimées quand les loges sont globuleuses ou renflées, en relief quand les loges sont aplaties. Chez les formes les plus

évoluées, au Campanien et au Maastrichtien, elles sont souvent très proéminentes à cause de l'ornementation des carènes, dans la majorité des cas "perlées".

Les sutures sont radiales chez les formes plus primitives, mais plus souvent inclinées en arrière. Une inclinaison en arrière particulièrement accentuée s'observe chez *G.fornicata* et *G.contusa*. Droites chez de rares formes spécialisées (voir *G.calcarata* et *G.stuarti*), elles sont d'habitude plus ou moins arquées (Fig. 14).

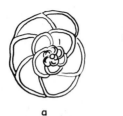

a   b

Fig. 14. Rapports entre les sutures et la forme des loges (en vue spirale). a. *Globotruncana stuarti* (DE LAPPARENT): sutures droites et obliques, loges trapezoïdales; b. *Globotruncana calcarata* CUSHMAN: sutures droites et obliques, loges fournies d'une tubulospine peripherique. (Dessins d'après SIGAL, 1952).

Du côté ombilical les sutures sont raremènt radiales et deprimées chez le genre *Globotruncana* s.str. Souvent on trouve des sutures à carène, qui se prolongent au bord de la cavité ombilicale. Chez les espèces à loges aplaties et allongées appartenant au groupe de la *G.lapparenti*, les sutures ont une allure sigmoïdale autour des loges réniformes.

(8) Ornementation. La surface est lisse, pointillée ou granuleuse. Il y a une évolution dans ce sens au cours du temps. Les espèces campaniennes et maastrichtiennes pourvues de costellae, un type d'ornementation caractérisé par de petites côtes discontinues, en relief, ont été groupées par BRÖNNIMANN et BROWN (1955) dans le morphogenre *Rugotruncana*.

Les carènes sont ornées de perles en relief chez de nombreuses espèces sénoniennes et maastrichtiennes, et parfois des perles sont parsemées sur la surface même du test (voir *Globotruncana arca*).

LES GENRES ET LEURS RAPPORTS PHYLÉTIQUES

Les genres décrits jusqu'à présent, qui sont plus ou moins liés à *Globotruncana* CUSHMAN sont les suivants (par ordre chronologique de création):

Globotruncana CUSHMAN 1927 (espèce-type *Pulvinulina arca* CUSHMAN 1926)

Rosalinella MARIE 1941 (espèce-type *Rosalina linneiana* D'ORBIGNY 1839)

Rotalipora BROTZEN 1942 (espèce-type *Rotalipora turonica* BROTZEN 1942)

Planomalina LOEBLICH et TAPPAN 1946 (espèce-type *Planomalina aspidostroba* LOEBLICH et TAPPAN 1946)

Thalmanninella SIGAL 1948 (espèce-type *Thalmanninella brotzeni* SIGAL 1948)

Globigerinelloides CUSHMAN et TEN DAM 1948 (espèce-type *Globigerinelloides algeriana* CUSHMAN *et* TEN DAM 1948)

Ticinella REICHEL 1949 (espèce-type *Anomalina roberti* GANDOLFI 1942)

Praeglobotruncana BERMÚDEZ 1952 (espèce-type *Globorotalia delrioensis* PLUMMER 1931)

Rugoglobigerina BRÖNNIMANN 1952 (espèce-type *Globigerina rugosa* PLUMMER 1926)

Plummerita BRÖNNIMANN 1952b (espèce-type *Rugoglobigerina* (*Plummerella*) *hantkenioides* BRÖNNIMANN 1952)

Trinitella BRÖNNIMANN 1952 (espèce-type *Trinitella scotti* BRÖNNIMANN 1952)

Rotundina SUBBOTINA 1953 (espèce-type *Globotruncana stephani* GANDOLFI 1942)

Rugotruncana BRÖNNIMANN et BROWN 1955 (espèce-type *Rugotruncana tilevi* BRÖNNIMANN et BROWN 1955)

Kuglerina BRÖNNIMANN et BROWN 1955 (espèce-type *Rugoglobigerina rugosa rotundata* BRÖNNIMANN 1952)

Bucherina BRÖNNIMANN et BROWN 1955 (espèce-type *Bucherina sandidgei* BRÖNNIMANN et BROWN 1955)

Biticinella SIGAL 1956 (espèce-type *Anomalina breggiensis* GANDOLFI 1942)

Marginotruncana HOFKER 1956 (espèce-type *Rosalina marginata* REUSS 1845)

Globotruncanella REISS 1957 (espèce-type *Globotruncana citae* BOLLI 1951)

Globotruncanita REISS 1957 (espèce-type *Rosalina stuarti* DE LAPPARENT 1918)

Helvetoglobotruncana REISS 1957 (espèce-type *Globotruncana helvetica* BOLLI 1945)

Abathomphalus BOLLI, LOEBLICH et TAPPAN 1957 (espèce-type *Globotruncana mayaroensis* BOLLI 1951)

Hedbergella BRÖNNIMANN et BROWN 1958, emend. (espèce-type *Anomalina lorneiana* var. *trochoidea* GANDOLFI 1942)

Clavihedbergella BANNER et BLOW 1959 (espèce-type *Hastigerinella subcretacea* TAPPAN 1943)

Parmi ces genres, quelques-uns tombent en synonymie avec d'autres genres; d'autres ne sont que des morphogenres et d'autres encore n'ont pas de rapports étroits avec *Globotruncana*.

Les rapports phylétiques entre les genres considérés ici comme valables et liés strictement à *Globotruncana* sont indiqués dans le schéma (Planche I).

Comme commentaire à ce schéma on peut observer que la distribution stratigraphique du genre *Globotruncana* est strictement limitée au Crétacé supérieur, allant du Turonien jusqu'au sommet du Maastrichtien.

Quant à l'origine des Globotruncanae, elle ne se trouve pas dans les Rotaliporae comme on le croyait autrefois: aucune transition ne s'observe en effet au cours de l'évolution dans les caractères considérés par la plupart des auteurs comme étant d'importance générique, à savoir ceux qui concernent les carènes et ceux qui concernent les ouvertures.

Le genre *Globotruncana* est considéré ici comme polyphylétique dans ce sens qu'il

PLANCHE I

Schéma des rapports phylétiques entre les genres proches de *Globotruncana*.

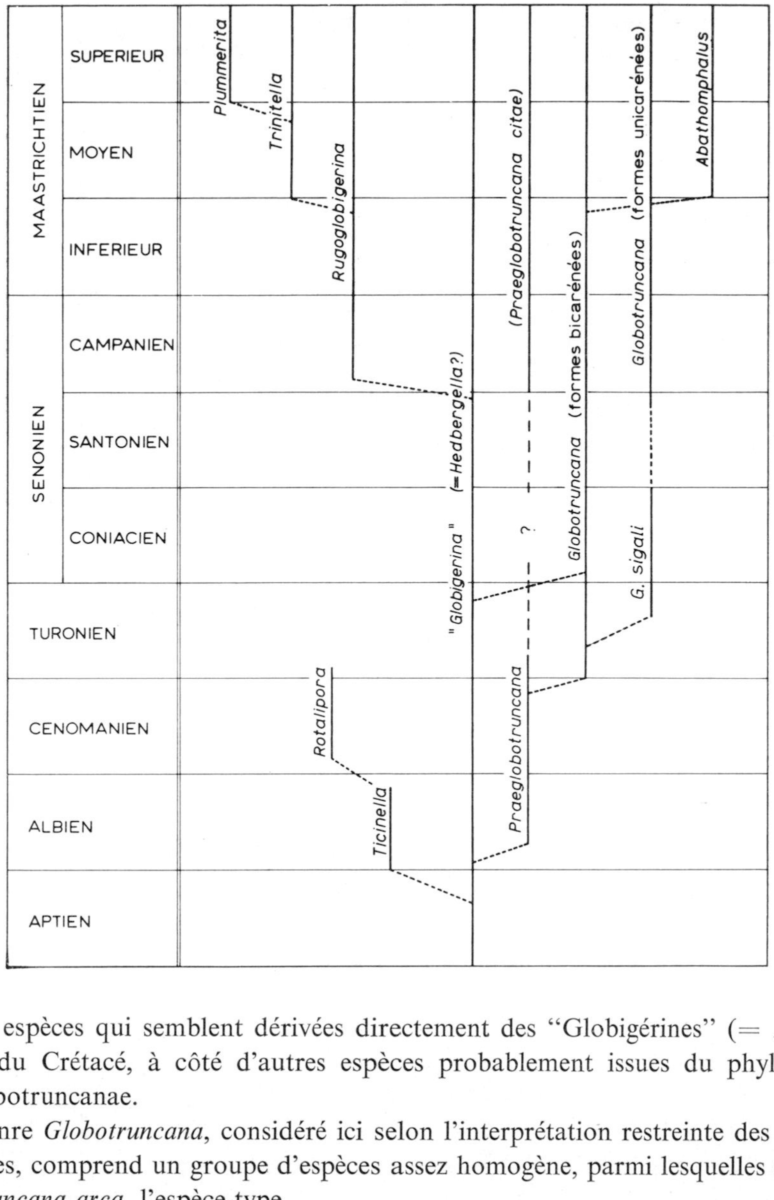

y a des espèces qui semblent dérivées directement des "Globigérines" (= *Hedber-gella*?) du Crétacé, à côté d'autres espèces probablement issues du phylum des Praeglobotruncanae.

Le genre *Globotruncana*, considéré ici selon l'interprétation restreinte des auteurs modernes, comprend un groupe d'espèces assez homogène, parmi lesquelles se place *Globotruncana arca*, l'espèce-type.

Les caractères taxonomiques, qui ont déjà été examinés en détail auparavant, varient souvent d'une façon progressive au cours de l'évolution.

Parmi les caractères qui affectent la position générique, on dispose de nombreuses observations sur les carènes. Les Globotruncanae bicarénées et celles unicarénées (dont la carène unique est due à la fusion de deux bourrelets carénaux très rapprochés)

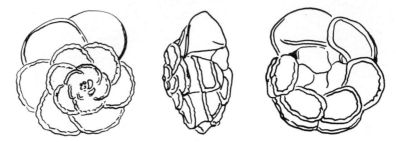

Fig. 15. *Globotruncana arca* CUSHMAN, espèce-type du genre *Globotruncana* CUSHMAN 1927. (d'Après BOLLI *et al.*, 1957).

du Sénonien supérieur–Maastrichtien sont considérées par la plupart des auteurs comme congénères. Pour d'autres espèces à carène unique et aux loges renflées, telles que *Globotruncana helvetica*, la position générique est douteuse (espèce-type du genre *Helvetoglobotruncana* REISS 1957, elle appartiendrait à *Ticinella* selon BANNER et BLOW, 1959, à *Praeglobotruncana* selon KLAUS, 1959).

En ce qui concerne les ouvertures, les observations sur les Globotruncanae sont beaucoup moins nombreuses et détaillées que chez les genres pré-turoniens *Ticinella*, *Rotalipora*, etc.

Bien différenciée des genres précités par le manque d'ouvertures supplémentaires intériomarginales suturales, *Globotruncana* se rapproche de *Praeglobotruncana*, qui en est également dépourvue. Mais chez *Praeglobotruncana* il n'y a pas de tegilla bien

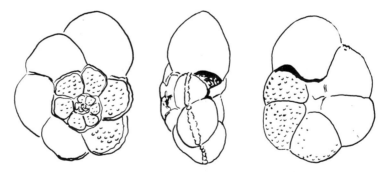

Fig. 16. *Praeglobotruncana delrioensis* (PLUMMER), espèce-type du genre *Praeglobotruncana* BERMÚDEZ 1952. (d'Après BOLLI *et al.*, 1957).

développés comme chez *Globotruncana*, et on n'y observe pas non plus d'ouvertures accessoires infralaminales.

Le phylum des Praeglobotruncanae, qui s'est différencié de celui des Hedbergellae dès l'Albien, se développe dans les étages suivants, atteignant son maximum au Cénomanien. Ensuite on ne trouve pas de Praeglobotruncanae dans le Sénonien. Mais des formes qui se rapprochent beaucoup de ce genre par leurs carènes peu différenciées et leur ouverture simple, réapparaissent plus haut dans le Crétacé supérieur, au

Campanien et au Maastrichtien. Il s'agit en partie de formes groupées par REISS (1957) sous le nom générique *Globotruncanella* (espèce-type *Globotruncana citae*).

Le genre *Globotruncana* est très proche aussi du genre *Abathomphalus*, le dernier qui se soit différencié de son phylum, au cours du Maastrichtien, soit par les caractères

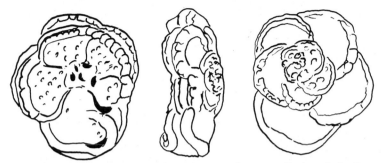

Fig. 17. *Abathomphalus mayaroensis* (BOLLI), espèce-type du genre *Abathomphalus* BOLLI, LOEBLICH et TAPPAN 1957. (d'Après BOLLI *et al.*, 1957).

concernant les ouvertures, soit par les carènes. Celles-ci sont particulièrement fortes et bien développées dans les Abathomphali: chez *A. mayaroensis*, l'espèce-type du genre, elles se présentent imbriquées.

C'est surtout la position de l'ouverture primaire (extraombilicale chez *Abathomphalus*, ombilicale chez *Globotruncana*) qui différencie les deux genres.

ONTOGÉNÈSE ET TENDANCES ÉVOLUTIVES

Dans l'histoire évolutive des Globotruncanae on rencontre trois moments de développement particulièrement intense, explosif: le premier est daté à l'Albien, et correspond au développement maximum des genres *Hedbergella* et *Ticinella* (celle-ci à la fin de l'Albien, jusqu'à la base du Cénomanien). Le deuxième date du Cénomanien, et correspond à la floraison du phylum des Rotaliporae, accompagné de celui des Praeglobotruncanae.

Le troisième commence dans la partie supérieure du Sénonien et se complète au Maastrichtien, en correspondance avec développement maximum des Globotruncanae et des Abathomphali. Il précède l'extinction complète de tous les phyla, qui a lieu à la fin du Maastrichtien.

Les faunes cénomaniennes sont bien différenciées de celles de l'Albien, mais les différences ne sont pas aussi marquées que celles entre le Turonien et le Cénomanien. Au Turonien les associations sont complètement renouvelées, et, en complexe, appauvries par rapport à celles des étages précédents. Peu à peu au Turonien et surtout dans le Sénonien inférieur le phylum des Globotruncanae, commencé dès le Turonien, se développe en donnant lieu à un grand nombre d'espèces: les associations maastrichtiennes sont les plus riches en espèces de toutes les populations à *Globotruncana*.

Parler de développement ontogénétique chez des protozoaires planctiques dont les dimensions sont toujours inférieures au millimètre, et souvent moindres, c'est chose bien problématique. D'autant plus qu'on ne connaît jusqu'ici aucune manifestation de dimorphisme chez les Globotruncanae. La génération microsphérique — qui, parcequ'elle est la plus persistante des deux, est la plus intéressante pour l'étude de l'ontogénèse — ne se distingue pas pour le moment de la génération mégalosphérique.

De tous les caractères que l'on a analysés précédemment, quelques-uns seulement peuvent être étudiés dans les premiers stades de leur évolution, à cause de la taille des exemplaires. L'étude est effectuée en règle générale en coupe mince, où on peut observer:

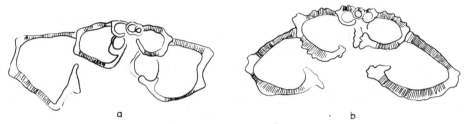

a   b

Fig. 18. Coupes axiales de *Globotruncana* du Turonien. On observe une variation progressive soit dans la forme des loges (les premières sont globuleuses, de type globigérinoïde), soit dans le développement du bandeau carénal. a. *Globotruncana wicheri* (HOFKER); b. *Globotruncana marginata* (REUSS); (Dessins d'après HOFKER, 1956).

(*1*) le mode d'enroulement
(*2*) la variation de forme des loges
(*3*) la variation dans les caractères concernant les carènes

Par contre, on ne peut pas faire d'observations précises sur les ouvertures, qui ne se prêtent pas à l'étude sur des coupes minces. Ainsi le caractère le plus important pour distinguer les genres échappe aux observations sur le développement ontogénétique, ce qui rend parfois discutable l'interprétation de quelques lignées phylétiques concernant les genres.

Mais la dérivation de toutes les Globotruncanae des "Globigérines" (= *Hedbergella*?) est bien démontrée par la présence, dans tous les individus appartenant à un genre quelconque de "*Globotruncana*" s.l., d'un premier stade de développement de type globigérinoïde, à loges globuleuses[1].

Une autre conclusion à laquelle on arrive à travers l'étude du développement ontogénétique est que les premières Globotruncanae bicarénées du Turonien ne sont pas dérivées des Rotaliporae cénomaniennes. Les observations de RENZ (1936) et de GANDOLFI (1942) semblaient contredire cette affirmation. RENZ décrivait en 1936 une "Zwischenform *Globotruncana appenninica – Globotruncana linnei*" qui, après le

---

[1] Il faut pourtant mentionner qu'un stade initial de type globigérinoïde a récemment été décrit par GLAESSNER et WADE (1959) pour des foraminifères très éloignés des globigérines, tels que les Victoriellidae.

premier tour à loges de type globigérinoïde, développait des loges à double carène et à bandeau caréné bien développé; ces loges étaient suivies, dans un stade successif, de loges unicarénées. La même forme était décrite en 1942 presqu'à la même époque par THALMANN et par GANDOLFI comme *Globotruncana renzi*. En effet la carène, apparemment unique, due à la fusion des deux carènes, qu'on observe dans les dernières loges de *Globotruncana renzi* (une espèce qui est d'ailleurs considérée douteuse actuellement) n'est pas assimilable à la carène vraiment unique de *Rotalipora appenninica*.

En passant des critères généraux et des rapports évolutifs au niveau des genres, aux tendances évolutives au niveau de l'espèce, on observe que presque tous les caractères changent d'une façon progressive, permettant ainsi de reconnaître des séries phylétiques d'espèces.

En ce qui concerne les d i m e n s i o n s d u t e s t, elles tendent à augmenter. Au fur et à mesure que les différents phyla évoluent, leurs dimensions deviennent de plus en plus grandes. Le maximum est atteint avant l'extinction du phylum. Cela se vérifie avec une évidence tout à fait particulière pour les Globotruncanae et Abathomphali du Maastrichtien supérieur, mais est bien évident aussi pour les Ticinellae de l'Albien supérieur, pour les Rotaliporae du Cénomanien supérieur, etc. Les Globotruncanae les plus grandes (appartenant aux espèces *G.arca*, *G.stuarti*, *G.contusa* particulièrement) se trouvent au Maastrichtien.

En ce qui concerne la s p i r e, elle a une tendance à s'élever de plus en plus chez de nombreuses espèces. Les formes les plus primitives, chez tous les phyla, sont très aplaties. Les formes les plus hautes se trouvent au Maastrichtien: *Globotruncana conica*, *G.caliciformis* et, tout particulièrement, *G.contusa* sont les espèces les plus caractéristiques dans ce sens et très utiles pour la stratigraphie.

En ce qui concerne la f o r m e d e s l o g e s, leur variation progressive s'observe, soit au cours de l'ontogénèse, soit par évolution phylogénétique. Chez *Globotruncana* les loges de type globigérinoïde sont limitées en général au premier stade de développement, sauf dans l'espèce *G. globigerinoides*. Les loges à forme pétaloïde sont le type le plus répandu. Mais on observe des variations très fortes, qui mènent à des loges trapézoïdales (comme chez *G.stuarti*) ou bien allongées (*G.fornicata*), ou bien pliées ainsi qu'alongées (*G.contusa*). Cette tendance se manifeste surtout dans le Sénonien et le Maastrichtien (Fig. 12).

Une tendance qui concerne la forme des loges et qui ne se manifeste que dans deux lignes évolutives, consiste en la formation d'une tubulospine périphérique. *Globotruncana calcarata*, à carène singulière serait dérivée, selon l'interprétation de BRÖNNIMANN et BROWN (1955) d'une *Rugoglobigerina*. Mais les caractères génériques de cette forme lui font défaut; l'allure des sutures septales et la forme trapézoïdale des loges rappellent de près celles de *Globotruncana stuarti* ou mieux de *G.stuartiformis*, d'où *G.calcarata* serait sortie. *Globotruncana spinea*, qui possède une double carène, dérive peut-être de *G.ventricosa*, dont elle rappelle beaucoup la morphologie externe.

En ce qui concerne la d i r e c t i o n d ' e n r o u l e m e n t, des observations intéressantes ont été faites surtout sur les associations cénomaniennes. Il semble que — dans la même espèce — les rapports entre les individus enroulés à droite ou bien à gauche soient variables dans le temps. BOLLI (1950) a observé que certaines espèces qui, lors de leur apparition présentent un rapport de 50 %, dans des couches successives montraient une direction préférentielle bien définie, c'est-à-dire un rapport beaucoup plus haut (ou plus bas). Ce que nous venons de dire ne s'applique qu'à quelques espèces de l'Albien et du Cénomanien, telles que *Rotalipora ticinensis*, *R.appenninica* ou *Praeglobotruncana stephani*. Les vraies Globotruncanae du Crétacé supérieur sont toujours enroulées à droite (CITA, 1948).

En ce qui concerne l'ornementation du test et les carènes (ce dernier caractère est ici examiné au niveau de l'espèce), on observe qu'elles tendent à devenir de plus en plus compliquées au cours de l'évolution, chez tous les phyla. L'ornementation n'est d'ordinaire pas très accentuée. Mais les formes les plus ornées sont toujours les plus tardives, tandis que chez les plus primitives il n'y a presque pas d'ornementation. De même les carènes très élevées et parsemées de petites perles se trouvent en général chez les formes les plus évoluées.

Fréquemment enfin, on observe chez les différents phyla que les formes les plus primitives ont une vie assez longue, tandis que les plus spécialisées ont une distribution stratigraphique beaucoup plus limitée. Voir par exemple *Globotruncana contusa*, qui est limitée au Maastrichtien, tandis que ses ancêtres *G.fornicata* et *G.caliciformis* ont une distribution assez ample dans le Sénonien, ou bien *G.gagnebini*, elle aussi limitée au Maastrichtien, tandis que ses ancêtres *G.renzi* et *G.ventricosa* ont une distribution beaucoup plus ample.

Étant donné que de nombreux caractères varient d'une façon progressive au cours de l'évolution, on est porté naturellement à établir plus ou moins hypothétiquement des suites ou lignées évolutives d'espèces de *Globotruncana*, basées sur des analogies formelles. C'est ce que de nombreux auteurs ont fait, sans tenir compte parfois, malheureusement, de deux conditions qui sont nécessaires pour que ces lignes évolutives aient une certaine probabilité de correspondre à la réalité, à savoir:

(*1*) que dans chaque ligne évolutive les formes primitives soient plus anciennes que celles dérivées d'elles,

(*2*) que ces différentes espèces aient été trouvées, dans l'ordre stratigraphique indiqué, si possible, dans la même région.

Parfois on a mis dans la même lignée phylogénétique des formes qui ont été trouvées même dans des continents différents.

BRÖNNIMANN et BROWN (1955, pp. 521, 523), par exemple, parlent d'une série évolutive *Globigerina infracretacea* – *Praeglobotruncana delrioensis* – *P.benacensis* – *Rotalipora montsalvensis minor* – *R.montsalvensis* – *R.appenninica* – *R.cushmani*. Or, *Praeglobotruncana delrioensis* (= *Globotruncana stephani* GANDOLFI) n'est pas plus ancienne que les espèces qui seraient dérivées d'elle. Au contraire, *Rotalipora appenninica* est souvent citée dans des couches inférieures à celles qui renferment les premières *P.stephani*. *Praeglobotruncana benacensis*, décrite à l'origine comme *Globotruncana*, est probablement une *Rotalipora*; elle n'a jamais été trouvée hors de l'Italie du nord, où elle apparaît bien après la première apparition de *Rotalipora appenninica*, qui ne peut donc pas être considérée comme une forme phylogénétiquement plus jeune.

Les séries évolutives qui nous semblent actuellement assez bien définies sont les suivantes:

Globotruncana lapparenti coronata – *G.lapparenti lapparenti* – *G.lapparenti tricarinata* – *G.arca* (Turonien–Maastrichtien)

Globotruncana renzi – *G. concava* – *G.ventricosa* – *G.gagnebini* (évolution parallèle *G.ventricosa* – *G.spinea*) (Turonien–Maastrichtien)

Globotruncana fornicata – *G.caliciformis* – *G.contusa* (Sénonien–Maastrichtien)

Globotruncana elevata elevata – *G.elevata stuartiformis* – *G.stuarti* (évolution parallèle *G.stuartiformis* – *G.calcarata*) (Sénonien–Maastrichtien).

L'ÉVOLUTION DES POPULATIONS À GLOBOTRUNCANA DU CRÉTACÉ DANS LES DIFFÉRENTES PARTIES DU MONDE

Il semble que les Globotruncanae aient été des foraminifères planctiques. C'est une opinion généralement admise, bien qu'on ne puisse pas avoir une certitude absolue, à cause de la complète extinction de ces formes à la fin du Crétacé. Mais leur dérivation des "globigérines" crétacées est bien démontrée, autant que la dérivation des Globorotaliidae des Globigerinidae tertiaires. Par analogie avec ces formes — dont les représentants sont actuellement planctiques — on arrive à l'affirmation précédente.

Quelques auteurs par contre, tout en admettant en général l'habitat planctique des Globotruncanae, font des réserves à l'égard de quelques groupes particuliers. BERMÚDEZ (1952), par exemple, place chez les Rotaliidae la sous-famille des Globotruncaninae et chez les Cymbaloporidae les Rotaliporae, ce qui implique un mode de vie différent. GANDOLFI (1955) considère comme probablement benthiques, soit *Rotalipora*, à cause de sa forme, soit les formes coniques du Maastrichtien, en particulier *Globotruncana contusa*. Il affirme que sa forme à convexité spirale très accentuée est tellement différente de la forme idéale d'une "globigérine", que l'on ne peut pas admettre qu'elle vivait à la surface de la mer.

Mais ces considérations ne nous semblent pas convaincantes; au contraire, nous sommes tout à fait d'accord avec le professeur GLAESSNER, qui aime comparer, à ce propos, la forme d'une *Globorotalia menardii* (très aplatie, biconvexe, à carène aiguë) et celle de *Globorotalia truncatulinoides* (fortement ombilico-convexe) à la forme d'une *Orbulina universa* (Fig. 19). Toutes les trois sont vivantes, et on ne peut donc pas douter de leur mode de vie, malgré leur morphologie si différente.

Une fois admis, donc, le mode de vie planctique de toutes les Globotruncanae, on s'explique leur diffusion géographique étendue sur le monde entier. Nombre d'espèces connues — parmi lesquelles on compte les formes les plus importantes au point de vue stratigraphique — sont vraiment cosmopolites: on les a citées aux Amériques, en Europe, en Afrique (outre l'Afrique méditerranéenne, on les a signalées récemment au Gabon, au Nigéria et au Madagascar), en Proche-Orient, aux Indes, en Extrême-Orient et en Australie.

On a déjà souligné auparavant la grande valeur stratigraphique des Globotruncanae,

qui sont d'excellents fossiles-guides du Crétacé supérieur, très utiles pour l'établissement des corrélations à grande distance, même intercontinentales.

Dans les nombreuses monographies sur ces formes qui ont paru récemment, on
trouve des tentatives plus ou moins poussées d'identifier exactement la distribution
des espèces et de définir des biozones. BOLLI (1957) a proposé pour la série de Trinidad
la zonation suivante (planche II).

Cette zonation, la première vraiment complète, et qui paraît, au moins en grande
partie, applicable, est basée surtout sur des coupes de forage, faute d'affleurements
suffisamment continus à la surface. Malheureusement, la série-type n'est pas vraiment
continue: deux hiatus l'interrompent, dont le premier, entre les formations Gautier et

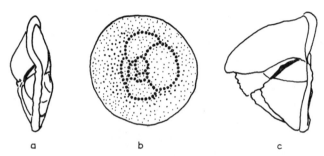

a   b   c

Fig. 19. Formes du test for différenciées réalisées chez des foraminifères planctiques vivants. a. *Globorotalia menardii* (D'ORBIGNY); b. *Orbulina universa* D'ORBIGNY; c. *Globorotalia truncatulinoides*
(D'ORBIGNY). (Dessins d'après BOLLI *et al.*, 1957).

Naparima Hill, est plus remarquable que le deuxième, situé entre Naparima Hill et
Guayaguayare. Dans cette zonation les corrélations avec les formations de la Gulf
Coast et les étages classiques d'Europe sont suggérées. Pendant que les premières
(Austin, Taylor, Navarro, etc.) renferment réellement les mêmes espèces de *Globotruncana* présentes à l'Ile de la Trinité, les stratotypes européens — sauf en partie le
Maastrichtien — sont dépourvus de foraminifères planctiques. Voilà une difficulté
que tous les chercheurs européens qui ont travaillé sur les Globotruncanae, connais-
sent très bien. On utilise couramment les noms d'étage, mais souvent ils n'ont qu'une
signification abstraite, pour indiquer une suite chronologiquement continue.

En effet les stratotypes, choisis autrefois sur la base de critères complètement différents de ceux qui informent la stratigraphie moderne, sont souvent situés aux bords
des bassins sédimentaires et correspondent à des faciès particuliers, en général
côtiers.

D'autre côté les associations à *Globotruncana* sont souvent exclusives et ne renferment pas d'autres fossiles: entre les lithofaciès les plus connus des couches à *Globotruncana* on a des calcaires très fins, pélagiques, ou bien des marnes plus ou moins
calcaires, qui renferment des millions de foraminifères planctiques dans un volume de
roche très petit, mais peu ou pas d'organismes plus évolués.

Le fait de retrouver des fossiles stratigraphiquement significatifs (ammonites) surtout en Afrique (Tunisie, Algérie, Madagascar) et en Europe occidentale, est donc

PLANCHE II

Zones à *Globotruncana* et formes voisines reconnues par BOLLI (1957) dans les formations crétacées de Trinidad (Gautier, Naparima Hill, Guayaguayare) et tentative de corrélation avec les formations de la Gulf Coast (colonne de gauche) et avec les étages classiques de l'Europe.

MENDEZ		GUAYAGUAYARE	*Abathomphalus mayaroensis*
	MAASTRICHTIEN		*Globotruncana gansseri*
NAVARRO			*Globotruncana lapparenti tricarinata*
	CAMPANIEN	NAPARIMA HILL	*Globotruncana stuarti*
TAYLOR			*Globotruncana fornicate*
	SANTONIEN		*Globotruncana concavata*
AUSTIN			*Globotruncana renzi*
	CONIACIEN		
EAGLE FORD	TURONIEN		*Globotruncana inornata*
WASHITA	CENOMANIEN MOYEN – INF.	GAUTIER	*Rotalipora appenninica appenninica*
			Globigerina washitensis
	? ALBIEN		*Rotalipora ticinensis ticinensis*

particulièrement important, puisqu'il permet de donner une consistance plus grande aux déterminations d'âge basées uniquement sur les Globotruncanae.

En ce qui concerne la répartition géographique des Globotruncanae, elles s'avèrent, d'après les études récentes, largement cosmopolite. Dans le passé, les idées à cet égard étaient bien différentes: d'après la littérature, il semblait que les faunes européennes (avec les espèces *Globotruncana canaliculata*, *G.marginata*, *G.stuarti*, *G.appenninica*, etc.) et américaines (*G.arca*, *G.rosetta*, *G.fornicata*, *G.conica*, *G.ventricosa* etc.) n'aient rien de commun. Mais les études conduites, soit en Europe (CITA, 1948), soit dans l'Amérique centrale (BOLLI, 1951; BRÖNNIMANN, 1952; GANDOLFI, 1955; etc.) ont démontré que les associations étaient en grande partie identiques, et que parfois les mêmes formes étaient connues dans les deux continents sous des noms spécifiques différents.

Les faunes à *Globotruncana*, typiques pour la Téthys, se trouvent même au dehors de cet immense bassin, caractérisé par des conditions climatiques de type tempéré à tropical. Mais les associations sont souvent appauvries. Dans le bassin boréal, par exemple, de nombreuses espèces endémiques de la région méditerranéenne manquent complètement.

On ne peut pas terminer cet exposé sur l'évolution des Globotruncanae sans dire un mot sur leur extinction qui, d'après les données disponibles, semble parallèle dans toutes les coupes étudiées, dans les divers continents, et qui est située au sommet du Maastrichtien.

Le "faunal break", que l'on observe dans les associations à foraminifères plancti-ques lors du passage du Maastrichtien au Danien est extrêmement net et profond, même dans les séries apparemment continues, à lithologie homogène.

Il s'agit d'un changement complet: de nombreux genres caractéristiques du Crétacé supérieur (parmi lesquels *Globotruncana* et *Abathomphalus*) avec des dizaines d'espèces disparaissent tout d'un coup. Au Danien ne se retrouvent que de rares espèces de *Globigerina* ensemble avec les premières Globorotaliae, de type globi-gérinoïde. C'est le changement le plus complet de toute l'histoire des foraminifères planctiques. Quelle est la cause qui a déterminé ce brusque arrêt de l'évolution, chez de différents groupes de planctiques?

Plusieurs faits nous font supposer qu'il s'agit d'une cause externe et non pas d'une cause liée à l'évolution elle-même, donc interne.

BOLLI et CITA (1960) avancent l'hypothèse qu'une variation dans la température ou dans la composition chimique des eaux peut être à l'origine de ce phénomène. En effet, seuls les foraminifères planctiques changent complètement au passage du Maastrichtien au Danien: mais les formes benthiques franchissent en grande partie la limite Crétacé–Tertiaire (qui est considérée ici comme correspondant à la limite entre les étages précités).

Si l'on passe des protozoaires aux animaux d'ordre supérieur, on trouve que les vertébrés continentaux et les mollusques planctiques se comportent comme les fora-minifères planctiques, tandis que l'évolution de nombreuses autres formes qui vivaient au fond de la mer (comme p.ex. les spongiaires, les échinides, plusieurs pélécipodes, etc.) ne s'est pas arrêtée à la fin du Crétacé.

Il serait donc un changement climatique à caractère très accentué, peut-être catastro-phique, qui a déterminé la disparition parallèle des grands reptiles, des ammonites, des Globotruncanae et d'autres foraminifères planctiques spécialisés.

Il est souhaitable que des analyses sur les isotopes de l'oxygène (O_{18}) présents dans la calcite qui constitue le test des foraminifères, permettront à l'avenir de vérifier la validité de cette interprétation.

SUMMARY

During the Upper Cretaceous, the evolution of planctonic Foraminifera followed different directions, producing more and more specialized genera, among which the genus *Globotruncana*. By following either the ontogenetic development, or the stratigraphic evolution, cleary defined evolutionary trends can be observed which influence some of the taxonomic characteristics and permit the identification of the evolutionary lineage.

The evolution, which is more or less regular during the Upper Cretaceous, comes to a sudden halt at the end of the Maastrichtian. According to the results of the latest research, the development of the various phyla, either directly or indirectly related to the group of *Globotruncana*, appears to be interrupted at the end of the Cretaceous.

The author attributes the lack of uniformity in the classification of *Globotruncana* and closely related genera largely to the different evaluation of the importance of the taxonomic characteristics.

BIBLIOGRAPHIE

ALLARD, P. L., CUVILLIER, J., DALBIEZ, F., DELMAS, M., DUFAURE, PH., FABER, J., FRANCOIS, S., GUBLER, Y., LACASSAGNE, R., LAPLAICHE, N., LYS, M., MAILLARD, J., MALMOUSTIER, G., MARIE, P., MAYNC, W., NEULANN, M., NOUET, G., PEREBASKINE, V., SÉRONIE-VIVIEN, M. et SIGAL, J., 1959. Les foraminifères et le Crétacé supérieur français. Mise au point et données nouvelles. *84e Congr. Soc. Sav. Dijon, Colloque Crétacé*, pp. 591–660.

AYALA CASTAÑARES, A., 1954. El genero *Globotruncana* CUSHMAN 1927 y su importancia en estratigrafia. *Bol. Asoc. Mex. Geol. Petrol.*, 6 (11–12) : 353–474.

BANDY, O. L., 1951. Upper Cretaceous Foraminifera from the Carlsbad area, San Diego County, Calif. *J. Paleontol.*, 25 : 448–513.

BANNER, F. T. and BLOW, W. H., 1959. The classification and stratigraphical distribution of the Globigerinaceae. *Paleontology*, 2 : 1–27.

BANNER, F. T. and BLOW, W. H., 1960. Some primary types belonging to the superfamily Globigerinacea. *Contrib. Cushman Found. Foraminiferal Research*, 11 : 1–41.

BERMÚDEZ, P. J., 1952. Estudio sistematico de los foraminiferos rotaliformes. *Ministerio Minas Hidrocarb. Venezuela Bol. Geol.*, 2 (4) : 7–230.

BETTENSTAEDT, F. and WICHER, C. A., 1955. Stratigraphic correlation of Upper Cretaceous and Lower Cretaceous in the Tethys and Boreal by the aid of microfossils. *Proc. IV World Petrol. Congr., Sect. I/D*, 5 : 494–516.

BOLLI, H. M., 1944. Zur Stratigraphie des Oberen Kreide in den höheren helvetischen Decken. *Eclogae Geol. Helv.*, 37 (2) : 217–328.

BOLLI, H. M., 1950. The direction of coiling in the evolution of some Globorotaliidae. *Contrib. Cushman Found. Foraminiferal Research*, 1 (3–4) : 82–89.

BOLLI, H. M., 1951. The genus *Globotruncana* in Trinidad, B.W.I. *J. Paleontol.*, 25 : 187–199.

BOLLI, H. M., 1957. The genera *Praeglobotruncana, Rotalipora, Globotruncana* and *Abathomphalus* in the Upper Cretaceous of Trinidad, B.W.I. *U.S. Natl. Museum Bull.*, 215 : 51–60.

BOLLI, H. M., 1959. Planktonic Foraminifera from the Cretaceous of Trinidad, B.W.I. *Bull. Am. Paleontol.*, 39 (179) : 257–276.

BOLLI, H. M. and CITA, M. B., 1960. Upper Cretaceous and Lower Tertiary planktonic Foraminifera from the Paderno d'Adda section, northern Italy. *Repts. XXI Intern. Geol. Congr.*, 5 : 150–161.

BOLLI, H. M., LOEBLICH A. R. and TAPPAN, H., 1957. Planktonic foraminiferal families Hantkeninidae, Orbulinidae, Globorotaliidae and Globotruncanidae. *U.S. Natl. Museum Bull.*, 215 : 3–50.

BRÖNNIMANN, P., 1952a. Globigerinidae from the Upper Cretaceous (Cenomanian–Maestrichtian) of Trinidad, B.W.I. *Bull. Am. Paleontol.*, 34 (140) : 1–61.

BRÖNNIMANN, P., 1952b. *Plummerita*, new name for *Plummerella* BRÖNNIMANN 1952. *Contrib. Cushman Found. Foraminiferal Research*, 3 : 146.

BRÖNNIMANN, P. and BROWN, N. K., 1955. Taxonomy of the Globotruncanidae. *Eclogae Geol. Helv.*, 48 : 503–561.

BRÖNNIMANN, P. and BROWN, N. K., 1958. *Hedbergella*, a new name for a Cretaceous planktonic foraminiferal genus. *Washington Acad. Sci. J.*, 48 : 15–17.

BROTZEN, F., 1936. Foraminiferen aus dem schwedischen untersten Senon von Eriksdal in Schonen. *Sveriges Geol. Undersökn., Ser. C*, 396 (Årsbok 30, 3) : 1–194.

BROTZEN, F., 1942. Die Foraminiferengattung *Gavelinella* nov.gen. und die Systematik der Rotaliiformes. *Sveriges Geol. Undersökn., Ser. C*, 451 (Årsbok 36, 8) : 1–60.

CARBONNIER, A., 1952. Sur un gisement de foraminifères d'âge Cénomanien supérieur provenant de la région de Teza (Maroc). *Bull. Soc. géol. France, 6e sér.* 2 : 111–122.

CARSEY, D. D., 1926. Foraminifera of the Cretaceous of central Texas. *Texas Univ. Bull.*, 2612 : 1–56.

CITA, M. B., 1948. Ricerche stratigrafiche e micropaleontologiche sul Cretacico e sull'Eocene di Tignale (Lago di Garda). *Riv. Ital. paleontol.*, 54 (2, 3, 4) : 49–74, 117–133, 143–168.

CITA, M. B., 1955. The Cretaceous–Eocene boundary in Italy. *Proc. IV World Petrol. Congr., Sect. I/D*, 2 : 427–452.

COLLIGNON, M. et SIGAL, J., 1955. Première note sur quelques foraminifères du Crétacé supérieur de Madagascar. *Compt. rend. Soc. géol. France*, 1955 : 291–293.

CUSHMAN, J. A., 1926. Some Foraminifera from the Mendez shale of eastern Mexico. *Contrib. Cushman Lab. Foraminiferal Research*, 3 (1) : 16–26.

CUSHMAN, J. A., 1927. Some characteristic Mexicanfossil Foraminifera. *J. Paleontol.*, 1 : 147–172.

CUSHMAN, J. A., 1928. Foraminifera, their classification and economic use. *Cushman Lab. Foraminiferal Research Spec. Publ.*, 4 : 1–349.

CUSHMAN, J. A., 1946. Upper Cretaceous Foraminifera of the Gulf Coast region of the United States and adjacent areas. *U.S. Geol. Surv., Profess. Paper*, 206 : 1–241.

CUSHMAN, J. A. and TEN DAM, A., 1948. *Globigerinelloides*, a new genus of the Globigerinidae. *Contrib. Cushman Lab. Foraminiferal Research*, 24 : 42–43.

DALBIEZ, F., 1955. The genus *Globotruncana* in Tunisia. *Micropaleontol.*, 1 : 161–171.

DE KLASZ, I., 1953. Einige neue oder wenig bekannte Foraminiferen aus der helvetischen Oberkreide der bayerischen Alpen südlich Traunstein (Oberbayern). *Geol. Bavarica*, 17 : 223–244.

DE KLASZ, I., 1961. Présence de *Globotruncana concavata* (BROTZEN) et *Gl. concavata carinata* Dalbiez (foraminifères) dans le Coniacien du Gabon (Afrique équatoriale). *Compt. rend. Soc. géol. France*, 1961 : 123–124.

DE LAPPARENT, J., 1918. Etude lithologique des terrains crétacés de la région d'Hendaye. *Mém. Serv. Carte géol. France*, pp. 1–155.

DE LAPPARENT, J., 1930. À propos du genre de foraminifères *Globotruncana* créé par J. A. CUSHMAN. *Compt. rend. Soc. géol. France*, 1930 : 64–66.

DI NAPOLI ALLIATA, E., 1952. Foraminiferi pelagici e facies in Italia. *Atti VII Conv. Metano e Petrol.*, pp. 1–34.

D'ORBIGNY, A., 1839. Foraminifères. In: R. DE LA SAGRA, *Histoire physique, politique et naturelle de l'île de Cuba*, Bertrand, Paris, 224 pp.

DROOGER, C. W., 1960. Some early rotaliid Foraminifera. I–III. *Proc. Koninkl. Ned. Akad. Wetenschap. Amsterdam, Ser. B*, 63 : 287–334.

EDGELL, H. S., 1957. The genus *Globotruncana* in northwest Australia. *Micropaleontol.*, 3 : 101–122.

FRANKE, A., 1928. Die Foraminiferen der oberen Kreide Nord- und Mitteldeutschlands. *Abhandl. preuss. geol. Landesanstalt, N.F.*, 111 : 1–208.

FRIZZELL, D. L., 1954. Handbook of Cretaceous Foraminifera of Texas. *Texas Univ. Bur. Econ. Geol. Rep. Invest.*, 22 : 1–232.

GANDOLFI, R., 1942. Ricerche micropaleontologiche e stratigrafiche sulla Scaglia e sul Flysch cretacici dei dintorni di Balerna (Canton Ticino). *Riv. ital. paleontol.*, 48 (4) : 1–160.

GANDOLFI, R., 1955. The genus *Globotruncana* in northeastern Colombia. *Bull. Am. Paleontol.*, 36 (155) : 7–117.

GANDOLFI, R., 1957. Notes on some species of *Globotruncana*. *Contrib. Cushman Found. Foraminiferal Research*, 8 : 59–65.

GLAESSNER, M. F., 1937. Planktonforaminiferen aus der Kreide und dem Eozän und ihre stratigraphische Bedeutung. *Moscow Univ. Lab. Paleontol. Stud. Micropaleontol.*, 1 : 27–46.

GLAESSNER, M. F., 1945. *Principles of Micropaleontology*. Melbourne Univ. Press, Melbourne, 296 pp.

GLAESSNER, M. F. and WADE, M., 1959. Revision of the foraminiferal family Victoriellidae. *Micropaleontol.*, 5 : 193–212.

GLINTZBOECKEL, C. et MAGNÉ, J., 1959. Répartition des microfaunes à plancton et à Ostracodes dans le Crétacé supérieur de la Tunisie et de l'Est Algérien. *Rev. Micropaléontol.*, 2 : 57–67.

HAGN, H., 1953. Die Foraminiferen der Pinswanger Schichten (unteres Obercampan): ein Beitrag zur Mikropalaeontologie der helvetischen Oberkreide Südbayerns. *Palaeontographica*, 104 (Pt. A, 1–3) : 1–119.

HAGN, H. und ZEIL, W., 1954. Globotruncanen aus dem Ober-Cenoman und Unter-Turon der Bayerischen Alpen. *Eclogae Geol. Helv.*, 47 : 1–60.

HAMILTON, E. L., 1953. Upper Cretaceous, Tertiary and Recent planktonic Foraminifera from the Mid-Pacific flat-topped seamounts. *J. Paleontol.*, 27 : 204–237.

HOFKER, J., 1951. The toothplate-Foraminifera. *Arch. Néerl. Zool.*, 8 : 353–373.

HOFKER, J., 1956. Die Globotruncanen von Nordwest Deutschland und Holland. *Neues Jahrb. Geol. Paläontol.*, 103 : 312–340.

HOFKER, J., 1960. The taxonomic status of *Praeglobotruncana, Planomalina, Globigerinella* and *Biglobigerinella. Micropaleontol.*, 6 : 315–322.

KIKOINE, J., 1947. Les Globotruncana du Crétacé supérieur nordpyrenéen. *Compt. rend. Soc. géol. France*, 2 : 19–21.

KLAUS, J., 1959. Le "Complexe schisteux intermédiaire" dans le synclinal de la Gruyère (Préalpes médianes). *Eclogae Geol. Helv.*, 52 : 753–851.

KLAUS, J., 1960a. Rotalipores et Thalmanninelles d'un niveau des Couches rouges de l'Anticlinal d'Aï. *Eclogae Geol. Helv.*, 53 : 704–709.

KLAUS, J., 1960b. Étude biométrique de quelques espèces de Globotruncanidés. 1. Les espèces du genre *Praeglobotruncana* dans le Cénomanien de la Breggia. *Eclogae Geol. Helv.*, 53 : 285–308.

KSIAZKIEWICZ, M., 1956. The Jurassic and Cretaceous of Bachowice. *Ann. Soc. géol. Pologne*, 24 (2–3) : 1–405.

KSIAZKIEWICZ, M., 1958. On the Turonian in the Pieniny Klippes belt. *Bull. Acad. polon. sci.*, 6 : 537–544.

KÜPPER, K., 1956. Upper Cretaceous pelagic Foraminifera from the "Antelope shale", Glenn and Colusa counties, Calif. *Contrib. Cushman Found. Foraminiferal Research*, 7 : 40–47.

LOEBLICH, A. R. and TAPPAN, H., 1946. New Washita Foraminifera. *J. Paleontol.*, 20 : 238–258.

LOEBLICH, A. R. and TAPPAN, H., 1961a. Suprageneric classification of the Rhizopodea. *J. Paleontol.*, 35 : 245–330.

LOEBLICH, A. R. and TAPPAN, H., 1961b. Cretaceous planktonic Foraminifera: Part I – Cenomanian. *Micropaleontol.*, 7 : 257–304.

MARIE, P., 1941. Les foraminifères de la Craie à *Belemnitella mucronata* du Bassin de Paris. *Mém. Musée natl. hist. nat. Paris, n. sér.*, 14 : 1–296.

MONTANARO GALLITELLI, E., 1958. Globotruncane campaniano-maestrichtiane nella formazione a facies di flysch di Serramazzoni nell'Appennino settentrionale modenese. *Boll. Soc. geol. ital.*, 77 : 171–191.

MORNOD, L., 1950. Les Globorotalidés du Crétacé supérieur du Montsalvens. *Eclogae Geol. Helv.*, 42 : 573–593.

MOROZOVA, V. G., 1957. The foraminiferal superfamily Globigerinidea superfam.nova and some of its representatives. *Doklady Akad. Sci. S.S.S.R.*, 114 : 1109–1112.

MORROW, A. L., 1934. Foraminifera and Ostracoda from the Upper Cretaceous of Kansas. *J. Paleontol.*, 8 : 186–205.

MULLER, S. W. and SCHENCK, H. G., 1943. Standard of Cretaceous System. *Am. Bull. Assoc. Petrol. Geologists*, 27 : 262–278.

NAGAPPA, Y., 1959. Foraminiferal biostratigraphy of the Cretaceous–Eocene succession in the India–Pakistan–Burma region. *Micropaleontol.*, 5 : 145–192.

NAKKADY, S. E., 1950. A new foraminiferal fauna from the Esna shales and Upper Cretaceous chalk of Egypt. *J. Paleontol.*, 24 : 675–692.

NAKKADY, S. E. and OSMAN, A., 1952. The genus *Globotruncana* in Egypt, taxonomy and stratigraphic value. *Compt. rend. 19e Congr. géol. intern.*, 13 (15) : 75–95.

NOTH, R., 1951. Foraminiferen aus Unter- und Oberkreide des oesterreichischen Anteils an Flysch, Helvetikum und Vorlandvorkommen. *Jahrb. Geol. Bundesanstalt. Austria, Sonderbd.*, 3 : 1–91.

PAPP, A. und KÜPPER, K., 1953. Die Foraminiferenfauna von Guttering und Kl. St. Paul (Kärnten); 1 – Ueber Globotruncanen südlich Pembergen bei Kl. St. Paul. *Oesterr. Akad. Wiss., Math.-Naturwiss. Kl. Sitzberrichte*, 1962 (1–2) : 31–48.

PESSAGNO, E. K., 1960. Stratigraphy and micropaleontology of the Cretaceous and Lower Tertiary of Puerto Rico. *Micropaleontol.*, 6 : 87–110.

PLUMMER, H. J., 1926. Foraminifera of the Midway formation in Texas. *Texas Univ. Bull.*, 2644 : 1–206

PLUMMER, H. J., 1931. Some Cretaceous Foraminifera in Texas. *Texas Univ. Bull.*, 3101 : 109–203.

POKORNÝ, V., 1958. *Grundzüge der zoologischen Mikropaläontologie*. I. VEB Deutscher Verlag Wiss., Berlin, 583 pp.

QUEREAU, E. C., 1893. Die Klippenregion von Iberg (Sihltal). *Beitr. Geol. Karte Schweiz*, 33 : 3–153.

RAUZER-CHERNOUSOVA, D. M., 1956. Les unités taxonomiques élémentaires dans la systématique des foraminifères. *Voprosy Mikropaleontol. S.S.S.R.*, 1 : 5–22.

REICHEL, M., 1949. Observations sur les *Globotruncana* du gisement de la Breggia (Tessin). *Eclogae Geol. Helv.*, 42 : 596–617.

REISS, Z., 1957. The Bilamellidea, nov. superfam. and remarks on Cretaceous Globorotaliids. *Contrib. Cushman Found. Foraminiferal Research*, 8 : 127–145.

RENZ, O., 1936a. Stratigraphische und mikropalaeontologische Untersuchung der Scaglia (Obere Kreide–Tertiaer) im zentralen Apennin. *Eclogae Geol. Helv.*, 29 : 1–149.

RENZ, O., 1936b. Ueber Globotruncanen im Cenomanien der Schweizer Jura. *Eclogae Geol. Helv.*, 29 : 500–503.

REUSS, A. E., 1845. *Die Versteinerungen der bömischen Kreideformation.* E. Schweizerbart, Stuttgart, 1 : 25–40.

REUSS, A. E., 1854. Beiträge zur Charakteristik der Kreideschichten in den Oestalpen besonders in Gosauthale, und am Wolfgangsee. *Denkschr. Akad. Wiss. Wien, Math. Nat. Kl.*, 7 : 1–156.

REYMENT, R. A., 1960. Notes on the Cretaceous–Tertiary transition in Nigeria. *Repts. XXI Intern. Geol. Congr.*, 5 : 131–135.

SACAL, V. ET DEBOURLE, A., 1957. Foraminifères d'Aquitaine. 2e partie. Peneroplidae à Victoriellidae. *Mém. Soc. géol. France, n. Sér.*, 78 : 1–87.

SIGAL, J., 1948. Notes sur les genres de foraminifères *Rotalipora* BROTZEN 1942 et *Thalmanninella*. *Rev. Inst. Franç. Pétrole*, 3 : 95–103.

SIGAL, J., 1952a. Foraminifères. In: J. PIVETEAU, *Traité de Paléontologie.* Masson, et Cie, Paris, 1 : 138–178, 192–301.

SIGAL, J., 1952b. Aperçu stratigraphique sur la micropaléontologie du Crétacé. *XIX Congr. Géol. Intern., Monograph, Rég., sér. I (Algérie)*, 26 : 1–45.

SIGAL, J., 1956a. Notes micropaléontologiques nord-africaines. 4. *Biticinella breggiensis* (GANDOLFI) nouveau morphogenre. *Compt. rend. Soc. géol. France*, 1956 : 35–37.

SIGAL, J., 1956b. Notes micropaléontologiques malgaches. 2. Microfaunes albiennes et cénomaniennes. *Compt. rend. Soc. géol. France*, 1956 : 210–214.

SIGAL, J., 1958. La classification actuelle des familles de foraminifères planctoniques du Crétacé. *Compt. rend. Soc. géol. France*, 1958 : 262–265.

SUBBOTINA, N. N., 1953. Fossil Foraminifera of the U.S.S.R. Globigerinidae, Hantkeninidae and Globorotaliidae. *Vnigri, N. Ser.*, 76 : 1–294.

TAPPAN, H., 1943. Foraminifera from the Duck Creek formation of Oklahoma and Texas. *J. Paleontol.*, 17 : 476–517.

THALMANN, H. E., 1933. Validité du nom générique "*Globotruncana* CUSHMAN 1927". *Compt. rend. Soc. géol. France*, 1933 : 200–201.

THALMANN, H. E., 1934. Die regional-stratigraphische Verbreitung der oberkretazischen Foraminiferen-Gattung *Globotruncana* CUSHMAN 1927. *Eclogae Geol. Helv.*, 27 : 413–429.

THALMANN, H. E., 1942. The genus *Globotruncana* and its species. *Am. Assoc. Petrol. Geologists, 27th Ann. Convention Program*, pp. 51, 52.

TILEV, N., 1952. Étude des Rosalines maestrichtiennes (genre *Globotruncana*) du sud-est de la Turquie (sondage de Ramandag). *Bull. Lab. géol. min. géophys. Musée géol. Univ. Lausanne*, 103 : 1–101.

TROELSEN, J. C., 1955. *Globotruncana contusa* in the White Chalk of Denmark. *Micropaleontol.*, 1 : 76–82.

TSCHATCHLI, B. S., 1941. *Ueber Flysch und Couches rouges in den Decken der oestlichen Préalpes Romandes (Simmenthal-Saanen).* Thesis, Bern, 78 pp.

VOGLER, J., 1941. Beiträge zur Geologie von Niederländisch-Indien. Ober Jura und Kreide von Misol. *Palaeontographica*, 4 (Suppl. Bd. 4) : 245–293.

WHITE, M. P., 1928. Some index Foraminifera of the Tampico embayment area of Mexico. Part II. *J. Paleontol.*, 2 : 280–317.

WICHER, C. A., 1956. Die Gosau-Schichten in Becken vom Gams (Oesterreich) und die Foraminiferengliederung der höheren Oberkreide in der Tethys. *Paläontol. Z.*, 30 : 87–136.

Note éditoriale: Il semble être préférable en français de faire d'après le Nouveau Larousse Universel la distinction entre „planctique" = qui erre, qui flotte au gré des eaux, et „planctonique" ou „planktonique" = qui a rapport au plancton.

PHYLOMORPHOGENESIS AND EVOLUTIONARY TRENDS OF CRETACEOUS ORBITOIDAL FORAMINIFERA

H. J. MAC GILLAVRY

Geological Institute, University of Amsterdam, Amsterdam (The Netherlands)

INTRODUCTION

When, as a young paleontologist, I started work in Indonesia twenty-four years ago, larger Foraminifera formed the main basis for biostratigraphic correlations in this region. VAN DER VLERK and UMBGROVE (1927) had introduced their well-known letter-classification (see also VAN DER VLERK, 1955), while a further refinement was being worked out by TAN SIN HOK by means of his method of phylomorphogenetic analysis. Ever since, I have been fascinated by these forms and have been studying them more or less continuously. Inevitably, during these years, I have developed a system of description which, however, has never appeared in writing, because of company interests and lack of spare time.[1] This system does not differ in essentials from that developed by TAN SIN HOK, except perhaps in the stress laid upon the first ontogenetic appearance of a retrovert aperture. During these years, furthermore, I independently discovered the interruption of the *Helicolepidina* spiral through nepionic reduction (BRÖNNIMANN, 1944; VAN RAADSHOOVEN, 1951), the essential difference between the microspheric arrangement in *Asterocyclina* and *Discocyclina* (BRÖNNIMANN, 1945), and the presence of a nepionic gümbeline stage in microspheric Orbitoididae (KÜPPER, 1954b). This is not mentioned here to establish a spurious claim to priority, but in order to show why I feel confident that the observations of these authors are correct.

What exactly are orbitoids, or better orbitoidal Foraminifera? Are they to be defined by the presence of a equatorial layer and two layers of lateral chambers? This would result in an completely artificial separation of closely allied forms and cut arbitrarily through taxonomical units. Or is the presence of secondary chambers in the equatorial layer to be taken as the hall-mark for these forms? In that case one cannot regard the Discocyclinidae as orbitoidal. In short, the term orbitoidal Foraminifera does not signify a taxonomic unit, but lumps (*a*) a number of homoeomorphs, developed by different means from different ancestors (*Orbitoides* and *Lepidorbitoides*), (*b*) forms which developed by analogous phylomorphogenetic means or parallel evolution, but likewise from different ancestors (*Helicolepidina* and *Helicorbitoides* nov. gen.), and finally (*c*) lineages belonging to one family or even one genus, which evolve

---

[1] Several indications have already been given in MAC GILLAVRY (1955).

from similar ancestors by similar means, but nevertheless independently one from the other. The term orbitoidal thus is merely a loose term, only to be used in a general sense. POKORNÝ (1958) has consistently separated unrelated forms into their respective families.

GENERAL PART

For a better understanding of evolutionary trends in larger Foraminifera, it will be necessary to give a summary of the descriptive system mentioned in the introduction. It will not be possible, within the scope of this paper, to mention which ideas have been derived from previous authors; it may be stated forthwith that most of the ideas expressed have first been developed by TAN SIN HOK and other authors. Neither will it be possible to give a complete discussion and justification for the modifications introduced by me. I must, therefore, apologize for neglecting to give honour to previous authors, where this is due; furthermore for the too concise, unpalatable, and apodictic form in which this system is presented.

In order to describe the evolution of larger Foraminifera, a distinction is to be made between (a) the phylogenetic introduction of new features, which presumably have a genetic basis, (b) types of phylomorphogenesis, characterized by a definite phylogenetic succession of introduction of such new features, (c) evolutionary trends, the most important of which is nepionic reduction.

PHYLOGENETIC INTRODUCTION OF NEW FEATURES

Under this heading come more in particular such new features as result in an important modification of morphologic pattern. This phylogenetic introduction of new features may follow different modes, but usually the deuterogenetic mode is followed, i.e., these features make their first phylogenetic appearance at a late ontogenetic stage; the word ontogeny is used to denote the entire life-span; furthermore they make their first phylogenetic appearance only in part of the population (quoted from POKORNÝ, 1958, pp. 147, 148). In fact they behave exactly as the "hopeful monsters" which are now quite out of fashion. Both palingenesis and the coexistence of new forms with unchanged ancestral ones, go against modern trends of thoughts on evolution, which try to belittle the role played by deuterogenesis and its accompaniment of palingenesis and tachygenesis, and which postulate the plastic transformation of entire populations through population genetics. This cannot be helped and must be excused on the ground that Foraminifera are primitive organisms. When the term palingenesis is understood in a purely descriptive sense, devoid of any mystic implications, I do not see any need for other words such as pseudoanaboly (POKORNÝ, 1958, p. 147).

The following new phylogenetic features follow the deuterogenetic mode: (1) the introduction of additional apertures, which occurs in a wide variety of forms, (2) the introduction of a retrovert aperture, which is an important step towards the orbitoidal pattern, (3) the introduction of new stolon passages, and probably also (4) the introduction of lateral chambers.

Very few features follow the proterogenetic mode. A case in point may be the introduction of radial apertures in some Soritidae, which apertures seem first to develop at the deuteroconch, and from there to spread outward.

Neither of these modes is followed by the introduction of adauxiliary apertures, which are restricted to the embryonic chambers, usually to the deuteroconch, but also occurring, in exceptional cases, in the protoconch (BRÖNNIMANN, 1940, p. 9).

TYPES OF PHYLOMORPHOGENESIS

Characteristic morphologic patterns are obtained through a definite sequence of phylogenetic introduction of new features. As all features which are of importance in this connection are deuterogenetic, this means that they appear ontogenetically in the same succession. Modifications of pattern result not merely from the introduction of a new feature, but the particular type of modification attained also depends upon the phylogenetic succession in which these features are introduced.

Fig. 1. Equatorial pattern of different types of phylomorphogenesis.
Type I: *Cycloclypeus*-type. Copied from TAN SIN HOK (1932, p. 18).
Type IIA: *Planorbulinella*-type. Diagrammatic figure, based upon BARKER and GRIMSDALE (1936, pl. 35, fig. 3), *Eulinderina semiradiata* BARKER and GRIMSDALE.
Type IIB: *Helicolepidina*-type. Diagrammatic figure, based upon BARKER and GRIMSDALE, (1936, pl. 38, fig. 4), *Helicocyclina paucispira* (BARKER and GRIMSDALE).
Type III: *Omphalocyclus*-type. After NEUMANN (1958, pl. VI, fig. 8), *Omphalocyclus macroporus* (LAMARCK). For explanation see text.

Type I. Cycloclypeus-type

The sequence of introduction of new features is: (*1*) additional apertures (*Operculina* to *Heterostegina*); (*2*) retrovert apertures (*Heterostegina* to *Cycloclypeus*).

(*1*) The introduction of additional apertures permits a retrovert lengthening of the primary chambers, and thus leads to a widening of the spiral. It furthermore leads to the subdivision of subsequent chambers into chamberlets. The succession of chambers and the direction of growth still follow the ancestral spiral, but this spiral mode is slackened on the external side because of the widening of the whorl.

(2) The introduction of a retrovert aperture, situated here at the margin, leads onto-genetically from a *Heterostegina*-stage to a juvenile *Cycloclypeus*. It is accompanied by the termination of the external spiral wall, and leads to retrovert growth and over-lap outside of the spiral wall of previous chambers through the retrovert extension of subsequent chambers. Retrovert overlap may not be immediate but may be delayed. As each chamberlet must be formed through an aperture in one of the preceding chambers (TAN SIN HOK, 1932, p. 19), one can determine where the first retrovert aperture occurs by analysing the position of chamberlets in the overlapping part of subsequent chambers. The introduction of the retrovert aperture means a further step in the relaxation of the ancestral spiral tendency. The spiral tendency is terminated on the external side, but the succession of chambers and the direction of growth, on the internal side, still follow the ancestral spiral mode.

(3) The retrovert overlap of primary chambers outside the spiral wall eventually leads to the formation of annular chambers and hence to cyclical growth: when growth in the direction of the primary spiral, and retrovert growth overlapping the spiral wall, meet, they join in a first annular chamber, which is comparable to the symmetrical peri-nepionic chamber of the next two types of phylomorphogenesis. Thus a nepionic stage, preceding annular growth, is delimited, not by the introduction of a new feature, but as a consequence of the modifications resulting from the introduction of the retro-vert aperture. However, there are reasons to regard this delimitation of a nepionic stage preceding annular growth as a fundamental datum. The chambers which con-stitute this stage are called the primary chambers.

(4) Finally, for a full description, it will be useful to record the total number of chambers, as this may also be subject to evolutionary change.

A description of the relevant stages will be: (*a*) number of chambers without addi-tional apertures, (*b*) number of chambers without retrovert aperture, (*c*) number of chambers preceding annular growth, (*d*) total number of chambers. It is preferred, for reasons to be discussed, to count all chambers preceding the introduction of the new modification of pattern, thus starting each time counting with the protoconch, rather than to describe the phylomorphogenesis in terms of successive ontogenetic stages (see also p. 148).

This type of morphogenesis occurs in *Discospirina*, the Soritidae, *Cycloclypeus*, and the Discocyclinidae (microspheric forms).

Type II

This is a group of different subtypes, all characterized by the introduction of a retro-vert aperture, not preceded by the acquisition of additional apertures. In this case a retrovert lengthening of primary chambers cannot be effected, because of the absence of additional, frontal, apertures. Instead a new type of chambers is formed, the secondary chambers. Primary chambers are those which have a basal aperture which is homologous with the ancestral aperture; they continue the direction of growth of the ancestral spire, and their walls foot, on the internal side, upon the spiral wall of a preceding whorl. Secondary chambers are all other equatorial chambers. The first retrovert aperture occurring ontogenetically leads to the formation of the first secondary chamber.

Type IIA. Planorbulinella–type

(*1*) Almost simultaneously with the appearance of the first retrovert aperture, the spiral wall terminates. This spiral wall is subsequently covered externally by a series of asymmetric secondary chambers, covering it in a retrovert direction. Termination of the spiral wall and retrovert overlap outside this wall may again be slightly delayed: sometimes one or a few secondary chambers are found within the spiral wall, similar to standard behaviour in type IIB. The ancestral spiral of chambers is continued by a spiral succession of primary chambers, which now, however, have two apertures, one basal, one retrovert. Normal secondary chambers have likewise two apertures.

(*2*) At a certain point the spiral of primary chambers meets the retrovert series of asymmetric secondary chambers around the spiral wall of the previous whorl. At this point a symmetrical chamber is formed, and thus again there is a delimitation of a nepionic stage: the total number of primary chambers. From there on growth is only effected by the addition of secondary chambers. This growth is not truly cyclical but in the manner of intersecting spirals. Again the delimitation of the number of primary chambers, though not due to the ontogenetic appearance of a new feature, is considered fundamental.

(*3*) Each secondary chamber can be assigned a certain rank by tracing its origin backwards through the succession of chambers which has led up to its formation. In this manner one might determine the total number of budding stages of an adult animal, which again might have evolutionary significance. However, whereas in *Cycloclypeus* it is comparatively easy to count the total number of chambers, it is less easy to count the total number of budding stages in this type of phylomorphogenesis, for a chamber may have a different rank, depending on which path is followed in tracing its origin backwards, inasmuch as growth rate, or rather budding rate, need not be the same in different directions.

The description of relevant stages is: (*a*) number of primary chambers without retrovert aperture, (*b*) total number of primary chambers, (*c*) total number of budding stages, which usually can not be reliably determined.

This type of morphogenesis is followed by *Lepidorbitoides minor* (microspheric forms), *Lepidocyclina*, *Planorbulinella*, and *Asterocyclina* (microspheric forms).

Type IIB. Helicolepidina–type

The spiral wall does not terminate at the introduction of the first retrovert aperture, but continues up to the periphery of the adult animal. Retrovert growth, effected by retrovert series of consecutive secondary chambers, takes place within the spiral wall. There is no retrovert overlapping growth outside of the spiral wall. This wall is covered externally only by the primary chambers of the next whorl. The retrovert aperture is therefore not to be called a marginal aperture, hence the more awkward word retrovert aperture. As shown by those specimens of type IIA, in which retrovert overlap outside the spiral wall is delayed, it can not properly be considered as marginal in that type either.

This pattern again enables the spiral to widen out. When this widening out goes so far, that the same point on the spiral wall is reached at the same time, externally by the primary chambers, and internally by the secondary chambers, the spiral wall may be discontinued, as in the controversial *Helicocyclina*. The spiral wall, though continuing up to the periphery, may also show a general dissolution, when interrupted, throughout its length, by frequent apertures as in *Helicolepidina vichayalensis* (L. RUTTEN) (neither *Actinosiphon* or *Polylepidina*). That this species belongs to the genus *Helicolepidina* is shown by the continued spiral of larger primary chambers and by the presence of a spiral wall which, though reduced to a series of thickened dashes, is still recognisable.[1]

The description of relevant stages in type IIB is: (*a*) number of primary chambers without retrovert aperture, (*b*) total number of primary chambers. The total number of primary chambers can be established with relative ease, and may be taken as indicative for total growth.

This type of morphogenesis is followed by *Helicolepidina*, *Helicorbitoides* (nov. gen.) *longispiralis* (PAPP and KÜPPER), and possibly by *Heterosteginoides panamensis* CUSHMAN.

Type IIC. Miogypsinoides–type

This subtype is similar to the preceding one, but the number of primary chambers is autonomously reduced (see further under evolutionary trends). The number of primary chambers is therefore not indicative for the total number of budding stages, which again cannot be established definitely, as it depends upon which path is taken in counting the number of budding stages leading up to a certain peripheral secondary chamber.

The relevant data are: (*a*) the number of primary chambers without retrovert aperture, (*b*) the total number of primary chambers, (*c*) the total number of budding stages.

This type of morphogenesis is followed by most Miogypsinidae. *Helicocyclina*, and

---

[1] The remarks on the species *vichayalensis* L. RUTTEN are based upon personal examination of the material in the Geological Institute of Utrecht. The spiral of larger primary chambers is just visible in Plate II, fig. 25, of L. RUTTEN (1928). The assignment to the genus *Helicolepidina* is in accordance with the opinion of VAUGHAN and L. RUTTEN in BARKER (1934, p. 351) and of BARKER and GRIMSDALE (1936, p. 240, note). The spiral wall of *Helicolepidina spiralis* is already pierced by apertures (BRÖNNIMANN, 1944, p. 26). It should be interesting to investigate, whether, in primitive species of *Helicolepidina*, one can distinguish an inner, ancestral part, which is not pierced by apertures, and an outer part, which is pierced by such apertures. In any case, there is but a gradual difference between the spiral wall of *Helicolepidina spiralis*, with long narrow apertures piercing this wall, and that of *H.vichayalensis*, where this wall is interrupted by wide apertures.

possibly also the more advanced species of *Helicorbitoides*, show a parallel trend, but the reduction of the number of primary chambers is not effected in the autonomous manner of primitive Miogypsinidae.

Type III. Omphalocyclus–type

This type starts with a gümbeline ancestral stage of alternate growth. Instead of spiral growth through primary apertures continuously in one spiral direction, growth takes place in alternate directions through primary apertures placed in alternate position in successive chambers. The term "biserial", usually employed for this kind of growth, will not be used here, because it would lead to confusion with the term biserial nepionic arrangement.

At a certain point a second aperture is formed on the "wrong" side of a chamber, again resulting in the formation of a first secondary chamber; in this case it furthermore leads to growth in other directions than alternate. In fact, as may be seen from the figures given by KÜPPER (1954b), the alternate gümbeline growth is not clearly continued once the new aperture has been introduced ontogenetically. The new aperture could be called marginal in this case. However, from analogy with the term used for the other groups, it will be called a contravert aperture.

The ancestral stage of alternate growth is usually delimited marginally by a thickened wall on either side. These flanks are subsequently covered by two series of asymmetric secondary chambers, one series on each side. Again the two rows meet to form a symmetric secondary chamber. Neither of these two series is to be considered as a series of primary chambers, as both grow in a contravert direction. Nevertheless, it is advisable to count the total number of budding stages preceding the formation of the symmetric peri-nepionic secondary chamber. If the ancestor is indeed gümbeline, one would expect a first ontogenetic stage with spiral growth. The description of relevant stages would then be: (*a*) total number of spirally arranged chambers preceding alternate growth, (*b*) total number of chambers preceding the first appearance of a contravert aperture, (*c*) number of budding stages preceding the formation of the peri-nepionic symmetric chamber, (*d*) total number of budding stages, which again will not be definite.

The chief merit of this system is that it stresses the importance of the first appearance of the retrovert aperture, which is seldom given in the literature, but which is of fundamental importance for the separation and recognition of independent but related lineages. Secondly it permits a consistent evaluation of nepionic reduction as well in uniserial nepionts as in more advanced, *i.e.*, more reduced, forms.

If we review the preceding, it is seen that type I is characterized by lengthened chambers subdivided into chamberlets, types II and III by the formation of secondary chambers. If the chambers of type I become constricted, between chamberlets, they will mimic the equatorial arrangement of advanced forms of types II and III, as happens in some Soritidae. If a form of type II develops chambers with radial walls and a rectangular shape, it will mimic forms of type I; this occurs in the Orbitoclypeidae and in *Eoannularia*. Types I and II derive from spiral ancestors. It appears that forms of type I derive from planispiral ancestors, those of type II from trochospiral ancestors.

These types of phylomorphogenesis are to be regarded in a purely descriptive sense. They do not have any specific taxonomic significance, for the same type of phylomorphogenesis may be followed by forms which are only distantly related. They may, however, indicate that the potentialities for phylomorphogenesis, within a certain major group, are restricted, and in this sense they have taxonomic significance. A comparable case is the introduction of canals in the inner shell layer in various groups of Rudists *(Caprina, Torreites, Chiapasella)*. Conversely elephants do not become snake-like through loss of limbs, whereas lizards frequently do.

Neither is it implied that *e.g.*, the retrovert aperture of *Cycloclypeus* is to be considered as strictly homologous with the retrovert aperture in *Helicolepidina*, the secondary chambers of *Miogypsinoides* homologous with those of *Omphalocyclus*. Secondary chambers may perhaps develop out of the ventral chambers of *Tremastegina* in the Lepidocyclinidae, out of the intramural lumina in *Miogypsinoides*, out of dorsal lateral chambers in the Pseudorbitoididae (*cf.* BRÖNNIMANN, 1954a, pl. 10, fig. 1, *Sulcorbitoides*). There are few data about the exact anatomical manner in which these features are developed in the different groups.

It is furthermore to be stressed that the same type of phylomorphogenesis may be followed independently by closely related groups, possibly at different times (*cf.* MAC GILLAVRY in TAN SIN HOK, 1939a, p. 78; PAPP and KÜPPER, 1954, p. 125; MAC GILLAVRY, 1959). This may account for discrepancies in world-wide correlations, particularly in forms which are benthonic, derive from benthonic ancestors, and which, accordingly, may evolve independently through geographic, or even through biologic isolation.

In the previous descriptions we have not considered the introduction of stolon complications. Little is known about the exact ontogenetic onset of such complications. In the second place analysis has been limited to the equatorial layer. In all types some or most of the forms may develop lateral chambers. As juvenile specimens of *e.g.*, primitive *Lepidorbitoides* appear to be devoid of lateral chambers, it is likely that this feature is also deuterogenetic. Thus it would be interesting to find out how many budding stages precede the formation of the first lateral chambers, but this will be difficult to ascertain.

EVOLUTIONARY TRENDS

The new features which define the different types of phylomorphogenesis all follow the deuterogenetic mode, *i.e.*, the phylogenetic sequence of the introduction of the new features is repeated by the sequence of their ontogenetic appearance and morphologic expression. Thus there is an ontogenetic lag of manifestation of the new genetic property. Ontogenetic lag of manifestation is universal, except in morphologic changes of the chromosomes themselves, for *e.g.*, peloric flower in *Antirrhinum* can only find morphologic expression when the plant is in flower. In Foraminifera, however, the ontogenetic lag is more fundamental, because not so obviously connected.

The most important trend of evolution, in all cases, is the acceleration or tachygenesis of this ontogenetic lag: the nepionic reduction. It results in an elaboration of the morphologic consequences of the new feature, as ever larger parts of the adult shell are characterised by it.

The ultimate stages of nepionic reduction may lead, in each type of morphogenesis, to further modifications of pattern, which are characteristic for each type. These will be discussed in a separate paragraph.

Similar to nepionic reduction, but not of the same status, for not in relation to the introduction of a new feature, is the reduction in the number of primary chambers. In *Helicolepidina*, conversely, there appears to be an increase in the number of primary chambers. In the other forms there may actually be an increase in the number of primary chambers in the first stages of phylomorphogenesis, soon, however, to be followed by reduction. The final stages of reduction of the number of primary chambers lead to the suppression of the ancestral ontogenetic stage.

The proterogenetic mode would require a concomitant bradygenesis. A possible instance may occur in the Pseudorbitoididae.

Of entirely different status is the phylogenetic increase in the number of adauxiliary chambers, once this feature has been phylogenetically introduced. This increase again means the elaboration of a new feature, but has no important morphologic consequences. By its nature it is neither deuterogenetic nor proterogenetic; nor can it be called coenogenetic.

Other tendencies of a more general nature are: increase in the diameter of the adult shell, increase in size of the deuteroconch, the trend of the deuteroconch to envelop the protoconch (Cretaceous forms are conservative in this respect), the trend which leads to a displacement of the protostolon from a marginal to a central position, decrease in the relative size of the peri-embryonic chambers and many other trends. The increase in the size of the protoconch has been studied in *Lepidorbitoides*. It is a complex feature, for it depends upon the bulk size of the B-generation, divided by the number of nuclei.

RATE OF EVOLUTION

After the phylogenetic introduction of a new feature the rate of evolution may be rapid, for in many cases nothing is known about the ancestor of a group. In those cases, where the new feature at first appears in part of the population only, the initial rate is obviously slow. The trends enumerated, in particular that of the nepionic reduction, have a low rate of change; this is already more or less implicit in the word trend.

The ontogenetic appearance of two or more features in one lineage may be affected by different rates of acceleration. Conversely, the acceleration of the appearance of a homologous feature may proceed at different rates in different lineages or side-branches. When a side-branch originates there may be a sudden evolutionary change in the rate of nepionic reduction, as in the case of *Katacycloclypeus* (TAN SIN HOK, 1936 c, p. 119).

NEPIONIC REDUCTION

In general, once a new feature is expressed ontogenetically in one chamber or budding stage, it will be expressed in all subsequent chambers or budding stages. If this were not the case, the idea of the ontogenetic lag, and hence the determination of the stage of nepionic reduction, would become rather indefinite. Nevertheless, an ontogenetic relapse to a more primitive stage may occasionally occur. This will be illustrated in *Monolepidorbis*.

The notion of ontogenetic lag implies that each nepionic stage is defined as the stage preceding the first ontogenetic appearance of the relevant feature. Consequently all chambers preceding this first appearance are counted as belonging to the relevant nepionic stage. It soon became apparent that the embryonic chambers were to be included in counting (see p. 152). Nepionic stages are thus not given as successive ontogenetic stages. Furthermore the term nepionic stage is always to be defined with reference to a certain feature. Thus in *Cycloclypeus* I count:

(*a*) The number of chambers without additional apertures = the number of *Operculina* chambers *sensu* TAN SIN HOK, plus two for the embryonic chambers, minus one because the last undivided chamber already has the additional apertures. In the case of the specimen figured (Fig. 1, type I) this is one chamber, because the deuteroconch already has one additional aperture. (*b*) The number of chambers without retrovert apertures = the number of *Heterostegina* chambers *sensu* TAN SIN HOK (usually not given by him), plus the number of preceding chambers. (*c*) The number of primary chambers = number of chambers preceding annular growth = number of nepionic septa *sensu* TAN SIN HOK, plus two for the embryonic chambers. The number of primary chambers is treated as an ontogenetic lag from analogy. Its different status is made clear by the wording: not "number of chambers without something", but "number of primary chambers". In the forms of type II the protoconch is counted as primary chamber 1, the deuteroconch as primary chamber 2, the primary auxiliary chamber as primary chamber 3, the peri-protoconchal series out of the primary auxiliary chamber as primary chambers 4, 5, etc. The symmetrical chamber is not consider ed as a primary chamber and is not included.

In order to bring out the changes of morphologic pattern brought about by the ultimate stages of nepionic reduction in each pattern, I have herewith figured the effect produced, when the different nepionic stages are reduced to three chambers, two chambers or one chamber only (Fig. 2). Some of the terms in use to denote these stages are added for comparison. The figures give a far better idea of these morphologic changes than long descriptions could do. The following comments must be made, however.

In the stage in which there are only two chambers without retrovert or contravert aperture, types IIA and III have become entirely homoeomorphic. It is important to realise that in this stage the primary aperture of the third primary chamber (the primary auxiliary chamber) and the fourth primary chamber are to be taken on the protoconchal side in forms of type IIA, on the deuteroconchal side in type III (Fig. 2, type IIA_1 and III, stage 2). When only forms with this stage of nepionic reduction (biserial nepionts) are found, it will not be possible to say, whether the animal belongs to type IIA or to type III. This holds a f o r t i o r i for the more advanced forms, where this nepionic stage is reduced to one chamber (triserial and quadriserial nepionts).

At the stage, in type II, in which there is only one chamber without retrovert aperture, a second auxiliary chamber is formed. This is considered as a retrovert secondary chamber issued out of a retrovert aperture of the deuteroconch. Similarly, in type III, a second auxiliary chamber will be formed at the comparable stage of nepionic reduction; this chamber will have to be considered as a secondary chamber issued out of a contravert aperture of the deuteroconch. In type II a further refinement has been introduced by TAN SIN HOK (1939a), who makes a distinction between triserial types (only one series of peri-embryonic secondary chambers issued out of the second auxiliary chamber), asymmetric quadriserial types (two such series, which are smaller than those issued out of the primary auxiliary chamber), and symmetric quadriserial types, the case figured (Fig. 2: type IIA_1, stage 1). Only the chambers issued out of the primary auxiliary chamber in the direction of the protoconch are considered as primary chambers. The chambers of the other three peri-embryonic series are regarded as secondary chambers.

There is a tendency to attain perfect symmetry. When, in type I and II, the two auxiliary chambers are of equal size, and when the protostolon has attained a central position, it becomes immaterial which of the two peri-protoconchal series is regarded as the series of primary chambers. One will usually take that series which has the largest number of chambers.

In *Helicolepidina* (type IIB), at the attainment of the stage with only one chamber without retrovert aperture, the spiral wall may become interrupted in the centre. After a while, however, both the spiral wall and the spiral of larger primary chambers may be reasserted ontogenetically. Initially this reasserted series of primary chambers can

---

Fig. 2 (pp. 150–151). Diagrammatic figures of pattern modifications in the three ultimate stages of nepionic reduction for the various basic nepionts in different types of phylomorphogenesis.

Solid black indicates spiral wall and thickened flank wall. Short arrows indicate first ontogenetic occurrence of retrovert or of contravert aperture.

Dashes indicate the succession of primary chambers. In symmetrical forms, the choice may be arbitrary.

The nepionic formulae are given for each example. The relevant values are underlined. Last value indicates the total number of chambers or of budding stages. Dots indicate that a value can not be determined from the drawing, brackets that the evaluation is likely to be indefinite.

Various terms in general use for some of the nepionic stages are also given. Those mentioned under type IIA include the comparable stages of Miogypsinidae which in reality have a *Miogypsinoides* or type IIC build.

	I_1 ADDITIONAL APERTURES	I_2 RETROVERT APERTURE	I_3 NUMBER OF PRIMARY CHAMBERS

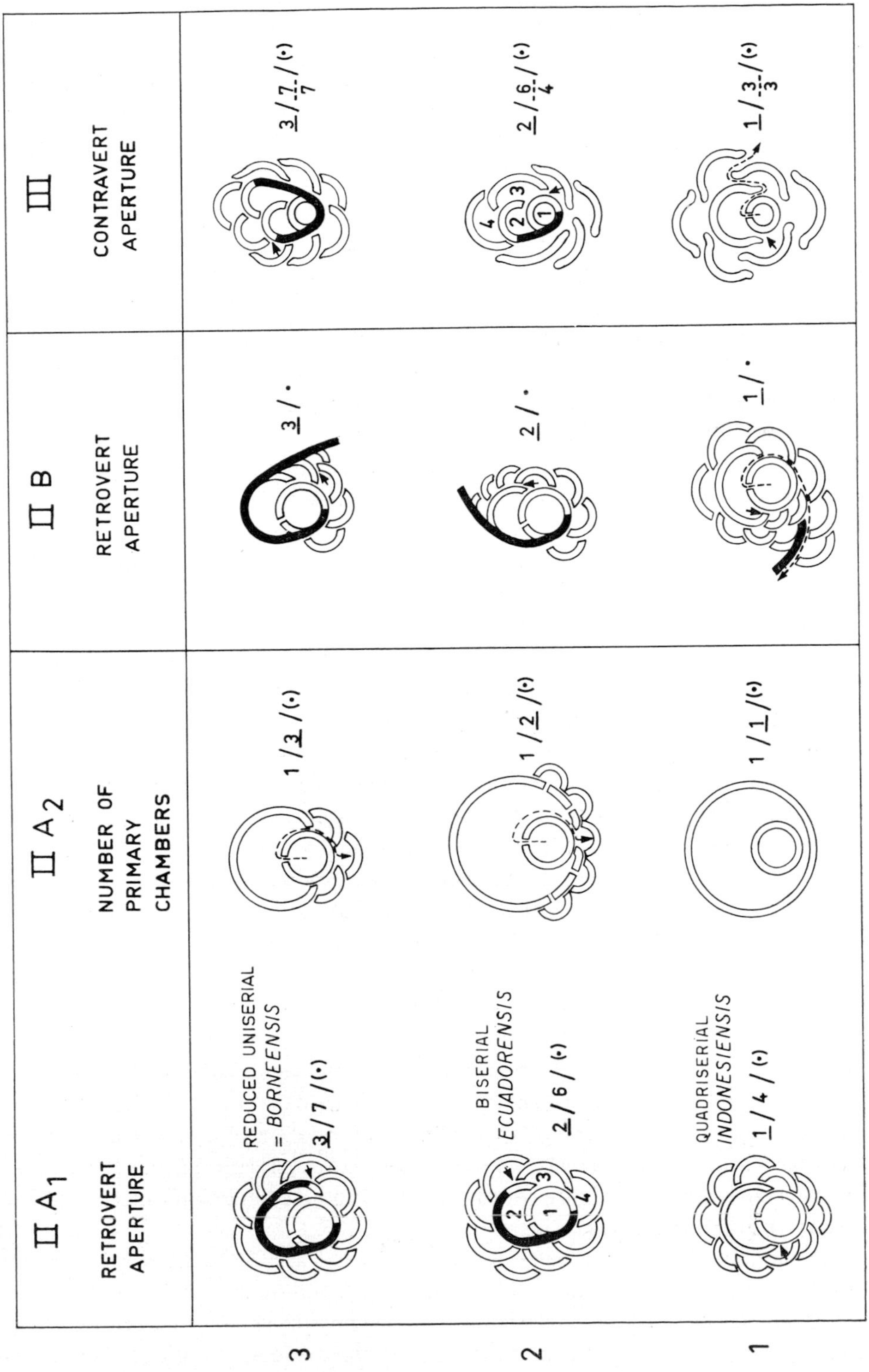
II A1
RETROVERT APERTURE
II A2
NUMBER OF PRIMARY CHAMBERS
II B
RETROVERT APERTURE
III
CONTRAVERT APERTURE
REDUCED UNISERIAL
= BORNEENSIS
3/7/(•)
BISERIAL
ECUADORENSIS
2/6/(•)
QUADRISERIAL
INDONESIENSIS
1/4/(•)
1/3/(•)
1/2/(•)
1/1/(•)
3/•
2/•
1/•
3
2
1

be traced back directly to the peri-protoconchal series of primary chambers, but in more advanced cases this is sometimes not so; the animal, as it were, has temporarily lost track of its primary chamber spiral. The reduction of the helicolepidine spiral wall may thus be effected in three ways: (*a*) from the periphery inward through the simultaneous attainment of a certain point by growth within and without the spiral wall, as in *Helicocyclina*, (*b*) from the centre proterogenetically outward, through the attainment of the stage with only one chamber without retrovert aperture, (*c*) through general dissolution as in *Helicolepidina vichayalensis*. All three modes may ultimately lead to homoeomorphs of *Lepidocyclina*. In view of the results of GRIMSDALE (1959) and VAN DER VLERK (1957, p. 26), indicating that "*Lepidocyclina*" is polyphyletic, this may be of importance. It would be interesting to investigate whether GRIMSDALE's lineage X could not have derived from *H. vichayalensis*, in view of the fact that "*Lepidocyclina*" *vichayalensis* is considered by GRIMSDALE (1959, p. 18) to form one of the oldest representatives of that lineage.

The situation in *Helicolepidina* shows that the formation of a symmetrical chamber on the protoconchal side may not signify the true termination of the formation of primary chambers. This may throw some doubt on the counting of primary chambers in type IIA. However, whether this doubt is justified will become apparent, if the nepionic reduction of these forms is plotted graphically. That the number of primary chambers is fundamental in type IIC is evident, because here this number is reduced autonomously. It is necessary to point out these facts, because most authors give the number of primary chambers, but hardly ever the number of chambers without retrovert aperture, which is a more fundamental datum.

The necessity of including the deuteroconch in counting is evident from Fig. 2: it is affected by the nepionic reduction in the same manner as any other primary chamber, though with somewhat exceptional results. There is no such direct reason for the inclusion of the protoconch, but it would be unreasonable to make a distinction.

Nevertheless, both embryonic chambers have a special significance. The special nature of the deuteroconch is best shown by the feature of the adauxiliary chambers. These are formed through adauxiliary apertures, a new form of aperture. Adauxiliary apertures are not to be compared with the additional apertures of type I, for they occur in types II and III which do not have the feature of the additional apertures. Neither are they to be regarded as radial stolons, for they occur in forms, which do not have radial solons. These adauxiliary apertures are in some degree comparable to the incidental additional apertures which may occur in the middle of the wall of exceptionally large secondary chambers and which lead to the formation of a rider chamber. The adauxiliary apertures and adauxiliary chambers, however, are not incidental but a fundamentally new feature, afterwards subjected to an evolutionary increase in the number of such apertures and chambers.

The special nature of the deuteroconch is further shown by its behaviour with regard to some of the evolutionary trends mentioned, and by the special modifications of morphologic pattern resulting when it is attained by the nepionic reduction.

The special position of the protoconch is even more evident, for it does not participate in any of the nepionic reductions. All nepionic stages are ultimately reduced to one chamber, the protoconch. In some cases it would be a physical impossibility for the protoconch to be affected: thus the deuteroconch can become annular, but the protoconch can not, because it can not encircle something which is not there.

The ultimate stages of nepionic reduction are not reached in all lineages. Thus *Cycloclypeus* never attains the stage of one chamber without retrovert aperture, nor any of the stages of three, two, or one primary chambers; *Lepidorbitoides* does not attain the stage of two primary chambers; the stage of one primary chamber is reported to occur in *Orbitoclypeus*; I do not know whether this stage is reached in *Eulepidina*.

One final word about the stolon-systems. The secondary chambers of types II and III have two apertures each, but they are issued out of two preceding chambers through apertures belonging to those preceding chambers. This is the so-called four-stolon system, a misnomer, for the chamber itself has only two apertures, and these are to be regarded as true apertures from homology with the two apertures occurring in chambers in the centre.

SPECIAL PART

The Cretaceous orbitoidal Foraminifera belong to the following separate and only remotely related groups: the Orbitoididae, Pseudorbitoididae, and Lepidorbitoididae. *Hellenocyclina* is not considered to belong to the Lepidorbitoididae; its taxonomic position is entirely obscure.

Tertiary forms are mentioned when this is necessary for an understanding of possible relationships. Some generic names are used without considering whether they are valid or whether they are to be deleted. We are concerned here with matters of a more general nature and not with specific nomenclatural problems.

It is to be noted that many of the Cretaceous orbitoidal Foraminifera have attained a nepionic arrangement which, from a comparison with what is known about Tertiary forms, is to be considered as an advanced stage of nepionic reduction. This suggests that a multitude of interesting forms may still have to be discovered.

Furthermore it will become clear that an appalling amount of work is yet to be done before we have a really adequate picture of even some of the most classical forms.

FAMILY ORBITOIDIDAE

Ancestor

According to the investigations of KÜPPER (1954b), this family, as shown by the microspheric generation, must have developed from an ancestor with alternate growth. As the validity of KÜPPER's discovery has been doubted by NEUMANN (1958, p. 39), HOFKER (1958a) and others (personal communications), it will be necessary to discuss this question in detail.

The presence of a gümbeline stage in both *Orbitoides* and *Omphalocyclus* is well shown in Küpper's photographs. It can also be seen in the photograph of an *Omphalocyclus* from the Schlumberger collection given by Neumann (1958, pl. VI, fig. 8) and represented by our pen-drawing of Fig. 1, type III, and of Fig. 3 right. These are to be compared with Neumann's analysis of the animal reproduced in Fig. 3 left.

Fig. 3. Microspheric *Omphalocyclus macroporus* from Maastricht, The Netherlands. Left: interpretation by Neumann (1958, textfig. 10). Right: drawn after the photograph given by Neumann (1958 pl VI, fig. 8). First chamber with contravert aperture indicated with an X.

The best way to analyse the centre, is to start with the chamber designated as X by Neumann, and to proceed backwards, considering that the wall of a chamber foots at least at one end upon the wall of the chamber from which it is issued. It is assumed that Neumann's textfig. 10 represents the same specimen as that of her plate VI, fig. 8. From chamber "X" two chambers are issued so that it must have two apertures. Chamber "X" is issued out of chamber "L" through an aperture on the left side of that chamber; chamber "L" has no aperture on the other side, where it is limited by a thickened marginal wall. The position of the adjacent secondary chamber outside the marginal wall proves that there is indeed no aperture. Chamber "L" is issued out of chamber "4" through an aperture on the right side of that chamber, and "4" again out of "3" through an aperture on the left side of "3". Thus far my analysis agrees with that of Neumann, but this already means alternate growth through three steps. Neumann assumes a spiral arrangement of three chambers preceding chamber "3". If this were true, it would only strengthen the supposition of a gümbeline centre, for Gümbelinidae start with a short spiral preceding alternate growth. However, I do not believe that the chambers preceding chamber 3 are spirally arranged, for the chamber at the tip of the nepiont — considered as chamber 2 by Neumann (Fig. 3a) — is the smallest, has the spherical shape of a protoconch, and is separated from chamber 3 by a knob or ledge of solid shell material protruding inward from the thickened marginal wall (Fig. 3b). Actually the true arrangement of the first chambers is not quite clear, and neither is it in

| 3 | 2 | (=) | 1 |

NUMBER OF SPIRAL CHAMBERS
PRECEDING ALTERNATE GROWTH

Fig. 4. Diagrammatic figures representing ultimate stages of nepionic reduction in the case of a spiral stage preceding alternate growth. The spiral stage is still recognisable when it is reduced to three chambers, but no longer when reduced to two chambers, or to one chamber. The latter two stages are identical.

the pictures given by KÜPPER (1954b). For this reason I have here given a picture of a microspheric specimen from the Maastricht type section (E.N.C.I. quarry, Pietersberg, Maastricht), which shows a gümbeline nepiont without initial spiral stage (Plate I, 1 and 2).

Accordingly, if a pre-alternate spiral stage is to be assumed, it is already reduced in this specimen to the point, where it can no longer be recognised (less than three chambers; the theoretical stages two and one spiral chambers preceding alternate growth cannot be distinguished; they are identical; see Fig. 4).

The photograph of ASTRE's microspheric type-specimen of *Monolepidorbis*, reproduced (reversed!) by NEUMANN (1958; my Fig. 5) can also only be understood if a stage of alternate growth is assumed, but of this I will only be able to convince those, who are already convinced of the validity of KÜPPER's observations. The analysis is made easier because of the little piece of chamber wall (marked by a * in our figure) which is still visible in ASTRE's figure (1927, pl. XX, fig. 12) but apparently lost when the photograph, given by NEUMANN, was taken. The first chamber with two apertures is again marked by an X. The thickened wall on the left of the nepionic stage, which has been noted by NEUMANN, is indeed abnormal; it means a relapse of the ancestral marginal wall at a later stage so that it is not marginal to the juvenarium. This is shown by the fact that it covers a symmetric secondary chamber

Fig. 5. Microspheric *Monolepidorbis sanctae-pelagiae* ASTRE. After ASTRE (1927, pl. XX, fig. 12) and NEUMANN (1958, pl. I, fig. 5). The initial stages are damaged. The arrangement of the chambers surrounding the nepiont indicates that there is no connection between them and the nepionic chambers, even in those places where the nepionic wall shows gaps, caused by the damaging; the only connections existing are the two apertures of the chamber indicated with an X; this is the first chamber, ontogenetically, in which a contravert aperture occurs.

from which two short series of asymmetric chambers are issued on either side. The symmetric chamber thus has two apertures, the subsequent asymmetric chambers have only one. That this is the case is shown by the arrangement of the two series of large asymmetric secondary chambers (each with two apertures) outside this wall, meeting in a symmetric chamber in the middle. Thus the relapse of the ancestral marginal wall also means a relapse of the one-aperture stage (but not of alternate growth!). I have also observed such a relapse in a *Planorbulinella* from the Tertiary of Borneo. A similar relapse appears to occur also in av few chambers of the microspheric *Omphalocyclus* figured (Fig. 1, type III), which makes it difficult to trace the path of growth of chambers around the nepiont, and thus to evaluate the total number of budding stages preceding the formation of the peri-nepionic symmetrical chamber (S).

It is to be noted that the drawings given by KÜPPER (1954b) do not exactly fit his photographs, even if the reversal of one of them is taken into account. Furthermore I do not agree with his statement (KÜPPER, 1954b, p. 181) that: "the last two chambers" — which still show alternate growth — "do not communicate through terminal apertures with the annular stage, but through apertures at their base". According to his figures these chambers have two apertures. Also I would prefer to call his "terminal" aperture: basal, or better primary, his "basal" aperture: marginal, or better contravert; also I do not like the word "annular" growth, and would furthermore prefer to let this kind of growth start later, namely with the formation of the peri–nepionic symmetric chamber, from analogy with the situation in types I and II.

HOFKER (1958b) again denies the presence of a stage with alternate growth in *Omphalocyclus*. According to him there is a clew of spatially arranged chambers in the centre of microspheric specimens. This we could not observe in our own axial sections, which are admittedly few; instead we find that the protoconch is situated on one side and that subsequent chambers in the centre are embracing on the other side (Fig. 6a). This gives the aspect, in vertical section, of alternate growth as in a reversed *Pavonina*. In order to understand the actual situation one must imagine the chambers on all sides to have such embracing alar prolongations. An occasional apparently additional chamber seen on the ventral side may well be the alar prolongation of a chamber on either side of the section. A horizontal section through these alar prolongations can be recognised, because it does not permit an analysis by the method of consecutive chamber growth (Plate II, 3). When a horizontal section is cut exactly right, such an analysis becomes possible. It may be seen from the axial vertical sections figured that such well centred horizontal sections can be made. There are, of course, specimens, in which the nepionic stage does not lie in the same plane as the rest of the animal (Fig. 6b), in which case one may not obtain an intelligible picture in a horizontal section.

The nepionic stage of alternate growth is not seen in all microspheric specimens as it is also subject to nepionic reduction. In the ultimate stages of nepionic reduction, as shown by Fig. 2, the stage of alternate growth can no longer be recognized. Such specimens are found together with others which do show this stage. Whether nepionic reduction progresses with time, as is to be expected, has still to be investigated. In fact

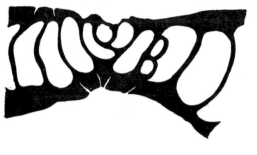

Fig. 6a: E.N.C.I. quarry, Pietersberg, Maastricht, The Netherlands, section ROMEIN 23.50 m, specimen no. 6, Maastrichtian (Md), × 50. Showing the lateral position of the protoconch and the alar projections of surrounding chambers.

Fig. 6b: same locality, section ROMEIN 22.00 m, specimen no. 1, Maastrichtian (Md), × 48. The first chambers lie in a plane which is at an angle to the ultimate equatorial plane. If allowance is made for this, it is seen that the protoconch has a lateral position, and that the situation is similar to that of Fig. 6a. Even in this case a well-centred horizontal section will cut through all chambers.

Fig. 6. Axial sections through microspheric specimens of *Omphalocyclus macroporus*.

the entire analysis for which the recipe has been given in the general part, is still to be made. Plate II, 1 shows a microspheric *Omphalocyclus* with "biserial nepiont", *i.e.*, with alternate stage reduced to two chambers; Plate II, 2 shows a microspheric *Orbitoides* with "quadriserial nepiont" (alternate stage reduced to one chamber).

The importance of the existence of a gümbeline nepionic stage has already been noted by KÜPPER (1954b, p. 183): it could mean that this stage was a temporarily planktonic floater and this could explain the wide geographical distribution of the species of *Orbitoides* and *Omphalocyclus*. This supposition becomes difficult because of the absence thus far of a microspheric generation in the most primitive form known, *Monolepidorbis* cf. *dordoniensis* (HOFKER), to be described below. In any case, it may be said that, if the family derives from a gümbeline ancestor, this would mean a phylogenetic change from a planktonic to a benthonic life, and this could account for the fact that *Monolepidorbis* cf. *dordoniensis* already has an advanced stage of nepionic reduction, for such a change could have induced a rapid initial evolution.

Megalospheric forms

The megalospheric "embryo" is surrounded by a thick wall. This wall is pierced by apertures which lead to secondary chambers outside the embryonic wall, squatting it as rider chambers. This thickened wall is therefore not to be compared with the thickened marginal walls along the flank of microspheric nepionts, nor with the thickened walls due to the relapse of the uniapertural stage, for these walls are not pierced by apertures. Probably a thickened wall merely means a pause in development, that part of the shell, where such a wall is formed, being subjected, during a certain length of time, to the addition of shell material by the ectoplasma. Thus it is possible that the megalospheric "embryo" represents a stage of some duration, before further growth takes place.

According to the literature, there is a general evolutionary trend to reduce the number of "embryonic" chambers as seen in horizontal section. The simplest forms appear to have four such chambers, more advanced forms only two. Conversely there is an increase in the number of enclosed chambers in *Simplorbites*. The enclosed chambers of *Simplorbites* are arranged in such a manner as to show that they originate from a protoconch situated close to, or almost within, the enclosing wall. I consider the arrangement in *Simplorbites* to be a proliferation, comparable to that which occurs in *Gublerina* and in *Racemiguembelina*, which strengthens the hypothesis of a gümbeline ancestor. *Simplorbites* certainly does not represent a primitive stage, for the genus branches off at a late stage in the evolution of *Orbitoides*. Moreover the arrangement is not simply alternate or "biserial", but "multiserial". The gigantic size of the animal also suggests an advanced form.

The primitive arrangement of four "embryonic" chambers has been explained as a tetrad (DOUVILLÉ, 1920, p. 211). This supposition is unlikely in view of the situation in *Simplorbites*. KÜPPER (1954a) regards one chamber as the protoconch, the second as the deuteroconch, and the two lateral ones as auxiliary chambers. This appears the more likely hypothesis. That the "embryonic" chambers of *Simplorbites* are formed in a consecutive manner is evident from any good section. The reduction in the number of "embryonic" chambers has been explained as due to the fusion of two chambers into one. But this again is unlikely, because it is rather to be expected that the reduction of the number of enclosed chambers is effected as a discontinuous process. In other words, it is difficult to see how two auxiliary chambers can unite, or how, when united, they can unite again with the deuteroconch.

That KÜPPER's interpretation of the four "embryonic" chambers of primitive forms may be correct, is suggested by some specimens (Plate III, 2) of *Monolepidorbis* cf. *dordoniensis* (HOFKER) (1959, p, 303, fig. 177A).

Monolepidorbis cf. *dordoniensis* (HOFKER). (Plate III, 1, 2; Plate IV, 1). Diagnosis: Size small to moderate (1–2.5 mm). External shape slightly conical to almost flat, periphery lobate, the peripheral equatorial chambers shining through in weathered forms. Vertical section: equatorial layer slightly conical, arrangement of equatorial chambers irregular, typically orbitoidid: apertures single; differs from HOFKER's *Monolepidorbis dordoniensis*, the vertical section of which I have been able to examine, in having a thicker wall of solid shell material in the centre; this wall is finely layered and traversed by many pores, perpendicular to the surface; it is not thickened to an umbonate centre as in typical *Linderina*. Horizontal section: inner diameter of protoconch 75–100 µ; nepiont biserial to quadriserial, walls of first chambers not or hardly thickened, certainly not joined to a thick "peri-embryonic" wall as in other species of *Monolepidorbis*; equatorial chambers typically orbitoidid, somewhat irregularly arranged, arcuate throughout; equatorial chamber walls with orbitoidid lip at base, and distinct dark median line; apertures at base of wall may be wide; no stolon complication. No dimorphism observed. A full description will be given at a later date. Differs from the species *M.sanctae-pelagiae* ASTRE and *M.douvillei* (SILVESTRI, 1910) which appear to have an "embryon" as in *Orbitoides* (NEUMANN 1954, pl. Va, fig. 4; HOFKER, 1959, p. 304). Dimorphism is known in *M.sanctae-pelagiae* (the holotype is microspheric). The species *M.douvillei* may have a few vacuoles, according to DOUVILLÉ's plate XVIII, fig. 18 (DOUVILLÉ, 1906), in which case it would already belong to *Orbitoides*; *M.vacuolaris* ASTRE (1927) would then be a synonym of *M. douvillei*. Whether our material is specifically different from or equal to *M.dordoniensis* (HOFKER) cannot be ascertained: the description and type specimen of HOFKER's *M.dordoniensis* are entirely inadequate. I have examined the sample from which the type was obtained, but failed to find a single specimen. Our specimens have a thicker wall of solid shell material than HOFKER's type specimen.

Type locality of *Planorbulinella dordoniensis* HOFKER: sample AI 40, G.D. 29893 "Saintes, Gisement no. 21, Santonien moyen (loc. type)", southern France; deposited in the collections of the Geological Survey, Haarlem. Our material has been collected by DR. G. J. BYVANK at Cuesta de la Mazorra, 60.7 km on the road from Burgos to Villarcayo, northern Spain. It is associated with *Lacazina* and *Nummofallotia*. Age: basal Campanian, according to CIRY (1939, p. 258). CIRY, however, also mentions the occurrence of *Monolepidorbis* in the Santonian of the same region.

Monolepidorbis cf. *dordoniensis* is primitive in having a more normal type of centre, without thickened common wall. It is already advanced because it has reached the stage of two to one chambers without contravert aperture. All conclusions concerning the derivation and fundamental construction of this family, are therefore exclusively based upon the microspheric generation. It is concluded that the initial evolution has been very rapid.

Peri–embryonic arrangement

The use of the terms "embryo" and "peri-embryonic" arrangement is confusing, because they refer tot he "embryo" surrounded by the thickened wall. But, as has been seen, this wall contains, what may have to be considered as the two embryonic chambers of other orbitoidal forms and of *Monolepidorbis* cf. *dordoniensis*, plus two auxiliary chambers. When one refers to the rider chambers issued through apertures piercing the thickened walls as auxiliary chambers, as has been done by KÜPPER (1954 a), the terminology becomes confusing.

In primitive forms, such as *Orbitoides tissoti*, there are usually four rider-chambers outside the "embryonic" wall. These would have to be considered as (*a*) the fourth primary chamber, (*b*) the contravert secondary chamber out of primary chamber 3 (the primary auxiliary chamber), (*c*) and (*d*) the two chambers issued out of the second auxiliary chamber, which is the contravert chamber issued out of the deuteroconch. The fact that there are four such chambers again strengthens the supposition that the primitive quadrilocular centre consists of two embryonic- plus two auxiliary chambers.

During further evolution the number of rider chambers increases. From my own observations, it is likely, that this increase is caused by the formation of adauxiliary chambers. The analysis is made difficult, because, as seen in vertical sections, the arrangement of equatorial chambers around the centre with thickened wall, is not restricted to one layer.

Stolon complication

The orbitoid equatorial chambers are conservative: always arcuate and devoid of stolon complication in horizontal section. In vertical sections it is seen that the apertures tend to multiply in a vertical direction. Up to seven apertures have been counted at the periphery in advanced species. It will not be possible, in view of this situation, to ascertain the budding stage at which the duplication, triplication, etc. of the apertures is introduced, ontogenetically. What can be done, however, is to ascertain in vertical axial section, how many chambers, counted from the centre, have less than two, less than three, etc., apertures. When this is done statistically it may be useful for stratigraphic purposes.

FAMILY LEPIDORBITOIDIDAE

Ancestor, primitive forms and microspheric centre

All the well-known Maastrichtian forms of this group have attained an advanced stage of nepionic reduction: *Orbitocyclina* and *Asterorbis* have only two chambers without retrovert aperture, *Orbitocyclinoides* and *Lepidorbitoides* only one such chamber. *Lepidorbitoides* is moreover characterized by the development of adauxiliary chambers in most populations. From these advanced stages, as has been seen, it cannot be decided through which process of phylomorphogenesis these forms have passed. For this purpose one has to study the microspheric generation. Therefore I here give a figure of a good section through the centre of a microspheric specimen of *Lepidorbitoides minor* from the Maastricht tuff-chalk of southern Limburg (Plate VI, 2). The arrangement is spiral and typically planorbulinellid, *i.e.*, type IIA, with a nepionic formula 5/10. The spiral of primary chambers is not continued as a spiral of larger primary chambers beyond the symmetric chamber.

It is therefore of the greatest interest, that PAPP and KÜPPER (1953) and PAPP (1954, 1955) have found forms, of Campanian age, which show a more primitive megalospheric nepionic stage. These are:

(*a*) *Pseudorbitoides longispiralis* PAPP and KÜPPER (1953, p. 352, pl. 2, fig. 3); with uniserial spiral of more than 33 primary chambers (EI + EII + PI + more than 30). I count 37 such chambers in the pen-drawing, more than 40 in the photograph. Campanian of Silberegg, Carinthia.

(*b*) *Pseudorbitoides* cf. *trechmanni* H. DOUVILLÉ (in PAPP, 1954, p. 163, fig. 2) with fourteen primary chambers. Campanian (higher level than *a*) of Pemberger Riegel, Carinthia.

(*c*) *Lepidorbitoides minima pembergeri* PAPP (1954, p. 163, fig. 3, 4); with ten to fourteen primary chambers, but with a retrovert series of secondary chambers issued out of the primary auxiliary chamber (= primary chamber 3) (biserial nepiont; last chamber of retrovert series has budding stage 4 or 6). Pemberger Riegel, same level as (b).

(d) *Lepidorbitoides minima minima* H. DOUVILLÉ (in PAPP, 1954, p. 165, fig. 5, 6); with six to seven primary chambers, biserial nepiont, last chamber of retrovert series out of primary chamber 3 has budding stage 6 and 9 according to the drawings. Forest edge north of Pemberg, Carinthia; Bisamberg, north of Vienna. Campanian, higher level than (b) and (c).

(e) *Lepidorbitoides bisambergensis* JÄGER (in PAPP, 1954, p. 166, fig. 7, 8); quadriserial nepionts with four primary chambers and no adauxiliary chambers. Uppermost Campanian (higher level than d). (MAC GILLAVRY, 1955, mentions primitive specimens of *Lepidorbitoides minor* which have no adauxiliary chambers).

In the primitive species *P. longispiralis* the authors see a similarity to *Siderolites*, so that a derivation from *Siderolites* is assumed. This corresponds with the hypothesis of DOUVILLÉ (1906, p. 599) who postulates a derivation of the "orbitoïdés" from *Siderolites* through *Arnaudiella*. The two embryonic chambers of *Siderolites vidali*, found in the same Carinthian localities, are very similar to those of the Campanian forms described.

The most surprising thing about these forms is, that the three most primitive ones (a), (b), and (c) are shown to have a helicolepidine, or type IIB arrangement, *i.e.*, the formation of secondary chambers takes place inside the prolonged spiral of primary chambers of the next whorl! This continued spiral of primary chambers is no longer drawn in the forms mentioned under (d) and (e). The situation is therefore in flagrant contrast to that of the microspheric *Lepidorbitoides minor*. Fortunately I have been able to collect samples at the localities of PAPP and KÜPPER in 1955. It is difficult to obtain isolated specimens and I have only been able to find the forms (a) and (d). The results confirm the conclusions derived from PAPP's drawings. The species *P. longispiralis* indeed has a type IIB arrangement, the spiral even continues up to the periphery. This is probably also the case in the specimen figured by PAPP and KÜPPER (1953, pl. II, fig. 3). The animal is very similar to a uniserial *Helicolepidina*, from which it can best be distinguished by the fact, that the deuteroconch is not smaller than the protoconch and that it has not so many secondary chambers. In the biserial forms, on the other hand, there is no spiral of larger primary chambers continued beyond the periembryonic symmetric chamber.

It appears to me necessary to create a new genus for the form *longispiralis*. Whether the forms (b) and (c) are also to be reckoned to this genus will depend on further investigations.

Helicorbitoides nov. gen.[1]

Diagnosis of genus: orbitoidal genus with equatorial layer and layers of lateral chambers on both sides. Equatorial layer with spiral of larger primary chambers opening out to admit formation of secondary chambers; secondary chambers formed within spiral wall, in the helicolepidine manner

---

[1] The name *Helicorbitoides* is a hybrid name, half greek, half latin, in the tradition of the generic names *Orbitoides, Pseudorbitoides, Rhabdorbitoides*, etc. The name *Helicorbitoides* expresses so exactly the curious features of this new genus, that it is preferred to a linguistically more proper name.

(type IIA of phylomorphogenesis). Type species similar to *Helicolepidina* but deuteroconch not smaller than protoconch.

Genoholotype: *Pseudorbitoides longispiralis* PAPP and KÜPPER, 1953, from the Campanian of Silberegg, Carinthia, Austria.

Helicorbitoides longispiralis (PAPP and KÜPPER) (Plate V, 1, 2; Plate VI, 1).

Diagnosis: small, often rather rotund orbitoidal form, possibly with flange; diameter without flange: 1–1.5 mm. Vertical section: lateral chambers in regular involute tiers, walls consecutively superposed, and superposed upon the walls of equatorial chambers at the contact with the equatorial layer; equatorial layer not sharply differentiated, without continuous roof and floor; spiral wall of inner volutions sometimes visible, carried around on either side in an involute manner, blocked out by a series of thickened consecutive walls of lateral chambers; all chamber walls traversed by numerous pores; surface of shell in sections through hard rock ill defined; the entire picture exactlylike that of "*Orbitocyclina minima*" from Afghanistan, DE CIZANCOURT (1938, pl. 38, fig. 1); pillars present.

Horizontal section: inner diameter of protoconch 100–125 µ; deuteroconch subequal to protoconch; spiral of primary chambers up to periphery; first ± 6–9 primary chambers without retrovert aperture; later ones with such an aperture, leading to the formation of secondary chambers; arrangement helicolepidine; secondary equatorial chambers difficult to distinguish from lateral chambers, irregularly arcuate; the whorl surrounded by spiral wall, forming the base to the primary chambers of the next whorl; this wall is thick in the equatorial layer and traversed by numerous pores; in tangential horizontal sections, this wall may appear as a rather compact layer, traversed by pores, with a mosaic of lines, corresponding with the walls of adjacent lateral chambers; in other cases it loses its identity just laterally from the equatorial plane, the slightly embracing walls of primary chambers of the next whorl footing directly upon walls of chambers of the preceding whorl.

Type locality: Silberegg, Carinthia, Austria.

Age: Campanian.

Associated fauna: *Orbitoides tissoti tissoti* SCHLUMBERGER, *O.tissoti minima* VREDENBURG, *Siderolites vidali* H. DOUVILLÉ, *Nummofallotia* sp.

The following hypotheses may account for the apparent discrepancy between the arrangement in *Helicorbitoides* and that of the microspheric *Lepidorbitoides minor*:

(*1*) The spiral of primary chambers disappears in the helicocycline manner, in the *vichayalensis* manner, or through nepionic reduction of the uni-apertural stage. Only the first supposition can account for the situation as recorded by PAPP (1954, p. 163, 164), who mentions a limited number of primary chambers in forms (b) and (c); it might account for the arrangement observed in the microspheric *Lepidorbitoides minor* specimen, which, however, does not show any helicolepidine secondary chambers.

(*2*) Forms (*a*) to (*c*) are not ancestral to *Lepidorbitoides*; this appears unlikely, in view of their occurrence in the same area, and their general similarity.

(*3*) These forms are ancestral to *Lepidorbitoides socialis*, but not ancestral to *Lepidorbitoides minor*. In this connection it is to be noted, that MAC GILLAVRY (1955) postulates an independent origin for these two species on entirely different grounds.

The least radical supposition is that both *L.socialis* and *L. minor* originated by the same phylomorphogenetic method, probably the helicocycline method, and that there was a greater difference between the number of uni–apertural chambers and that of primary chambers in the ancestry of *L. socialis* than in the ancestry of *L. minor*. In the microspheric specimen of *L. minor*, the number of uni–apertural chambers is already very small. There is no difficulty in considering the forms (*d*) and (*e*) as ancestral to *L.socialis*. My specimens of biserial forms from Pemberger Riegel — species (*d*) — have wall-pores which are exactly similar to those of *Helicorbitoides*.

I have not been able to observe any pseudorbitoid layer in vertical sections. The *Siderolites*-like canals, described by PAPP and KÜPPER (1953), occur in the spiral wall, are not limited to the equatorial layer, are comparable to the pores observed in all lateral chamber walls, and are fundamentally different from the spaces between the radial plates of *Pseudorbitoides*. As will be seen, moreover, *Pseudorbitoides* is judged to develop according to the phylomorphogenetic type IIA. In any case adjacent whorls of the primary chamber spiral are contiguous in all Pseudorbitoididae, with the exception of *Vaughanina jordanae* BRÖNNIMANN (1958b), where, however, the two whorls are separated by an area with densely packed radial plates, and apparently with no annular walls. Thus no secondary chambers are formed in a helicolepidine manner as in *Helicorbitoides*.

The dimensions of the pores in the spiral wall are much smaller than those of the gigantic *Siderolites vidali* with which the genus is associated. Also they do not show the same complex structure. A derivation of the family from *Siderolites* or *Arnaudiella* thus remains to be proved. *Helicorbitoides* differs from *Arnaudiella* in that the latter genus (DOUVILLÉ, 1906, pl. 18, fig. 17) presents a typical *Siderolites*-like vertical section, with the lateral chambers located in the normal *Siderolites*-wall.

A relationship to *Orbitocyclina*, as suggested by the species determination *minima minima* also seems unlikely, for the Campanian *bisambergensis* is already more advanced than the Maastrichtian *Orbitocyclina*. The species mentioned under (b) and (d) will thus have to be renamed. The name *O. minima* H. DOUVILLÉ 1927, as has been remarked by TAN SIN HOK (1939a, p. 71), may be preoccupied by *Orbitoides minima* VREDENBURG 1908, if this should turn out to be an *Orbitocyclina* (or a *Lepidorbitoides*, as this is the generic assignment of DOUVILLÉ). The species mentioned under (c) can be designated by the specific name *pembergeri* PAPP.

If we now turn to the Maastrichtian forms, it seems likely that *Orbitocyclina* and *Orbitocyclinoides*, with their retarded nepionic reduction, do not belong to the same lineage as *Lepidorbitoides*. One can but agree with PAPP (1954, p. 167) that, since biserial nepionts are found in forms which are probably ancestral to *Lepidorbitoides socialis*, a distinction between *Orbitocyclina* and *Lepidorbitoides* cannot be made on the basis of this. Nevertheless, as the forms from Carinthia which have biserial nepionts are thought to be Campanian, whereas *Orbitocyclina* is considered to be Maastrichtian and associated with higher evolved species of *Orbitoides*, it would still seem that the two genera belong to independent lineages. Conversely if, as I prefer, one maintains *Orbitocyclina* as a valid genus, one cannot assign all forms with biserial nepionts to the genus *Orbitocyclina*. Hence it will be necessary to reconsider the geographic range of this genus as recorded by DE CIZANCOURT (1938).

It is quite possible, accordingly, that the family Lepidorbitoididae consists of a complex bundle of independent lineages. Only a very careful analysis of these forms, preferably in consecutive populations collected from continuous stratigraphic sections, a thorough study of their phylomorphogenesis and all their anatomical details, even seemingly minor ones, can serve to unravel the problems presented by this group.

Of great interest is the occurrence of a number of mysterious forms in the Paleocene of the western hemisphere and of Asia, *i.e.*, the very regions from which the two relatively retarded Maastrichtian genera *Orbitocyclina* and *Orbitocyclinoides* have been described. CAUDRI (1948) has insisted upon the similarity of the Paleocene American forms to *Lepidorbitoides* (*Orbitocyclina* in our terminology), BRÖNNIMANN (1944) upon the resemblance of *Orbitocyclina punjabensis* DAVIES to *Orbitocyclinoides*. Since none of these forms can have any relationship to true lepidocyclines (lineage Y of GRIMSDALE in VAN DER VLERK, 1957, 1959; GRIMSDALE, 1959), which derive from *Tremastegina* at the base of the Middle Eocene, it is far more reasonable to admit their derivation from the Lepidorbitoididae. In other words, *Lepidocyclina*-like animals could originate in yet another way. This is not meant to imply that these Paleocene species derive from any known form. In view of the fact that several independent lineages are already to be assumed for the Cretaceous forms, there may be more such lineages. There may, for instance, be a significant difference between lineages with normal deuteroconch, and those which have a small deuteroconch. The Paleocene forms, in so far as they did not escape my attention, have therefore been given in Table I, together with the Cretaceous forms. This table shows the various shifts in evolutionary stage of one feature or another in various lineages.

Finally, as shown by BRÖNNIMANN (1945), the Orbitoclypeidae, which include *Asterocyclina*, are found to have a microspheric centre of the type IIA (see BRÖNNIMANN, 1945, pl. XXI, fig. 1). An excellent picture of such a centre can also be seen in VAUGHAN (1945, pl. 8, fig. 3) for *Discocyclina anconensis* BARKER. Thus far

---

On Tables I and II (pp. 164–165) have been indicated:
(*a*)   the number of chambers without retrovert aperture / number of primary chambers.
(*b*)   the shape of equatorial chambers (arc. = arcuate; spat. = spatulate or hexagonal; rect. = rectangular; arrow means variation from centre to periphery or variation between species).
(*c*)   the presence of radial stolons (rad.).
(*d*)   whether the deuteroconch is smaller than the protoconch.
Notes:
[1]   VAN DER VLERK (1957, 1959), (GRIMSDALE, 1959).
[2]   VAN RAADSHOOVEN (1951).
[3]   *Pseudolepidina trimera* BARKER and GRIMSDALE 1932, which occurs at the boundary between Lower and Middle Eocene (GRIMSDALE, 1959), can not be included: it appears to have a quadriserial nepiont in equatorial sections but a biserial nepiont in axial sections; equatorial chambers arcuate.
[4]   data from TAN SIN HOK (1939); *Asterorbis* is included in *Orbitocyclina*: according to COLE (1942, pl, 10, fig. 3), it has the nepionic formula 2/6; *Cryptasterorbis* is insufficiently known.
[5]   VAUGHAN (1929a).
[6]   VAUGHAN (1945, pl. 19, fig. 5, 7).
[7]   VAUGHAN (1929b, pl. 2, fig. 1), VAUGHAN (1945, pl. 25, fig. 1), CAUDRI (1948, pl. 74, fig. 5).
[8]   own observations; the equatorial chambers can only be described as wide hexagonal; they are arranged in radial rows.
[9]   BRÖNNIMANN (1944).
[10]   TAN SIN HOK (1939), MAC GILLAVRY (1955).
[11]   PAPP (1954), 1955; supplemented with our own observations in the case of *"minima minima"*.
[12]   PAPP and KÜPPER (1953), Papp (1954, 1955), supplemented by our own observations.
[13]   COLE (1942, pl. 15, fig. 10).
[14]   COLE and BERMUDEZ (1944, pl. 1, fig. 14, 15; fig. 13).
[15]   own observations; variation range for both nepionic series.
[16]   own observations; variation range for all peri–embryonic series.

TABLE I

EVOLUTIONARY STAGES OF LEPIDORBITOIDIDAE, HELLENOCYCLINA AND ORBITOIDIDAE COMPARED WITH THOSE OF A NUMBER OF EARLY TERTIARY FORMS

	Primary spiral up to periphery	uniserial	reduced uniserial	reduced uniserial and biserial	biserial	biserial and quadriserial	quadriserial (incl. triserial)	adauxiliary chambers	quadriserial	adauxiliary chambers	adauxiliary chambers adjoining
MIDDLE EOCENE	*Lepidocyclina* lineage Y[1] EII small					"*Lepidocyclina*" sp. B[2] 2/8; 1/5 arc. → ? EII small					
LOWER EOCENE				"*Lepidocyclina*" sp. A[2] 3/11; 2/10 arc. → ? EII small						*Asterocyclina* usually 1/4 spat. → rect. rad.	*Orbitoclypeus* 1/1 spat. → **rect.** rad.
PALEOCENE				"*Lep.*" *barbadensis*[2] 4/9; 3/8; 2/X arc. rad. present EII small		*punjabensis*[1] 2/6; 1/(4-5) arc. → spat. rad.	*Actinosiphon*[5] 1/6 arc. → short spat. rad. — "*Lep.*" *barbadensis*[6] 1/5 arc. → short spat. EII small		*Bontourina*[7] 1/5 ogival → spat. rad. EII small or not		
MAASTRICHTIAN				*Clypeorbis*[8] ?3; ?11 and 2/7 wide hex.	*Orbitocyclina*[1] 2/(4-7) arc. → spat.		*Orbitocyclinoides*[9] 1/(4-5) arc. → ogival rad.	*Lepidorbitoides*[10] *minor socialis* 1/(4-6) 1/(4-6) arc. → spat. spat.			
CAMPANIAN	*Helicorbitoides longispiralis*[12] 6/> 40 irreg. arc.		?*Helicorbitoides* "*trechmanni*"[11] 3/14	*Lepidorbitoides* "*minima minima*"[11] 2/(6-9) arc. → short og. — ?*Helicorbitoides pembergeri* 2/(11–> 14)			*Lepidorbitoides bisambergensis*[11] 1/(4-6)				

TABLE II

	primary spiral up to periphery	uniserial	reduced uniserial	reduced uniserial and biserial	biserial	biserial and quadriserial	quadriserial (incl. triserial)	adauxiliary chambers
MIDDLE EOCENE			13 Linderina floridensis 3/7 arc.				11 Eoannularia 1/3 0 and 4 adaux. arc. → rect.	
LOWER EOCENE								
PALEOCENE								
MAASTRICHT-IAN					15 Hellenocyclina visserae 2/(6–8) arc. → short spat.			
CAMPANIAN							Orbitoididae →	
SANTONIAN						16 Monolepidorbis cf. dordoniensis 2/(5–6); 1 (3–6) arc. (orbitoidid)		

nobody has offered any suggestion as to their origin. It may therefore be significant, that *Asterocyclina* is reported to appear earlier in the western hemisphere than elsewhere, and that the Paleocene *Bontourina* CAUDRI shows some intermediate characteristics between the Orbitoclypeidae and Lepidorbitoididae. All good figures show a quadriserial nepionic arrangement devoid of adauxiliary chambers. It is therefore here tentatively suggested, that the Orbitoclypeidae may have originated out of the Lepidorbitoididae. This supposition is only offered as a suggestion, largely intended to instigate further examination of these Paleocene forms. The Orbitoclypeidae would differ from the Lepidorbitoididae by the possession of intramural lumina. VAUGHAN's (1929b) pl. 2, fig. 1, suggests that such intramural lumina are already present in *Bontourina*. It is not known, however, how fundamental this difference is, and whether these lumina could not evolve from the "median dark line" of chamber walls in the Lepidorbitoididae. If it can be shown that such lumina are definitely absent in the Lepidorbitoididae, and that they are already present in the earliest stages of microspheric Orbitoclypeidae, my tentative supposition can be disproved.

It would be an anticlimax to proceed to the description of some minor evolutionary trends in *Lepidorbitoides*. They have been investigated by MAC GILLAVRY (1955), but a rigorous check has still to be made.

A few words must be added, however, about the enigmatic genus *Clypeorbis*. The nepionic arrangement has been described by NEUMANN (1958, p. 68). I can but confirm her description from my own observations: the nepionic arrangement forms a little cone, with the protoconch at the top, the deuteroconch and nepionic chambers forming the base of the cone. They are spirally arranged. In some axial sections there are a few additional equatorial chambers adjacent to the protoconch. Under these circumstances it is exceedingly difficult to establish the exact nepionic stage attained. As far as can be made out (NEUMANN, 1958; and my own observations) the nepionic arrangement appears to be biserial, although in one of our sections there appears to be a reduced uniserial nepiont. The genus thus must be regarded to belong to type II, subtype unknown, with three to two primary chambers without retrovert aperture. The shape of the chambers of the nepionic spiral is different from that in other genera of the Lepidorbitoididae. The equatorial chambers have a wide hexagonal shape; nevertheless, we have only found normal apertures and no stolon complication. In axial sections the arrangement of the equatorial chambers is found to be regular as in *Lepidorbitoides*. The arrangement of the lateral chambers on the flat side resembles that of *Lepidorbitoides*. In a horizontal tangential section the lateral chambers resemble those of *Orbitoides*.

It is difficult to account for this isolated form. In order to establish whether it really belongs to this family, one must look for more primitive forms, or study a good horizontal section through a microspheric specimen. A connection with *Orbitoides* is precluded by the spiral arrangement of the nepionic chambers.

Genus Hellenocyclina REICHEL 1949, (Table II).

This enigmatic genus has been placed among the Lepidorbitoididae by its author

REICHEL (1949) and also by POKORNÝ (1958). The genoholotype *Hellenocyclina beotica* REICHEL has been described from thin sections through hard rock from Greece. It is an exceedingly small animal, slightly conical in section; in vertical section the equatorial layer may also be conical; the equatorial chambers are arranged in a more regular succession than in *Monolepidorbis*; in equatorial section, the equatorial chambers are seen to be arcuate in the centre, to low ogival towards the periphery. In the only specimen in which the centre can be observed it is found that there are some six chambers which have thickened walls. The genus differs from *Monolepidorbis* by the more regular succession of equatorial chambers, from *Monolepidorbis* and *Linderina*, because of the ogival or low hexagonal form of the equatorial chambers in horizontal section; from the Lepidorbitoididae because of the absence of lateral chambers at a stratigraphic level where *e.g.*, *Lepidorbitoides* has reached an advanced stage of evolution in all respects. Furthermore, in whatever manner the nepionic arrangement of the type specimen is to be interpreted, it is certainly less advanced than in the contemporary *Lepidorbitoides*. According to NEUMANN (1958, p. 68) the genus occurs exclusively in the Upper Maastrichtian, for which it is an excellent index fossil.

In the tuff-chalk of Maastricht a small form occurs, which has been described by VISSER (1950, p. 292) as *Linderina douvillei* SILVESTRI, and which has been renamed *Linderina visserae* by HOFKER. This form has all the characteristics of a *Hellenocyclina* in which genus it is to be included although it appears to differ in its nepionic arrangement from the type species. We have in our collections isolated specimens from both the region of St. Marcet and from Maastricht (MAC GILLAVRY, 1955, p. 37).

Hellenocyclina visserae (HOFKER) (Plate IV, 2; Plate VII, 1, 2) (HOFKER, 1958b).
Diagnosis: exceedingly small (0.5 – 1 mm). External shape: distinctly conical to almost flat[1], periphery lobate, peripheral equatorial chambers shining through. Vertical section: equatorial layer slightly conical; equatorial chambers regularly arranged, slightly embracing on concave side; lateral wall compact, traversed by fine pores. Horizontal section: inner diameter of protoconch 30–40 µ; protoconch and deuteroconch subequal, with slightly thickened common wall; nepiont invariably biserial; primary auxiliary chamber subspherical, with thickened wall, often larger than either of the two embryonic chambers; two chambers issued out of primary auxiliary chambers sometimes also with thickened wall; equatorial chambers regularly arranged, arcuate throughout, or short hexagonal or short spatulate towards periphery; no additional stolons or apertures observed; pores of lateral layer seen to be somewhat radially oblique at periphery. No dimorphism observed. A full description will be given at a later date.
Geographical range: Neighbourhood of Maastricht and Haute Garonne (several localities).
Age: Upper Maastrichtian. At Maastricht found in uppermost Mb, and throughout Mc and Md (HOFKER, 1958b).
Associated fauna: *Orbitoides*, *Omphalocyclus*, *Siderolites*, etc. At Maastricht this form is associated with *Lepidorbitoides minor*, near St. Marcet with *L. socialis*.

The arrangement in the centre is very characteristic. Protoconch and deuteroconch are often very similar, and can only be distinguished if there is a slight curvature in the wall between them. The resemblance of the primary auxiliary chamber to an embryon-

---

[1] The supposition of REICHEL that the apparent conical shape, in arbitrary vertical sections, might be caused by a sellate form, thus does not apply to *H.visserae* which is truly conical.

ic chamber, caused by its large size and thickened wall, gives the centre a trilocular aspect: at first one often has difficulty in recognizing which two chambers out of these three are the embryonic chambers. The thickened wall of the primary auxiliary chamber is not a spiral wall, nor a thickened gümbeline-stage wall, for it must have apertures on both sides to permit the formation of the two chambers of budding stage four. The two peri-embryonic series are subequal and usually meet around the embryonic chambers in a symmetric chamber situated on the side opposite to that of the primary auxiliary chamber. HOFKER (1958b, fig. 8), in a pen-drawing, shows three symmetric peri-embryonic chambers, which can not be correct.

The centre of *H.visserae* resembles that of *H.beotica*, because of the occurrence of a thickened wall around several of the nepionic chambers.

Thus, if one interpretes the nepionic arrangement in a different manner from that presented by REICHEL (1949) as shown in Fig. 7, a comparable situation ensues:

REICHEL   *alternative interpretation*
    P (= EI)   EI
    AA (on the right)   EII
    D1   prim. aux. ch. = prim. ch. 3
    A (on the left)   prim. ch. 4
    D2   prim. ch. 5
                             etc.

The alternative interpretation would give a biserial nepiont with seven primary chambers. In *H. visserae* we normally find six to seven primary chambers. Nevertheless, none of our specimens will exactly fit the figure of REICHEL's typespecimen. Through the courtesy of REICHEL, I have been able to examine the type specimen in Basel. I could not confirm the alternative interpretation; one has to disregard the apparent doubling of REICHEL's auxiliary chamber on the right, and the apparent separation by a treu wall between REICHEL's auxiliary chamber on the left and his second deuteroconch. Either *H. beotica* has a different centre, in which case the two forms may be considered as separate species, or the centre of *beotica* is abnormal — which it would be, if there are indeed two deuteroconchs — or else misleading because cut laterally, in which two cases the two species may be identical. The species name *beotica* then has priority.

Fig. 7. Centre of *Hellenocyclina beotica* REICHEL. Left: interpretation of REICHEL (1949, textfig. 10). Right: alternative interpretation (see text), based upon REICHEL (1949, fig. 8). An examination of the original material did not confirm this interpretation, but the situation is not clear in any case.

REICHEL mentions the possible occurrence of dimorphism, because some forms are larger and flatter. We have also found such specimens, but they always gave the same, megalospheric, arrangement.

In the preceding we have assumed that the animal belongs to the type II of phylo-morphogenesis. Actually, as only biserial nepionts are found (two chambers without retrovert or contravert aperture) it is not possible to decide, whether the animal belongs to type II or to type III. In the latter case, what has been called primary chambers, would not be primary chambers (see pp. 145, 149).

The genus might be thought to derive from some primitive orbitoidid, inasmuch as neither REICHEL nor I could observe any stolon complication in horizontal section, in spite of the advanced shape of peripheral equatorial chambers. Such a supposition is not likely, however, because the animal is considerably younger than any orbitoi-did without lateral chambers, and nevertheless, has a nepionic stage which is more primitive than that of *Monolepidorbis* cf. *dordoniensis*. Neither is it likely that it belongs to the Lepidorbitoididae, since the Campanian *Helicorbitoides longispiralis* already has well-developed lateral layers. Also the equatorial chambers of *Hellenocy-clina* are much smaller than in any other orbitoidal form. A connection with *Linderina* is likewise improbable: the only good photograph of the centre of a true *Linderina* that I have been able to find in the literature is that given by COLE (1942, pl. 15, fig. 10): it shows a reduced uniserial centre with the formula 3/7, and equatorial chambers which remain arcuate up to the periphery. *Linderina*, it may be noted, thus definitely belongs to type II, and probably to subtype IIA, the planorbulinellid type.

All considered, one has to wait until either a microspheric centre or a more primi-tive megalospheric centre is found, before it can be decided whether this genus belongs to type IIA or to type III. Whatever the result, it cannot be placed in any relationship to the known forms, and has to be treated as separate. At the present stage of know-ledge, however, it is not justified to create a new family for this form. It is primitive because of the absence of lateral chambers, and possibly because of the absence of dimorphism (cf. Orbitoididae and Pseudorbitoididae). Nepionic reduction, however, has already advanced to the biserial stage (two uni–apertural chambers), a stage of evolution equal to that of *Orbitocyclina* but much more primitive than that of the associated species of *Lepidorbitoides*.

FAMILY PSEUDORBITOIDIDAE

Thanks to the work of BRÖNNIMANN (1954 – 1958), the different forms belonging to the family Pseudorbitoididae are among the best known, morphologically. There is no doubt about the origin of this group, which developed from *Sulcoperculina*. In all forms, with the exception of the more advanced ones, a sulcoperculinid juvena-rium can be demonstrated. A table for the determination of the different genera is given by BRÖNNIMANN (1958, p. 166). This table is based upon the evolutionary com-plications of the radial elements and on general shape.

Nevertheless, there are difficulties if one tries to understand the phylomorphogenesis of these forms and the manner in which they must have grown. Thus the juvenarium is invariably described as a uniserial spiral of primary chambers, *i.e.*, a simple trochospiral arrangement of a single row of chambers. Thus none of the features used here to define the different types of phylomorphogenesis would be acquired. If that were the case, it cannot be understood, how a quadriserial nepiont could be formed in *Pseudorbitoides*, for this means the formation of a second auxiliary chamber, which is here considered to be a secondary chamber issued out of the retrovert aperture of the deuteroconch. Only in *Vaughanina* and its allies would true equatorial chambers be formed, while the possibility of the presence of such chambers in microspheric *Pseudorbitoides* is left open.

Characteristic for the family is the presence of a layer with radial rods or plates, issued out of the sulcus of the sulcoperculinid juvenarium. These radial elements are already present in orimental form in *Sulcoperculina*. In *Vaughanina* and its allies this layer is traversed by the annular walls, considered as the walls of true equatorial chambers. In the other forms a distinction is made by BRÖNNIMANN between secondary lateral chambers and primary lateral chambers. The latter are not separated from the pseudorbitoid layer, but rest with their lumen upon the radial elements. BRÖNNIMANN regards these "primary lateral chambers" as lateral chambers, but nevertheless considers them to belong to the equatorial layer, which would consist of the two layers of primary lateral chambers and the pseudorbitoid layer of radial elements separating them. Apparently BRÖNNIMANN is undecided how to regard these chambers. In my opinion they are to be considered as true equatorial chambers, seen to be subdivided, in vertical section, by the radial elements of the pseudorbitoid layer (BRÖNNIMANN, 1955a, pl. 10, fig. 1).

For a possible interpretation of the phylomorphogenesis within this group, it will be easiest to start with *Vaughanina* and the related genera *Aktinorbitoides* and *Ctenorbitoides*. Here the spiral row is surrounded by annular chambers. However, the annular chambers are not formed immediately; there is a transitional stage in which concentrically elongate chambers are formed which do not completely surround the juvenarium (BRÖNNIMANN, 1954b, pl. 16, fig. 3; p. 96, textfig. 8). A close scrutiny of plate 16, fig. 3 has led me to the conclusion that these elongate chambers are formed through retrovert apertures, and thus in the manner of secondary chambers.

Fig. 8. Centre of *Vaughanina cubensis* PALMER. After BRÖNNIMANN (1954b, pl, 16, fig. 3). Interpretation in text.

This is illustrated by the interpretative Fig. 8: there are six primary chambers without retrovert aperture; a small secondary chamber of normal shape is issued through a retrovert aperture out of primary chamber 7; it behaves as a symmetrical chamber issued on its retrovert side out of primary chamber 15; out of primary chamber 8 again a very small secondary chamber is formed, which leads to a symmetrical secondary chamber issued, on its retrovert side, out of the retrovert chamber out of

primary chamber 7; this symmetric secondary chamber is already somewhat elongate; it leads in retrovert sense to another elongate secondary chamber which already shows a radial passage; on its retrovert side this elongate chamber appears to be issued out of a retrovert aperture of the secondary
chamber issued out of primary chamber 7; out of primary chamber 9 there is a short series of small
retrovert secondary chambers leading in the same direction to a secondary chamber which is very
elongate in a retrovert direction, behaving as a symmetrical chamber issued on its retrovert side out of
a small secondary chamber issued out of primary chamber 13.[1]

Thus in this specimen there would be: (a) six chambers without retrovert aperture, (b) a total number of fifteen primary chambers, (c) an indefinite number of budding stages preceding annular growth,
(d) an unknown total number of budding stages. The number of budding stages of nepiont (c) and
hence of nepionic stage (d) is indefinite because of the short-circuiting caused by the retrovert lengthening. Thus the secondary chamber out of primary chamber 7 has budding stage 8 if counted in that
way, whereas it has budding stage 16 on the other side, where it is issued out of primary chamber 15.

That the elongate chambers are secondary chambers and not, for instance, primary
chambers lengthened in a direction leading to retrovert overlap and annular growth, as
in *Cycloclypeus*, is clear from the figures cited. It explains why "annular walls" occur
only in the radii of *Aktinorbitoides*, which are separated by interradii where only lateral chambers are found. For, if the origin of the neanic chambers is in the manner of
secondary chambers, a sectorial growth is a priori possible, whereas it could not be
realised without further innovations, if these chambers were lengthened primary
chambers. It is also understandable why the radii start with their pointed inner ends
at the partition between two primary chambers, for at this point a secondary chamber
is issued, which forms a focal point for the formation of sectorial growth of "annular"
chambers. In any case, the annular walls of *Aktinorbitoides* can not be truly annular.

The elongation of the equatorial chambers is made possible by the introduction of
radial passages. These are situated in two rows close to the roof and floor of the equatorial layer and thus are probably not to be regarded as additional apertures but as
stolon passages. The *Vaughanina*-arrangement, though fundamentally of type IIA, is
then a kind of reversed type I, with the introduction of additional passages and retrovert lengthening of equatorial chambers after the introduction of a retrovert aperture.

As the three genera mentioned are the only ones with this type of equatorial phylomorphogenesis, it may be significant that they are also the only genera where the
pseudorbitoid layer is delimited by a distinct roof and floor. It is therefore justified to
separate them as a subfamily, the Vaughanininae.

This leads us to the more difficult interpretation of the other forms, which may be
separated as the Pseudorbitoidinae. As has already been seen, it is concluded, from
the presence of quadriserial nepoints in *Pseudorbitoides trechmanni*, to be likely
that a retrovert aperture does occur, and thus that secondary equatorial chambers are
present. These, in the more primitive forms, can only be the primary lateral chambers,
which would be subdivided down the middle by the layer of radial elements.

The question then becomes whether, in the more advanced forms, there are undivided secondary equatorial chambers. This is reported to be the case in microspheric
specimens of advanced species of *Pseudorbitoides*. However, it is to be concluded that

---

[1] This interpretation may be wrong in one or the other particular, but I believe it to be correct in
principle.

they also exist in the megalospheric generation, for BRÖNNIMANN (1955 a) apparently regards the peri–embryonic chambers of quadriserial forms as undivided, and only one of the series around the protoconch is considered by me as a series of primary chambers, the other three being regarded as series of secondary chambers. One obtains the impression from BRÖNNIMANN's figures (1955a, pl. 10, fig. 2, 4; p. 62, textfig. 2a–d) that there are even some undivided secondary chambers which are not peri–embryonic (see also BRÖNNIMANN, 1955a, pl. 3, fig. 17). The fact that these occur in the more advanced species, suggests that the occurrence of undivided chambers may be a proterogenetic feature. Since the radial elements are thought to have developed from incipient elements of the same nature in the ancestral sulcus, it is only reasonable to suppose that they behave proterogenetically. Should this supposition be true, then it could be expected that the pseudorbitoid layer could, as it were, be pushed outward phylogenetically. If this should continue to the entire disappearance of this layer, one would finally obtain a very misleading *Orbitocyclina*-like homoeomorph. It remains curious, as already mentioned by BRÖNNIMANN (1955a, p. 67), that the microspheric generation would be the more advanced. Perhaps this is less curious than it may seem, because the rule that the microspheric generation is the more conservative is based upon deuterogenetic features.

I have attempted to check these suppositions on isolated specimens of *Historbitoides*, collected by me on the Chiapas excursion of the Mexican congress. As BRÖNNIMANN (1956) had only random sections in hard rock at his disposal, a few supplementary

Fig. 9. *Historbitoides* sp., megalospheric, from Chiapas, Mexico, 10.6 km west of Tuxtla Gutierrez, Coll. MAC GILLAVRY, 1955, 19–IX–I (specimen no. 4). Same specimen as Plate VIII, 1. The deformation of the chambers in the proximity of the radii makes it difficult to determine the nepionic formula. × 100.

observations may here be given (Fig. 9; Plate VIII, 1, 2). I have one vertical axial megalospheric section, three vertical tangential, and two horizontal sections. One of the latter is microspheric (diameter of shell 2 mm), the other megalospheric (diameter 1.2 mm). The characteristics of the genus can be observed. The layer of radial elements is continuous even in the interradii; the radial plates in the radii nevertheless fan out towards the periphery. The nepionts of the Mexican material are uniserial, the megalospheric specimen having the nepionic formula ?4/>7?, the microspheric 12/18 (first number indicates primary chambers without retrovert aperture; the second the number of primary chambers). The inner diameter of the megalospheric protoconch is 50 μ. It is difficult to see where the radial elements begin on the inner side. Brönni-mann (1958b, p. 170) states that the radial elements of *Aktinorbitoides* proceed invariably from a partition between two of the primary chambers, though this is not apparent from his textfigs. 4a and 4c (Brönnimann, 1958b, p. 169). In the megalospheric specimen of *Historbitoides* from Mexico, this is not the case; the pointed inner end of the radii here starts at the partition between two secondary chambers which are adjacent to the primary chambers. These secondary chambers are lengthened in a radial direction to a triangular shape, with the apex lying alongside the inner end of the radius and pointing outward. This might be considered as an argument that there is indeed a slight proterogenetic shift, the inner points of the radii not starting from the partition between chambers of the primary spiral, but starting here from the partition between chambers of the next row. It is true that *Aktinorbitoides* is supposed to have a different build, but this does not affect the reasoning.

The geographical range of the genus can thus be extended to include Mexico. The locality is km 1075.4 Carretera Panamericana, 10.6 km west of Tuxtla Gutierrez, in the direction of Ocozocoautla. The associated fauna contains Rudists, *Sulcoperculina*, and a badly preserved fauna of *Globotruncana* species, which, according to Dr. J. J. Hermes, indicates a Campanian to Maastrichtian age. The age of the genoholotype of Brönnimann is Maastrichtian.

The evolutionary trends within the family comprise: reduction of the number of primary chambers, and presumably also reduction of the number of primary chambers without retrovert aperture; decrease of the proportion, in vertical section, between the diameter of the juvenarium and the diameter of the shell. Within one species there is an increase of the number of layers of lateral chambers as the number of primary chambers becomes smaller. This trend also holds for the group as a whole, for if Brönnimann's data for the different forms are plotted, there is found to be a vague negative correlation between number of layers of lateral chambers and the number of

---

In Table III (p. 174) the following data are given:
(a) the number of uni-apertural chambers / number of primary chambers.
(b) proportion, in axial section, between diameter juvenarium and diameter of shell.
(c) shape of juvenarium.
(d) inner diameter of protoconch, in μ.
(e) the number of layers of lateral chambers (primary lateral chambers of Pseudorbitoidinae not included).
Notes:
[1] own observations.
[2] since the genus is sulcoperculinid throughout, the proportion: diameter juvenariumh/sell is 1.0.
[3] Brönnimann gives the diameter inclusive the walls in these two genera. The values given here are obtained by subtracting twice 14 μ from the value given by Brönnimann, 14 μ being the average wall thickness for all forms. The protoconchal wall thickness does not show any correlation with the number of primary chambers, and thus is supposed not to be subject to progressive change.
[4] the proportion between diameter juvenarium and shell has not been given by Brönnimann; I have calculated it from the range values given for the two diameters.
[5] the inner diameter of the protoconch has not been given by Brönnimann; it has been measured from his pl. 9, fig. 1 (Brönnimann, 1954a).

TABLE III

EVOLUTION AND TAXONOMY OF PSEUDORBITOIDIDAE

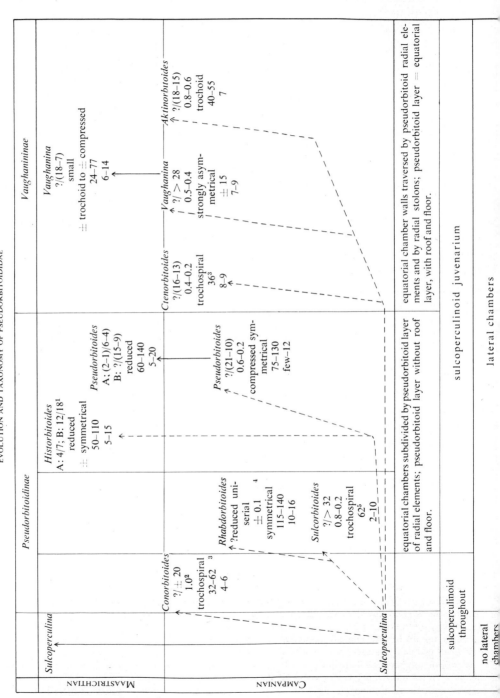

TABLE IV

BEHAVIOUR OF DIFFERENT GROUPS OF CRETACEOUS ORBITOIDAL FORAMINIFERA WITH REGARD TO THE MORE IMPORTANT EVOLUTIONARY TRENDS

	nepionic reduction of uni-apertural stage	nepionic reduction of the number of primary chambers	development of adauxiliary chambers	development of hexagonal or spatulate equatorial chambers	development of stolon complications	development of lateral chambers	development of dimorphism
Orbitoididae	immediate	immediate (converse trend with proliferation in *Simplorbites*)	early	none	not in horizontal plane	early, asymmetric	early
Lepidorbitoididae *Helicorbitoides* and *Lepidorbitoides*	fairly early	regular and rapid; does not attain ultimate stages	in *Lepidorbitoides*	characteristic for *Lepidorbitoides*	present	immediate	at least in *Lepidorbitoides*
Orbitoclyclina etc.	slowed down at 2-chamber stage	slowed down	none	present	present	present	present
Clypeorbis	slowed down at 2-chamber stage	slowed down	none	present	?	present, asymmetric	present
Hellenocyclina	slowed down at 2-chamber stage	slowed down	none	present	none?	none	none
Pseudorbitoididae Pseudorbitoidinae	regular and fairly early	regular and fairly rapid; does not attain ultimate stages	none	radially elongate at periphery	?	immediate	late
Vaughaninae	regular; does not attain ultimate stages	regular, but slow; does not attain ultimate stages	none	special evolution of concentrically elongate chambers	radial stolons	immediate	none

primary chambers. There is also a vague negative correlation between the inner diameter of the protoconch and the number of primary chambers; it is therefore likely
that there is a tendency for the protoconch to increase in size. Only the advanced
forms are known to have dimorphism.

The different values in these trends for the various forms have been plotted on
Table III. The data are obtained from BRÖNNIMANN's papers. The genera have been
arranged according to the taxonomic interpretation given here, which agrees in all
respects with the genetic relationships proposed by BRÖNNIMANN. The stratigraphic
age of many forms is often uncertain. Nevertheless it will be evident that the different
evolutionary trends operate independently, some forms being more advanced in one
respect but less in another.

It may finally be remarked that this is the only family in which primitive nepionic
arrangements prevail.

The following table for the determination of genera is given, in order to take into account
the considerations presented. It is based upon the table given by BRÖNNIMANN (1958b).

I. No lateral chambers: *Sulcoperculina* THALMANN
II. Lateral chambers present: Pseudorbitoididae
   (*1*) Sulcoperculinoid throughout: *Conorbitoides* BRÖNNIMANN[1]
   (*2*) Sulcoperculinoid juvenarium.
      (*A*) Equatorial chambers subdivided, ver-
         tically, by pseudorbitoid layer of
         radial elements: Pseudorbitoidinae[1]
        (*a*) Radial rods.
            (α) Two sets of radial rods only: *Sulcorbitoides* BRÖNNIMANN
            (β) More than two sets of radial
                rods with complex intercon-
                nections: *Rhabdorbitoides* BRÖNNIMANN
        (*b*) Radial plates. Nepionic stage
            reduced.
            (α) Single set of radial plates, as a
                rule not interconnected, later-
                ally: *Pseudorbitoides* H. DOUVILLÉ
            (β) Single set of radial plates, irre-
                gularly interconnected, later-
                ally. Incipient radii and inter-
                radii: *Historbitoides* BRÖNNIMANN
      (*B*) Equatorial chambers and chamber
         walls traversed by radial plates. Later
         equatorial chambers concentrically
         elongated, with chamber walls perfo-
         rated by radial stolon passages. Equa-

---

[1] It seems best to include *Conorbitoides* in the Pseudorbitoidinae.

torial layer = pseudorbitoid layer,
with roof and floor: Vaughanininae
    (*a*) circular forms: *Vaughanina* D. K. PALMER
    (*b*) conical forms, with comb-like
        adventitious equatorial layer: *Ctenorbitoides* BRÖNNIMANN
    (*c*) actinate forms, with equatori-
        al layer restricted to the radii: *Aktinorbitoides* BRÖNNIMANN

FINAL REMARKS

The evolutionary behaviour of the different families and subfamilies with regard to the most important features is summarised in Table IV. The table shows how different these families behave and how *Hellenocyclina* does not fit into any of them. It may furthermore be noted that dimorphism appears to be absent in the earliest members of each group.

ACKNOWLEDGEMENTS

The author is greatly indebted to Mr. P. H. DE BUISONJÉ and Mr. D. VAN HARTEN for their skillful preparation of the most difficult thin sections, their discussions, criticism and comments. Without them this paper could not have been written.

My thanks are also due to Dr. J. J. HERMES, for much useful criticism, and for the age determination of the Mexican fauna of Globotruncanidae.

To Dr. G. J. BIJVANK I am indebted for valuable material from northern Spain. My observations on *Clypeorbis* and on the primitive species of *Monolepidorbis* are based upon this material.

Some of the ideas presented in this paper were first laid down in an unpublished manuscript written in 1947. I am indebted to Dr. H. E. THALMANN, Dr. P. BRÖNNIMANN and Don L. FRIZZELL for their correspondence, advice and suggestions at that time. The late Dr. W. S. ADKINS generously provided me with photocopies of literature which was not otherwise available to me.

Professor M. REICHEL of the University of Basel, Dr. J. B. REESIDE and Dr. L. G. HENBEST of the National Museum, Washington, the late professor S. G. TROOSTER of the Geological Institute, Utrecht, and Dr. J. H. VAN VOORTHUYSEN of the Geological Survey, Haarlem, enabled me to examine material which has been of importance for the writing of this paper.

SUMMARY

A distinction is made between the phylogenetic introduction of new features and evolutionary trends. A type of phylomorphogenesis is defined as a definite succession of phylogenetic introduction of specific new features. The following types of phylomorphogenesis are distinguished: I. *Cycloclypeus*-type with (*1*) introduction of additional apertures, (2) introduction of retrovert apertures, (3) delimitation of the number of primary chambers; IIA. *Planorbulinella*-type: with (*a*) introduction of retrovert aperture leading to retrovert growth outside the spiral wall; (*b*) delimitation of the number of primary chambers; IIB. *Helicolepidina*-type, similar to IIA, but with the formation of secondary chambers inside the spiral wall, and without delimitation of the number of primary chambers; IIC. *Miogypsinoides*-type, as IIB, but with autonomous reduction of the number of primary chambers; III. *Omphalocyclus*-type with incipient alternate growth, (*a*) introduction of contravert aperture, (*b*) delimitation of number of peri-nepionic budding stages.

Each type of phylomorphogenesis is characterized by a definite ontogenetic succession of changes of morphologic pattern. Nepionic reduction effects further modifications, which are characteristic for each type. Development of Cretaceous orbitoidal Foraminifera is analysed on the basis of these concepts.

Orbitoididae. The presence of a gümbeline nepiont in microspheric forms is confirmed. *Monolepidorbis* cf. *dordoniensis* (HOFKER), with normal biserial and quadriserial nepionts, is described. It is devoid of the thickened "embryonic" wall characteristic for other members of the family.

Lepidorbitoididae. This family is considered to be a bundle of independant parallel lineages. Microspheric forms of *Lepidorbitoides minor* have a type IIA centre. Campanian forms, possibly ancestral to *L. socialis*, have a type IIB centre. A new genus *Helicorbitoides* is introduced for *Pseudorbitoides longispiralis* PAPP and KÜPPER 1953. It is suggested that Paleocene "Lepidocyclinae" and *Actinosiphon* may belong to this family. It is tentatively suggested, that the Orbitoclypeidae, which include *Asterocyclina*, are derived from such Paleocene forms through the intermediary of *Bontourina*. The question is raised, whether the *Lepidocyclina*-lineage X of GRIMSDALE (1959) may have derived from *Helicolepidina*. The species *Lepidocyclina vichayalensis* L. RUTTEN 1928 is placed in the genus *Helicolepidina*. Whether the genus *Clypeorbis* belongs to this family is considered uncertain.

Hellenocyclina is considered an isolated genus not to be placed in the Lepidorbitoididae. The species *H. visserae* (HOFKER) is described. It has a biserial nepionic arrangement.

Pseudorbitoididae. A new interpretation is given of the phylomorphogenesis within this group. Two subfamilies are distinguished: the Pseudorbitoidinae and Vaughaninae. Additional data are given on *Historbitoides* BRÖNNIMANN 1956. The geographical range of *Historbitoides* is extended to include Mexico. A revised table for the determination of genera is given, based on the phylomorphogenetic views presented.

A final table gives the different evolutionary behaviour of groups and subgroups with regard to the more important features.

REFERENCES

AKERS, W. H. and DROOGER, C. W., 1957. Miogypsinids, planktonic Foraminifera, and Gulf Coast Oligocene-Miocene correlations. *Bull. Am. Assoc. Petrol. Geologists*, 41 : 656–678.

ASTRE, G., 1927. Sur *Monolepidorbis*, Foraminifère voisin des Lindérines et des Orbitoïdes. *Bull. Soc. géol. France, 4e sér.*, 27 : 387–394.

BARKER, R. W., 1934. Some notes on the genus *Helicolepidina* TOBLER. *J. Paleontol.*, 8 : 344–351.

BARKER, R. W. and GRIMSDALE, T. F., 1936. A contribution to the phylogeny of the Orbitoidal Foraminifera, with descriptions of new forms from the Eocene of Mexico. *J. Paleontol.*, 10 : 231–247.

BARKER, R. W. and GRIMSDALE, T. F., 1937. Studies of Mexican fossil Foraminifera. *Ann. Mag. Nat. Hist.*, Ser. 10, 19 : 161–178.

BRÖNNIMANN, P., 1940. Über die tertiären Orbitoididen und die Miogypsiniden von Nordwest-Marokko. *Schweiz. Paleontol. Abhandl.*, 63 : 1–113.

BRÖNNIMANN, P., 1944. Ein neues Subgenus von *Orbitocyclina* aus Iran nebst Bemerkungen über *Helicolepidina* TOBLER und verwandte Formen. *Schweiz. Paleontol. Abhandl.*, 64 : 2–42.

BRÖNNIMANN, P., 1945. Zur Frage der verwandtschaftlichen Beziehungen zwischen *Discocyclina* s.s. und *Asterocyclina*. *Eclogae Geol. Helv.*, 38 : 579–615.

BRÖNNIMANN, P., 1954a. Upper Cretaceous Orbitoidal Foraminifera from Cuba, Part I. *Sulcorbitoides* nov. gen. *Contrib. Cushman Found. Foraminiferal Research*, 5 : 55–61.

BRÖNNIMANN, P., 1954b. Upper Cretaceous Orbitoidal Foraminifera from Cuba, Part II. *Vaughanina* PALMER 1934. *Contrib. Cushman Found. Foraminiferal Research*, 5 : 91–105.

BRÖNNIMANN, P., 1955a. Upper Cretaceous Orbitoidal Foraminifera from Cuba, Part III. *Pseudorbitoides* H. DOUVILLÉ, 1922. *Contrib. Cushman Found. Foraminiferal Research*, 6 : 57–76.

BRÖNNIMANN, P., 1955b. Upper Cretaceous Orbitoidal Foraminifera from Cuba, Part IV. *Rhabdorbitoides*, nov. gen. *Contrib. Cushman Found. Foraminiferal Research*, pp. 97–104.

BRÖNNIMANN, P., 1956. Upper Cretaceous Orbitoidal Foraminifera from Cuba, Part V. *Historbitoides*, nov. gen. *Contrib. Cushman Found. Foraminiferal Research*, 7 : 60–66.

BRÖNNIMANN, P., 1957. Morphology and stratigraphic significance of *Pseudorbitoides israelskyi* VAUGHAN and COLE. *Eclogae Geol. Helv.*, 50 : 582–604.

BRÖNNIMANN, P., 1958a. New Pseudorbitoids from the Upper Cretaceous of Guatemala, Texas and Florida. *Eclogae Geol. Helv.*, 51 : 422–437.

BRÖNNIMANN, P., 1958b. New Pseudorbitoididae from the Upper Cretaceous of Cuba, with remarks on encrusting Foraminifera. *Micropaleontol.*, 4 : 165–186.

CAUDRI, C. M. B., 1944. The Larger Foraminifera from San Juan de los Morros, State of Guarico, Venezuela. *Bull. Am. Paleontol.*, 28 : 5–45.

CAUDRI, C. M. B., 1948. Note on the stratigraphic distribution of *Lepidorbitoides. J.Paleontol.*, 22 : 473–481.

CIRY, R., 1939. *Étude géologique d'une Partie des Provinces de Burgos, Palencia, Léon et Santander.* Thèse (Paris). Toulouse, 519 pp.

COLE, W. S., 1942. Stratigraphic and paleontologic studies of wells in Florida — No. 2. *State of Florida Dept. of Conserv., Geol. Bull.*, 20 : 1–56.

COLE, W. S., and BERMÚDEZ, P. J., 1944. New Foraminiferal Genera from the Cuban Middle Eocene. *Bull. Am. Paleontol.*, 28 (113) : 3–16.

DE CIZANCOURT, H., 1938. Remarques sur le genre *Orbitocyclina* VAUGHAN. *Bull. Soc. géol. France, 5e sér.*, 8 : 645–652.

DOUVILLÉ, H., 1906. Evolution et enchaînements des Foraminifères. *Bull. Soc. géol. France, 4e sér.*, 6 : 588–602.

DOUVILLÉ, H., 1920. Révision des Orbitoides. *Bull. Soc. géol. France, 4e sér.*, 20 : 209–232.

DROOGER, C. W., 1956. Parallel evolutionary trends in larger Foraminifera. *Proc. Koninkl. Ned. Akad. Wetenschap., Ser. B*, 59 (5) : 458–469.

GRIMSDALE, T. F., 1959. Evolution in the American Lepidocyclinidae (Cainozoic Foraminifera): An interim review. I, II. *Proc. Koninkl. Ned. Akad. Wetenschap., Ser. B*, 62, (1) : 8–33.

HOFKER, J., 1958a. Foraminifera from the Cretaceous of Limburg, Netherlands, XXXV. On the initial stages of *Omphalocyclus macroporus* (LAMARCK). *Natuurhist. Maandbl.*, 47 : 98–100.

HOFKER, J., 1958b. Foraminifera from the Cretaceous of Limburg, Netherlands, XXXVII. *Linderina visserae* nov. spec. *Natuurhist, Maandbl.*, 47 : 125–127.

HOFKER, J., 1959. Les Foraminifères des Craies tuffoides de Charente et Dordogne de l'Aquitaine, France du Sud-Ouest. *84e Congr. Soc. Savantes, Dijon*, pp. 253–368.

KÜPPER, K., 1954a. Notes on Cretaceous larger Foraminifera I. Genus *Orbitoides* in America. *Contrib. Cushman Found. Foraminiferal Research*, 5 : 63–67.

KÜPPER, K., 1954b. Notes on Upper Cretaceous larger Foraminifera, II. Genera of the subfamily Orbitoidinae with remarks on the microspheric generation of *Orbitoides* and *Omphalocyclus. Contrib. Cushman Found. Foraminiferal Research*, 5 : 179-184.

MAC GILLAVRY, H. J., 1955. Two evolving species of the genus *Lepidorbitoides* SILVESTRI, a biometrical study. *Mededel. Geol. Stichting, N. Ser.*, 9 : 11–43.

MAC GILLAVRY, H. J., 1959. Danger of world-wide correlations based on evolving features. XX *Congr. Geol. Internacional, Mex.*, 1956 *Symp. del Cret.*, pp. 77–84.

NEUMANN, M., 1954. Le genre *Linderina* et quelques autres Foraminifères l'accompagnant dans le Nummulitique d'Aquitaine. *Bull. Soc. géol. France, 6e sér.*, 4 : 55–59.

NEUMANN, M., 1958. Révision des Orbitoididés du Crétacé et de l'Éocène en Aquitaine occidentale. *Mém. Soc. géol. France, sér. 37* 83 : 1–174.

PAPP, A., 1954. Über die Entwicklung von *Pseudorbitoides* und *Lepidorbitoides* in Europa. *Verhandl. Geol. Bundesanstalt*, 3 : 162–170.

PAPP, A., 1955. Morphologisch-genetische Untersuchungen an Foraminiferen. *Paläontol. Z.*, 29 : 74–78.

PAPP, A. und KÜPPER, K., 1953. Die Foraminiferenfauna von Guttaring und Klein St. Paul (Kärnten). III. Foraminiferen aus dem Campan von Silberegg. *Sitzungsberichten Österr. Akad. Wissensch., Math. naturwiss., Abt. I*, 162 : 345–357.

PAPP, A. und KÜPPER, K., 1954. The genus *Heterostegina* in the Upper Tertiary of Europe. *Contrib. Cushman Found. Foraminiferal Research*, 5: 108–127.

POKORNÝ, V., 1958. *Grundzüge der Zoologischen Mikropaläontologie*, I. VEB, Deutscher Verlag der Wissenschaften, Berlin, 582 pp.

REICHEL, M., 1949. Sur un nouvel orbitoïdé du Crétacé supérieur hellénique. *Eclogae Geol. Helv.*, 42 : 480–485.

RENZ, O. und KÜPPER, H., 1946. Über morphogenetische Untersuchungen an Grossforaminiferen. *Eclogae Geol. Helv.*, 39 : 317–342.

RUTTEN, L., 1928. On Tertiary rocks and Foraminifera from North-Western Peru. *Proc. Koninkl. Ned. Akad. Wetenschap.*, 31 (6–10) : 931–946.

RUTTEN, M. G., 1935. A note on *Actinosiphon vichayalensis* (RUTTEN). *J. Paleontol.*, 9 : 546–547.

RUTTEN, M. G., 1941. A synopsis of the Orbitoididae. *Geol. Mijnbouw*, 3 : 34–62.

TAN SIN HOK, 1932. On the genus *Cycloclypeus* CARPENTER, Part I. *Wetenschap. Mededeel. Dienst Mijnbouw Ned.Indië*, 19 : 3–194.

TAN SIN HOK, 1935. Die peri-embryonalen Äquatorialkammern bei einigen Orbitoididen. *De Ingr. in Ned. Indië*, 2 (IV) : 113–126.

TAN SIN HOK, 1936a. Zur Kenntnis der Lepidocycliniden. *Natl. Tijdschr. Ned. Indië*, 96 (4) : 235–280.

TAN SIN HOK, 1936b. Beitrag zur Kenntnis der Lepidocycliniden. *Proc. Koninkl. Ned. Akad. Wetenschap.*, 39 (8) : 3–12.

TAN SIN HOK, 1936c. Zur Kenntnis der Miogypsiniden. *De Ingr. in Ned. Indië*, 3 (IV) : 45–61, 84–98, 109–123.

TAN SIN HOK, 1936d. Over verschillende paleontologische criteria voor de geleding van het Tertiair. *De Ingr. in Ned. Indië*, 3 (IV) : 173–179.

TAN SIN HOK, 1937a. Note on *Miogypsina kotôi* HANZAWA. *De Ingr. in Ned. Indië*, 4 (IV) : 31–32.

TAN SIN HOK, 1937b. Weitere Untersuchungen über die Miogypsiniden. I, II. *De Ingr. in Ned. Indië*, 4 (IV) : 35–45, 87–111.

TAN SIN HOK, 1939a. On *Polylepidina, Orbitocyclina* and *Lepidorbitoides*. *De Ingr. in Ned. Indië*, 6 (IV) : 53–84.

TAN SIN HOK, 1939b. The results of phylomorphogenetic studies of some larger Foraminifera (a review). *De Ingr. in Ned. Indië*, 6 (IV) : 93–97.

TODD, J. U. and BARKER, R. W., 1932. Tertiary Orbitoids from North-Western Peru. *Geol. Mag.*, 69 : 529–543.

VAN RAADSHOOVEN, B., 1951. On some Paleocene and Eocene Larger Foraminifera of Western Venezuela. *World Petrol. Congr., Proc. 3rd Congr., Hague*, Section 1 : 476–489.

VAUGHAN, T. W., 1929a. *Actinosiphon semmesi*, a new genus and species of Orbitoidal Foraminifera, and *Pseudorbitoides trechmanni* H. DOUVILLÉ. *J. Paleontol.*, 3 : 163–169.

VAUGHAN, T. W., 1929b. Descriptions of new species of Foraminifera of the genus *Discocyclina* from the Eocene of Mexico. *Proc. U.S. Natl. Museum*, No. 2800, 76 (Art. 3) : 1–18.

VAUGHAN, T. W., 1945. American Paleocene and Eocene Larger Foraminifera. *Geol. Soc. Am., Mem.* 9 : 1–175.

VISSER, A. M., 1950. *Monograph on the Foraminifera of the type locality of the Maestrichtian*. Thesis Univ. Leyden, 359 pp.

VAN DER VLERK, I. M., 1955. Correlation of the Tertiary of the Far East and Europe. *Micropaleontol.*, 1 : 72–75.

VAN DER VLERK, I. M., 1957. De stratigrafische betekenis van het "genus" Lepidocyclina. *Koninkl. Ned. Akad. Wetenschap., Verslagen der afdel. Nat.*, 66 (1) : 23–27.

VAN DER VLERK, I. M., 1959. Problems and principles of Tertiary and Quaternary stratigraphy. *Quart. J. Geol. Soc. London*, 65 : 49–63.

VAN DER VLERK, I. M. en UMBGROVE, J. H. F., 1927. Tertiaire gidsforaminiferen van Nederlandsch Oost-Indië. *Wetenschap. Mededeel., Dienst Mijnbouw Ned. Indië*, 6 : 1–35.

PLATES I–VIII

PLATE I

1. *Omphalocyclus macroporus*, microspheric centre. E.N.C.I. quarry, Pietersberg, Maastricht, The Netherlands (type-locality Maastrichtian), section ROMEIN 28.00 m, specimen no. 1, Maastrichtian (Md), × 200. The figure shows the position of the gümbelinid nepiont.

2. *Omphalocyclus macroporus*, same specimen as in 1, showing the gümbelinid nepiont (stage of alternate growth), enlarged. Chambers on the right are less clear because they lie at a slightly lower level. 2b × 800.

PLATE I

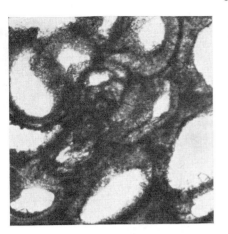

1

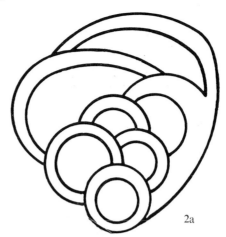

2a

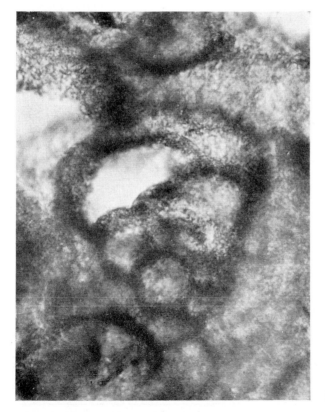

2b

PLATE II

1. *Omphalocyclus macroporus*. Same locality as Plate I. Section ROMEIN 28.00 m, specimen no. 2, Maastrichtian (Md), 1a × 200. Microspheric specimen with "biserial nepionic arrangement", *i.e.*, the stage of alternate growth is reduced to two chambers and therefore not recognisable as such. The alternate mode of growth is still expressed through seven budding stages. No thickened walls along flanks of reduced nepiont; there is a thickened wall (relapse), covering primary chamber 3 and three other chambers; the latter with relapse to the uni-apertural stage. Nepionic formula: $2\left/\frac{5}{5}\right.$

2. *Orbitoides apiculata*. Coll. J. J. ROZEBOOM, St. Marcet no. 121 (see MAC GILLAVRY, 1955, for locality), Haute Garonne, southern France, PA 675, Maastrichtian, 2a × 200. Microspheric specimen with "symmetric quadriserial nepiont", *i.e.*, the stage of alternate growth is reduced to one chamber. Nepionic formula: $1\left/\frac{4}{4}\right.$

. *Omphalocyclus macroporus*. Coll. J. J. ROZEBOOM, Latoue 39, Haute Garonne, southern France, PA 587, Maastrichtian, × 150. Microspheric specimen, cut tangentially. Analysis of the succession of central chambers not possible.

PLATE II

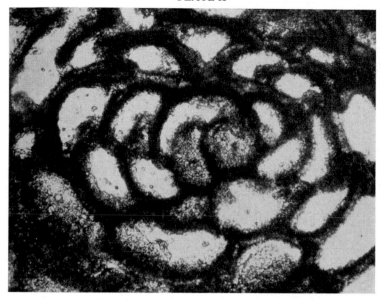

1a

2b

1b

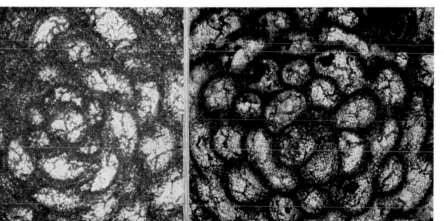

2a   3

PLATE III

1. *Monolepidorbis* cf. *dordoniensis* (HOFKER). Coll. Dr. G. J. BIJVANK, Cuesta de la Mazorra, at 60.7 km on the road from Burgos to Villarcayo, northern Spain. Specimen no. 16. Basal Campanian, fide CIRY (1939), 1a × 200. Megalospheric specimen (no dimorphism observed) with "biserial nepionic arrangement", *i.e.*, stage of alternate growth reduced to two chambers. Nepionic formula: $2\big/\frac{6}{6}$

2. *Monolepidorbis* cf. *dordoniensis* (HOFKER). Coll. Dr. G. J. BIJVANK. Same locality and age. Specimen no. 18, 2a × 200. "Quadriserial nepiont" *i.e.*, stage of alternate growth reduced to one chamber. Auxiliary chambers of unequal size. The centre shows some resemblance to that of a normal primitive orbitoidid, but the walls of the two embryonic chambers and of the two auxiliary chambers do not form a common thickened wall; walls of the auxiliary chambers not thicker than those of other equatorial chambers. Nepionic formula: $1\big/\frac{4}{4}$; peri-deuteroconchal series have five and five budding stages.

PLATE III

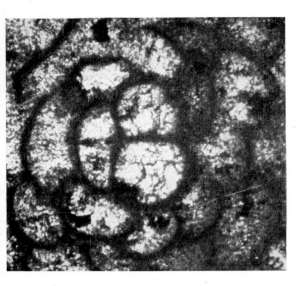

1a

1b

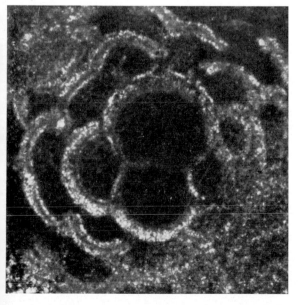

2a

2b

PLATE IV

1. *Monolepidorbis* cf. *dordoniensis* (Hofker). Coll. Dr. G. J. Bijvank. Cuesta de la Mazorra, at 60.7 km on the road from Burgos to Villacayo, northern Spain. Specimen no. 23, × 75. One axial and one vertical tangential section. Showing irregular orbitoidid arrangement of equatorial chambers and single aperture. Lateral walls perforated by numerous pores. Lateral walls thicker in centre than those of *M. dordoniensis*, type–specimen of Hofker.

2. *Hellenocyclina visserae* (Hofker). Tennis court E.N.C.I., Pietersberg, Maastricht, The Netherlands (for locality see Mac Gillavry, 1955). Maastrichtian (Mc). Axial section of megalospheric specimen (no dimorphism observed), showing more regular arrangement of equatorial chambers, × 200.

PLATE IV

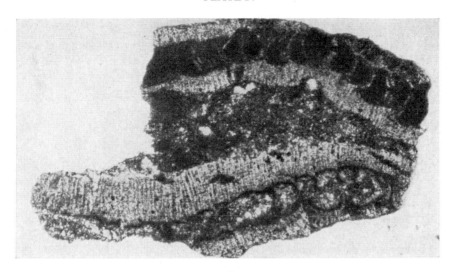

1

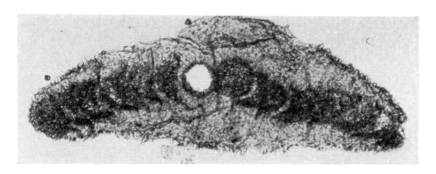

2

PLATE V

1. *Helicorbitoides* nov. gen. *longispiralis* (Papp and Küpper). Coll. Mac Gillavry 1955, loc. 6, Silberegg, Carinthia, Austria. Specimen no. 2, Campanian, × 75. The photograph shows the spiral of primary chambers which opens out in the third whorl to admit the formation of helicolepidine secondary chambers. It is not clear from the figure that the spiral of primary chambers continues up to the periphery. There are approximately seven primary chambers without retrovert aperture.

2. *Helicorbitoides longispiralis* (Papp and Küpper), same specimen as in 1. Centre enlarged, × 200. Wall pores visible at several points.

PLATE V

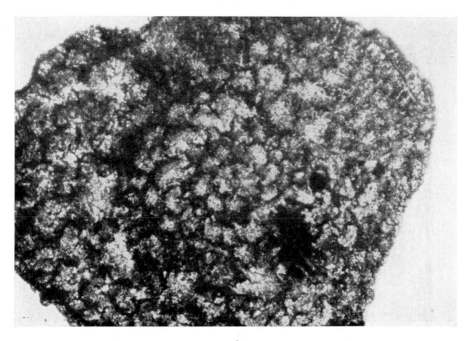

1

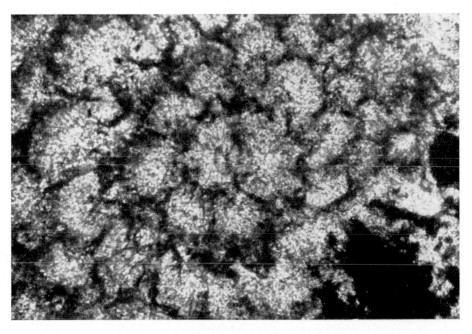

2

PLATE VI

1. *Helicorbitoides longispiralis* (Papp and Küpper). Coll. Mac Gillavry 1955 loc. 7, Silberegg, Carinthia, Austria. Campanian. Thin-section through hard rock, × 75. Vertical, almost axial section, showing features mentioned in the text. Note involute build in centre. A large primary chamber is seen on the left.

2. *Lepidorbitoides minor* Schlumbeager, microspheric specimen. Schooverberg 174, Limburg, The Netherlands (for locality see Mac Gillavry, 1955). Specimen no. 15, PA 2749, Maastrichtian (Md), × 330. This figure shows the *Planorbulinella*-type of phylomorphogenesis (type IIA). Nepionic formula: 5 / 10. Deuteroconch and primary chamber 3 with recrystallised filling. First retrovert secondary chamber small.

PLATE VI

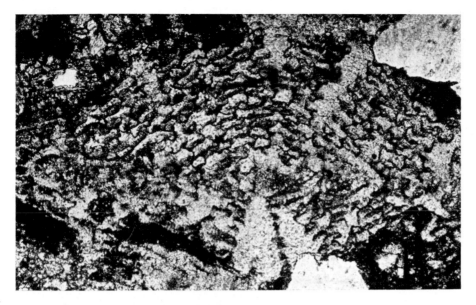

1

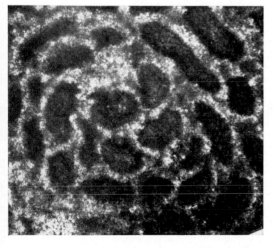

2a

2b

PLATE VII

1. *Hellenocyclina visserae* (Hofker). Coll. J. J. Rozeboom, St. Marcet no. 32, Haute Garonne, southern France (for locality see MacGillavry, 1955). PA 557, 1a × 200. Characteristic biserial nepionic arrangement, trilocular appearance, and large primary auxiliary chamber with slightly thickened wall. The black line in the lumen of the auxiliary chamber is caused by recrystallisation of the filling. Nepionic formula: 2 / 6.

2. *Hellenocyclina visserae* (Hofker). Coll. J. J. Rozeboom, Naouarret no. 48, Haute Garonne, southern France. PA 622, 2a × 200. Biserial nepiont. Large primary auxiliary chamber to the left of the two embryonic chambers. Nepionic formula: 2 / ?7. Several chambers in the centre have a somewhat thickened wall. The resulting picture shows some resemblance to the centre of *H. beotica* figured by Reichel (our Fig. 7, left), especially if the photograph is turned around.

PLATE VII

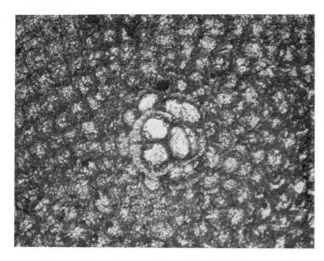

1b

1a

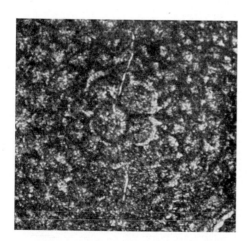

2b

2a

PLATE VIII

1. *Historbitoides* sp. Coll. MAC GILLAVRY 1956, Mexico 19–IX–I, Carretera Panamericana 1075.4 km, 10.6 km west of Tuxtla Gutierrez, in the direction of Ocozocoautla. Specimen no. 4. Upper Senonian, × 75. Megalospheric specimen. For an analysis of the centre see Fig. 9. The photograph shows the actinate equatorial layer and, in the left upper corner, the layer of radial elements. The fanning out towards the periphery of the radial elements in a radius is seen on the left side.

2. *Historbitoides* sp. Same locality. Specimen no. 3, × 200. Axial section through megalospheric specimen, showing about seven undivided equatorial chambers.

PLATE VIII

1

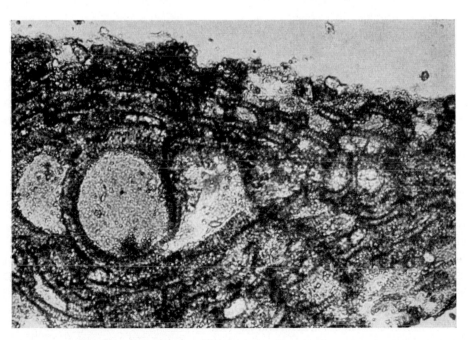

2

ZUR ENTWICKLUNG DER BENTHOS-FORAMINIFERE BOLIVINOIDES

HEINRICH HILTERMANN

Bundesanstalt für Bodenforschung, Hannover (Deutschland)

EINLEITENDE BEMERKUNGEN UND MATERIAL

Vorliegende Darstellung von Entwicklungsreihen der Gattung *Bolivinoides* mit ihrer weltweiten Verbreitung und ihren Analogien soll die taxonomische Überprüfung im Hinblick auf evolutorische Zusammenhänge einerseits und geographisch bedingte Einflüsse andererseits anregen. Fossile Kleinforaminiferen sind ja durch ihr zahlreiches Auftreten sowie durch die Gewinnungsmöglichkeit von grossen Individuenmengen in engsten Proben-Abständen praedestiniert für die Erfassung phylogenetischer Reihen. Bisherige Ergebnisse und ihre praktische Anwendung für die Feinstratigraphie ermutigen zur Verfolgung weiterer solcher Entwicklungsreihen hinsichtlich ihrer vertikalen Evolution. Einige Beispiele stellten BETTENSTAEDT (1958) und HILTERMANN (1958) zusammen. Diese Ergebnisse gehen auf Arbeiten zurück, die von WEDEKIND (1940) bei Neoflabellinen und von WICHER bei *Bolivinoides* 1937 bis 1939 völlig unabhängig voneinander durchgeführt wurden. Die in verschiedenen Gebieten auch ausserhalb NW-Deutschlands besonders häufigen *Bolivinoides* ergaben auch in weit auseinander liegenden Punkten gleichgerichtete Tendenzen der Entwicklung, die für Altersvergleiche ausserordentlich wertvoll sind. Solche Gesetzmässigkeiten konnten 1954 durch EDGELL, POZARYSKA und REISS für Australien, Polen und Israel angewandt und in ihrer Richtigkeit biostratigraphisch bestätigt werden. Von einigen Arten und Arten-Gruppen sind variationsstatistische Messungen einiger Einzelmerkmale von BETTENSTAEDT, HILTERMANN, HOFKER und KOCH begonnen worden. Eine ausreichende taxonomische Durcharbeitung war noch nicht möglich.

Ganz besonders wichtig und schwierig ist die richtige Fassung der Variationsbreite und die Abgrenzung der Arten bzw. Unterarten unter gleichwertiger Berücksichtigung der Morphologie und Stratigraphie. Je gründlicher und vollständiger morphologisch Zusammengehörendes in seinem Entwicklungablauf erarbeitet und bekannt ist, desto grösser ist die Möglichkeit, unabhängig von Fazies- und Faunen-Änderungen überregionale bis weltweite zeitliche Abläufe zu erkennen und zu vergleichen. Auf Vorteile und Schwierigkeiten in der Art-Fassung, die die fossilen Lebewesen im Vergleich zu den rezenten der Taxonomie bieten, wurde von HILTERMANN (1951, 1954, 1956) hingewiesen. Nachfolgend werden dementsprechend die kleinen taxonomischen Einheiten in den Vordergrund gestellt.

Bei der Fassung der Gattung *Bolivinoides* wird in Übereinstimmung mit fast allen Bearbeitern die überlappende Skulptur und Schalenverdickung als ausreichend für die Abtrennung von *Bolivina* angesehen. Hierdurch ist eine nomenklatorische Zusammenfassung dieser in der Oberkreide schnell abändernden Arten möglich, für die sich auch CUSHMAN (1927) durch die Wahl von *Bolivina draco* MARSSON als Genotyp entschieden hat. CUSHMAN behielt auch später im Gegensatz zu anderen Autoren diese Fassung von *Bolivinoides* bei. Die Vereinigung überlappender Bolivinen des Tertiärs und Quartärs mit *Bolivinoides* CUSHMAN 1927 kann kein Grund dafür sein, diese zu liquidieren, wie es REYMENT (1959, S. 14) vorschlug. Wir möchten vielmehr die Tatsache, dass CUSHMAN (1937, S. 89) die jüngeren grobskulptierten Formen zu *Bolivina* und nicht zu *Bolivinoides* stellte, als Hinweis für die Gültigkeit seiner *Bolivinoides* ansehen. Auch das andersartige Auftreten der *Bolivina*-Arten der Oberkreide, etwa von *Bolivina incrassata* REUSS, weist auf eine selbständige Entwicklung der *Bolivinoides*-Gruppe.

Während zwanzigjähriger Beobachtungen an sehr grossen Material wurde eine Veröffentlichung unsererseits immer wieder hinausgeschoben, da diese Fragen ebenso wie die nach der Abstammung und Herkunft mit norddeutschen Profilen allein nicht zu klären waren. Durch freundliches Entgegenkommen von G. C. ADAMS, E. ALLEMANN, H. ARNOLD, J. P. BECKMANN, F. BROTZEN, H. S. EDGELL, H. GERTH, H. HAGN, F. HODSON, J. HOFKER, TH. KRUCKOW, A. R. LOEBLICH, A. MCGUGAN, E. MALZAHN, H. J. PLUMMER, J. B. REESIDE, Z. REISS, M. L. ROBLES-RAMOS, B. J. ROMEIN, F. SCHMID, D. J. SMITH, R. TODD, E. VOIGT und J. H. ZIEGLER gelangten wir in den Besitz von Proben aus Nord- und Mittel-Amerika, Trinidad, Australien, Asien, Israel, Iran, Afrika und dem gesamten Europa. Von aussereuropäischen Funden liegen dieser Arbeit über 280 fossilführende Schlämmrückstände aus der Oberkreide zugrunde. Die Zahl der europäischen Proben überschreitet das 20fache dieser Zahl wesentlich.

Eine Sichtung und Vorarbeitung dieser oft aus mehreren 100 *Bolivinoides* bestehenden Populationen ist noch in keiner Weise abgeschlossen. In erster Linie bin ich meinem Mitarbeiter, Herrn W. KOCH, für seine langjährige Hilfe und Anregungen zu grossem Dank verpflichtet. Den oben genannten Kollegen habe ich dafür zu danken, dass sie die Mühen und Schwierigkeiten nicht gescheut haben, mir teilweise ganze Profile und Probenserien zu verschaffen. Nicht zuletzt gilt mein Dank Herrn H. DEITERS für seine wertvollen präparativen Arbeiten und die Anfertigung der beigegebenen Mikrophotos.

ZUSAMMENHÄNGE ZWISCHEN VERSCHIEDENEN FORMEN

Schon die aus nordwest-Deutschland publizierten Unterlagen, besonders die Darstellung der zeitlichen Abfolge 64 verschiedener *Bolivinoides* (HILTERMANN und KOCH, 1950, Abb. 2–4), zeigten bestimmte Zusammenhänge. Die Entwicklungstendenz der dort behandelten Formen wurde besonders durch die Zunahme der Gehäusebreite (Abnahme des L/Br-Index) gekennzeichnet. In Korrelation dazu ändern sich Skulptur und Querschnitt. Die schmalen Typen, *B. strigillatus*, bilden den Ausgangspunkt. Im unteren Campan erfolgte mit einer Zunahme der Grösse eine Aufspaltung in zwei Reihen, einmal in *B. decoratus* und etwas später in *B. draco*. Beide Reihen ändern schon im Laufe des Ober-Campan ihre Skulptur deutlich in zwei verschiedenen Richtungen ab. Bei *Bolivinoides decoratus decoratus* sind etwa von der siebenten Kammer an überlappende Knotenrippen vorhanden, die auf den Kammerwänden senkrecht stehen und diese verdecken. Diese Entwicklung führte schliesslich im mittleren Unter-Maastricht zu der bis 0.8 mm grossen *B. decoratus giganteus*, die durch starke und besonders gleichmässige Überlappungen gekennzeichnet ist. Bei der parallel erfolgten Weiterentwicklung von den ersten gekörnelten Formen der *B. draco miliaris* zu *B. draco draco* treten noch andere Merkmale hinzu, vor allem Betonung einer Mittelfurche, zugespitzter Querschnitt mit Kiel und starkes Breitenwachstum, wobei der L/Br-Index bis auf 1.1 absinkt.

Neben diesen phyletisch zusammengehörenden und gut definierbaren Gruppen treten aber noch verschiedene Formen auf, die eine Sonderentwicklung darstellen. Nachfolgend soll versucht werden, diesbezügliche neue Zusammenhänge aufzudecken und in der neueren Literatur publizierte Formen in diesen Rahmen zu bringen. Vergleichende morphologische und biostratigraphische Untersuchungen zeigen, dass sich einige auch unter anderen Namen beschriebene Formen um diese Arten gruppieren.

Bolivinoides strigillatus (CHAPMAN, 1892) ist älteste Art dieses Formenkreises mit übergreifenden Kammerknoten und stellt nach bisherigen Kenntnissen als "Stammform" eine Entwicklüngsbasis dar. Diese Art ist weltweit verbreitet. Morphologische Abweichungen zeigen sich in der Verlagerung ihrer Wachstums-Tendenz, vor allem der Variations-Breite und des -Maximums. Nach unserem Material handelt es sich um infraspezifische Merkmals-Verschiebungen, wie sie bei vikariierenden geographischen Rassen vorkommen. Dies gilt ganz besonders für *Bolivinoides angulatus* REISS aus Israel und auch für einen Teil der aus Nord- und Mittel-Amerika vorliegenden Exemplare aus dem Kreis um *Bolivinoides austinanus* CUSHMAN. In Australien konnte dank EDGELL's enger Zusammenarbeit und Material-Austausch ein weiterer neuer Artname vermieden werden, obwohl EDGELL (1954, S. 71) die australischen Formen von den europäischen folgendermassen unterscheiden konnte: "Sie sind insgesamt kleiner, mehr gerundet (im Gehäusequerschnitt) und mit stärkerer sekundärer Verdickung des Gehäuses". Wenn es nötig ist, Formen mit solchen Merkmalen, die als geographische Abweichungen bewertbar sind, zu benennen, so geschieht es von uns ternär als Subspezies. Dass eine solche Unterart nicht ohne weiteres überregional verwendet, d.h. in ihrer taxonomischen Einheit übertragen werden kann, muss in ihrer Fassung dann ausreichend begründet sein. So sind andererseits die bisher in Nord- und Mittel-Amerika nur vereinzelt gefundenen Exemplare von *B. strigillatus* weniger rund, sondern mit mehr ovalem Querschnitt ausgebildet und haben eine etwas weniger stark ausgeprägte Knotenbildung sowohl zahlen- als stärkenmässig. Diese Formen zeigen im Gegensatz zu denen aus anderen Gebieten deutlich die Entwicklung und den Übergang zu *B. austinanus* CISHMAN, so dass deren Entstehung etwa hier angenommen werden kann. Gegenüber der australischen *B. strigillatus* und besonders der *B. angulatus* aus Israel könnte man die amerikanische Form von *B. strigillatus* als entgegengesetztes Extrem innerhalb der Variationsbreite dieses Formenkreises ansehen, dessen Mitte etwa von den europäischen Individuen gebildet wird. Das von HILTERMANN und KOCH (1950, S. 624, Abb. 5, 68) aus dem lower Taylor von Texas abgebildete Exemplar von *B. strigillatus* zeigt sowohl einen ovalen Gehäuse-Quer schnitt wie auch an Zahl und Stärke geringere Skulptur-Verdickungen gegenüber den europäischen Formen; es wird dadurch eine zu der Entwicklung von *B. austinanus* tendierende Schwerpunktbildung angedeutet. Alle hier erwähnten Formen überschneiden sich innerhalb der Variationsbreite der Art. *B. strigillatus*. Allerdings ist — abgesehen von dem obigen Exemplar — aus den Sedimenträumen Amerikas *B. strigillatus* s.str. weder unter diesem noch unter einem anderen Namen bekannt geworden. Diese ausgesprochene Seltenheit der typisch ausgebildeten Form deutet — gegenüber der häufiger auftretenden, evolutorisch aber schon als Nachfolgeform anzusehende *B. austinanus* — auf z.T. weit auseinanderliegende Entstehungsräume bei den *Bolivinoides*-Arten hin.

Durch Vergleiche mit der Verbreitung in Europa und Amerika konnten auch in Australien ähnliche grundlegende stratigraphische Ergebnisse erzielt werden (EDGELL, 1954, S. 69). — Die Verbreitung der ältesten *Bolivinoides*-Art im Ober-Santon und im tieferen Unter-Campan konnte immer wieder bestätigt und als relativ sichere Basis in der Stratigraphie benutzt werden.

Die Entwicklung von *B. decoratus* aus *B. strigillatus* vollzieht sich in Europa in einer verhältnismässig kurzen, sprunghaften Phase, wie dies auch schon von HILTERMANN und KOCH (1950, S. 618–620, Abb. 2–4) angedeutet wurde. In einer besonders in Mittel- und Nord-Europa nur geringmächtigen Schicht von selten mehr als 0.5 m treten beide Arten zusammen auf und charakterisieren so einen stratigraphisch wichtigen Leithorizont des hohen Unter-Campan. Allerdings treten beide Arten im Gegensatz zu den anderen Horizonten nur relativ selten auf: Aus 1 kg Rohprobe lassen sich höchstens etwa zehn Exemplare jeder Art gewinnen. In diesem Horizont und besonders im unmittelbar Hangenden überschneiden sich die Längen–Breiten–Indices (L/Br) von *B. decoratus* mit denen von *B. strigillatus* im Bereich der Werte von 1,6–2,2. Doch ist eine Unterscheidung möglich: "Bei *B. decorata* ist der Querschnitt immer flacher und der Rand zugespitzt gegenüber dem breit gerundeten Rand von *B. strigillata*" (HILTERMANN und KOCH, 1950, S. 607). So sprechen die für die Art-Zugehörigkeit ebenfalls entscheidenden Verhältnisse von Gehäuse-Dicke zur Breite neben den nebeneinanderliegenden Knotenreihen klar für die eine oder die andere Art (vgl. hierzu auch BETTENSTAEDT, 1958, S. 132, 4). Häufig fällt *B. decoratus decoratus* in diesem Bereich auch durch kleine Populationen von besonders gut ausgebildeten, typischen Individuen auf, wie sie sich in den darüber folgenden Schichten noch keineswegs durchsetzen, sondern in dieser bereits "hochentwickelten" Ausbildung das Populationsbild erst viel später, im Ober-Campan bestimmen. Eine derartige frühe, richtungweisende und sprunghafte "Beschleunigung der Entwicklung" ist jedoch auch schon im Ober-Santon bei *B. strigillatus*-Populationen zu beobachten: Das L/Br-Index-Maximum von 1,7 wird erst im Ober-Campan durch *B. decoratus* wieder erreicht (BETTENSTAEDT, 1958, S. 134, Abb. 3).

Im oberen Unter-Campan und im unteren Ober-Campan, vor dem Einsetzen von *B. draco miliaris*, treten — immer nur vereinzelt, aber weltweit verbreitet — Exemplare von *B. decoratus* auf, bei denen Gehäuseform und besonders die Skulpturanordnung so starke Anklänge an *B. draco miliaris* zeigen, dass damit deren Herkunft von *B. decoratus* deutlich angezeigt wird. Dabei ist der bei *B. decoratus decoratus* noch gerundete Gehäuse-Rand bereits etwas zugeschärft, und die Anordnung der Knoten zeigt zwei Reihen an einer angedeuteten Mittel-Furche. Dies ist auch eine Bestätigung der Annahme von HOFKER (1957, S. 269, Abb. 324), der *B. draco miliaris* ebenfalls von *B. decoratus decoratus* ableitet. Neben diesen scheinbaren Entwicklungssprüngen stehen allmählich und gleitend abwandelnde phylogenetische Reihen. So entwickelt sich *B. laevigatus* zu *B. peterssoni* von welcher die ersten "Zwischen"-Formen bereits an der Grenze Maastricht/Campan zu finden sind. In dem Material von Lüneburg fanden sich Exemplare, "bei denen die Herabbiegung der Suturen allmählich abnimmt und gleichzeitig die Knötchen-Skulptur kräftiger wird" (HILTERMANN und KOCH, 1955, S. 367). Während des ganzen unteren Unter-Maastricht findet eine solche evolutorisch fliessende Populations-Änderung in Form einer allmählichen Schwerpunkt-Verlagerung von *B. laevigatus* zu *B. peterssoni* über alle Stufen von Zwischenformen hinweg statt, die man in grossen Individuenzahlen beobachten kann und die daher offenbar auch lokal hier stattgefunden hat.

Ganz ähnlich und nur wenig später, erst im unteren Unter-Maastricht beginnend und im oberen Unter-Maastricht endend, findet die Entwicklung von *B. decoratus decoratus* zu *B. decoratus giganteus* statt. Das Fehlen grosser Individuenzahlen besonders im Unter-Maastricht deutet jedoch hier auf eine regionale Verschiebung des Entwicklungs-Zentrums hin.

Diese Beobachtungen zeigen, dass nicht nur trinomisch zu kennzeichnende "geographische Rassen", sondern in erster Linie sogar die verschiedenen regelrechten Arten in z.T. verschiedenen Räumen entstanden sein müssen. Dies gilt auch für *B. delicatulus*. Individuen- und formenreiche Populationen sprechen dafür, dass viele Entwicklungs-Impulse vom amerikanischen Lebensraum ausgegangen sind. So ist die enge Verwandtschaft mit *B. strigillatus*, die schon von CUSHMAN (1927) bei Aufstellung von *B. delicatulus* als Unterart von *B. decoratus* betont wird, im mittleren und nördlichen Europa nur durch vereinzelt vorkommende "Zwischenformen" (= "*B.* cf. *austinanus*") angedeutet. Dagegen sind in Amerika fliessende Übergänge von *B. strigillatus* zu *B. austinanus* und zu *B. delicatulus* an zahlreichen Individuen festzustellen. Auch die frühen *B. delicatulus*-Populationen des europäischen Unter-Campan sind im Vergleich zu den amerikanischen Vorkommen in Europa meistens individuenarm und von geringer Variationsbreite. CUSHMAN (1927) gibt von *B. decoratus delicatulus* als Verbreitung "Upper Cretaceous. Velasco shale." an und erweitert in nachfolgenden Arbeiten an Hand weiterer Proben deren vertikale Reichweite und Variabilität, wie von HILTERMANN und KOCH (1950, S. 614) näher ausgeführt wurde.

Wichtig erscheint dabei die später erfolgte Ausdehnung bis auf das Unter-Campan! Die Zusammengehörigkeit dieser alten Formen mit den jüngeren aus dem Bereich um das Dan, die von CUSHMAN (1946) sogar subspezifisch zusammengefasst wurden, lässt sich an ausreichendem Material feststellen und belegen. Neben dem ovalen Querschnitt und der durchweg schlanken Gehäuseform ist besonders die schwächere, verwaschene Knotenskulptur charakteristisch. Im Ober-Campan und im Unter-Maastricht nimmt auch in Europa der Individuenreichtum der Populationen zu. Eine allmähliche Verschiebung der Variationsbreite führt zu der stratigraphisch an diesen Bereich gebundenen mit feiner Skulptur gleichmässig bedeckten Form: Diese europäische Hauptform gehört in der von HILTERMANN und KOCH (1950) vorgenommenen Determination zur selbständigen Entwicklungsreihe der *delicatulus-*Formen. Dabei ist eine Zusammenfassung und eine Rangerhöhung zur Art richtig: Die CUSHMAN'sche Erstbeschreibung wäre als *B. delicatulus delicatulus* zu bezeichnen; die Form aus dem Ober-Campan und Unter-Maastricht, die REISS (1954, S. 158) *B. regularis* nennt, ist dann *B. delicatulus regularis*. Während Verbreitung und Entwicklung dieser Reihe in Amerika und im nördlichen Europa etwa gleich sind — von Schwankungen beim Einsetzen, in der Häufigkeit und der Variationsbreite abgesehen — treten bereits in der europäischen Tethys die älteren Entwicklungsformen zurück. Es besteht also die Tatsache, dass in Amerika und Europa morphologisch nicht unterscheidbare Exemplare einmal im Unter-Campan und dann im Dan auftreten. Auseinandergehende Auffassungen über Zugehörigkeit und Benennung dieser morphologisch zusammengehörenden älteren und jüngeren Entwicklungsformen dürften hauptsächlich dadurch entstanden sein, dass in den verschiedenen Lebensräumen nicht alle Entwicklungsstufen auftreten. Bei Weiterverfolgung der *delicatulus-*Gruppe sind in Israel von REISS (1954) bisher nur noch jüngste Vertreter im "Dano-Paleocene" festgestellt worden, die *B. delicatulus delicatulus* und *B. delicatulus curtus* genannt werden müssen und beide mit amerikanischen und europäischen Funden zu identifizieren sind. In Australien wurde dagegen bisher nur die ältere im Unter-Campan an *B. strigillatus* anschliessende Form von EDGELL (1954, S. 74, Tafel 14, 7) gefunden ("*B.* cf. *delicatulus*").

Etwa parallel zur *delicatulus-*Reihe verläuft eine weitere, ebenfalls von *B.* cf. *austinanus* als Ausgangsform abzuleitende Entwicklungsfolge mit den bekanntesten Formen *B. laevigatus* und *B. peterssoni*. Charakteristisch sind hier die zu einem scharfen Rand flach auslaufenden Gehäuseformen, die im mittleren Teil Knotenskulptur tragen und aussen die Suturen sichtbar werden lassen. Von dieser ist in Deutschland die älteste abtrennbare Art von HOFKER (1957) *B. granulatus* (unterteilt in *B. granulatus* und *B. granulatus primitivus*) genannt worden. Phyletisch vergleichbare Äquivalente sind in Amerika *B. texanus*, in Israel *B. pustulatus*. Im mittleren Europa ist die im Ober-Campan phyletisch nachfolgende Form *B. laevigatus* völlig ident mit den in gleichaltem amerikanischem Probenmaterial gefundenen Exemplaren. Das gleiche gilt für die nachfolgende jüngere Entwicklungsform dieser Reihe: *B. peterssoni*. Im mittleren und nördlichen Europa sind jedoch Variationsbreite und besonders der Individuen-Reichtum der *laevigatus-* und *peterssoni-*Populationen bedeutend reicher. In Kleinasien verläuft die Entwicklung ganz ähnlich, soweit das uns zur Verfügung stehende Material schon eine solche Verallgemeinerung zulässt. Nach REISS (1954) wird lediglich die specifische Unterteilung der Reihe anders aufgefasst: *B. pustulatus* leitet phylogenetisch über *B. compressus* und *B. praecursor* ebenfalls zu *B. peterssoni*. Es ist auch die Möglichkeit geographisch bedingter Sonderentwicklungen nicht auszuschliessen. Für die Beurteilung der Frage, inwieweit *B. texanus* CUSHMAN 1937, *B. pustulatus* REISS 1954 und *B. granulatus* HOFKER 1957 synonym sind, reicht unser Material noch nicht aus.

TABELLE I

SCHEMATISCHE DARSTELLUNG DER BESCHRIEBENEN PHYLOGENETISCHEN ZUSAMMENHÄNGE
BEI BOLIVINOIDES

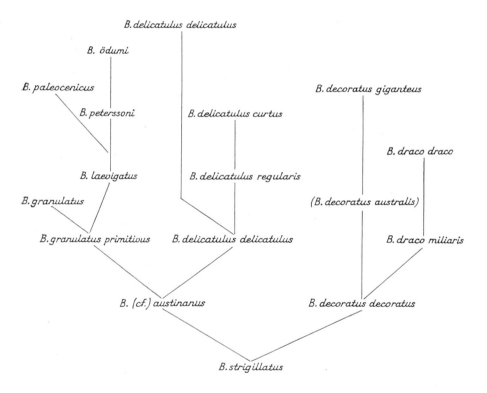

Die bereits erwähnte Entwicklungsreihe der *B. decoratus*-Gruppe zeigt bereits im höheren Campan die Entwicklungsrichtung zu *B. decoratus giganteus* an: Vergrösserung und Verbreiterung der Gehäuse, Entwicklung der Knotenskulptur zu Rippen und Ausdehnung über fast das ganze Gehäuse. Lokale bis regionale Verschiebungen von Entwicklungsstufen deuten auf das Wandern von Entwicklungszentren hin. Tatsächlich ist jedoch fast überall in der Welt die Identität sowohl der Anfangs- als auch der Endstufe der *B. decoratus*-Reihe feststellbar; auch stratigraphisch sind diese an die gleichen Schichten, nämlich an das mittlere Campan und das Ober-Maastricht gebunden!

TABELLE II

DIE STRATIGRAPHISCHE VERBREITUNG VON BOLIVINOIDES-FORMEN AUS DEM UNTERSUCHTEN MATERIAL

	B. strigillatus	B. decoratus decoratus	B. decoratus giganteus	B. draco miliaris	B. draco draco	B. (cf.) austinanus	B. delicatulus delicatulus	B. delicatulus regularis	B. delicatulus curtus	B. granulatus primitivus	B. granulatus	B. laevigatus	B. peterssoni	B. paleocenicus	B. ödumi
Dan (bis Paläozän)							● ● ●		● ● ●					●	● ●
Ober-Maastricht			█		█		● ● ●	● ●	●					●	● ●
Unter-Maastricht	● ●	●	█	●	█ ●		● ● ●	█				●	█ ●	▮	
Ober-Campan	█		●	█		●	● ● ●	█ ●		█	● ●	● ●	●		
Unter-Campan	●	●				● ●	● ●			█ ●	●	●			
Ober-Santon	█														

■■ = Normalvorkommen, ● ● ● ● = Vereinzelt

Eine von EDGELL (1954) in Australien gefundene Form stellt stratigraphisch und evolutorisch die unmittelbar vor *B. decoratus giganteus* auftretende und zu dieser überleitende Entwicklungsform dar (*B. decoratus australis*, eine Form, die zumindest in nordwest Deutschland relativ selten ist, da hier im tieferen Unter-Maastricht durchweg nur vereinzelte Individuen der *decoratus*-Gruppe auftreten. HILTERMANN und KOCH (1950) trennten *B. decoratus giganteus* von *B. decoratus decoratus* in erster Linie —

von der Gehäusegrösse und dem L/Br-Index abgesehen — durch das Vorherrschen der zu Rippen verschmolzenen Knotenreihen und deren Ausdehnung ab. Da dies gleichzeitig mit der wieder eintretenden grösseren Häufigkeit der Art vom oberen Unter-Maastricht an der Fall ist, hat sich unsere Unterteilung als zweckmässig erwiesen. Das Vorhandensein von fliessenden Übergängen spricht dagegen, diese beiden Formenkreise als gesonderte Arten zu trennen. Es besteht ohne weiteres die Möglichkeit, aus diesen noch weitere Formen morphologisch abzutrennen. Ob es richtig ist, solche Zwischenformen noch weiter subspezifisch zu determinieren, muss die Erfassung möglichst vieler Merkmale und ihre objektive metrische Auswertung ergeben.

Wie schon erwähnt wurde, setzt in Mittel-Europa im Ober-Campan — nach vorherigem Auftreten von vereinzelten von *B. decoratus* herleitenden "Übergangsformen" — *B. draco miliaris* ein, und zwar verhältnismässig abrupt mit reichen Populationen. Dieser Übergang ist in südlichen Faziesbereichen, besonders aber auch im amerikanischen Raum kontinuierlich und mit grösseren Individuenzahlen belegt. Auch die Variationsbreite ist hier grösser. Es liegen Populationen vor, in denen eine Trennung von *B. draco miliaris* und *B. decoratus* nur schwer und teilweise nicht möglich ist. Die Entwicklung zu *B. draco draco* ist demgegenüber im mittleren und nördlichen Europa wieder besonders gut zu beobachten. Die nur allmählich abwandelnden, verschiedenen phylogenetischen Stadien (in der Ausrichtung der Knoten an der Mittelfurche und bei den quer über die Kammern verlaufenden Reihen bis zur Verschmelzung zu durchlaufenden Rippen) können für feinstratigraphische Datierungen benutzt werden. Vom oberen Unter-Maastricht an (in nordwest Deutschland) tritt dann in der Häufigkeit mit *B. decoratus giganteus* wechselnd nur noch *B. draco draco* auf.

Unter Voraussetzung stratigraphischer Äquivalenz der Fundschicht Neuseelands dürfte *B. dorreeni* FINLAY 1940 als eine "geographische Rasse" von *B. draco* anzusehen sein und sollte trinomisch benannt werden: *Bolivinoides draco dorreeni*, wie dies auch schon von REISS (1954) durchgeführt wurde. In Überbewertung von unregelmässigen Kammerverdickungen bei *B. draco draco*, die eine scheinbare zusätzliche Querrippung verursachen, ist von einigen Autoren auch bei europäischen und anderen Funden die Bezeichnung *B. dorreeni*, und zwar als Art oder Unterart angewandt worden. Bei diesen Formen erheben sich die seitlichen Kanten besonders dicker Kammern zwischen den senkrecht dazu verlaufenden Rippen und können so den Eindruck von Querverbindungen erwecken. Derartige Erscheinungen treten mehr oder weniger häufig neben der normalen Ausbildung von *B. draco draco* auf und sind nach bisherigen Beobachtungen ökologisch abhängig und können allenfalls lokalstratigraphisch von Bedeutung sein. Die Vertikalverbreitung von *B. draco dorreeni* liegt daher auch immer innerhalb der von *B. draco draco*. Die von HILTERMANN und KOCH (1950) zugunsten von *B. draco draco* eingezogene *B. rhomboidea* CUSHMAN 1926 ist als echtes Synonym invalid. Es ist also damit in der amerikanischen Oberkreide die echte *B. draco draco* nachgewiesen.

TAXONOMISCHE HINWEISE

Für die meisten behandelten Formen befinden sich im Oberkreide-Kapitel (HILTER-MANN und KOCH, 1962) des SIMON'schen Abrisses "Leitfossilien der Mikropaläontologie" Diagnosen und Bestimmungszitate. Dies betrifft:

Bolivinoides strigillatus (CHAPMAN 1892)
Bolivinoides granulatus HOFKER 1957
Bolivinoides laevigatus (MARIE 1941)
Bolivinoides peterssoni BROTZEN 1945
Bolivinoides paleocenicus (BROTZEN 1948)
Bolivinoides decoratus decoratus (JONES 1886)
Bolivinoides decoratus giganteus HILTERMANN und KOCH 1950
Bolivinoides draco miliaris HILTERMANN und KOCH 1950
Bolivinoides draco draco (MARSSON 1878)
Bolivinoides delicatulus regularis (REISS 1954), dort noch aufgeführt als *B. decoratus delicatulus*.

Ergänzend, besonders in Bezug auf Synonymik und weitere ausführliche Angaben sind die Arbeiten von HILTERMANN und KOCH (1950, 1955), EDGELL (1954), POZARYSKA (1954), REISS (1954) und HOFKER (1957) wichtig.

Als Fassungen von *B. delicatulus delicatulus* (REISS 1954) und *B. delicatulus curtus* (REISS 1954) sind die von REISS (1954) für *B. delicatulus* und *B. curtus* aufgestellten Definitionen anzuwenden. Betreff *B. ödumi* (BROTZEN 1948) siehe BROTZEN (1948, S. 65) und HOFKER (1957, S. 255). *B. austinanus* CUSHMAN 1937 wurde zuletzt von CUSHMAN (1946, S. 112) noch einmal abgebildet und charakterisiert.

SUMMARY

The author adheres to the narrow concept of *Bolivinoides* as introduced by CUSHMAN, and discusses approximately twenty forms of stratigraphical importance from the Upper Cretaceous, of which he also gives illustrations. On the basis of very rich material in the shape of specimens from Europe and outside Europe, the connections between the species and subspecies are investigated. Attention is paid to the true biological correlations, and with them to the phylogeny and geographical-ecological influences. It can be proved that individual groups of forms show worldwide analogies in the course of development. Provided morphology agrees, they also bear a uniform nomenclature. The supposed phylogenetic relations are represented graphically, and a table gives the stratigraphic range of fifteen forms.

LITERATUR

BETTENSTAEDT, F., 1958. Phylogenetische Beobachtungen in der Mikropaläontologie. *Paläontol. Z.,* 32 : 115–140.
BROTZEN, F., 1948. The Swedish Paleocene and its foraminiferal fauna. *Sveriges Geol. Undersökn. Avhandl., Ser. C,* 493 : 1–140.

CUSHMAN, J. A., 1927. American Upper Cretaceous species of *Bolivina* and related species. *Contrib. Cushman Lab. Foraminiferal Research*, 2 : 85–91.

CUSHMAN, J. A., 1946. Upper Cretaceous Foraminifera of the Gulf Coastal Region of the United States and Adjacent Areas. *U.S. Geol. Surv. Profess. Papers*, 206 : 1–241.

EDGELL, H. S., 1954. The stratigraphical value of *Bolivinoides* in the Upper Cretaceous of Northwest Australia. *Contrib. Cushman Found. Foraminiferal Research*, 5 : 68–76.

FRIZZELL, D. L., 1954. *Handbook of Cretaceous Foraminifera of Texas*. Bur. Econ. Geol. Univ. Texas, Rept. 22, Austin, (Texas). 232 pp.

GALLITELLI, E. M., 1957. A revision of the foraminiferal family Heterohelicidae. *U.S. Natl. Museum, Bull.*, 215 : 133–154.

HAGN, H., 1953. Die Foraminiferen der Pinswanger Schichten (Unteres Obercampan). *Palaeontograph.*, 104 (A) : 1–119.

HILTERMANN, H., 1949. Foraminiferen als Leitfossilien der Oberkreide NW-Deutschlands. *Intern. Geol. Congr. 18. Sess., Gt. Brit.* 1948, 43–49.

HILTERMANN, H., 1951. Populationen in ihrer Bedeutung für die Paläontologie und Stratigraphie. *Z. Erdöl Kohle*, 4 : 244–249.

HILTERMANN, H., 1952. Stratigraphische Fragen des Campan und Maastricht unter besonderer Berücksichtigung der Mikropaläontologie. *Geol. Jahrb.*, 67 : 47–66.

HILTERMANN, H., 1954. Zur Artfassung in der Paläontologie. *Roemeriana*, 1 : 385–392.

HILTERMANN, H., 1956. Ten rules concerning the nomenclature and classification of the Foraminifera. *Micropaleontol.*, 2 : 296–298.

HILTERMANN, H., 1958. Spezielle Arbeitsgebiete der Mikropaläontologie 1. Foraminiferen. In: H. FREUND, *Handbuch der Mikroskopie in der Technik*, 2, (3) *(Mikropaläontol.)* Umschau Verlag, Frankfurt am Main, pp. 167–189.

HILTERMANN, H. und KOCH, W., 1950. Taxonomie und Vertikalverbreitung von Bolivinoides-Arten im Senon Nordwestdeutschlands. *Geol. Jahrb.*, 64 : 595–632. (hier weitere Literatur).

HILTERMANN, H. und KOCH, W., 1955. Biostratigraphie der Grenzschichten Maastricht-Campan in Lüneburg und in der Bohrung Brunhilde. 2 Teil: Foraminiferen. *Geol. Jahrb.*, 70 : 357–383.

HILTERMANN, H. und KOCH, W., 1962. Oberkreide, nördliches Mitteleuropa. In: W. SIMON, *Leitfossilien der Mikropaläontol.* Borntraeger, Berlin (im Druck) pp. 216–245.

HOFKER, J., 1952. Zur Fassung der Foraminiferengattung *Bolivinoides* CUSHMAN, 1927. *Geol. Jahrb.* 66 : 377–382.

HOFKER, J., 1956. Die *Pseudotextularia*-Zone der Bohrung Maasbüll I und ihre Foraminiferen-Fauna. *Paläontol. Z.*, 30 : 59–79.

HOFKER, J., 1957. Foraminiferen der Oberkreide von Nordwestdeutschland und Holland. *Geol. Jahrb., Beih.* 27 : 1–464.

HOFKER, J., 1958. The gliding change in *Bolivinoides* during time. *Natuurhist. Maandbl.*, 47 : 145–159.

HOFKER, J., 1958. Upper Cretaceous *Bolivinoides* guide forms. *Micropaleontol.*, 4 : 329–333.

HOFKER, J., 1961. Die Foraminiferen-Fauna der Gruben Hemmoor und Basbeck. *Paläontol. Z.*, 35 : 123–145.

POZARYSKA, K., 1954. The Upper Cretaceous Index Foraminifers from Central Poland. *Acta geol. Polon.*, 4 : 59–72, 249–276.

REISS, Z., 1954. Upper Cretaceous and Lower Tertiary *Bolivinoides* from Israel. *Contrib. Cushman Found. Foraminiferal Research*, 5 : 154–164.

REYMENT, R. A., 1959. The foraminiferal genera *Afrobolivina* gen. nov. and *Bolivina* in the Upper Cretaceous and Lower Tertiary of West Africa. *Stockholm Contrib. Geol.*, 3 : 1–57.

RICHTER, R., 1948. *Einführung in die Zoologische Nomenklatur durch Erläuterung der Internationalen Regeln*. Kramer, Frankfurt/M., 252 pp.

SIMPSON, G. G., 1951. *Zeitmasse und Ablaufformen der Evolution*. Messerschmidt, Göttingen, 331 pp.

WEDEKIND, R., 1940. Die papillaten Flabellinen der Kreide und die Stufengliederung des Senons. *Neues Jahrb. Mineral. Geol. Beil.* 84 (b) : 177–204.

TAFEL I

1. *Bolivinoides delicatulus delicatulus* (CUSHMAN).
Unteres Ober-Campan, Bl. Drensteinfurt, Westfalen. In einer Population mit *B. laevigatus* und *B. decoratus* vorkommend und durch die schmale Gehäuseform mit der verwaschenen Skulptur auffallend.
T.K. Nr. 4109. L: 0,35 mm.

2–3. Zwischenformen: *B. strigillatus* – *B. decoratus*.
Aus dem hohen Unter-Campan NE. Hannover. Sowohl Gehäuseform als auch Ausbildung der Knotenskulptur liegen zwischen den für die beiden Arten typischen Formen.
2. T.K. Nr. 4110. L : 0,38 mm.
3. T.K. Nr. 4111. L : 0,39 mm.

4–6. *B. delicatulus delicatulus* (CUSHMAN).
4. Unteres Ober-Campan, Ahlen, Westfalen. Besonders der verflachte Rand weist auf die phyletische Herkunft von *B. austinanus*.
T.K. Nr. 4112. L: 0,41 mm.
5. Lower Taylor, E. New Braunfels, Texas. Nur durch geeignete Präparation konnte die verwaschene Skulptur plastisch sichtbar betont werden. In natürlicher Erhaltung: Tafel II, 19.
T.K. Nr. 4113. L: 0,40 mm.
6. Grenzbereich Unter-/Ober-Campan, E. Münster, Westfalen. Dieses Exemplar ist dem von CUSHMAN 1927 (Tafel 12, Fig. 8) abgebildeten Holotypus aus dem Velasco shale (in Mexico) besonders ähnlich.
T.K. Nr. 4114. L: 0,51 mm.

7–9. Zwischenformen: *B. strigillatus* – *B. decoratus*.
Aus dem hohen Unter-Campan.
7. NE. Hannover. Die "*strigillatus*-Skulptur" hat sich bei diesem Exemplar nicht mit dem Gehäuse in die Breite ausgedehnt, sondern bleibt vielmehr eng zusammen (wie auf schmalen *strigillatus*-Typen!), ohne den Aussenrand zu bedecken.
T.K. Nr. 4115. L: 0,56 mm.
8. Hardivilliers, N. Paris.
T.K. Nr. 4116. L: 0,43 mm.
9. NE. Hannover.
T.K. Nr. 4117. L: 0,38 mm.

10. *B. delicatulus delicatulus* (CUSHMAN).
Upper Austin, Lamar County, Texas.
T.K. Nr. 4118. L: 0,48 mm.

11. *B. austinanus* CUSHMAN.
. Mooreville Chalk, Pickens County, Alabama.
Die für diese schmale Art typische schwache Skulptur konnte nur durch geeignete Präparation und entsprechende Beleuchtung so plastisch sichtbar gemacht werden. Bei normaler Erhaltung sind nur die Vertiefungen zu sehen, wie sie bisher auch alle Abbildungen von dieser Art zeigen.
T.K. Nr. 4119. L: 0,53 mm.

12–13. *B. strigillatus* (CHAPMAN).
Austin, Bell County, Texas. Knotenausbildung und Gehäuseumriss stellen diese Formen zu *B. strigillatus*; der ovale Querschnitt zeigt jedoch bereits unverkennbar die Entwicklungstendenz zu *B. austinanus* an.
12. T.K. Nr. 4120. L: 0,41 mm.
13. T.K. Nr. 4121. L: 0,33 mm.

14. Zwischenform: *B. strigillatus* – *B. austinanus*.
Burdit chalk member, Travis County, Texas.
T.K. Nr. 4122. L: 0,33 mm.

15. *B. austinanus* Cushman.

Austin, Collin County, Texas. Auch diese breitere Ausbildung der Art besitzt (neben dem ovalen Querschnitt) die charakteristische schwache "Grübchen-Skulptur", die auf der breiteren Gehäuse-oberfläche auch entsprechend verbreitert und vergröbert ist (im Verhältnis zum schmaleren Exemplar 11).
T.K. Nr. 4123. L: 0,37 mm.

16. *B. strigillatus* (Chapman).

Unter-Campan, Hannover. Breite Form mit 2–3 Knotenreihen je Seitenhälfte. Nicht präpariert; die belassenen Sedimentreste (weiss) zwischen den Knoten machen diese deutlich.
T.K. Nr. 4124. L: 0,43 mm.

17, 20. *B.* cf. *austinanus*.

Unter-Campan, Bohrung im Emsland. Vergleiche dieser nordwestdeutschen Formen mit den Exemplaren 14 und 15 zeigen deutlich ihre phyletische Stellung: Es sind die unmittelbaren Nach-folgeformen von *B. strigillatus*, von denen nach bisherigen Beobachtungen *B. delicatulus* und *B. granulatus* abzuleiten sind. Charakteristisch sind die "reduzierte *strigillatus*-Skulptur" und der ovale Querschnitt dieser flacheren Gehäuse als die von *B. strigillatus*.
17. T.K. Nr. 4125. L: 0,41 mm.
20. T. K. Nr. 4128. L: 0,50 mm.

18. *B. strigillatus* (Chapman).

Unter-Campan, Hannover. Schmale Form mit anfangs einer, in der jüngeren Hälfte mit zwe Knotenreihen je Seitenhälfte. Ebenfalls wie Expl. 16 nicht präpariert.
T.K. Nr. 4126. L: 0,44 mm.

19. *B. strigillatus* (Chapman).

Austin, Bell County, Texas. Eines der relativ seltenen Exemplare mit ausgeprägter Knotenbildung. Jedoch sind diese Formen im Querschnitt nicht so aufgetrieben wie die aus Europa, Australien oder Vorderasien: Die Entwicklungsrichtung zu *B. austinanus* erscheint bereits angezeigt.
T.K. Nr. 4127. L: 0,33 mm.

20. Siehe bei 17.

21. *B. angulatus* Reiss.

Unter-Campan, Israel. Dieses breit-keilförmige Gehäuse besitzt nur eine Reihe länglicher Über-lappungsknoten auf jeder Seitenhälfte; zusammen mit den beiden auf der Gehäuseschmalseite sind es vier auf jeder Kammerzeile, wie bei den schmalen Formen von *B. strigillatus*. Die hier ohne Zunahme von Knotenreihen erfolgte Verbreiterung dürfte die hohlkehlenartige Vertiefung dieser Extremform (Reiss 1954, Tafel 28 zeigt bei seinen abgebildeten Exemplaren mehr Knotenreihen) bewirkt haben. Auch die an *Eouvigerina* erinnernde Kammerform rührt daher. Das gleiche Exem-plar von verschiedenen Seiten: (*a*) präpariert, (*b*) unpräpariert.
T.K. Nr. 4129. L : 0,28 mm.

22–23. *B. strigillatus* (Chapman).

Unter-Campan, NE. Hannover. Bis zu sieben Knotenreihen werden auf einer Kammerzeile am Mündungsende erreicht!
22. T.K. Nr. 4130. L: 0,43 mm.
23. T.K. Nr. 4131. L: 0,36 mm.

24. *B. strigillatus* (Chapman).

Ober-Santon, NW. Australien. Das typische, im Querschnitt fast runde Gehäuse weist 6–7 Knoten-reihen auf jeder Kammerzeile auf. Die vorliegenden Exemplare sind durchweg etwas zierlicher und feiner ausgebildet als die europäischen.
T.K. Nr. 4190. L: 0,31 mm.

Die Exemplare Nr. 8, 16, 18, 21b sind in natürlicher Erhaltung, alle anderen nach besonderer Präpa-rierung (meist chemische Versilberung) photographiert worden.
Alle abgebildeten Exemplare befinden sich in der Bundesanstalt für Bodenforschung, Hannover, unter der angegebenen Typenkatalog-Nr. (T.K. Nr.).
L = Längenabmessung.

TAFEL I

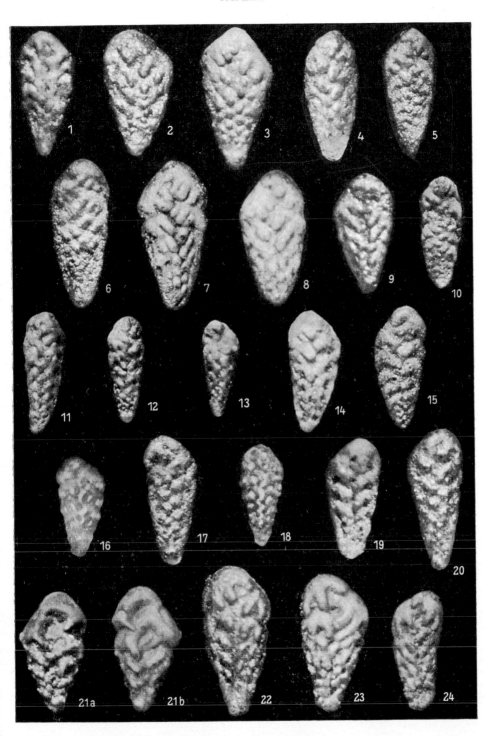

TAFEL II

1–3. *B. peterssoni* BROTZEN.
1. Oberes Ober-Maastricht, Stevns Klint, Dänemark. Sehr stark (besonders im unteren Gehäuseteil) skulptiertes Exemplar.
T.K. Nr. 4132. L: 0,35 mm.
2. Unteres Unter-Maastricht, Lüneburg. (*a*) In natürlicher Erhaltung. (*b*) Präpariert, um photographisch die Knotenbildung plastischer darstellen zu können.
T.K. Nr. 4133. L: 0,38 mm.
3. Oberes Ober-Maastricht, Mariager, Dänemark. Exemplar mit zahlreichen, aber schwach ausgebildeten Skulpturknoten. (*a*) Präpariert. (*b*) Normale Erhaltung.
T.K. Nr. 4134. L: 0,41 mm.

4. Zwischenform: *B. laevigatus* – *B. granulatus*.
Oberes Ober-Campan, Lüneburg. (*a*) Präpariert erscheint die Oberflächenskulptur. (*b*) In normaler Erhaltung sind die stark abfallenden Suturen sichtbar.
T.K. Nr. 4135. L: 0,48 mm.

5. *B. granulatus* HOFKER.
Oberes Unter-Campan, S. Münster, Westfalen. Präpariert, um die charakteristische Knotenbildung deutlich zu machen, die sich als "Granulierung" auch auf den Initialteil erstreckt. Ebenfalls typisch sind die schräg abwärts gerichteten Suturen.
T.K. Nr. 4136. L: 0,46 mm.

6–10. *B. laevigatus* (MARIE).
Verschiedene Gehäuseformen, 7–10, unpräpariert.
6. Pecan Gap, W. Taylor, Texas. Exemplar mit besonders kräftiger Knotenbildung, die zudem durch Präparierung noch plastisch hervorgehoben wurde.
T.K. Nr. 4137. L: 0,37 mm.
7. Unteres Unter-Maastricht, Lüneburg.
T.K. Nr. 4138. L: 0,38 mm.
8–9. Ober-Campan, W. Kiel, Schleswig-Holstein.
8. T.K. Nr. 4139. L: 0,41 mm.
9. T.K. Nr. 4140. L: 0,39 mm.
10. Lower Taylor, E. New Braunfels, Texas.
T.K. Nr. 4141. L: 0,30 mm.

11–13. *B. granulatus* HOFKER.
11. Oberes Unter-Campan, S. Münster, Westfalen.
Die verwaschene Knotenskulptur auf dem jüngeren Gehäuseteil deutet auf *B. delicatulus*. Die rauhe Granulierung auf dem Initialteil, die stark abwärts gerichteten Suturen sowie der zugeschärfte Rand ermöglichen eine Determination.
T.K. Nr. 4142. L: 0,41 mm.
12. Annona (middle Taylor), NE. Clarksville, Texas. Breite Form, präpariert.
T.K. Nr. 4143. L: 0,27 mm.
13. Unteres Ober-Campan, S. Münster, Westfalen. Diese besonders charakteristische "ältere" Form ist gekennzeichnet durch verschiedene Skulpturknoten. Auf dem älteren Teil befindet sich anfangs eine rauhe Granulierung, der längliche, gratig-scharfe Knoten folgen. Die letzten Kammern dagegen sind mit runden, verwaschenen Überlappungsknoten (wie bei *B. laevigatus*) besetzt. Nicht präpariert.
T.K. Nr. 4144. L: 0,36 mm.

14. *B. texanus* CUSHMAN.
Lower Taylor, Collin County, Texas. Wegen der stärkeren Granulierung am Initialteil und der breiten Gehäuseform wurde das Expl. Nr. 12 zu *B. granulatus* gestellt. Vergleiche zwischen allen abgebildeten Exemplaren von *B. texanus* und *B. granulatus* zeigen aber, dass es sich offenbar um eine Art handelt, innerhalb welcher allenfalls feine, geographisch bedingte Unterschiede für eine subspezifische Unterteilung sprechen.
T.K. Nr. 4145. L: 0,34 mm.

15. *B.* cf. *delicatulus.*
Unterstes Ober-Campan, Ahlen, Westfalen. Diese Form gehört eng zu *B. delicatulus delicatulus,* wenn auch der verflachende Rand eine Tendenz zu *B. laevigatus* andeutet. Vergleiche mit diesen (Expl. 7–10) zeigt deutlich die nahe Stellung zur typischen Ausbildung (Expl. 19).
T.K. Nr. 4146. L: 0,39 mm.

16. *B. texanus* CUSHMAN.
Wolfe City sand member/Taylor, W. Farmersville, Texas. Präpariert, um die Knotenbildung hervorzuheben.
T.K. Nr. 4147. L: 0,43 mm.

17. *B. pustulatus* REISS.
Unter-Campan, Israel. Präpariert, da photographisch sonst keine Zeichnung der Oberfläche zu erkennen war. Vergleiche u.a. besonders mit Expl. 5, zeigen die enge Verwandtschaft und deuten auf die besprochene geographisch bedingte Verlagerung der Variationsbreite.
T.K. Nr. 4148. L: 0,43 mm.

18. *B. texanus* CUSHMAN.
Austin, Collin County, Texas. Zusammen mit den Expl. 12, 14 und 16 zeigt diese Form Entwicklungsrichtung und Herkunft: Expl. 19 (dasselbe präpariert: Tafel I/5) wurde zum Vergleich daneben gestellt und zeigt, dass Ausbildung der Kammern, Suturen und der Knoten auf dem jüngeren Gehäuseteil nahezu gleich sind. Lediglich die rauhe „Granulierung" des Initialteils fehlt, und der Rand ist mehr gerundet anstatt zugeschärft. Tafel I zeigt *B. austinanus,* die Stammart dieser beiden, im ersten Entwicklungsstadium scheinbar nur geringe Unterschiede aufweisenden selbständigen Artenreihen.
T.K. Nr. 4149. L: 0,45 mm.

19. *B. delicatulus delicatulus* (CUSHMAN).
Lower Taylor, E. New Braunfels, Texas. Unpräpariert. Dasselbe Exemplar präpariert auf Tafel I/5, wo ein Vergleich mit Expl. I/15 den Ursprung dieser Art und den von *B. texanus* (bezw. *B. granulatus*) andeutet: *B. austinanus* dürfte als Stammart von beiden anzusehen sein. Wegen der oft sehr ähnlichen Ausbildungen bei verschiedenen Formenkreisen wurde dieses Exemplar in natürlicher Erhaltung zum Vergleich nochmal gebracht.

Die Exemplare 2a, 3b, 4b, 7, 8, 9, 10, 13, 14b, 15, 18b und 19 sind in natürlicher Erhaltung, alle anderen nach besonderer Präparierung (meist chemischer Versilberung) photographiert worden.
Alle abgebildeten Exemplare befinden sich in der Bundesanstalt für Bodenforschung, Hannover, unter der angegebenen Typenkatalog-Nr. (T.K. Nr.).
L = Längenabmessung.

TAFEL II

TAFEL III

1–2. *B. delicatulus delicatulus* (Cushman).
Beide unpräpariert; so scheinen unter der verwaschenen Knotenskulptur die Suturen schwach dunkel durch.
1. Aus dem Bereich Dan–Paleozän in Israel.
T.K. Nr. 4150. L: 0,47 mm.
2. Aus der *Globorotalia uncinata*-Zone Bolli, im tiefen Paleozän (Lower Lizard Springs) von Trinidad.
T.K. Nr. 4151. L: 0,60 mm.

3. *B. paleocenicus* (Brotzen).
Unteres Unter-Maastricht, Lüneburg. (Siehe Hiltermann und Koch, 1955, Tafel 27, Fig. 3). Nicht präpariert, da sich die unregelmässige, knotige Skulptur über dazwischen befindlichen Kreideresten besser abhebt.
T.K. Nr. 1047. L: 0,33 mm.

4. *B. delicatulus curtus* (Reiss).
Aus dem Bereich Dan–Paleozän in Israel. (*a*) Unpräpariert, normale Erhaltung, die hellen Kalkreste lassen die Knotenskulptur dunkel erscheinen. (*b*) Nach der Präparation treten bei dem selben Exemplar die Knoten gegenüber den dunklen Vertiefungen plastisch hervor.
T.K. Nr. 4152. L: 0,36 mm.

5–6. *B. delicatulus delicatulus* (Cushman).
Beide präpariert, so dass die Oberfläche mit der verwaschenen Knotenskulptur plastischer hervortritt als bei den Exemplaren 1 und 2.
5. Aus dem Bereich Dan–Paleozän in Israel.
T.K. Nr. 4153. L: 0,48 mm.
6. Aus dem Dan N. Bidart (bei Biarritz), Frankreich.
T.K. Nr. 4154. L: 0,48 mm.

7. *B. delicatulus regularis* (Reiss).
Aus dem Unter-Maastricht in Lüneburg. (Siehe Hiltermann und Koch, 1955, S. 355, Tabelle 1: Probe Nr. 10887). Breites Exemplar.
T.K. Nr. 4155. L: 0,44 mm.

8–9. *B. delicatulus curtus* (Reiss).
Beide unpräpariert, zeigen auch in normaler Erhaltung die charakteristischen Skulpturelemente.
8. Ober-Maastricht N. Bidart (bei Biarritz), Frankreich. Die schmale Form hat noch keine so ausgeprägte und ausgedehnte Knotenbildung (wie dies bei den Exemplaren 4 und 9 der Fall ist) und kann daher als Vor- oder Zwischenform angesehen werden.
T.K. Nr. 4156. L: 0,34 mm.
9. Von der Typlokalität der Velasco-Formation in Mexico: Typisches Exemplar.
T.K. Nr. 4157. L: 0,33 mm.

10. *B. delicatulus delicatulus* (Cushman).
Ober-Maastricht N. Bidart (bei Biarritz), Frankreich. Die gestreckte Gehäuseform zusammen mit der etwas verwaschenen Skulptur kennzeichnet die Nominatunterart. (*a*) Präpariert wirkt die Oberfläche besonders plastisch. (*b*) Dasselbe Exemplar in normaler Erhaltung lässt die Skulptur weniger deutlich hervortreten.
T.K. Nr. 4158. L: 0,44 mm.

11–12. *B. delicatulus regularis* (Reiss).
11. Aus der Marshalltown Formation, New Yersey. Breites Exemplar.
T.K. Nr. 4159. L: 0,42 mm.
12. Unter-Maastricht, Lüneburg. (Siehe Hiltermann und Koch, 1955, S. 355, Tabelle 1 : Probe Nr. 15463). Schmales Exemplar. (*a*) Durch die Präparation wird Oberfläche mit Skulptur betont. (*b*) In normaler Erhaltung fällt bei demselben Exemplar die Knotenbildung durch die glasige Oberfläche weniger plastisch auf; dafür scheinen die Suturen schwach (dunkel) durch.
T.K. Nr. 4160. L: 0,55 mm.

13–14. *B. delicatulus delicatulus* (CUSHMAN).
13. Unteres Ober-Campan, S. Münster, Westfalen. Typisches Exemplar. (*a* + *c*) Präpariert, beide Seiten. (*b*) Unpräpariert, natürlich erhalten. (Die drei Abbildungen desselben Exemplars sollen Darstellungsfehler weitgehend und möglichst objektiv ausschalten).
T.K. Nr. 4161. L: 0,50 mm.
14. Pecan Gap Chalk/Taylor Marl, SW. Wolfe City, Texas. Präpariert, um die schwache Skulptur möglichst plastisch sichtbar zu machen.
T.K. Nr. 4162. L: 0,38 mm.

15. *B. decoratus decoratus* (JONES).
Ober-Campan, SE. Münster, Westfalen. Solche kleinwüchsigen, fein und oft sehr regelmässig skulptierten Exemplare, die lokal ganze Populationen bilden, können den Eindruck von "Zwischenformen" (zw. *B. decoratus* und *B. delicatulus regularis*) erwecken. Beobachtungen an stratigraphisch aufeinanderfolgenden Populationen in verschiedenen Profilen klärten die taxonomische Stellung und deuten auf oekologische Einflüsse hinsichtlich Wachstum und Ausbildung. Um die Skulpturverhältnisse genau zu erkennen, sind wegen der verschiedenen Vergrösserungsmassstäbe Vergleiche mit den Grössenangaben der abgebildeten Exemplare von *B. delicatulus regularis* erforderlich.
T.K. Nr. 4163. L: 0,48 mm.

16. *B. delicatulus delicatulus* (CUSHMAN).
Unteres Ober-Campan, Ahlen, Westfalen. In natürlicher Erhaltung, unpräpariert. Die typische verwaschene Skulptur lässt die Suturen schwach durchscheinen.
T.K. Nr. 4164. L: 0,48 mm.

17–18. *B. delicatulus delicatulus* (CUSHMAN).
Annona Chalk (Middle Taylor), Red River County, Texas. Beide Exemplare wurden präpariert, um die schwache, typisch-verwaschene Skulptur deutlich zu machen.
17. Mikrosphär.
T.K. Nr. 4165. L: 0,32 mm.
18. Megalosphär.
T.K. Nr. 4166. L: 0,46 mm.

19. Zwischenform: *B. delicatulus delicatulus* – *B. delicatulus regularis*.
Unteres Ober-Campan, Ahlen, Westfalen. Das nicht präparierte Exemplar zeigt im Vergleich zu Expl. 16 eine Zunahme und Verdeutlichung schlanker Knoten, wie sie in grösserer Zahl und regelmässig angeordnet für *B. delicatulus regularis* kennzeichnend sind.
T.K. Nr. 4167. L: 0,44 mm.

20. *B. delicatulus regularis* (REISS).
Demopolis Chalk, Lowndes County, Alabama. Ein Vergleich mit der Grösse von Nr. 15 dürfte die verschiedenen Namen trotz der Ähnlichkeit erklären. Hinzu kommt, dass dieses (kleinere) Exemplar präpariert wurde, um die feine Skulptur überhaupt für die Photographie sichtbar zu machen.
T.K. Nr. 4168. L: 0,33 mm.

Die Exemplare Nr. 1, 2, 3, 4a, 8, 9, 10b, 12b, 13b, 15, 16 und 19 sind in natürlicher Erhaltung, alle anderen nach besonderer Präparierung (meist chemischer Versilberung) photographiert worden.
Alle abgebildeten Exemplare befinden sich in der Bundesanstalt für Bodenforschung, Hannover, unter der angegebenen Typenkatalog-Nr. (T.K. Nr.).
L = Längenabmessung.

TAFEL III

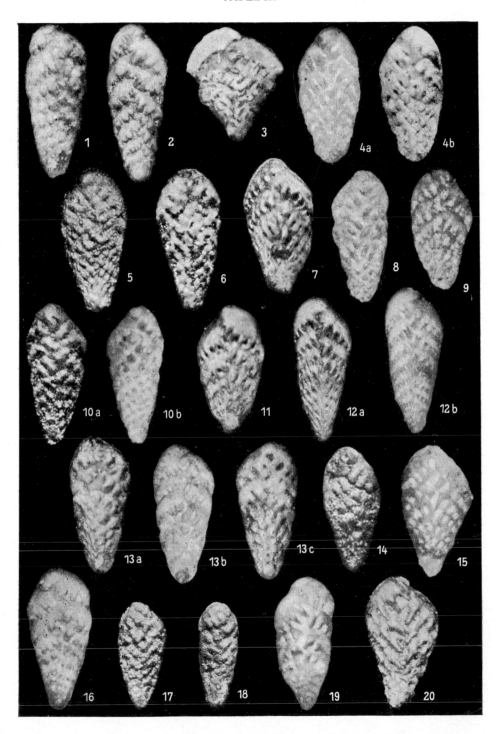

TAFEL IV

1–5. *B. decoratus giganteus* HILTERMANN und KOCH.
Gegenüber den folgenden ist bei diesen fünf Exemplaren eine Rippenbildung als vorherrschend klar zu erkennen — auch bei unregelmässigem Wachstum.
1. Oberes Ober-Maastricht, Mariager, Dänemark.
T.K. Nr. 4169. L: 0,76 mm.
2. Oberes Unter-Maastricht, Hemmoor, N. Deutschland. Dieses Exemplar zeigt die typische gleichmässige Rippenskulptur, wie sie im Unter-Maastricht einsetzt. Daneben kommen — bis in das Ober-Maastricht hineinreichend — unregelmässig unterbrochene und zu Einzelknoten aufgelöste oder versetzte Knotenreihen vor (wie z.B. Expl. 4).
T.K. Nr. 4170. L: 0,67 mm.
3, 4, 5. Oberes Ober-Maastricht, Mariager, Dänemark. 3. Breites Exemplar.
T.K. Nr. 4171. L: 0,58 mm.
4. Exemplar mit Einzelknoten.
T.K. Nr. 4172. L: 0,60 mm.
5. Exemplar, bei dem die verdickten Kammerseiten (ähnlich und von gleicher Ursache wie bei *B. draco* "*doreeni*"! — Vgl. Expl. 17) zwischen den Knotenreihen hervortreten und den Eindruck der durchlaufenden Rippen stören.
T.K. Nr. 4173. L: 0,73 mm.

6, 7. Zum Vergleich nebeneinander gestellt:
6. *B. decoratus decoratus* (JONES).
Oberes Ober-Campan, Lüneburg. (Siehe HILTERMANN und KOCH, 1955, S. 354, Tabelle 1 : Probe 17588).
T.K. Nr. 4174. L: 0,61 mm.
7. *B. decoratus australis* EDGELL.
Ober-Campan, NW. Australien.
T.K. Nr. 301. L: 0,62 mm.

8–9. *B. decoratus decoratus* (JONES).
Oberes Ober-Campan, Montereau, Frankreich.
8. T.K. Nr. 4175. L: 0,61 mm.
9. T.K. Nr. 4176. L: 0,52 mm.

10. *B. decoratus decoratus* (JONES).
Pecan Gap Chalk/Taylor, Wolfe City, Texas. Extrem schmales Exemplar.
T.K. Nr. 4177. L: 0,59 mm.

11. *B. decoratus decoratus* (JONES).
Ozan, Little River County, Arkansas. Relativ breites Exemplar.
T.K. Nr. 4178. L: 0,62 mm.

12 *B. decoratus decoratus* (JONES).
Oberes Ober-Campan, Lüneburg. Breites Exemplar. (Siehe HILTERMANN und KOCH, 1955, S. 354, Tabelle 1 : Probe Nr. 17587).
T.K. Nr. 4179. L: 0,55 mm.

13. *B. decoratus decoratus* (JONES).
Unterstes Maastricht, Abu Zehaima bei Suez.
T.K. Nr. 4180. L: 0,31 mm.

14. *B. decoratus decoratus* (JONES).
Unteres Ober-Campan, Ahlen, Westfalen. Schmales Exemplar.
T.K. Nr. 4181. L: 0,39 mm.

15. Zwischenform: *B. draco miliaris* – *B. decoratus*.
Annona Chalk, Middle Taylor, Red River County, Texas. Dieses schmale Exemplar hat zwar eine dem Expl. 14 ähnliche Gehäuseform, wird jedoch durch den zugeschärften Rand, die schmalen, gratigen Knoten und die angedeutete Mittelfurche als "Zwischenform" ausgewiesen.
T.K. Nr. 4182. L: 0,45 mm.

16–19. *B. draco draco* (MARSSON).
  16. Maastricht, NW. Australien.
  T.K. Nr. 4191. L: 0,48 mm.
  17, 18. Oberes Ober-Maastricht, Mariager, Dänemark.
  17. In natürlicher Erhaltung, mit Kreideresten zwischen den Rippen als Kontrast sind die hervortretenden Kammerseiten am besten zu erkennen, die eine scheinbare, zusätzliche Querrippung verursachen.
  T.K. Nr. 4183. L: 0,66 mm.
  18. Exemplar ohne hervortretende Kammerseiten.
  (*a*) Präpariert, um die Oberfläche möglichst plastisch erscheinen zu lassen. (*b*) Dasselbe Exemplar in natürlicher Erhaltung mit weissen Kreideresten.
  T.K. Nr. 4184. L: 0,56 mm.
  19. Ober-Maastricht, N. Bidart (bei Biarritz), Frankreich.
  T.K. Nr. 4185. L: 0,43 mm.

20. Zwischenform: *B. draco miliaris* – *B. draco draco*.
  Höheres Unter-Maastricht, Israel. Die Bezeichnung "Zwischenform" wurde hier zur besonderen Kennzeichnung gegeben, und ein Vergleich mit Exemplar 21 dürfte die Begründung dafür liefern: Wenn auch noch einige einzelne Knoten erkennbar sind (die aber schon in einer Richtung stehen), so ist doch bereits weitgehend eine Verschmelzung zu durchlaufenden Rippen erfolgt. Regulär wäre diese Form noch zu *B. draco miliaris* zu stellen, da *B. draco draco* erst bei vollständiger Rippenbildung abgetrennt wird. (*a*) In natürlicher Erhaltung. (*b*) Präpariert, um zu zeigen, dass verschiedene Erhaltungszustände (und Lichteffekte) sich morphologisch unterschiedlich auswirken können.
  T.K. Nr. 4186. L: 0,53 mm.

21–23. *B. draco miliaris* HILTERMANN und KOCH.
  21. Oberes Ober-Campan, Lüneburg. Das frühe Entwicklungsstadium dieses Exemplars ist an den schräg liegenden Knoten beiderseits der Mittelfurche zu erkennen: Sie weisen in die gleiche Richtung wie die übrigen auf den Kammern befindlichen—im Gegensatz zu den Knoten der Exemplare 20 und 22, bei denen diese Knoten mehr in der Richtung der Mittelfurche stehen.
  T.K. Nr. 4187. L: 0,53 mm.
  22. Unteres Unter-Maastricht, Lüneburg.
  T.K. Nr. 4188. L: 0,62 mm.
  23. Oberes Ober-Campan, Lüneburg.
  T.K. Nr. 4189. L: 0,51 mm.

Die Exemplare Nr. 15, 17, 18b, 20a und 21 sind in natürlicher Erhaltung, alle anderen nach besonderer Präparierung (meist chemische Versilberung) photographiert worden.
Alle abgebildeten Exemplare befinden sich in der Bundesanstalt für Bodenforschung, Hannover, unter der angegebenen Typenkatalog-Nr. (T.K. Nr.).
L = Längenabmessung.

TAFEL IV

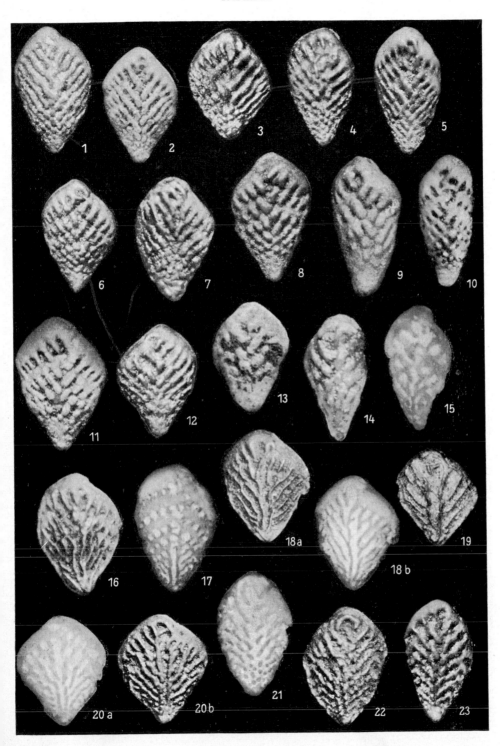

THE GENUS PSEUDEDOMIA AND ITS PHYLETIC RELATIONSHIPS, WITH REMARKS ON ORBITOLITES AND OTHER COMPLEX FORAMINIFERA

A. H. SMOUT

The British Petroleum Company Ltd., Sunbury-on-Thames, Middlesex (Great Britain)

GENERAL

Pseudedomia HENSON 1948 is the only genus known to occur stratigraphically to form a link between the older Cretaceous Alveolinidae and the Tertiary genera of that family. Although showing similarities to the Cretaceous genera, *Pseudedomia* has characters suggestive of closer relationship to complex Miliolidae such as *Fabularia* and *Raadshoovenia*. Tertiary Alveolinidae are more probably derived from Miliolidae than from *Pseudedomia*. The tracing of phyletic links between larger Foraminifera is very difficult because most species present themselves as quite isolated, or as members of a very small group of obviously related species. This can be partly ascribed to imperfections of the geological record, but is in part due to their stability for considerable periods of geological time.

The justification for regarding *Pseudedomia* as a genus of the family Alveolinidae involves an accurate knowledge of the morphology of other larger Foraminifera and some appreciation of their possible phylogeny. In some cases, the distinctions can be summarily stated; in others there have been confusions about the morphology and a redescription has had to be made. In a number of cases, the taxonomy has been gravely confused and it has not been possible to refer to genera and species without taxonomic revision. Where possible, this is definitive but in a number of cases there are further investigations to be made and a summary of the present position is given. It is hoped that this will provide a useful point of departure for further taxonomic and phyletic work. The writer attaches great importance to the rigorous application of taxonomy in phyletic discussions, for two reasons. The first is the danger of misunderstanding. The second is because the taxonomy should be closely related to phyletic theory. Of course, it can not conform to it in every detail for this would be logically impossible and in practice too nomenclaturally disturbing. It will be noted that there is a great deal in common between the writer's opinions on the phylogeny of the Alveolinidae and those of GALLOWAY (1933). However, much has been learnt about the Alveolinidae since then and the generic changes affect the statement of relationships as well as their assessment.

The diagnosis and description of the foraminiferal family Alveolinidae was placed on a firm basis by REICHEL (1937) in his monograph "Étude sur les Alveolines". This has been widely accepted, excepting for the usage of the genera *Alveolina*, *Borelis* and *Flosculina* by American authors, who usually prefer the classification suggested by CUSHMAN (1927) and the family name "Alveolinellidae". REICHEL's system is in better accord with European usage before 1937 and is normally followed by European workers at present. Alveolinidae are much more common in the Old World than in the New World and, accordingly, REICHEL's classification has a substantial preponderance of usage over CUSHMAN's. The use of "Alveolinidae" in preference to "Alveolinellidae" is clearly correct but minor taxonomic doubts about REICHEL's use of *Alveolina* and *Neoalveolina* do exist. However, their descriptions are clear and unambiguous while the alternative classification (CUSHMAN, 1955) is confused by inadequate descriptions of the morphology of the genera. This is particularly true of *Flosculina*, which is presumably the genus to which *Alveolina* as defined by REICHEL (1937) would be assigned. It is obviously desirable that REICHEL's system should be stabilised by appropriate designation of types or even by plenary decision if necessary. GLAESSNER (1945) provided an adequate account in English of the generic definitions given by REICHEL (1937) but textbooks in English do not yet include the genera *Cisalveolina* REICHEL 1941 and *Multispirina* REICHEL 1947. EAMES and SMOUT (1955) recognised that *Pseudedomia* HENSON 1948 is a complanate genus of the Alveolinidae and emended its description, but the type species *P. multistriata* HENSON 1948 has not yet been fully described. The holotype is still the only microspheric specimen known and the description given below is still incomplete, but the megalospheric generation has now been identified and is here described. REICHEL (1937, p. 136, footnote) mentioned specimens from Istria that had received the manuscript name "*Cosinella*" SCHLUMBERGER and stated that *Borelis cardenasensis* BARKER and GRIMSDALE 1937 was similar. "*Cosinella*" has never been validly named, figured or described and no more can be said about it. *B. cardenasensis*, according to the original description, has a globular, streptospiral test, except for a single terminal planispiral whorl, but REICHEL stated that a uniserial stage was developed in the largest individuals. If this is correct, and GRIMSDALE (verbal communication) has informed me that it is possibly so, *B. cardenasensis* should be regarded as a species of *Raadshoovenia* VAN DEN BOLD 1946 and formally excluded from the Alveolinidae. Some doubt must be attached to any record of uniserial habit that is not fully substantiated by illustrations, because a globular test with a thin complanate flange developed terminally will appear terminally uniserial in most random sections and only the globular early part of the test can normally be separated from the rock matrix.

There are a considerable number of species of larger Foraminifera that have a superficial resemblance to *Pseudedomia* and an investigation has been made into the basis of classification of such forms to determine whether any known species require to be transferred to the family Alveolinidae. Foraminiferal tests of globular or fusiform shape are readily separated from rock matrix and the loss of one or two of the outer whorls does not materially change their appearance or affect their description. In the case of compressed lenticular and discoidal tests, it is usually impossible to separate specimens from the rock matrix without serious damage. The general appearance therefore has to be reconstructed from sections, often random in direction, and the interpretation of the structure can be very difficult. The problem is further aggravated by gross homeomorphy between genera of several families of the porcellaneous Foraminifera, so that an accurate knowledge of their comparative morphology is necessary. Further difficulties are introduced because the porcellaneous shell material often alters in fossilisation to a microgranular texture. Tests of the Lituolidea have a microgranular texture that cannot be distinguished from the altered porcellaneous texture unless there are agglutinated grains incorporated in it. There are, however, many species of the Lituolidea, scattered among many genera, that do not have agglutinated grains. Conversely, porcellaneous Foraminifera may have agglutinated grains attached to the outside of the chamber walls, although this is not recorded in any of the complex species with which we are concerned here. It follows that, although there is no intention to alter REICHEL's description of the Alveolinidae, it is necessary to discuss the characters of relevant genera of the families Peneroplidae, Miliolidae, Ophthalmidiidae and the superfamily Lituolidea to establish the criteria on which the differential diagnosis rests.

REICHEL (1937, p. 17), defined the family Alveolinidae as follows:

(*1*) Nature of test... porcellaneous.

(*2*) Mode of coiling: (*a*) nepionic stage: streptospiral or planispiral, (*b*) adult stage: planispiral (symmetrical-spiral).

(*3*) Division of chambers... into tubular chamberlets in the direction of coiling.

(*4*) The number of chambers per whorl... progressive, more than two per whorl in the adult.

REICHEL explicitly included any species that might be found with an outer agglutinated layer of the chamber wall or with only the last whorl planispiral. He regarded the tubular chamberlets as a fundamental character and noted that all known species have a preseptal canal. The guiding principle is exclusiveness; the Alveolinidae can only be distinguished from the Miliolidae that have endoskeleton by arbitrary definition and in practice it is found that a species that does not confirm in all ways to the alveolinid structure differs in more than one character and is best regarded as miliolid. To REICHEL's definition we may add that all known species are strictly involute and that no case of cyclical growth is known. It is still true that all species have a preseptal canal and this is probably an essential character. REICHEL excluded species with a uniserial termination by implication. The only difficult case is that of *B. cardenasensis*, but information on this species is inadequate for treatment at present.

Under the headings of various families, their validity is discussed when in doubt, and the characters by which their complex genera can be recognised are demonstrated. LOEBLICH and TAPPAN (1961) have recently revived the family Meandropsinidae, abolished by HENSON (1950), and this is shown to be inadvisable. The classification of the family Peneroplidae by HENSON (1950) has long been regarded by him as obsolescent; he proposed it as a necessary but interim step towards a final assessment. The present work was instigated by him and carried out with his help, although the writer takes sole responsibility for the observations and opinions recorded. HOFKER (1950,

1951 a, b, 1952 a, b, 1953) reclassified the living species of the Peneroplidae, but omitted some of the more complex living forms and did not consider fossil species, so that his work has little direct bearing on the present investigation. MARIE (1940, 1958) has published important notes on the identity of certain species. LACROIX (1959) has made a similar contribution but this cannot be accepted without reservations.

The morphology and classification of the family Peneroplidae has been discussed at some length because the existing summaries on the subject provide an inadequate basis on which to discuss the differential diagnosis of the Peneroplidae from the Alveolinidae. In order to give meaning to many common names, it has been necessary to redescribe some species and nominate types for them, particularly for Orbitolitinae, which may resemble *Pseudedomia* when seen in fragmentary condition.

Careful scrutiny of the published species of larger Foraminifera, especially those classified by HENSON (1948) in the obsolete family Meandropsinidae, has not yielded any more that should be transferred to the family Alveolinidae. *Pseudedomia multistriata* has been fully described, including the megalospheric generation, and *P.globularis* nov. sp. has been described.

COMPARATIVE ANATOMY OF THE ENDOSKELETON IN SELECTED GENERA OF THE SUPERFAMILIES MILIOLIDEA AND LITUOLIDEA

In many complex Foraminifera of the superfamilies Miliolidea and Lituolidea, the chambers are partly infilled by shell material that was formed at the same time as the formation of the chamber wall. This endoskeleton usually consists of a subepidermal part and a part in the central zone of the chamber, the structure of the two being independent, although often the two zones are fused together. In the special case of the Alveolinidae, it is more convenient to regard the chamber as entirely filled with endoskeleton excepting for more or less tubular "canals" and "chamberlets". The greater degree of development of endoskeleton usually enables the Alveolinidae to be distinguished from other families without hesitation, but in some species the proportion of lumen is great enough to make the endoskeleton appear as either general infilling or as partitions of a general space, according to the prejudice of the viewer. Similarly, the endoskeleton of the other families can be thick enough in some species to approach the condition in Alveolinidae. It is therefore desirable to have additional criteria to resolve cases of doubt.

Some Peneroplidae develop subepidermal partitions which run from septum to septum and are of constant thickness. They are only approximately constant in spacing and are randomly arranged from chamber to chamber, and on opposite sides of the same chamber in cases where the chamber is compressed or equitant. The apertures always lie in the central zone of the chamber, not in the subepidermal zone. Partitions may occur in this central zone and these may be extensions of the subepidermal partition or fused with them, but there are nevertheless recognisable subepidermal and central zones of the chamber.

Some Lituolidea have primary subepidermal partitions like those of the Peneroplidae, with the addition of transverse secondary and tertiary plates, dividing the subepidermal zone into cellules. When the endoskeleton is particularly heavy, these may be reduced to tubules and the structure can be described as a thick wall with quadrichotomous alveoles. As in the Peneroplidae, apertures never appear in the part of the apertural face corresponding to the subepidermal zone. When lituolid subepidermal partitions are reduced to the primary plates, they are closely similar to the condition in the Peneroplidae and have the same possibilities of confusion with the internal structures of Alveolinidae.

Complex species of both Peneroplidae and Lituolidea often have characters of the central zone of the chamber which immediately distinguish them from the Alveolinidae, but there are cases where the central zone is too reduced to be distinctive.

Some Alveolinidae, particularly Cretaceous species, have a "continuous" layer of chamberlets and the apertures are in alignment with these. In a number of species, this chamberlet layer is subepidermal and a more solid endoskeleton, in which more scattered chamberlets lie, occupies the central zone of the chamber. The preseptal canal lies more in the central than in the subepidermal zone of the chamber and in the complex species the primary chamberlets open into it but it does not intervene between each and its corresponding aperture. In other cases, the preseptal canal intervenes but the apertures are still mostly aligned with the chamberlets. The primary chamber layer can appear very similar to the subepidermal layer of a peneroplid or even lituolid species, but the "continuous" alignment of chamberlets from chamber to chamber, caused by the continuity of the apertures with them, serves as a diagnostic character. In yet other alveolines the apertures regularly alternate with the chamberlets, again a character not parallelled in other families. The increase of the number of chamberlets from chamber to chamber in Alveolinidae necessarily causes some disturbance of the regular "continuous" or "alternating" chamberlets. In many species this is negligible but in some it causes sufficient irregularity to make the simple statement that the apertures are regularly arranged with respect to the chamberlets open to objection. However, the Alveolinidae often have a single layer of chamberlets and there is no question of subepidermal zones being present in such cases, this only arises when there is more than one layer of chamberlets.

REICHEL (1952) raised the question of the resemblance of *Meandropsina* to the Alveolinidae and similar queries could arise with *Edomia* and other peneroplids. For this reason, a considerable digression on selected Peneroplidae is made below. It is concluded that the structure of the endoskeleton in these genera is not homologous with that of alveolinids.

Family Peneroplidae REUSS 1860.

The family Peneroplidae (Soritidae, Orbitolitidae auct.) is in use for planispiral, porcellaneous Foraminifera and related genera with uniserial or cyclical terminal stages, provided the chambers are without endoskeleton, or the endoskeleton takes the form of subepidermal partitions, with or without fusions and with or without interseptal buttresses in the central region. The apertures are sometimes single but usually cribrate and always in the central part of the apertural face, avoiding the subepidermal zone. When subepidermal partitions are present, their spacing tends to be roughly equal, but they are otherwise aligned at random in consecutive chambers and, when the chambers are compressed, they are also randomly arranged on the two sides of the chamber. The random arrangement necessarily includes the two cases; alternating and continuous alignment. These are normally observed in sections of the test and, rarely, one mode may be found throughout the test of an individual, simulating the regularity of an alveoline. In such cases the presence or absence of apertures in the subepidermal zone becomes critical evidence of family affinities. The Peneroplidae typically have discoidal, lenticular, cylindrical or flabelliform tests while the Alveolinidae typically have fusiform or globular tests, but REICHEL (1937, 1952) has made it quite clear that the shape of the test is not diagnostic. The chambers of Peneroplidae are usually involute in spiral tests, but they may be evolute, especially at late stages of ontogeny, in which case they contrast with the strictly involute alveolinid chamber.

The cyclical genera have no parallel in the Alveolinidae, nor have those in which the later chambers show shortening of the alar prolongations and progressive ontogenetic change from the spiral to the uniserial chamber arrangement.

The peneroplid test has a more or less spherical proloculus, followed in the microspheric generation by a spire of chambers and in the megalospheric generation by a "canal flexostyle" or elongate deuteroconch that may coil for 90° to nearly 360° around the proloculus, in the equatorial plane. In simple species, this is followed by a single spire of simple chambers, but even in such species, the aperture is often cribrate in the ephebic chambers. In species which have cyclical chambers in the later stages of growth, the initial spire becomes flaring or aduncate and the chambers are recurved; the next stage is reniform and the cyclical habit follows. In some species a similar initial spire is succeeded by uniserial chambers which may be cylindrical or may be compressed so that the uniserial part of the test is flabelliform. The early chambers are often involute, with alar prolongations that reach the poles. The alar prolongations may be shorter in the later chambers and the cyclical and uniserial chambers are always evolute.

In some cyclical species the megalospheric nepiont has a very abbreviated spire, making less than one whorl. Further abbreviation leads to a three-chambered nucleoconch that looks as if it were formed as a single unit; the third chamber is large and embraces the proloculus and deuteroconch almost completely. It has no endoskeleton, which distinguishes it from the ephebic chambers in many species, but it has the ephebic type of multiple, marginal, aperture and gives rise to a reniform or cyclical chamber of ephebic type. The ultimate reduction leaves only the proloculus and deuteroconch, the third chamber being reniform or cyclical and of ephebic type.

Some Peneroplidae have no endoskeleton in the chambers but in most, including most of the cyclical species, endoskeleton is present. The interior of each chamber can be thought of as consisting of two parts; the subepidermal zone and the central zone. All the apertures are marginal or areal and open into the central zone. The subepidermal zone, if it has endoskeleton at all, is occupied by subepidermal partitions, which are thin laminae that run from septum to septum. Endoskeleton may be present in the central zone, independantly of its presence in the subepidermal zone. It may consist of extensions of the subepidermal partitions, or of labyrinthic partitions fused with the edges of the subepidermal partitions, or of inter-septal buttresses (pillars).

In *Praerhapydionina* and *Rhapydionina* the cylindrical uniserial chambers have radially directed subepidermal partitions at approximately equal spacing. In *Rhipidionina* the cross-section of the uniserial chambers is oval and in the more compressed specimens it is evident that there is no correspondence between partitions on opposite sides of the same chamber. Cyclical chambers are analogous and also lack correspondance between partitions on opposite sides of the same chamber. Since the spacing between partitions is only roughly equal, considerable variation may occur, from virtual correspondence to complete irregularity or approximate alternation. In those species which have the partitions extended across the central zone, their course is not, in general, straight. Where the arrangement is least regular, two partitions of one side may fuse with one or more of the other side, or two from the same side may fuse. These irregularities are additional to the irregularities of position of the subepidermal partitions in successive chambers. HENSON (1948, 1950) and others have described species of the Peneroplidae as having "continuous" and "alternating" subepidermal partitions. In the Peneroplidae, these are limiting conditions of a fundamentally random arrangement and this must be contrasted with the fundamentally ordered arrangement of the Alveolinidae, which may be disturbed into a random arrangement in special cases.

The Peneroplidae are represented in the Cretaceous, from the Cenomanian onwards, by a number of large and complex genera but the family has only few records of simple forms in the Cretaceous. These do not become widespread and abundant until the Eocene. It is therefore reasonable to speculate whether the Aveolinidae and Peneroplidae of the Cretaceous have a common origin, especially as there is a resemblance between *Meandropsina*, *Edomia* and *Pseudedomia*. However, the detailed phyletic relationships of all these genera are obscure and no evolutionary pattern for the Peneroplidae as a whole can be discerned. The tendency of the Alveolinidae to reduction of the milioline coiling in favour of planispiral coiling could logically lead to the peneroplid spire but the apertural characters and those of the endoskeleton do not seem to be related.

Subfamily Peneroplinae (SCHULTZE, 1854, pro subfamily Peneroplida) nomen corr.

From those species which HENSON (1950) placed in the family Peneroplidae implicitly or explicitly, it is possible to state that the following belong to the subfamily Peneroplinae as here recognised, differentiated from the subfamily Orbitolitinae by the absence of a cyclical terminal stage of growth or by a substantial spiral stage occurring even in the megalospheric generation before the cyclical habit begins.

Archaias kirkukensis HENSON 1950.

A. operculiniformis HENSON 1950.

Nautilus angulatus FICHTEL and MOLL 1798 (type species of *Archaias* MONTFORT 1808 and, by substitution, of *Helenis* MONTFORT 1808, *Ilotes* MONTFORT 1808 and *Orbiculina* LAMARCK 1816).

Synonyms:

Nautilus aduncus FICHTEL and MOLL 1798; subjective synonym.

N. orbiculus FICHTEL and MOLL 1798; junior homonym of *N. orbiculus* FORSKAL 1775; subjective synonym.

Orbiculina nummata LAMARCK 1816; type species of *Orbiculina*; new name for *N. orbiculus* FICHTEL and MOLL 1798.

O. numismalis LAMARCK 1822; new name for *N. orbiculus* FICHTEL and MOLL 1798.

Ilotes rotalitatus MONTFORT 1808; new name for *N. orbiculus* FICHTEL and MOLL 1798.

Helenis spatosus MONTFORT 1808; new name for *N. aduncus*.

Archaias spirans MONTFORT 1808; new name for *N. angulatus*.

Orbiculina uncinata LAMARCK 1822; new name for *N. aduncus*.

Orbiculina compressa D'ORBIGNY 1839 (type species of *Cyclorbiculina* SILVESTRI 1937).

Orbitolites malabarica CARTER 1853 (*Taberina* auct.).

Pavonina liburnica STACHE 1889 (type species of *Rhipidionina* STACHE 1913).

Peneroplis liburnica STACHE 1889 (type species of *Rhapydionina* STACHE 1913).

Praerhapydionina cubana VAN WESSEM 1943 (type species of *Praerhapydionina* VAN WESSEM 1943).

P. delicata HENSON 1950.

P. huberi HENSON 1950.

Rhapydionina urensis HENSON 1948.

R. urensis var. *minima* HENSON 1948.

Rhipidionina macfadyeni HENSON 1948.

R. williamsoni HENSON 1948.

Sorites hofkeri LACROIX 1940 (*Cyclorbiculina* auct.).

Taberina cubana KEIJZER 1945 (type species of *Taberina* KEIJZER 1945).

Orbitolinella depressa HENSON 1948 is also included here in the Peneroplinae, although its strictly uniserial habit makes its affinities problematical (Plate III, Plate IV, 1, 2).

Genera in which the chambers do not develop endoskeleton can be omitted from the present discussion as there is no possibility of confusing them with Alveolinidae. Genera that have endoskeleton are particularly liable to confusion with Alveolinidae, for the planispiral, involute, adult habit is common and the external shape, although usually different, is not diagnostic.

Genus *Meandropsina* SCHLUMBERGER 1898 (attributed to MUNIER-CHALMAS). (Type species *Meandropsina vidali* SCHLUMBERGER 1898, designated by CUSHMAN, 1928).

Most specimens are lenticular and strictly involute with a tightly coiled spire and curved alar prolongations of the chambers. In this they closely parallel *Pseudedomia*, but in very large microspheric specimens the last few chambers are cyclical and evolute, with meandrine lateral chambers developed; a character alien to the Alveolinidae. The endoskeleton consists of subepidermal plates which run interseptally at their insertions but are not extended as far into the central zone of the chamber distally as proximally. REICHEL (1951) suggested that this might be an indication that the species *M. vidali* has affinities with the Alveolinidae, the distal void in the chamber corresponding to the alveolinid preseptal canal and the partitions to incomplete walls of primary chamberlets. This interpretation of the homologies is not accepted because the apertures lie in the central zone of the chamber and do not place the subepidermal cellules in continuity from chamber to chamber directly. A further discussion of this genus will be found under the heading of the obsolete family Meandropsinidae.

Genus *Taberina* KEIJZER 1945. (Type species *Taberina cubana* KEIJZER 1945, by original designation, monotypic).
Synonym: vide HENSON (1950): *Edomia* HENSON 1948; type species *Edomia reicheli* HENSON 1948.

The type species has a mainly spiral, involute, habit but is terminally uniserial, evolute. The chambers have interseptal subepidermal partitions and there are buttresses between the septa in the central zone of the chamber. The latter feature distinguishes this genus from *Meandropsina*, *Rhapydionina*, *Rhipidionina* and *Praerhapydionina*. *Edomia* is subjectively synonymous only; its species are Cretaceous rather than Tertiary and have no uniserial termination. *E. reicheli* has a superficial resemblance to *Pseudedomia*, as the names would indicate. One could suggest that the whole central zone of the chamber of *Edomia* is homologous with the preseptal canal of *Pseudedomia*, but this would imply that the subepidermal cellules are incompletely enclosed primary chamberlets and in that case they should be associated with apertures and be continuous or alternating from chamber to chamber. The point is very difficult to observe as the specimens are embedded and impregnated by sparitic calcite, but scattered apertures of peneroplid type in the central part of the apertural face seem to be the only ones present. The Cretaceous species *Taberina bingistani* HENSON 1948 agrees formally with the characters of *Taberina*, and so does *Orbitolites malabarica* CARTER 1853, referred to *Taberina* by HENSON (1950), excepting that its termination is aduncate, not uniserial. The varied appearance and occurrence of species of *Taberina* makes it likely that the genus is polyphyletic.

Taberina daviesi HENSON 1950 is so strongly cyclical and evolute that it must be regarded as belonging to the subfamily Orbitolitinae. It conforms to "*Orbitolites*" s.l. and might be regarded as a species of *Marginopora*.

Genus *Fusarchaias* REICHEL 1952 (for 1951). (Type species *Fusarchaias bermudezi* REICHEL 1952 (for 1951), original designation, monotypic).
This genus is very liable to confusion with Alveolinidae for it is fusiform in shape. Interseptal buttresses are present but no subepidermal partitions or other endoskeleton, which is considered by REICHEL to be incompatible with alveolinid affinities.

Genus *Archaias* MONTFORT 1808. (Type species *Archaias spirans* MONTFORT 1808 = *Nautilus angulatus* FICHTEL and MOLL 1798, original designation).

This genus is lenticular or discoidal, sometimes with cyclical chambers terminally. Interseptal buttresses are present in the chambers but no other endoskeleton.

Genus *Praerhapydionina* VAN WESSEM 1943. (Type species *Praerhapydionina cubana* VAN WESSEM 1943, original designation).

The chambers have subepidermal partitions and no other endoskeleton. The test is initially spiral with a large uniserial, cylindrical, termination and one aperture per chamber. There is therefore no resemblance to alveolinids.

Genus *Rhapydionina* STACHE 1913. (Type species *Peneroplis liburnica* STACHE 1889, monotypic).

This genus differs from *Praerhapydionina* only in having several apertures per chamber.

Genus *Rhipidionina* STACHE 1913. (Type species *Pavonina liburnica* STACHE 1889, monotypic).

There are subepidermal partitions in the chambers, which are initially spiral but mainly uniserial, flattened in a plane at right-angles to the equatorial plane of the spire. The entire test is therefore strikingly different from anything seen in the subfamily Orbitolitinae or family Alveolinidae. However, a broken portion of the flange looks much like "*Orbitolites*" s.l. and has the same chance of confusion with alveolinids.

Genus *Cyclorbiculina* SILVESTRI 1937. (Type species *Orbiculina compressa* D'ORBIGNY 1839).

The chambers have subepidermal partitions but no other endoskeleton. The apertures are confined to the central zone of the chambers. The involute, spiral, nepiont is very large, but the ephebic chambers are cyclical and evolute. This genus could equally well be placed in the Orbitolitinae and it is doubtful if its separation from *Amphisorus* is justified.

Genus *Orbitolinella* HENSON 1948. (Type species *Orbitolinella depressa* HENSON 1948, monotypic).

The shell material was probably porcellaneous but the preservation is defective and a mistake might have been made. The megalospheric form only is known, the proloculus being large and spherical. The nature of the first chamber is uncertain but all chambers that can be seen clearly are in straight uniserial series, forming a low cone. The dorsal surface has serried subepidermal partitions. As the species is known only in random section, it is difficult to be sure of their arrangement; probably they are randomly arranged from chamber to chamber. At first sight they seem to have corresponding apertures, but this is probably not so, the appearance being due to intersection of the open inner ends of the subepidermal cellules. Only "primary" partitions in the direction of growth are present. Within this layer, every second or third partition is produced to the ventral side of the chamber. These walls thicken and the central parts of the chambers have reticulate passages in them. Narrow, obliquely directed, pores serve as apertures on the ventral surface. They are comparatively widely spaced and open in a more marginal position externally than internally. The origin of this peculiar structure may have been from that of *Taberina bingistani*. Most of the differences of appearance in the uniserial chambers can be ascribed to the distortion to a low conical instead of a cylindrical shape. The reticulate passages of the central zone could be derived from the buttressed central zone of *Taberina* by thickening of the endoskeleton at the expense of the lumen. A somewhat similar change is known to occur in reverse in the ontogeny of *Marginopora vertebralis*. If an attempt is made to describe the structure of *Orbitolinella* in terms of an alveolinid origin, the general appearance of the axial section is at first sight encouraging, but on consideration, no homologue for the preseptal canal can be found. This is such a constant feature of alveolinid anatomy that its absence is regarded as highly significant. As no species of the Alveolinidae has a uniserial stage, this habit is suggestive of peneroplid origin in preference to alveolinid.

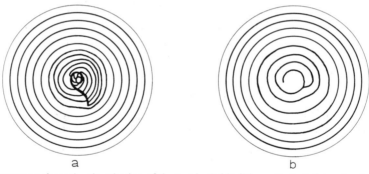

Fig. 1. Diagrams to show the chambering of the test in Orbitolitinae. Endoskeleton has been omitted. The megalospheric nucleoconch is only one of the three possible types. a. *"Orbitolites"* s.l., *Somalina* and *Opertorbitolites*, microspheric form, equatorial; b. *"Orbitolites"* s.l., *Somalina* and *Opertorbitolites*, megalospheric form, equatorial.

Subfamily Orbitolitinae BRADY 1881.

All genera of this subfamily have most of the chambers of the test cyclical and evolute, the nepiont being spiral in the microspheric form at least but rarely completing one whorl of divided chambers. The apertures are numerous and confined to the central zone of the chamber; they are arranged in one or two rows, in a band, or in transverse rows. Endoskeleton is normally present. Subepidermal plates are usual and may be the only endoskeleton. When endoskeleton is present in the central zone, it may be extensions of the subepidermal partitions, or independent partitions that may partly fuse with the subepidermal ones, or buttresses.

Formal distinction of members of this subfamily from the Alveolinidae is theoretically very simple; their apertures are confined to the central zone instead of having

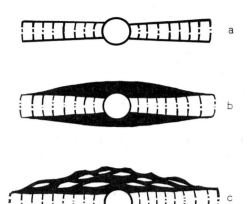

Fig. 2. Diagrams to show the chambering of the test in Orbitolitinae. Endoskeleton has been mitted. The megalospheric nucleoconch is only one of the three possible types. a. *"Orbitolites"* s.l., megalospheric form, axial; b. *Opertorbitolites*, megalospheric form, axial; c. *Somalina*, megalospheric form, axial.

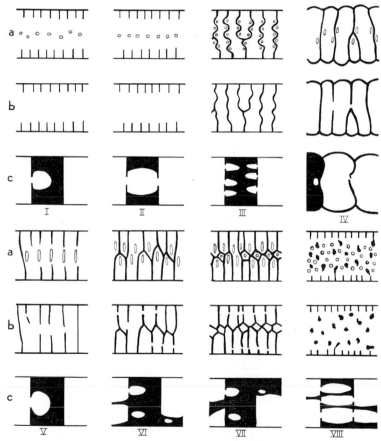

Fig. 3. Diagrams to show: a. apertural face; b. tangential section through one chamber; c. axial section through three chambers. The species represented are: I. *"O"*. moureti; II. *"O"*. anahensis, O. iranica, O. martini; III. *"O"*. carpenteri; IV. *"O"*. duplex; V. *"O"*. duplex (transitional to another species?); VI. O.complanata; VII. *"O"*. orbiculus; VIII. *"O"*. vertebralis plicata.

some correspondence to chamberlets, and the endoskeleton is organised as subepidermal plates and partitions or buttresses, instead of a tubulated mass. In practice, particularly in fossil specimens, the distinction is less easy and a good working knowledge of the orbitolitid organisation is a great help. Unfortunately there are wide differences of opinion current about the interpretation of the structure; for instance, HENSON (1950) described cycles of small chambers instead of subdivided annular chambers. Generic nomenclature is in a very confused state and the recognition of a number of species is open to debate. Some species, *e.g.*, *Orbulites marginalis* LAMARCK 1816, have two current interpretations. To refer to Orbitolitinae without close definition of names would merely add to confusion. For this reason, notes have been made on all critical species and type specimens have been designated where this is desirable. Application of generic names to the type species is of course easily done, and some of these genera are ostensibly worth separation, but their definition to include species other than the types is a problem that cannot be completely solved at present; more observation of the remaining species is necessary. The only practical course is to use the genus "*Orbitolites*" s.l. for such species, pending further generic revision. Generic distinctions will cut across lineages and stratigraphical associations if crudely based on some of the characters traditionally cited. The use of genera so defined would be disadvantageous compared to the use of a single genus.

Variation in the Orbitolitinae occurs in the megalospheric nucleoconch; some species having proloculus and deuteroconch followed by chambers arranged spirally but of normal type, sometimes without endoskeleton. Other species have reniform or cyclical chambers formed directly after the deuteroconch and some have a third chamber of the nucleoconch, distinguished from later chambers by the wall thickness and texture and without endoskeleton, directly followed by cyclical chambers of normal type.

Variations in the endoskeleton rarely suppress the subepidermal partitions, although their extension towards the centre of the chamber is variable. In the simplest case, the central zone of the chamber is quite empty. In others, the subepidermal partitions may extend across the central zone, leaving a central hole, which in some species has a distal situation but in others is central. Complete fusion in twos and threes, leaving no hole, is possible. Yet other species do not show extension of the subepidermal partitions but develop partitions in the central zone that may fuse with the subepidermal partitions, leaving holes at their junction. Such partitions may be simple or reticulate. Partitions in the central zone may have holes and if these are large, the partitions may be reduced to buttresses. The ultimate reduction is to slender interseptal pillars.

Variations in apertural pattern are confined to arrangements on the apertural face over the central zone of the chamber and are often associated with particular arrangements of endoskeleton. In some species the shape of the apertures varies with their arrangement. In some, the apertures alternate with partitions but in others the pores are aligned along partitions, which are then fluted, and the apertures inclined, to avoid them.

Inflation of the chamber walls between the sutures of the partitions occurs to a small degree in many species, but when it is conspicuous it changes the general appearance profoundly, particularly when it is greatest at the angles of the margin. Combination of this with fusion of subepidermal partitions across the central zone of the chambers can result in an appearance of cycles of chambers that resemble those of *Lepidocyclina* in many ways. The insistance here on regarding the chambers as annular is justified by close observation; there is continuity of gradation of character with specimens in which the chambers are more obviously annular, sometimes in the same specimen. In a number of species, a perfectly equatorial section will make the chambers appear annular, while sections slightly to either side will intersect the partitions and look as though cycles of small chambers had been intersected. In all Orbitolitinae, observation of the margin will show that the insertion of subepidermal partitions on either side of the chamber is random. The extensions of the partitions into the central zone may meet naturally but in some parts it will be found that the partitions bend in order to meet, or even fuse in threes, two from one side and one from the other, or two from the same side of the chamber fuse.

With a random arrangement of subepidermal partitions from chamber to chamber, definite alignment or alternation must be found sporadically by chance. In addition, the spacing between the subepidermal partitions conforms to an average value. If the deviation from this is small, the partitions will tend to appear regularly arranged.

The Orbitolitinae often tend to have supplementary flanges and other irregularities of growth, particularly in association with plastogamy in the megalospheric generation. This variability is accentuated by the possibility of regeneration of a complete test from a broken fragment and of continuation of growth after the margin has been severely worn. Morphogenetic principles are difficult to formulate to take care of such complexities.

Genus *Orbitolites* LAMARCK 1801. (Type species *Orbitolites complanata* LAMARCK 1801, virtually designated by DOUVILLÉ, 1902, explicitly designated by CUSHMAN, 1927).

DOUVILLÉ (1902) effectively reduced this genus to monotypy by emending the description to include only species with complete partitions across the chambers. Many authors have used *Orbitolites* in a much less restricted sense and most porcellaneous, cyclical, peneroplid species with subepidermal partitions have been referred to *Orbitolites* unless they have lateral chamber or shell layers. There are a number of nominally valid genera into which *Orbitolites* s.l. can be divided, but the correct basis on which species other than the types can be allocated to genera is not clear at the moment. For immediate purposes *Orbitolites* s.str. will be used with DOUVILLÉ's definition, characterised by partitions completely fused in twos and threes across the central zone leaving no holes. "*Orbitolites*" s.l. will be used for most species of the Orbitolitinae, reflecting the writer's opinion that the extant generic names and descriptions have arisen piecemeal as individuals have been impressed by the differences between pairs of species, without sufficient knowledge of the problem as a whole. Even

HENSON's classification, which attempted to create an empirical classification based strictly on morphology, is thrown into confusion if it is admitted that the Orbitolitinae have annular chambers, with complexities not considered in his system.

The identity of *Orbitolites complanata* LAMARCK 1801 is fortunately in no doubt although it must be noted that CARPENTER (1883) described *Marginopora vertebralis* under this name.

Genus "*Orbitolites*" s.l.

The following list of species comprises all those belonging to the subfamily Orbitoiltinae that lack lateral layers of shell material. A number of species that are the types of their genera have been included for consistency but there can be little objection to using these as monotypic genera if desired, other than that the genera so used are tautonymous with their type species. The problem of assignment of the remaining species to genera cannot be satisfactorily resolved on the information immediately available and it is for this reason that it is proposed to use "*Orbitolites*" s.l. for the present.

Orbitolites americanus CUSHMAN 1918.

Meandropsina anahensis HENSON 1950 (= ? *O.martini*).

Orbitolites complanata LAMARCK 1801 (type species of *Orbitolites* s.str.).

O.complanata d'archiaci DE GREGORIO 1894.

O.complanata gigantea SACCO 1922.

O.complanata minima HENSON 1950.

O.complanata perundata SACCO 1922.

Taberina daviesi HENSON 1950.

Orbitolites disculus LEYMERIE 1851 (= ? *O.complanata*).

Qataria dukhani HENSON 1948 (type species of *Qataria*).

Orbitolites duplex CARPENTER 1883 (type species of *Bradyella*).

Orbitolites elliptica MICHELIN 1846 (= ? *O.complanata*).

Sorites grecoensis HENSON 1950.

Amphisorus hemprichii EHRENBERG 1840 (type species of *Amphisorus*).

Meandropsina iranica HENSON 1950.

Orbitolites laciniatus BRADY 1881 (= "*O*". *vertebralis plicata*).

Orbulites marginalis LAMARCK 1816.

Orbitolites martini VERBEEK 1896 (*Sorites* auct.).

Praesorites moureti DOUVILLÉ 1902 (type species of *Praesorites*).

Nautilus orbiculus FORSKÅL 1775 (not FICHTEL and MOLL 1798).

Dohaia planata HENSON 1948 (type species of *Dohaia*).

Marginopora vertebralis plicata DANA 1846.

Orbitolites tonga WILLIAMSON 1856 (= "*O*." *vertebralis*).

Marginopora vertebralis QUOY and GAYMARD in BLAINVILLE 1830 (type species of *Marginopora*).

Archiacina verworni RHUMBLER 1911.

To this list may be added "*Orbitolites*" *carpenteri* new name for *Orbitolites marginalis* CARPENTER 1883; not *Orbulites marginalis* LAMARCK 1816.

Sorites dominicensis EHRENBERG 1840 and ? *S.edentulus* EHRENBERG 1840 possibly belong to "*Orbitolites*" but are nomina dubia that cannot be placed with certainty.

Genus *Amphisorus* EHRENBERG 1840. (Type species *Amphisorus hemprichii* EHRENBERG 1840, by monotypy).

As *A.hemprichii*, *Orbulites marginalis* LAMARCK 1816 and *Nautilus orbiculus* FORSKÅL 1775 are very closely similar and probably represent variants of one species, EHRENBERG's distinction (1840) between *Sorites* and *Amphisorus* cannot be maintained. "*O.*"*hemprichii* was described as having two layers of chambers; in fact it has one layer with the subepidermal cellules inflated, leaving a marginal sulcus in which the apertural pores lie. "*O.*"*marginalis* and "*O.*"*orbiculus* have the same structure without as much inflation between the sutures, causing them to look single-layered. Some authors, *e.g.*, HENSON (1950) have stated that these species have cycles of small chambers. This is a deceptive appearance due to the partitions and the inflation of the chamber walls between them; the chambers are essentially annular with subepidermal partitions randomly inserted on the two sides of the chamber and partially fused across the central zone of the chamber.

As *Sorites* is apparently based on an indeterminable species and was proposed at the same time as *Amphisorus*, it is best regarded as a potential synonym and as effectively junior to *Amphisorus*.

Genus *Bradyella* MUNIER-CHALMAS 1902. (Type species *Orbitolites duplex* CARPENTER 1883, original designation).

In the type species, the structure seems to agree with that of "*O.*" *carpenteri* in the earlier chambers (*Sorites* of DOUVILLÉ, 1902), but in later chambers the subepidermal partitions are distinct and only partly fused with partitions that are complete across the central zone, a hole being left at their junctions with the subepidermal partitions. In later chambers of some specimens where there are more than two rows of apertures, the partitions of the central zone are reticulate, each aperture corresponding to a cellule.

This genus has never been popular, but has more claim to being distinct than several others. *Marginopora* has a similar structure, except that the central zone is occupied by interseptal buttresses.

Genus *Dohaia* HENSON 1948. (Type species *Dohaia planata* HENSON 1948, original designation, monotypic).

The chamber structure is closely similar to that of *Amphisorus* and *Praesorites*, the subepidermal partitions leaving a small, empty, central zone of the chamber. They are, however, not shortened distally and the nepiont appears to be symmetrical.

Qataria differs from *Dohaia* in having the partitions alternating in successive chambers instead of being aligned. In other respects the similarity is so close that it is suspected that both are random arrangements in reality.

Genus *Qataria* HENSON 1948. (Type species *Qataria dukhani* HENSON 1948, original designation, monotypic). See *Dohaia*.

Genus *Marginopora* QUOY and GAYMARD 1830. (Type species *Marginopora vertebralis* QUOY and GAYMARD in BLAINVILLE 1830, monotypic).

The subepidermal zone with partitions is distinct from the central zone of the chamber with interseptal buttresses. These are often so crowded that they could be described as partitions with holes, but sometimes appear as discrete, slim, pillars.

Apart from "*Orbitolites*" s.l., this seems to be the only reasonable generic name for *Taberina daviesi* HENSON 1950, if one believes that the cyclical species should not be classified in the same genera as spiral species with a uniserial termination.

Genus *Praesorites* DOUVILLÉ 1902. (Type species *Praesorites moureti* DOUVILLÉ 1902, by monotypy).

This genus differs from all others of the Orbitolitidae in having a slightly skew nepiont, if the description by MARIE (1958) is correct. The subepidermal partitions are normal and complete, but their distal extensions into the central zone are not so well developed as the proximal ones, which usually fuse in pairs. The apertures are in one or two rows.

The chamber structure is very like that described by DOUVILLÉ for *Sorites* (based on "*O.*"*carpenteri*) or *Amphisorus* as described here. In *O. carpenteri* the partitions even show the same distal shortening in the central zone. Provisionally, the genus is kept distinct as the nepiont shows slight asymmetry. The latter character however has probably been overemphasised in importance, as peneroplids often show irregular asymmetry without structural differentiation.

Genus *Opertorbitolites* NUTTALL 1925. (Type species *Opertorbitolites douvillei* NUTTALL 1925).

O.douvillei is an Eocene species with considerable resemblance to *Orbitolites complanata*, but with thick lateral layers of shell material.

Genus *Somalina* SILVESTRI 1939 (1937 nomen nudum). (Type species *Somalina stefaninii* SILVESTRI 1939).

S. stefaninii is an Eocene species which is closely related to *Opertorbitolites*, differing in the presence of cavities between the lateral layers of shell material.

Generic names that should not be used at present are:

Broeckina MUNIER-CHALMAS 1882, nomen dubium. (Type species *Cyclolina dufrenoyi* D'ARCHIAC 1854, nomen dubium, original designation).

The type species cannot be identified with certainty with any known specimens. MARIE (1958) has reported that he failed to find authentic specimens known to have been seen by D'ARCHIAC. *Praesorites moureti* DOUVILLÉ 1902 has characters sufficiently close to *C. dufrenoyi* to make it probable that the two are in fact synonymous. However, there is no proof of this. *C. dufrenoyi* is best suppressed to protect the well-known name *P. moureti*. *Broeckina* therefore has the status of nomen dubium and should be suppressed to protect *Praesorites*.

Sorites EHRENBERG 1840, nomen dubium. (Type species *Sorites dominicensis* EHRENBERG 1840 nomen dubium, designated by CUSHMAN, 1927).

Two species of the original list of species were available for designation as the type of *Sorites*; *S. dominicensis* and *Nautilus orbiculus* FORSKÅL 1775. CUSHMAN unfortunately designated *S. dominicensis*. This species cannot be recognised at present. EHRENBERG's collections are believed to be preserved in East Berlin and an authentic specimen might be found there. However, this is not certain, for the publication will give little help in the identification of the specimen unless it is adequately labelled. Subsequent attempts to use the name have not been impressive. Only RENZ (1948) has explicitly determined a specimen as *S. dominicensis*. His specimen came from Venezuela, not San Domingo, and he wrote no explanation of his grounds for identification. His description and figures are not adequate for reliable identification. They might apply to "*O.*" *orbiculus* but could be of "*O.*" *carpenteri* or some other species. DOUVILLÉ (1902) found a specimen from San Domingo in the DESHAYES collection but concluded that it was unlikely to be *S. dominicensis*. Lacking an explicit type locality or even an assurance that the specimen was either fossil or recent, identification seems impossible without a paratypic specimen as a guide.

Objection to the use of *Sorites* is based on further considerations. DOUVILLÉ emended *Sorites*, mentioning "*Orbitolites marginalis* et *Hemprichi* (*duplex*, CARPENTER)", but not designating a type. The text figure seems to represent "*O.*" *carpenteri*, which was almost certainly the species meant by "*O. marginalis*", following CARPENTER (1883). On DOUVILLÉ's descriptions, the distinction between *Praesorites* and *Sorites* seems quite inadequate; the annular stolon formed by the distal shortening of the partitions in the central zone is present in both and the difference of size has been exaggerated, to judge by direct comparison of *P. moureti* with "*O.*" *carpenteri*. If *Sorites* were to be conserved, DOUVILLÉ's description would need amendment if it were to be of any distinctive value. By "*O. Hemprichi*" there is little doubt that DOUVILLÉ meant "*O.*" *duplex*. This species seems to be very closely related to "*O.*" *carpenteri*, perhaps some cline between the two exists. Nevertheless, "*O.*" *duplex* has a complexity of the partitions of the central zone that contrasts with the simplicity of "*O.*" *carpenteri*, "*O.*" *orbiculus* and *P. moureti*. The figure given by DOUVILLÉ for "*Marginopora*" is a crude representation of the condition in "*O.*" *duplex*. The difference between the megalospheric nucleoconch of "*O.*" *carpenteri*, which is followed by a spiral nepiont, and "*O.*" *duplex*, which is not, is not at present fully understood. It may be a generic distinction, but is more probably a varietal character and is likely to be associated with trimorphic differences between successive generations, possibly differing in detail in different geographical races.

Amphisorus hemprichii, *Orbulites marginalis* and *Nautilus orbiculus* are shown in the appendix to be exceedingly closely related, to the point of doubt that specific distinction can be maintained. EHRENBERG (1840) assumed that these were Bryozoa and his generic distinction between *Amphisorus* and *Sorites* was based on being two-layered or one. In fact, the distinction is quite spurious; being based only on the degree of inflation of the chamber walls at the margin, between the sutures of the partitions. *"O."orbiculus* resembles *"O."carpenteri* in many ways, the main differences being in proportions and in the shift of the hole in the fused partitions to a lower level, so that the partitions fuse distally as well as proximally around it. EHRENBERG strongly emphasised the similarity between *A.hemprichii* and *S.orbiculus* (sic!) in his descriptions and figures.

If *Sorites* is to be used as a genus at present, *Nautilus orbiculus* FORSKÅL 1775 must be taken as the effective type species; in this case it unquestionably would be a synonym of *Amphisorus*. Since *Amphisorus* is a valid genus at present, whatever opinion one may hold about its synonymy, and it was proposed in the same work as *Sorites* and therefore has the same seniority, it is obvious that only a plenary decision bluntly contrary to the *Règles internationales de la Nomenclature zoologique* (1953) could validate it, in any meaning yet proposed. It has been shown that the facts of morphology give no support to the idea that this might be desirable. Should *S.dominicensis* be identified and found to be congeneric with *"O."orbiculus*, this would merely mean that *Sorites* would be established as an effectively junior synonym of *Amphisorus*. Should it be found to be generically distinct, it is likely that it would be conspecific with some subsequently named species and liable to upset the nomenclature of some other established genus. Both these effects would be highly undesirable.

Taramellina MUNIER-CHALMAS 1902, nomen nudum.

No named species have ever been attached to this genus. MUNIER-CHALMAS stated that the type was based on specimens like the simple type of *Orbitolites* described by CARPENTER (1853) but he did not state that they were identical.

Family Meandropsinidae HENSON 1948 (obsolete).

The type species of the family Meandropsinidae, *Meandropsina vidali* SCHLUMBERGER 1898, was placed in the Peneroplidae by HENSON (1950) and he therefore could not continue the use of the name Meandropsinidae. Although very different views on the genus *Meandropsina* SCHLUMBERGER 1898 are taken here from those of HENSON (1950) it is maintained that the genus is correctly assigned to the family Peneroplidae. The genera of the Meandropsinidae are now distributed between the families Peneroplidae, Alveolinidae, Cyclamminidae and Lituolidae. LOEBLICH and TAPPAN (1961) advocate that the Meandropsinidae should be reduced to the rank of subfamily but retained in the family Soritidae. Retaining HENSON's diagnosis, the Meandropsinidae would comprise all peneroplid genera with endoskeleton in the chambers. The diagnosis given by LOEBLICH and TAPPAN is invalid as it would not admit the type genus *Meandropsina*. *Meandropsina vidali* is found in Upper Cretaceous strata. It has a lenticular, involute, spiral test with very recurved septa and strongly vorticiform alar prolongations that reach the poles accurately except in the latest stage of growth of the microspheric form, where the median chamber layer is cyclical and there are meandriform lateral chambers. REICHEL (1952) stated that in *M. vidali* the partitions are mainly arranged in alignment from chamber to chamber and extend through the thickness of the chamber, leaving a continuous space at the distal end of the chamber that could be regarded as homologous with the preseptal canal of an alveoline. However, re-examination leads the writer to the belief that the organisation is more like the peneroplid than the alveolinid condition. The subepidermal partitions of *M. vidali* seem really to be arranged randomly from chamber to chamber, the natural consequence being that they quite often appear in alignment. The apertures all seem to lie in the central part of the chamber and not to be aligned with the spaces between the partitions, as is typical of those alveolinid species that show "continuous" chamberlets most clearly. The occasional terminal development of cyclical chambers is a character paralleled in the Peneroplidae but not in the Alveolinidae. These features are all shown in SCHLUMBERGER's type figures. For these reasons the genus *Meandropsina* is classified in the family Peneroplidae, although there is a remote possibility that its features may indicate a phyletic link between the Peneroplidae and the Alveolinidae in the Cretaceous.

A number of Upper Cretaceous species are congeneric with *Meandropsina vidali*: *Fallotia jacquoti* DOUVILLÉ 1902; *Fascispira colomi* SILVESTRI 1940, both the type species of their respective genera; probably also *M. larrazeti* SCHLUMBERGER 1898. SCHLUMBERGER suspected *Orbitolites chartacea* DES MOULINS 1864 of being conspecific with *M. vidali*, but this species remains a nomen dubium. *?M. rutteni* PALMER 1934 is not well enough described or figured to be assigned firmly to any genus. The Tertiary species *Meandropsina anahensis* HENSON 1950 and *M. iranica* HENSON 1950 agree more in structure with species described in the genus "*Orbitolites*" s.l. The assignment to families of the species of other genera that HENSON (1948) placed in the Meandropsinidae will be found in the discussions on these families.

Family Miliolidae EHRENBERG 1840.

The family Miliolidae is characterised by the streptospiral mode of coiling. There are two chambers per whorl, occasionally with an uncoiled uniserial termination. The degree of involution is variable; often it is slight but in some species, such as *Periloculina zitteli* MUNIER-CHALMAS and SCHLUMBERGER 1885 a progression from evolute to involute chambers progresses past the normal 180°, embracing to the hyper-involute condition where each chamber completely surrounds the previous test. *Lacazina* spp. (MUNIER-CHALMAS, 1882a) show most chambers in this hyperinvolute condition, the apertures alternating from pole to pole and therefore indicating that there are two chambers per whorl (not one as stated by REICHEL, 1937, p. 17). *Fabularia discolithes* DEFRANCE 1820 is remarkable in having normally involute adult chambers. The genera mentioned all have endoskeleton in the chambers. This is mainly on the chamber floor with ridges rising towards the outer wall in *Periloculina*. In *Lacazina* the ridges form incomplete partitions which are otherwise of alveolinid type and in *Fabularia* they are complete and form tubular chamberlets of alveolinid type and only the two-chambers-per-whorl distinguishes the genus from the Alveolinidae. *Raadshoovenia* VAN DEN BOLD 1946 seems to have the structure of *Fabularia*, but with a terminal uniserial stage. *Borelis cardenasensis* BARKER and GRIMSDALE 1937 was stated by REICHEL (1937) to have a uniserial termination and is therefore here regarded provisionally as a species of *Raadshoovenia* although the only description and figures show only a five-to six-chambered final planispiral whorl following a milioline stage. In all these genera with endoskeleton, the aperture is cribrate and opens in an anterior undivided part of the chamber that can be regarded as homologous to the preseptal canal of an alveo-line. It is probable that the Alveolinidae are polyphyletically derived from the Milio-lidae.

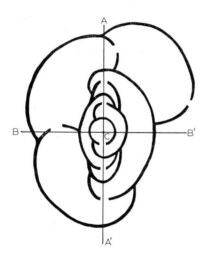

Fig. 4. Equatorial section; the megalosphere, "canal flex-ostyle", three milioline and three planispiral chambers are shown. Note how there are two milioline chambers per whorl, their apertures lying along one axis, alternately at each pole; while the planispiral chambers are typically more than two per whorl.

Family Ophthalmidiidae CUSHMAN 1927.

The Ophthalmidiidae are planispiral but otherwise resemble the Miliolidae. The chambers are typically long but there are usually rather more than two per whorl and a few species develop numerous chambers in the last whorl. *Discospirina italica* = *Pavo-nina italica* COSTA 1853 = *Orbitolites tenuissima* CARPENTER 1883, is classified in this family because the nepiont is obviously ophthalmiid but the later chambers are of peneroplid type with partitions that do not reach the distal septum. The Peneroplidae typically have many chambers per whorl when spiral, even in the microspheric nepiont, but they often have a deuteroconch in the megalospheric generation that occupies a half to a whole whorl. It is therefore possible that the Peneroplidae are derived from the Ophthalmidiidae, but this is not proven.

Superfamily Lituolidea GLAESSNER 1945.

Most of the species of the superfamily Lituolidea have shell material mainly formed of agglutinated grains, with a microgranular matrix. A considerable number of species lack obvious agglutinated grains but, when fresh, the texture of their shell material is

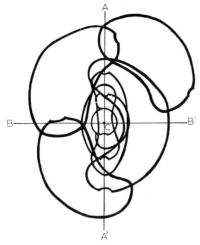

Fig. 5. Evolute test corresponding to Fig. 4, viewed as if transparent.

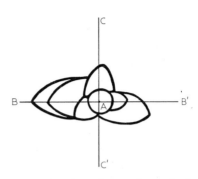

Fig. 6. Axial section of an evolute test of milioid type.

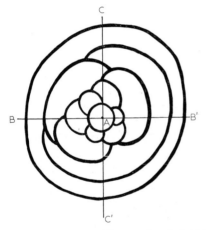

Fig. 7. Axial section of a test that is initially evolute but terminally hyperinvolute, after the manner of *Periloculina* and *Lacazina*.

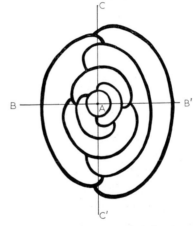

Fig. 8. Axial section of a precisely involute test, as is typical of the Alveolinidae.

Fig. 4–8. Diagrams to show the relationship of the milioline coiling to the equatorial plane, and the effect of variation in the degree of involution of the chambers in a streptospiral test.

obviously different from that of Foraminifera with porcellaneous test. Unfortunately the distinction between these types of shell material cannot be made in practice for many species of fossil Foraminifera, for minor diagenetic alteration produces the same final appearance in both, were there no agglutinated grains. In such cases, distinction between fossil porcellaneous genera and some of the Cyclamminidae becomes a matter of comparative anatomy and the nature of the shell material is deduced from this. The Lituolidea characteristically have the apertures in the central part of the chamber, as in the Peneroplidae and this feature serves to distinguish them from the Alveolinidae.

They commonly have subepidermal partitions; primary ones running in the direction of growth and secondary ones parallel and transverse to the septa, cutting the subepidermal region into roughly square cellules. When the partitions are exceptionally thick, the cavities of the cellules become tubular and are described as alveoles. When partitions parallel to the septa are present, the species cannot belong to the porcellaneous families. However, there are species of the Lituolidae that have primary subepidermal partitions only and distinction of such fossil species from the Peneroplidae, or sometimes even the Alveolinidae, can present difficulty.

Genera belonging to the superfamily Lituolidea that have been wrongly included in porcellaneous families are:

Saudia HENSON 1948; Meandropsinidae HENSON (1948), Peneroplidae HENSON (1950) and GRIMSDALE (1952).

S. discoidea HENSON 1948 (type species).

S. labyrinthica GRIMSDALE 1952.

Pseudorbitolina DOUVILLÉ 1910; Meandropsinidae HENSON (1948), Peneroplidae HENSON (1950).

P. marthae DOUVILLÉ 1910 (type species).

Broeckinella HENSON 1948; Meandropsinidae HENSON (1948), Peneroplidae HENSON (1950).

B.arabica HENSON 1948 (type species).

All the species listed have subepidermal cellules of lituolid type, formed by subepidermal partitions that are parallel to the septa as well as interseptal partitions.

The genera Mangashtia HENSON 1948, Zekritia HENSON 1948, Cyclolina D'ORBIGNY 1826 and Cyclopsinella GALLOWAY 1933 are insufficiently described for reliable classification. They all lack subepidermal partitions and the interpretation of their structure is therefore difficult. None of them seem to have any close relationship to the family Alveolinidae.

Family Alveolinidae (EHRENBERG 1840, pro fam. Alveolinea) nomen corr., STEINMANN 1881.

(1) Nomenclature.

Alveolinidae is the first name for this family to be correctly formed from a generic name and therefore stands. American authors have advocated the use of Alveolinellidae e.g., CUSHMAN (1928), GALLOWAY (1933), LOEBLICH and TAPPAN (1961) on the grounds that Alveolina is a junior synonym of Borelis, and therefore cannot serve as the type of the family. However, these authors do not remove Alveolina from this family and Clause 54 (1) (a) of the Additions to and modifications of the Règles internationales de la Nomenclature zoologique (1953), states that a junior synonym may serve as the type of a family and that its use as such is not subject to amendment when its status is discovered. "Alveolinidae" has been accepted throughout the European literature, e.g., by REICHEL (1937), GLAESSNER (1945), SIGAL in PIVETEAU, (1952), POKORNÝ (1958) and RAUZER-CHERNOUSOVA and FURSENKO (1959). Owing to difficulties with their type species, both Alveolina and Borelis are properly regarded as nomina dubia. However, *Alveolina* is in general use with a precise definition stated by Reichel (1936) and must be regarded as a nomen conservandum.

(2) Diagnosis.

The shell material is imperforate calcite of porcellaneous texture, without agglutinated material. The major part of the test consists of involute chambers, planispirally arranged, more than two and usually six or more per whorl, each with its independent wall which is never extended to cover other chambers. The chambers are always infilled with endoskeleton, in which there are chamberlets running in the direction of growth, all opening into a preseptal canal (open space below the apertural face). Minor complexities of the chamber cavity such as postseptal canals and bullae occur in some genera. The apertures are related to the chamberlets, often aligned with them or regularly alternating with them. In species where there is a subepidermal layer of serried chamberlets, there are corresponding apertures in alignment with them, making the chamberlets appear continuous from chamber to chamber when seen in tangential sections. The shape of the test is not diagnostic; it is usually fusiform or globular but may be lenticular or discoidal. Cyclical species are unknown and species with a uniserial termination are excluded. The microspheric nepiont usually shows milioline coiling. This is sometimes present in the megalospheric tests also, but more usually, the globular proloculus is succeeded by a "canal flexostyle" of about one half whorl, lying in the equatorial plane and succeeded directly by chambers of ephebic type.

(3) Discussion.

The precise structure of the milioline nepiont is very difficult to reconstruct. If it is truly milioline, the apertures of the chambers should lie on an approximately straight line in the equatorial plane, there being two per whorl and their centre lines being at progressively different angles to the equatorial plane. Reichel (1937, fig. 13, 22) illustrates nepionts in which the coiling seems even more complex, but the difficulties of drawing and interpretation are so great that these figures may contain some errors. Until someone examines a series of juvenile specimens, presumably of a living species, accurate description will not be possible.

The regularity of the involution of the ephebic chambers of Alveolinidae is remarkable. They usually overlap the poles regularly and only to the extent necessary to avoid the formation of umbilical depressions. Chambers with short alar prolongations, leading to ontogenetic change to the evolute condition, are never found. When a terminal flange is formed to the spire, the chambers become very recurved and the alar prolongations very vorticiform, sometimes with meandrine kinks in them, but they still reach to the poles regularly. The flange can be pseudevolute, but the extreme vorticity of the alar prolongations causes the chambers, even of part of the last whorl, to be partly covered. For the appreciation of the pseudevolute condition, we are indebted to Henson (1950). Where an involute test suffers a sudden increase in whorl height of the terminal flange, the later chambers have a very large part of their height above the margin of the previous whorl. The central part of the test, which alone receives the alar prolongations of the chambers and so appears involute, is then a very small part of the total, which appears to be evolute. The family Peneroplidae has a number of species that show the formation of a terminal flange with strongly recurved chambers, terminating in cyclical chambers. In those cases where the spiral chambers are all involute, the cyclical chambers are all evolute nevertheless. There may be no equivalent structures to the alar prolongations but in rare cases there are lateral chambers arranged in a meandrine manner. If, as seems likely, the Alveolinidae invariably have involute chambers, it follows that the cyclical habit is impossible for them.

Practical distinction between the Alveolinidae and the Peneroplidae is usually obvious on the external shape of the test but this is not reliable, for *Fusarchaias* REICHEL 1952 is a fusiform peneroplid, while complanate species of alveolines exist. Peneroplids with heavily developed subepidermal partitons can have some resemblance to alveolinids with unusually large lumina of the chamberlets. The apertures of the Peneroplidae avoid the subepidermal zone of the chamber, while the apertures of those Alveolinidae which are most likely to be confused with them lie in alignment with the cortical layer of chamberlets, as well as in the more central part of the apertural face. The central part of the chamber of an alveolinid, particularly in the later whorls, may contain massive endoskeleton (the "couche basale") in which supplementary chamberlets are less regularly arranged than in the primary chamberlet layer, but there is never an open space or a zone with reticulate partitions or interseptal pillars, as often occurs in the Peneroplidae.

There is no known case of a species without endoskeleton in the chambers that in other respects resembles the Alveolinidae.

REICHEL (1931, 1936–1937) makes much use of the distinction between the "continuous" mode of chamberlet arrangement and the "alternating" mode. Some genera show these modes very clearly and the "continuous" mode is very conspicuous in the cases where the primary chamberlets form a serried subepidermal layer and the preseptal canal lies internal to them, so that the chamberlets open into it by pores at their distal ends and it does not intervene between them and the septum. In such a case, the continuous alignment of the chamberlets from one chamber to the next is reinforced by the alignment of apertures putting the chamberlets into communication with those of the next chamber. In such cases, a tangential section through the cortical chamber layer may appear to show completely continuous chamberlets with no visible septa. One must remember that the necessity for the increase in the number of chamberlets in successive chambers causes irregularities in either mode of alignment and in some species this causes the alignment of chamberlets from chamber to chamber to be effectively random. It is usual to find that the apertures of one chamber are the origin of the chamberlets of the next.

REICHEL (1936–1937) produced the first clear account of the family Alveolinidae and adequate diagnoses of genera. Obviously, there is considerable value in conserving his generic nomenclature, which has come into wide use. Dissent from REICHEL's nomenclature is mainly from American authors, who have relatively few species represented by sparse records. Disturbance of American usage would be trivial compared to the large number of records from the Old World which have been given according to REICHEL's scheme.

The following genera have not been the subject of confusion and require no further comment:

Alveolinella DOUVILLÉ 1907 (type species *Alveolina quoyi* D'ORBIGNY 1826); Miocene – Recent.

Bullalveolina REICHEL 1936 (type species *Alveolina bulloides* D'ORBIGNY 1826); Oligocene.

Cisalveolina REICHEL 1941 (type species *Cisalveolina fallax* REICHEL 1941); Cenomanian.

Flosculinella RUTTEN 1914 (SCHUBERT in RICHARZ 1910, nomen nudum; type species *Alveolinella bontangensis* RUTTEN 1913); Oligocene and Miocene.

Multispirina REICHEL 1947 (type species *Multispirina iranensis* REICHEL 1947); Cenomanian.

Ovalveolina REICHEL 1936 (type species *Alveolina ovum* D'ORBIGNY 1826); Cenomanian and Turonian.

Praealveolina REICHEL 1933 (type species *Praealveolina tenuis* REICHEL 1933); Cenomanian – Senonian.

Pseudedomia HENSON 1948 (type species *Pseudedomia multistriata* HENSON 1948); Campanian and Maastrichtian. This genus was recognised by EAMES and SMOUT (1955) as belonging to the family Alveolinidae and an emended description is given below.

The remaining generic names, from which names for two major genera need to be taken, are the subject of serious nomenclatural difficulties. It is possible here only to state the difficulties and to indicate the designations which, if adopted by plenary decision, would establish the widely accepted usage based on REICHEL (1936–1937).

Genus *Alveolina* D'ORBIGNY 1826 (type species *Oryzaria boscii* DEFRANCE in BRONN 1825; designation of doubtful validity); Paleocene and Eocene.

There is no possibility of maintaining *Alveolina* as a valid name under the *Règles*, except by plenary decision. This is obviously essential, as *Alveolina*, as defined by REICHEL (1936), is in wide use with a precise meaning. American authors from CUSHMAN (1928) to LOEBLICH and TAPPAN (1961) have advocated its suppression, but the weight of usage in the Old World is so great that suppression would be quite impossible in practice. The American viewpoint has not been accepted in Europe because it offered no clear generic descriptions for the alternative names recommended in place of those used by REICHEL and because the reasons given for the suppression of *Alveolina* as a junior synonym were not entirely convincing. ELLES and MESSINA stated that PARKER and JONES (1860) have designated *Nautilus melo* FICHTEL and MOLL 1798 as the type of *Alveolina*. In fact, they stated that all specimens of *Alveolina* could be attributed to one species with several varieties and that "... for nomenclatorial purposes the first established specific appelation accompanied by varieties will serve well;... *Alveolina melo* vars. *sabulosa, elongata*, etc.". This cannot be taken as a valid designation of type. The statement that PARKER and JONES (1865) designated *Miliolites sabulosus* MONTFORT 1808 as the type of *Alveolina* is open to doubt; the writer has

not succeeded in finding the reference, but this species is believed to be synonymous
with *Oryzaria boscii* DEFRANCE in BRONN 1825 which was designated as the type of
Alveolina by DOUVILLÉ (1907). Unlike *M.sabulosus*, *O.boscii* is a species of the original
list of *Alveolina*.

 Alveolina has the following senior subjective synonyms;

Miliolites MONTFORT 1808 (type species *Miliolites sabulosus* MONTFORT 1808). This
 name is a junior homonym of *Miliolites* LAMARCK 1804 and is therefore invalid.

Fasciolites PARKINSON 1811 (type species *Alveolina schwageri* CHECCHIA-RISPOLI
 1905). No species were named in the original description and in the first revision
 by YABE and HANZAWA (1929), *A.schwageri* was designated as type. GALLOWAY
 (1933) determined PARKINSON's figures as of *Alveolina oblonga* D'ORBIGNY 1826
 and claimed, wrongly, that this species is the type. REICHEL (1936) placed *Fasciolites*
 as a subgenus of *Alveolina*; however, the nomenclature is doubly wrong for *Fasciolites* is (*a*) the senior name and must be applied to the whole genus if it is used at
 all, and (*b*) REICHEL left no species in *Alveolina* sensu stricto. The action that
 would restore legality with the least disturbance of REICHEL's nomenc·ature,
 would be the suppression of *Fasciolites*, having the effect of assigning to *Alv eolina*
 s.str. those species which REICHEL assigned to *Fasciolites*, which include *A.boscii*,
 and leaving *Alveolina* as the senior name for the genus.

 Junior names subjectively synonymous with part of *Alveolina* s.l. are:

Flosculina STACHE 1880 (type species *Flosculina decipiens* SCHWAGER 1883). *F.decipiens*
 was the first species to be attributed to this genus and was formally designated by
 GALLOWAY (1933) as the type. *Flosculina* was regarded by REICHEL (1936) as a
 synonym of *Alveolina* s.l. because in his opinion the presence of flosculinised
 whorls is a variable character of infra-specific value.

Eoalveolinella SILVESTRI 1928 (type species *Alveolina violae* CHECCHIA-RISPOLI 1905).
 This name was proposed as a subgenus of *Alveolina* and REICHEL (1936) perpetua-
 ted this.

Glomalveolina REICHEL 1936 (type species *Alveolina ovulum* STACHE in SCHWAGER
 1883). This name was proposed as a subgenus of *Alveolina*.

Genus *Neoalveolina* SILVESTRI 1928 emended bij REICHEL, 1937 (type species *Alveolina
bradyi* SILVESTRI 1927, designated by BAKX, 1932 = *Nautilus melo* var. *β* FICHTEL and
MOLL 1798 = *Nautilus melo* s.str. as emended by neotype, proposed p. 265). Miocene
to Recent.

 The identity of *Nautilus melo* is discussed in the Appendix on selected species. There
are three prior objective synonyms of *Neoalveolina*: *Borelis* MONTFORT 1808, p. 170,
Clausulus MONTFORT 1808, p. 178 and *Melonia* LAMARCK in DEFRANCE 1822. *Neoalveolina* therefore cannot be used unless these names are suppressed by the Commission
on Zoological Nomenclature, using its plenary powers.

 Clausulus and *Melonia* have never come into general use and their suppression is
unlikely to arouse any dissent. *Borelis* has been widely used. REICHEL (1937) advocated
its suppression to protect *Neoalveolina* and the same arguments apply today. Its type
species being *Nautilus melo* var. *β* FICHTEL and MOLL 1798, it is in fact the senior

synonym of *Neoalveolina* and it might seem a simple matter to substitute the name. Unfortunately, American authors have maintained that *Borelis* is a synonym of *Alveolina*. We have seen above that this is a misinterpretation of the nomenclatural situation. In view of the inadequate generic diagnoses given in American textbooks and the resulting confusion in naming species by those who attempt to follow them, it seems that the existing references would be more easily understood if *Neoalveolina* were used in preference to *Borelis* in future, forcing the reader to consider the correct generic meaning of each record of *Borelis*.

(4) Phylogeny.

The stratigraphical record of the family Alveolinidae begins low in the Cenomanian with small, globular species of *Praealveolina*. No contemporary or earlier species are known that look as if they might be ancestral to *Praealveolina*. At higher horizons, larger and more fusiform species of *Praealveolina* appear and three genera, *Cisalveolina*, *Ovalveolina* and *Multispirina* are found which may have been evolved from *Praealveolina*. *Praealveolina* alone is found in the Turonian and its only known successor, *Subalveolina*, is the sole Santonian–Lower Campanian representative of the Alveolinidae.

Complex Peneroplidae, such as *Edomia reicheli* and *Taberina bingistani*, occur in the Cenomanian. They are very unlike the Cenomanian Alveolinidae, being of typical peneroplid shapes and having the much more open type of endoskeleton. Their microspheric nepionts are planispiral rather than milioline and one would naturally look for an ancestral form among lenticular or ophthalmiid species rather than globular miliolid ones. A common origin of the Peneroplidae and the Alveolinidae seems unlikely.

Pseudedomia first occurs in the Campanian, possibly at a higher horizon than the last *Subalveolina*. It has no resemblance to that genus in detail but has the general praealveolinid organisation of "continuous" chamberlets and supplementary chamberlets in the "couche basale". The lenticular shape is merely a matter of proportions; the relationship of a globular form to it is the same in principle as to a fusiform test‘ the relationship being in the opposite sense, with the equatorial diameter increased relatively to the axial length.

Miliolidae that have tests suggestive of being ancestral to the Alveolinidae are not known certainly before the Lower Senonian. *Periloculina* MUNIER-CHALMAS and SCHLUMBERGER 1885, has endoskeleton that divided the chamber cavity incompletely into longitudinal chamberlets, leaving an open space below the cribrate aperture that can be compared to the preseptal canal of alveolines. However, *Periloculina* has milioline coiling and the chambers become increasingly involute, leading to *Lacazina* MUNIER-CHALMAS 1882, but not to genera of the Alveolinidae. *Fabularia* DEFRANCE 1820, has the same general type of endoskeleton but in the type species there are two chambers per whorl that are strictly involute, not hyperinvolute. In other species, possibly better placed in *Raadshoovenia* VAN DEN BOLD 1946, the test passes through a planispiral stage into a uniserial development. In spite of the close parallel in organisation, it seems most unlikely that the Cretaceous Alveolinidae can have evolved from these miliolids.

No direct link has been found between the Alveolinidae of the Cretaceous and the Tertiary. *Alveolina* is the only genus known from the Paleocene to the Middle Eocene. It parallels *Praealveolina* by starting with small, globular, species and developing larger, fusiform ones but it contrasts in having a strongly developed postseptal canal and alternating chamberlets. It has no resemblance to *Pseudedomia* and is most likely to have arisen independently of the Cretaceous Alveolinidae; possibly from *Raadshoovenia*. *Alveolina* became extinct early in the Auversian and Alveolinidae are absent from most of the Upper Eocene. *Borelis* has been recorded in the Upper Eocene, but very rarely and because the beds may involve severe reworking, there is a possibility of stratigraphical revision of the occurrence. *Borelis* occurs abundantly in the lower Miocene and probably arose from some miliolid rather than from *Alveolina*, because both the microspheric and megalospheric generations have a milioline nepiont. The other Alveolinidae have a planispiral megalospheric stage although the microspheric nepiont is milioline (except perhaps in *Pseudedomia*). *Bullalveolina*, known only from the Oligocene, is of unknown origin. It has the primitive globular shape but the details of its apertural complexities are not suggestive of its being a link between *Alveolina* and *Borelis*. *Borelis* survives to the present day and *Flosculinella* (Miocene) and *Alveolinella* (Miocene to Recent) are obviously derived from it, showing more complex chambers and being more fusiform.

It seems probable that the family Alveolinidae represents one particular mode of specialisation of the family Miliolidae that has been followed by several lineages independently.

THE GENUS PSEUDEDOMIA HENSON 1948, EMENDED.

Type species *Pseudedomia multistriata* HENSON 1948, original designation.

(*1*) Diagnosis.

HENSON's original description was based on inadequate material and, as he foresaw, it has needed amendment although the genus was sufficiently well described to be easily recognisable. EAMES and SMOUT (1955) gave the following amended description: "Test porcellaneous, imperforate, lenticular (probably to globular), becoming discoidal in the microspheric form, planispiral, involute, spire simple, chambers subdivided as in *Praealveolina*, with the addition of buttresses in the preseptal canal. Microspheric form with a terminal flange of strongly recurved chambers which may attain a final cyclical arrangement; alar prolongations becoming vorticiform and sometimes meandriform. Dimorphism pronounced." To this must be added: The earliest clearly visible whorls, even in the microspheric test, are planispiral, but the first one or two have not been clearly seen and may prove to be streptospirally coiled. Cyclical median chambers have not been observed, although the extreme recurvature of the later chambers approaches the cyclical condition. The alar prolongations of the later chambers of the microspheric form may be strongly vorticiform, with meandriform flexures, but in all cases where they are clearly visible, they run continuously from the median layer to the poles and there are no meandrine lateral chambers, such as are sometimes seen in *Meandropsina*. The buttresses in the preseptal canal are typically confined to a region near the equatorial plane; the earlier chambers have only one per chamber and these are then inconspicuous and easily overlooked. The primary chamberlets form a serried cortical layer with "continuous" arrangement. Less regularly arranged supplementary chambers are found in the "couche basale" of the later chambers only. Apertural pores correspond strictly to the chamberlets, except for irregularities caused by intercalation as the chambers become successively larger. No complexities associated with the apertures have been seen.

(2) Remarks.

The radical changes from HENSON's description of this genus are fully justified by the redescription of the type species, below. *P. multistriata* HENSON 1948 and *P. complanata* EAMES and SMOUT 1955, are very closely similar, differing in minor characters of size and proportions only. A third species is added here, again differing in proportions only. The generic differentiation from all previously named genera of the Alveolinidae is based on the presence of the complanate flange of the microspheric form. *Borelis cardenasensis* shows characters which seem to differentiate it from the species of *Pseudedomia*, and additional characters have been cited to provide a differential diagnosis from such species.

HENSON (1950) placed *Pseudedomia* in the synonymy of *Taberina* KEIJZER 1945, of the family Peneroplidae. *Taberina cubana* KEIJZER 1945, the type species, is a typical Tertiary peneroplid with a mainly spiral test that is terminally uniserial and has subepidermal partitions and interseptal pillars. The distinction of *Taberina* from *Pseudedomia* now made is not unexpected for HENSON (1950) remarked: "There is difficulty in accepting any direct linear relationship between the complex Cretaceous members of the Peneroplinae and those of Tertiary and Recent times that have similar structure".

(3) Occurrence.

Pseudedomia has so far been recorded only from the Campanian and Maastrichtian of Arabia and Iraq. It occurs mostly in shallow water limestones of lagoonal type.

(4) Key to species.

Test initially globular: . . . .*P. globularis*
Test initially lenticular:
    Form B over 5 mm diameter; form A with
    numerous supplementary chamberlets: . . . . *P. complanata*
    Form B under 5 mm diameter; form A with
    very rare supplementary chamberlets: . . . .*P. multistriata*

Pseudedomia multistriata HENSON 1948

See Plate I, 1–6.

Specimens: Holotype, British Museum (Natural History) P. 35961–2.
Topotypes, P. 42638, 42641.
Other specimens, P. 42639–40.

Redescription of the microspheric form

The holotype is still the only specimen known and it at present exists as two thin sections, one approximately equatorial, but varying because the test was thin and wavy. The second section is tangential – vertical and it is possible to see on the first section where the piece for the second was cut off. HENSON (1948) stated: "Test flabelliform; early stages planispiral, evolute, with whorls opening rapidly; later chambers serial, arcuate, tending to become cyclical; . . .". This description is not supported by drawings or photographs and it is not compatible with what is now known about comparative morphology. The chambers were probably pseudevolute rather than evolute, the last whorl being so much larger than the earlier ones that the involute central part went unnoticed. There seems to have been no polar swelling. "Serial" seems to imply that the later chambers formed an aduncate termination to the spire. The present appearance of the section suggests this, but a reconstruction could also be made showing persistance of the spiral habit. The later chambers are strongly arcuate and subtend a considerable part of the margin of the test, but there is no proof that cyclical chambers were present and it is more probable that the spiral habit held throughout, as in all other alveolines.

The internal structure revealed by the equatorial section shows the chambers occupied with massive endoskeleton. There is a narrow preseptal canal, traversed by numerous pillars. Where the section is deep within the chamber, the endoskeleton is traversed by thin, widely spaced, chamberlets. Where the section is superficial, the chamberlets are much more closely spaced and they are continuous from one chamber to the next, the apertures through the septa being of exactly the same diameter as the chamberlets, so that the septa are not distinguishable. The preseptal canals lie too deep in the chamber to be seen in this part of the section. The early whorls are not seen clearly but it seems that they were planispiral and had fairly widely spaced, nearly straight septa, with the usual infilling of endoskeleton. Comparison with the better-known species *P. complanata* EAMES and SMOUT 1955 and *P. globularis* nov. sp. leaves no doubt that there is identity of structure, the differences being only in size and proportions.

The vertical section was prepared from a portion cut from the outer part of the flange. It is very obscure and it is doubtful if any features described from it are trustworthy, but a drawing of its possible features is given (Plate I, 6). It shows a rounded margin with chamberlets or more probably the preseptal canals of three chambers on the right-hand side. Five large, black, spots in the central part of the section were thought by HENSON (1948) to be interseptal buttresses, but they are too large; more probably they are post-mortem damage to the test. Faint pattern on each side of this section may indicate alar prolongations of the last two or three chambers, although, because the section is confined to the last five chambers, it would indicate very extreme vorticity, and is more probably a false indication.

Description of the megalospheric form

The test is lenticular with a subacute margin and flat poles. The exterior is smooth and the septal sutures flush. There is no umbilical depression. Decorticated specimens show about six chambers per whorl with narrow preseptal canals and serried "continuous" chamberlets, their walls being slightly narrower than their cavities. The megalosphere is small and spherical. The margin is more acute in the early whorls than in the later ones. Occasional supplementary chamberlets occur in the "couche basale" of the chambers of the last two whorls, near the equatorial plane. No buttresses have been seen in the preseptal canal; one per chamber, near the equatorial plane would be expected but only an exceptionally well-orientated section would intersect one.

Dimensions of microspheric form:

Maximum observed equatorial diameter	3.5 mm
Thickness at periphery	0.26 mm
Primary chamberlets, diameter	0.007 mm
spacing	30 per mm
Subsidiary chamberlets, diameter	0.009 mm
spacing	17 per mm
Height of preseptal canal	0.01 mm
Diameter of buttress	0.04 mm

About three whorls are visible, with sixteen visible chambers in the last whorl. It is estimated that there were at least six whorls with about six chambers in the third to fifth whorls and over twenty in the last whorl.

Dimensions of megalospheric form:

Maximum observed diameter	2.3 mm
Thickness at axis	0.8 mm
Primary chamberlets, diameter	0.007 mm
spacing	30 per mm
Diameter of proloculus	0.15 mm

There are about seven whorls with six to seven chambers in the last whorl.

Remarks

After describing *Pseudedomia complanata* EAMES and SMOUT 1955, it was evident that the megalospheric form of *P. multistriata* HENSON 1948 should be lenticular, probably rather compressed, and about 2 mm in diameter. Its primary chamber layer would have the same characteristics as that of the holotype and there should be about 6 chambers in the last whorl. Examination of material of similar age to the type locality, and at the type locality itself, yielded a few specimens that conformed to expectations. They are nowhere abundant, mostly occurring in hard limestone, and only a single specimen showing the test in the round was found. It is only the knowledge gained from the more abundant material of *P. complanata* that has enabled *P. multistriata* to be described reliably.

Occurrence

Maastrichtian limestones of shallow water facies, in association with *Omphalocyclus macropora* (LAMARCK 1816); *Siderolites calcitrapoides* LAMARCK 1801, *Rotalia trochidiformis* (LAMARCK 1801); *Fissoelphidium operculiferum* SMOUT 1955; *Elphidiella multiscissurata* SMOUT 1955; *Orbitoides apiculata* SCHLUMBERGER 1901 and *Loftusia* spp.

Localities: Deep Boreholes at Jebel Dukhan, Qatar Peninsula of Arabia; Ratawi, Southern Iraq; other possible occurrences have been noted but poor preservation makes their recording undesirable.

Pseudedomia globularis nov. sp.

See Plate II, 1–18.

Specimens: Holotype, British Museum (Natural History) P. 42643.
　　　　　　Paratypes, P. 42642, 42644–6.

Description

Dimorphism is slight, the external appearance of the test being much the same in both generations and there being no known difference of size. The immature test is globular with about eight chambers per whorl, after which it becomes lenticular and

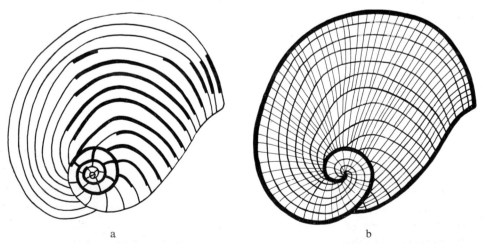

Fig. 9. *Pseudedomia multistriata* HENSON 1948. a. Reconstruction of the equatorial section of the holotype, lines actually seen bold, endoskeleton omitted; b. Reconstruction of the external appearance of the holotype, viewed from the side.

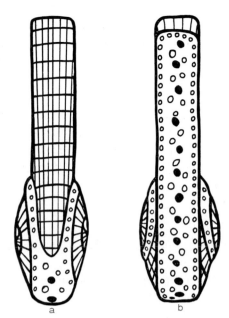

Fig 10. *Pseudedomia multistriata* HENSON 1948. Reconstructions of the external appearance of the holotype, viewed from the edge.

finally develops a large, narrow, pseudevolute flange with strongly recurved chambers. The alar prolongations of the final chambers have not been observed, which suggests that they are probably almost radially directed. There is a serried subepidermal layer of primary chamberlets of "continuous" type. Numerous supplementary chamberlets lie in the "couche basale". They are larger than the primary chamberlets and spaced more widely. They are very irregularly arranged. In the early chambers they disturb the regularity of the primary chamberlet layer and in the very early chambers only primary chamberlets are present. The preseptal canal is abundantly provided with buttresses of irregular shape. The megalosphere is succeeded by a "canal flexostyle" in the equatorial plane of about a quarter of the whorl length. The microspheric nepiont has been seen only obscurely but it is probable that it is milioline.

Dimensions

Estimated equatorial diameter of a large specimen	3.20 mm
Diameter of globular part of the test in the equatorial plane, approx. . .	2.0 mm
Thickness at axis of coiling	1.6 – 2.0 mm
Thickness of flange at periphery	0.6 – 0.8 mm
Primary chamberlets, diameter	0.003 – 0.007 mm
spacing.	11 – 25 per mm
Supplementary chamberlets, diameter	0.005 – 0.008 mm
Height of preseptal canal.	0.01 mm
Diameter of megalosphere	0.2 – 0.3 mm
Maximum chamber height in flange	1.1 mm

Occurrence

Known only from the Bekhme Limestone formation of Campanian age at Bekhme Gorge, Northeastern Iraq. The occurrence is in limestone of shallow water facies.

Remarks

This species is known only from very hard limestone and therefore has been seen only in random sections. The globular shape of the immature test and the strongly pseude-volute nature of the terminal flange distinguish it from the other spieces of the genus.

This species was referred to by Dunnington *et al.* (1960, p. 61) as *Cosinella* nov. sp. REICHEL M.S.

APPENDIX

Notes on selected species of taxonomic interest, mainly of *"Orbitolites"* s.l.

The locality of a number of type specimens is quoted as "Challenger station no. 172". BRADY (1884) stated that this material was collected on July 22, 1874 off Nukualofa, Tongatabu, Friendly Islands, from a coral botton at 18 fathoms.

Orbitolites complanata LAMARCK 1801

  Selected synonyms:

  Orbitolites complanata LAMARCK, 1801 [LAMARCK (1801), 376].
  Orbitolites complanata LAMARCK; CARPENTER [(1856), 226/tabula 6, fig. 9].
  Orbitolites complanata LAMARCK; DOUVILLÉ [(1902), 296–297/textfig. 5, 6].
  Non *Orbitolites complanata* LAMARCK; CARPENTER (1883).
  Non *Orbitolites complanata* LAMARCK; BRADY (1884).

This is a very well known and widespread species which has an authentic type depo-sited in the Musée d'Histoire naturelle, Paris. There is no other species with which it could easily be confused at the typelocality and it is readily distinguished from all other species of the Orbitolitinae. CARPENTER (1883) and BRADY (1884) wrongly deter-mined specimens of *Marginopora vertebralis* as this species, as was pointed out by DOUVILLÉ (1902).

In this species the subepidermal zone is very thin, almost vestigial, and the apertural pores are almost randomly scattered in a wide band that occupies almost the whole of the margin. The apertures are roughly aligned in transverse rows. Partitions run from side to side of the chamber, occasionally anastomosing with each other but mostly distinct. The partitions are strongly fluted with an aperture at the end of each groove. There are no holes through the partitions to put the cellules of the same chamber in direct communication with each other. The equatorial section and any sections parallel to it have a deceptive appearance of cycles of small arcuate chambers. This is caused by the twisted partitions, but it will be noted that superficial sections parallel to the axis show the partitions very clearly, and they can be observed readily on broken specimens.

"Orbitolites" orbiculus (FORSKÅL 1775)

See Plate IV, 3, 4.

    Nautilus orbiculus FORSKÅL, 1775 [FORSKÅL (1775), 125].

    Sorites orbiculus FORSKÅL; EHRENBERG [(1840), 144–145/tabula 1, tabula 2, fig. 2 a–d].

Neotype: British Museum (Nat. Hist.) specimen no. 1961.11.10.10.

Origin: Recent; Gulf of Aqaba, Red Sea, collected by Dr. F. R. S. HENSON.

The test is discoidal; outline sometimes irregular; margin only slightly thicker than the centre; sutures depressed. The chambers are annular, with subepidermal partitions that are randomly inserted on either side but fuse in pairs across the central zone in many cases, always leaving a central hole if not a gap. The cellules so formed are inflated marginally, giving the appearance of arcuate chambers disposed in cycles. The apertures lie in a slight central sulcus, roughly in a single to double row, roughly aligned with the partitions. The megalospheric (or very large microspheric?) proloculus is followed by an undivided deuteroconch, succeeded by about four spiral chambers with partitions and four or more reniform chambers. The spiral and reniform chambers are involute, their alar prolongations forming a small central star on the exterior. Maximum diameter of the test about 3 mm.

FORSKÅL's description is inadequate to differentiate this species from other *Orbitolites* and it is only by inference that the species is placed as originating in the Red Sea. EHRENBERG (1840) published a redescription and figures that have been widely accepted as characteristic of this species and the Neotype specimen has been chosen from specimens from the Red Sea which agree very closely with EHRENBERG's figures. There can be little doubt that the species described as *Sorites orbiculus* by LACROIX (1959) is the same species, but he did not figure external views.

Orbulites marginalis LAMARCK 1816 and *Amphisorus hemprichii* (EHRENBERG 1840) are only varietal forms of this species. *"O."marginalis* is small with a larger, bicellular, nucleoconch and reduced involute, spiral stage. *"O". hemprichii* is thicker with more inflated cellules and the apertures more definitely arranged in a double row; it should not be confused with *"O."duplex*.

"Orbitolites" marginalis (LAMARCK 1816)

See Plate IV, 5, 6.

    Orbulites marginalis LAMARCK 1816 [LAMARCK (1816), 196].

Neotype: British Museum (Nat. Hist.) specimen no. 1961.11.10.9.

Origin: Recent, shore near Priola, Sicily, Mediterranean Sea, collected by Dr. F. E. EAMES.

The test is discoidal; outline and chambering sometimes irregular; margin only slightly thicker than the centre; sutures depressed. The chambers are annular, with subepidermal partitions that are randomly inserted on either side but fuse in pairs across the central zone in many cases, always leaving a central hole if not a gap. The cellules so formed are inflated marginally, giving the appearance of arcuate chambers disposed in cycles. The apertures lie in a slight central sulcus, roughly in a single to double row, roughly aligned with the partitions. The nucleoconch is megalospheric, consisting of a deuteroconch enclosing the proloculus, followed by one undivided chamber and a few evolute spiral chambers that are divided by partitions, passing through a reniform stage of a few chambers before the annular ephebic type of chamber is produced. Maximum diameter of the test about 2 mm.

LAMARCK's description indicated a discoidal species of about 2 mm diameter with a porous margin found in the Mediterranean Sea. The specimen selected as a Neotype satisfies this in all details. MARIE (1940) stated that he had searched for LAMARCK's specimens and failed to find them, so the present erection of a new type is necessary. MARIE noted that DESHAYES and EDWARDS (1836) in their re-editing of LAMARCK's work stated that this species has two layers of chambers. This persistant error of description affects a number of species of the Orbitolitinae and need not be taken seriously. When the cellules of an annular chamber are marginally inflated, the test appears superficially to be two-layered. Specimens of this type are strictly regarded as "O."*hemprichii* but are thought to be conspecific with this species, which typically shows only slight marginal inflation of the cellules and has the apertures almost in a single row. "O."*orbiculus* seems to be a senior synonym. It typically differs in the nepiont; "O."*marginalis* may be the A_1 form of "O."*orbiculus*, which is itself probably B, or A_2.

CARPENTER (1883) applied the name O.*marginalis* LAMARCK to the species here named "O."*carpenteri*. This is a much larger Pacific species not reliably recorded from the Mediterranean Sea, in which the chambers are obviously annular and the apertures are transverse slits arranged in a single row. Many authors have erroneously followed CARPENTER's use of the name, but LACROIX (1955) has correctly placed it in the synonymy of "O."*orbiculus*. His opinion carries great weight since he made a special study of Red Sea and Mediterranean Sea species.

"*Orbitolites*" *hemprichii* (EHRENBERG 1840).

Amphisorus Hemprichii EHRENBERG 1840 [EHRENBERG (1840), 130/tabula 3, fig. 3].

Neotype: British Museum (Nat. Hist.) specimen no. 1962. 6. 26.1.
Origin: Recent, Gulf of Aqaba, Red Sea, collected by Dr. F. R. S. HENSON.

The test is discoidal; outline sometimes irregular; margin thicker than the centre, sutures strongly depressed. The chambers are annular, with subepidermal partitions that are randomly inserted on either side but fuse in pairs across the central zone in many cases, always leaving a central hole if not a gap. The cellules so formed are strongly inflated marginally, giving the appearance of arcuate chambers disposed in cycles. The apertures lie in a well-developed central sulcus in slightly offset pairs, rarely in threes in later chambers. The apertures thus form two rows. The type specimen is probably microspheric or A_2 megalospheric but the species is probably trimorphic. The microspheric test has the proloculus followed by two undivided chambers, succeeded by about four spiral chambers and a few reniform chambers. The nepionic chambers are involute, their alar prolongations forming a central star as in "*O*"*orbiculus*. Maximum diameter of the test about 3 mm.

The selection of a Neotype which is not from EHRENBERG's collection requires justification. It is understood from Dr. K. DIEBEL, who has generously offered any help in his power, that the EHRENBERG collection is preserved in East Berlin; most of the specimens being in spreads of canada balsam on glass. The identification of specimens as syntypes is likely to be subjective and there is no guarantee of even this limited success.

The specimen from Akaba in the British Museum (Nat. Hist.) agrees well with EHRENBERG's description and figure and there is no reason to doubt that it represents the species that EHRENBERG intended. A further consideration in making an immediate designation of type is the convenience in having the types of *A.hemprichii*, *Nautilus orbiculus* and *Orbitolites marginalis* in the same depository, where direct comparison is possible. It is also a matter of urgency because of the theoretical implications on the description of the subfamily Orbitolitinae and its genera.

EHRENBERG's description and figure leave no doubt that this species has the general appearance of "*O*."*orbiculus*, probably even to being the same size. The Neotype specimen has been chosen from specimens from the Red Sea that meet these requirements. No specimens are known in which two layers of chambers are actually present, but specimens such as that chosen have a high degree of inflation of the cellules marginally, which gives an appearance like two layers of chambers arranged in cycles.

CARPENTER (1883) identified specimens of "*O*."*duplex* or a species closely allied to it from the Red Sea as *A.hemprichii* and many subsequent authors have followed his synonymy. It seems unlikely that Ehrenberg would have omitted to mention the notable differences of this species from "*O*". *orbiculus*, if it were the species that he had in mind. In describing *A.hemprichii* as generically distinct from *S.orbiculus* (sic!), the distinction between one and two layers weighed very heavily with EHRENBERG, for he thought that he was describing Bryozoa.

A.hemprichii is merely a varietal form of "*O*."*orbiculus* and there seems to be complete gradation between them in some populations. They differ only in the degree of inflation of the cellules and a slight difference in the apertural pattern. Microspheric specimens are likely to show the *hemprichii* characters more often than megalospheric ones.

"*Orbitolites*" *carpenteri* nomen novum

    Orbitolites marginalis LAMARCK; CARPENTER [(1883), 20–25/tabula 3, fig. 1–7; tabula 4, fig. 1–5] non LAMARCK 1816.

Holotype: British Museum (Nat. Hist.) specimen no. 1961.11.10.7.
Origin: Recent, Fiji reef; Challenger station no. 172.

The test is discoidal, rarely fluted or flanged; margin only slightly thicker than the centre. The subepidermal partitions are spaced at about the chamber height and are strongly developed, leaving a hole in the central zone of the chamber. The apertural pores are transversely elongate and form a single row; each is aligned over the hole in the fused part of the subepidermal partition. The megalospheric nucleoconch consists of three chambers but the third is small and in obvious spiral succession; there are about four spiral chambers and about four reniform chambers before the annular habit is assumed. Maximum diameter of the test is about 6 mm. This species is trimorphic with some variation in the size of the test.

The specimens described by CARPENTER (1883) as "O."*marginalis* are most unlikely to be conspecific with the specimens given the name by LAMARCK; they were from the Pacific Ocean, not the Mediterranean Sea, and many specimens attain a size two or three times the 2 mm cited by LAMARCK. These specimens have a strong resemblance to "O."*duplex*, but differ in the structure of the megalospheric nucleoconch and in the possession of only a singly row of apertures. It is highly desirable that this form should receive a distinct name. It is the species described by DOUVILLÉ (1902) as typical of *Sorites*.

The specimen selected as Holotype may have been the original of the drawing by CARPENTER [(1883), tabula 3, fig. 1].

"*Orbitolites*" *duplex* CARPENTER 1883

Orbitolites duplex CARPENTER 1883 [CARPENTER (1883), 25–29/tabula 3, fig. 8–14; tabula 4, fig. 6–10; tabula 5, fig. 1–10].

Lectotype: British Museum (Nat. Hist.) specimen no. 1961.11.10.1.
Origin: Recent, Fiji reef; Challenger station no. 172.

The test is discoidal, sometimes with accessory flanges that are more or less radial, rarely slightly fluted; margin moderately thicker than the centre; sutures almost flush. The subepidermal partitions are spaced at about the chamber height and are strongly developed, leaving a small empty central zone which is sometimes crossed by buttresses. The apertural pores are transversely elongate and form two rows, the arrangement in each row being random with respect to the other. The megalospheric nucleoconch has three chambers and is directly succeeded by annular chambers. This species is trimorphic. Maximum diameter of the test about 8 mm.

The specimen here designated as lectotype is possibly the specimen used in drawing pl. 3, fig. 8 of CARPENTER (1883), selected from the syntypes of CARPENTER's collection; its authenticity is beyond doubt.

ELLIS and MESSINA state that this is a new name. If so, it would have to be considered a junior synonym of *Amphisorus hemprichii* EHRENBERG 1840, for this is the oldest species named in CARPENTER's synonymy. However, CARPENTER did not state that *duplex* was a new name formally; in his text he said "... these (specimens) I could pretty certainly identify with the forms on which Professor EHRENBERG had founded his genus *Amphisorus*...". This is a qualified identification and refers to specimens from the Red Sea, whereas the description of "O". *duplex* was explicitly founded on specimens from the Fiji reefs in the Pacific. The identity of *A.hemprichii* has been the subject of some discrepancies in the literature and therefore a Neotype has been proposed here which agrees in all respects with Ehrenberg's description and figure. It is a specimen closely resembling "*O.*" *orbiculus*. "*O. duplex* occurs in the same sample and is specifically quite distinct.

"*Orbitolites*" *vertebralis* (Quoy and Gaymard in Blainville, 1830)

> *Marginopora vertebralis* Quoy and Gaymard in Blainville, 1830 [Blainville (1830), 377 (Vol. 60)].
> *Orbitolites complanatus* Lamarck; Carpenter [(1883) 29–43/tabula 5, fig. 11–18; tabula 6–7], non Lamarck, 1801.

Neotype: British Museum (Nat. Hist.) specimen no. 1961.11.10.8.
Origin: Recent, Fiji reef; Brady collection, probably Challenger Station no. 172.

The test is discoidal, occasionally irregularly fluted; margin considerably thicker than the centre; sutures almost flush. The subepidermal partitions are spaced at less than the chamber height and the subepidermal zone is narrow. The central zone is traversed by irregular and incomplete partitions. The apertures are small, circular pores arranged randomly in a broad band. The megalospheric nucleoconch has three chambers, followed directly by annular chambers with partitions. This species is probably dimorphic. Maximum diameter of test 20 mm.

It is a reasonable inference from the mention of Quoy that this species is from the Pacific Ocean and the original description fits the specimen now designated as the Neotype. No indication has been found in the literature of the location of the specimens available to Blainville (1830).

This species is highly distinctive; the closeness of the subepidermal partitions and the small, numerous apertural pores scattered in a wide median band round the margin, are not parallelled by any other living species of the Orbitolitinae. It is sharply distinct from "*O.*"*duplex*, and has little resemblance to the Eocene species *O.complanatus*. The latter species has transverse rows of apertural pores associated with fluted partitions. Carpenter figures a protracted development of complex annular chambers with numerous pores and complex buttresses between them from simple chambers with subepidermal partitions only. In most megalospheric specimens the ephebic type of chamber is established by the fourth or fifth chamber.

"*Orbitolites*" *vertebralis* var. *plicata* (Dana 1848).

> *Marginopora vertebralis* Quoy and Gaymard in Blainville (1830), var. *plicata* Dana 1848 [Dana (1848), 706/tabula 60, fig. 9, 9a, 9b].
> *Orbitolites laciniatus* Brady 1881 [Brady (1881), 47].
> *Orbitolites complanata* var. *laciniata* Brady (sic!); Carpenter [(1883), tabula 7].
> *Orbitolites complanata* var. *laciniata* Brady 1884 [Brady (1884), 220–221/tabula 14, fig. 8–11].

Lectotype: British Museum (Nat. Hist.) specimen no. 1959.5.5.772, figured by Brady [(1884), tabula 16, fig. 10a, b].
Origin: Recent, Fiji Reef; Challenger station no. 172.

The test is discoidal but very highly fluted, the margin being doubled or trebled in most specimens. The margin is considerably thicker than the centre. The subepidermal partitions are spaces more closely than the chamber height and the subepidermal zone is very narrow. The central zone is filled in the earlier chambers by partitions with holes in them, but in later chambers the central zone is occupied by slender pillars. The apertures are small and circular and arranged in a broad band. The megalospheric nucleoconch is thought to be three-chambered and is probably not significantly different from that of *M.vertebralis*. Maximum diameter of test about 25 mm.

This form was described as a variety of *Marginopora vertebralis*, and this is probably correct. It should however be noted that it is a very distinct variety and that the very frank development of pillaring is not comparable in *M.vertebralis* s.str., being much more crowded into dubious partitions in that form. The majority of specimens fall into one of two groups, those with a more or less simple disc and those with the laciniate habit.

Orbitolites" moureti (DOUVILLÉ 1902)

Praesorites moureti DOUVILLÉ 1902, [DOUVILLÉ (1902), 291–293/tabula 9, fig. 1–4].
Praesorites moureti DOUVILLÉ; HENSON [(1950), 54–55/tabula 10, fig. 1].
Praesorites moureti DOUVILLÉ; MARIE [(1958), 130/tabula 1, fig. 9–11].

Lectotype: the specimen figured by DOUVILLÉ [(1902), tabula 9, fig. 1]; collection of the École des Mines, Paris; collected by M. ARNAUD; Lower Campanian P. I., Saint-André, Charentes, France.

This specimen has been seen by myself and has been redescribed by HENSON (1950) and MARIE (1958).

MARIE (1958) stated that the megalospheric nepiont of this species is slightly twisted to one side of the median plane. He figured partitions in a reniform deuteroconch; a very unusual feature in the Orbitolitinae, for most species have no endoskeleton until the third or some later chamber. MARIE's figures are conventionalised drawings. The figure by HENSON (1950, pl. 10, fig. 1), a topotype specimen, shows that the subepidermal partitions are completely inter-septal but that their extensions into the otherwise empty central zone of the chamber penetrate more deeply proximally than distally. DOUVILLÉ's figures show a double row of apertures (although not on topotype specimens), but MARIE reports a single row of apertures. DOUVILLÉ is more probably correct.

"Orbitolites" dufrenoyi (D'ARCHIAC 1854)

Cyclolina dufrenoyi D'ARCHIAC 1854 [D'ARCHIAC (1854), 203/tabula 2, fig. 1 a–d].
Broeckina dufrenoyi (D'ARCHIAC); MUNIER-CHALMAS [(1882), 470–471 partim].
Praesorites dufrenoyi (D'ARCHIAC); MARIE [(1958), 125–139].

MARIE has recorded that specimens seen by D'ARCHIAC cannot be found. He redescribed the species from D'ARCHIAC's description and figure but found no specimens from the type locality or elsewhere to fit the description. This species is very like *Prae-sorites moureti* DOUVILLÉ 1902 and there is naturally a grave suspicion that they are really synonymous. *B.dufrenoyi* is therefore at present a nomen dubium and it would be better to obtain a ruling against its use rather than risk the substitution of *dufrenoyi* for *moureti* and *Broeckina* for *Praesorites* at some future date.

Sorites dominicensis EHRENBERG 1840, nomen dubium
     Sorites dominicensis EHRENBERG, 1840 [EHRENBERG (1840), 134].

The brief latin description is inadequate for recognition of this species and there was no figure. Until the specimens of EHRENBERG's collection in Berlin are examined, it is uncertain whether authentic specimens can be established. Unless they are labelled adequately, the species will remain a nomen dubium. There seems to be a very strong case for the suppression of this name because it is highly probable that the species has received a name, probably of later date, by which it is now known.

Recognition of this species has been claimed by only one author, RENZ (1948) and he obtained his specimens from Venezuela and failed to give any justification for the application of this name to them. DOUVILLÉ (1902) mentioned a specimen in the DESHAYES collection from San Domingo that might be this species, but he did not describe or figure it. CUSHMAN and PONTON (1932) described a species from the Lower Miocene Chipola Marl of Florida that they thought might be *S.dominicensis*. There is therefore no established usage for this name.

Nautilus melo FICHTEL and MOLL 1798
     The following synonyms have been proposed:
     Nautilus melo var. α FICHTEL and MOLL 1798:
          Clausulus indicator MONTFORT 1808, 178–180 (type of *Clausulus* MONTFORT 1808); new name.
          Melonites sphaerica LAMARCK 1816 (type of *Melonites* LAMARCK 1816); new name.
          Alveolina haueri D'ORBIGNY 1846; subjective synonym.
     Nautilus melo var. β FICHTEL and MOLL 1798:
          Borelis melonoides MONTFORT 1808, 170–172 (type of *Borelis* MONTFORT 1808); new name.

Neotype: SCHLUMBERGER Collection, Sorbonne, Paris, specimen 2405 (3), figured by REICHEL [(1937), tabula 10, fig. 8].

The original description and figures indicate a globose alveoline with "continuous" arrangement of chamberlets. D'ORBIGNY (1852) included under this name specimens which would now probably be determined as the Eocene species *Alveolina globosa* (LEYMERIE 1846) but REICHEL (1937) gave an exceedingly careful account in which he concluded that *N.melo* var. *a* is synonymous with *Neoalveolina haueri* (D'ORBIGNY 1846) and *N. melo* var. *β* is synonymous with *Neoalveolina bradyi* (SILVESTRI 1927).

Application will be made to the Commission of Zoological Nomenclature for the suppression of *C. indicator*, *M. sphaerica* and *B. melonoides*.

The neotype has been deliberately selected to conform to *Nautilus melo* var. *β*, to maintain the usage of REICHEL (1937). One would normally select var. *α* as the type of *N. melo* but this form is commonly known as *Neoalveolina haueri* (D'ORBIGNY 1846). The suppressions recommended not only remove unfamiliar names but have the effect that *N. haueri* is the first accepted new name and applies to *N. melo* var. *α*, leaving var. *β* as *N. melo* s.str.

NOTE

A major work on *Orbitolites* has appeared while this paper was in press: LEHMANN R., 1961. Strukturanalyse einiger Gattungen der Subfamilie Orbitolitinae. *Eclogae Geol. Helv.*, 54 : 597–667. This gives an excellent account of the morphology of several of the species described here. LEHMANN has been uncritical in his adoption of names, except in the unfortunate case where his recognition of the similarity of chamber arrangement in *Orbitolites*, *Opertorbitolites* and *Somalina* has led him to place them in mutual synonymy, ignoring the perfectly usable diagnostic characters of the lateral layers on which the original differential diagnoses rest. He has ignored the difficulties surrounding the type of *Sorites*, assuming that *Orbitolites carpenteri* can be regarded as the type. The discussion and designation of types in this paper enables a synonymy to be given for LEHMANN's species:

Correct name:	LEHMANN's name:
Orbitolites complanata	*Orbitolites complanata*
Opertorbitolites douvillei	*Orbitolites douvillei*
Orbitolites (Amphisorus) orbiculus	*Sorites orbiculus*
Orbitolites carpenteri	*Sorites marginalis*
Orbitolites orbitolitoides	*Sorites orbitolitoides*
Orbitolites (Marginopora) vertebralis	*Marginopora vertebralis*
Orbitolites duplex (?juvenile)	*Amphisorus hemprichi*
Somalina stephanii	*Orbitolites stephanii*

The introduction of three new species closely resembling *Orbitolites complanata* raises problems for the practical palaeontologist who may have to determine poor specimens. This can easily be overcome by regarding *armoricensis*, *cotentinensis* and *reicheli* as subspecies of *O.complanata*, preserving the whole of LEHMANN's work but permitting laxer determination where necessary.

The subfamily definition of the Orbitolitinae proposed here would necessitate removal of *Yaberinella* to the subfamily Peneroplinae.

The discrepancies in the nomenclature have been emphasised here as it is evident that the paper by LEHMANN will deserve the position of a standard work and provides a most valuable source of information that has not hitherto been readily available.

ACKNOWLEDGMENTS

This paper is published by permission of the Managements of the Iraq Petroleum Co. Ltd. and The British Petroleum Co. Ltd. Thanks are due to Dr. F. R. S. HENSON, Dr. F. E. EAMES and Dr. F. T. BANNER for their help and kind criticism during the course of this work and to the Staff of the British Museum (Natural History) for access to their collections and records and their unfailing helpfulness. Gifts of separates of his works by Mr. P. MARIE have been particularly helpful in this connection.

SUMMARY

The taxonomy and phylogeny of the family Alveolinidae is discussed, directed to the understanding of the genus *Pseudedomia* HENSON 1948. The characters and relationships of many known species of large, complex Foraminifera, particularly those from the Middle East, are reviewed to establish their distinctive characters and assess their possible phyletic relationships to *Pseudedomia*. The genera concerned are mostly porcellaneous forms of the superfamily Miliolidea but some are crypto-agglutinating forms of the superfamily Lituolidea. Taxonomic notes are given where necessary for the families Peneroplidae and Alveolinidae; type designations and redescriptions being given where necessary. A formal emendation of *Pseudedomia* is based on a redescription of the type species *P.multistriata* HENSON 1948, the megalospheric form being described for the first time. A new species, *P.globularis*, is described.

REFERENCES

BAKX, L. A. J., 1932. De genera *Fasciolites* en *Neoalveolina* in het Indo-Pacifische gebied. *Verhandel. Ned. Geol. Mijnbouw. Genoot. Ned. en Koloniën*, 9: 205–266.

BARKER, R. W. and GRIMSDALE, T. F., 1937. Studies of Mexican fossil Foraminifera. *Ann. Mag. Nat. Hist., London*, Ser. 10, 19: 161–178.

BERMÚDEZ, P. J., 1935. Foraminiferos de la Costa Norte de Cuba. *Mem. Soc. Cubana Hist. Nat.*, 9: 129–224.

BRADY, H. B., 1881. Notes on some of the reticularian Rhizopoda of the Challenger Expedition, pt. 3. *Quart. J. Microscop. Sci., N. Ser.*, 21: 31–71.

BRADY, H. B., 1884. Report on the Foraminifera dredged by H.M.S. "Challenger" during the years 1873–1876. *Report on the sci. research of the Voyage of H.M.S. Challenger, Zoology*, 9: 210–212.

CARPENTER, W. B., 1850. On the microscopic structure of *Nummulina, Orbitolites* and *Orbitoides*. *Quart. J. Geol. Soc. London*, 6: 21–38.

CARPENTER, W. B., 1856. Researches on the Foraminifera. 1st. series; On *Orbitolites*. *Phil. Trans. Roy. Soc. London*, 146: 181–236.

CARPENTER, W. B., 1883a. Report on the specimens of the Genus *Orbitolites* collected by H. M. S. CHALLENGER during the years 1873–1876. *Report on the sci. research of the Voyage of H. M. S. Challenger, Zoology*, 7: 1–47.

CARPENTER, W. B., 1883b. Researches on the Foraminifera. Supplemental memoir: On an abyssal type of the genus *Orbitolites*; a study in the theory of descent. *Proc. Roy. Soc. London*, 35: 276–279.

CARTER, H. J., 1853. Description of *Orbitolites Malabarica* (H. J. C.) illustrative of the spiral and not concentric arrangement of chambers in D'ORBIGNY's order Cyclostègues. *Ann. Mag. Nat. Hist., London*, Ser. 2, 11: 425–427.

CHECCHIA-RISPOLI, G., 1905. Sopra alcune Alveoline eoceniche della Sicilia. *Palaeontografica ital.*, 11: 147–167.

COLOM, C. G., 1935. Las especies de la familia Peneroplidae actuales y fóssiles de las Baleares. *Bol. Soc. Española Hist. Nat.*, 35: 83–102.

COSTA O. G., 1856. Paleontologia del regno di Napoli, parte II, *Accad. Pontaniana, Atti*, 7: 113–378.

CUSHMAN, J. A., 1918. The smaller fossil Foraminifera of the Panama Canal Zone. *Bull. U.S. Natl. Museum*, 103: 45–87.

CUSHMAN, J. A., 1927a. An outline of a re-classification of the Foraminifera. *Contrib. Cushman Lab. Foraminiferal Research*, 3: 1–105.

CUSHMAN, J. A., 1927b. The designation of some genotypes in the Foraminifera. *Contrib. Cushman Lab. Foraminiferal Research*, 3: 188–190.

CUSHMAN, J. A., 1928. Foraminifera. Their classification and economic use. *Cushman Lab. Foraminiferal Research, Spec. Publ.*, 1: 1–401.

CUSHMAN, J. A., 1955. *Foraminifera. Their Classification and economic Use.* 4th. Ed. Harvard Univ. Press, Cambridge, Mass., 478 pp.

CUSHMAN, J. A. and PONTON, G., 1932. The Foraminifera of the Upper, Middle and part of the Lower Miocene of Florida. *Bull. Florida Geol. Surv.*, 9: 7–147.

DANA, J. D., 1846. Zoophytes. U.S. Exploring Expedition during the years 1838–1842 under the command of Charles Wilkes. *U.S. Navy*, 10: 1–740.

DEFRANCE, M. J. L., 1820. Minéralogie et Géologie. In: F. G. LEVRAULT *Dictionnaire des Sciences Naturelles.* Paris, 16 : 1–567.

D'ARCHIAC, A. and HAIME, J., 1854. Coupe géologique des environs de Bains de Rennes (Aude) suivie de la description de quelques fossiles de cette localité. *Bull. Soc. géol. France, 2e sér.*, 11: 205–206.

DE GREGORIO, A., 1894. Description des faunes Tertiaires de la Vénétie; Monographie des fossiles éocéniques (Étage Parisien) de Mont Postale. *Ann. géol. Palermo*, 14: 1–55.

DES MOULINS, C., 1864. Le bassin hydrographique du Couzeau dans ses rapports avec la vallée de la Dordogne, le question diluviale et les silex ouvrés. *Soc. Linn. Bordeaux, Actes, 25, 3e Sér.*, 5: 67–242.

D'ORBIGNY, A., 1826. Tableau méthodique de la classe des Céphalopodes. *Ann. Sci. Nat., Paris, 1e sér.*, 7: 96–314.

D'ORBIGNY, A., 1839. Foraminifères. In: DE LA SAGRE, R., *Histoire physique, politique et naturelle de l'Ile de Cuba.* A. Bertrand, Paris. 224 pp.

D'ORBIGNY, A., 1846. *Foraminifères fossiles du Bassin tertiaire de Vienne Autriche.* Gide et Comp., Paris. 303 pp.

DOUVILLÉ, H., 1902a. Essai d'une révision des *Orbitolites. Bull. Soc. géol. France, 4e sér.*, 2: 289–306.

DOUVILLÉ, H., 1902b. Distribution des *Orbitolites* et des *Orbitoïdes* dans la Craie du sud-ouest. *Bull. Soc. géol. France, 4e sér.*, 2: 307–313.

DOUVILLÉ, H., 1907 a (for 1906). Les Calcaires à Fusulines de l'Indo-Chine. *Bull. Soc. géol. France, 4e sér.*, 6: 576–587.

DOUVILLÉ, H., 1907b (for 1906). Evolution et enchaînements des Foraminifères. *Bull. Soc. géol. France, 4e sér.*, 6: 588–602.

DOUVILLÉ, H., 1910. La Craie et le Tertaire des environs de Royan. *Bull. Soc. géol. France, 4e sér.*, 10: 51–61.

DOUVILLÉ, H., 1919. Les Cyclostègues de D'ORBIGNY. *Compt. rend. Acad. Sci.*, 169: 1130–1135.

DOUVILLÉ, H., 1924 (for 1923). Les *Orbitoïdes* et leur évolution en Amérique. *Bull. Soc. géol. France, 4e sér.*, 23: 369–376.

DUNNINGTON, H. V., WETZEL, R. and MORTON, D. M., 1960. *Lexique Stratigraphique International* Vol. III: Asie; fasc. 10a: *Iraq, Mesozoic and Palaeozoic.* Centre Nat. Recherche Sci., Paris, 333 pp.

EAMES, F. E. and SMOUT, A. H., 1955. Complanate Alveolinids and associated Foraminifera from the Upper Cretaceous of the Middle East. *Ann. Mag. Nat. Hist., 12e sér.*, 8: 505–512.

EHRENBERG, C. G., 1840 (for 1838). Über die Bildung der Kreidefelsen und des Kreidemergels durch unsichtbare Organismen. *K. Akad. Wiss., Berlin, Physik. Abhandl.*, 1838: 59–147.

ELLIS, B. F. and MESSINA, A. *Catalogue of Foraminifera.* Loose- leaf publication.

FLINT, J. M., 1899 (for 1897). Recent Foraminifera. A descriptive catalogue of specimens dredged by the U.S. Fish Commission Steamer Albatross. *U.S. Natl. Museum Ann. Rept.*, 1: 249–349.

FORSKÅL, P., 1775. *Descriptiones animalium.* Hauniae Carsten Niebuhr, Copenhagen, 164 pp.

GALLOWAY, J. J., 1933. *A Manual of Foraminifera.* Bloomington, Indiana, 450 pp.

GEINITZ, H. B., 1846. *Grundriss der Versteinerungskunde.* Arnold, Dresden – Leipzig, 26 pp.

GLAESSNER, M. F., 1945. *Principles of Micropaleontology.* Melbourne Univ. Press, Melbourne, 296 pp.

GRIMSDALE, T. F., 1952. Cretaceous and Tertiary Foraminifera from the Middle East. *Bull. Brit. Museum, Geol.*, 1: 223–247.

HEMMING, F., 1953. *Copenhagen Decisions on Zoological Nomenclature.* International Trust for Zoological Nomenclature, London, 135 pp.

HENSON, F. R. S., 1948. *Larger imperforate Foraminifera of South-Western Asia.* Brit. Museum, London, monography, 127 pp.

HENSON, F. R. S., 1950. *Middle Eastern Tertiary Peneroplidae (Foraminifera), with Remarks on the Phylogeny and Taxonomy of the Family.* West Yorkshire Press Co., Wakefield, 70 pp.

HOFKER, J., 1930. *The Foraminifera of the Siboga Expedition,* pt. 2; Siboga Exped. Leiden, pt. 4a; 79–170.

HOFKER, J., 1950. Recent Peneroplidae, Pt. 1, *J. Roy. Microscop. Soc., London,* 70: 388–396.

HOFKER, J., 1951a. Recent Peneroplidae. Pt. 1 (continued). *J. Roy. Microscop. Soc., London,* 71: 223–239.

HOFKER, J., 1951b. Recent Peneroplidae. Pt. 2. *J. Roy. Microscop. Soc., London,* 71: 342–356.

HOFKER, J., 1952a. Recent Peneroplidae. Pt. 3. *J. Roy. Microscop. Soc., London,* 71: 450–463.

HOFKER, J., 1952b. Recent Peneroplidae. Pt. 4. *J. Roy. Microscop. Soc., London,* 102–122.

HOFKER, J., 1953. Recent Peneroplidae. Pt. 5. *J. Roy. Microscop. Soc., London,* 73: 40–46.

KEIJZER, F. G., 1945. *Outline of the Geology of the eastern Part of the Province of Oriente, Cuba (E. of 76° WL) with notes on the Geology of other Parts of the island.* Thesis Univ. Utrecht, 238 pp.

LACROIX, E., 1940. Les *Orbitolites* de la Baie de Cauda. *Bull. Inst. Océanografie, Monaco,* 787: 1–16.

LACROIX, E., 1941. Les *Orbitolites* du Golfe d'Akaba. *Bull. Inst. Océanografie, Monaco,* 794: 1–38.

LACROIX, E., 1959. Les *Orbitolites* du Golfe d'Akaba. In: Mission Robert Ph. Dollfus en Égypte. Pt. 3, 23, Foraminifera I: 7–34. *Centre Natl. Recherche Scientifique, Paris.*

LAMARCK, J. B., 1801. *Système des Animaux sans Vertèbres.,* Paris. 432 pp.

LAMARCK, J. B., 1804. Suite des mémoires sur les fossiles des environs de Paris. Paris. *Musée Natl. Hist. Nat., Ann., Paris,* 5: 349–357.

LAMARCK, J. B., 1816. *Tableau encyclopédique et méthodique des trois Regnes de la Nature; Pt. 23; Mollusques et Polypes divers.* Paris, 3: 1–16.

LAMARCK, J. B., 1845. *Histoire naturelle des Animaux sans Vertèbres.* Revue et augmentée par G. P. DESHAYES et H. MILNE EDWARDS. 2e Ed., Paris, 11 : 665 pp.

LEYMERIE, A., 1851. Mémoire sur un nouveau type pyrénéen. *Mém. Soc. géol. France, 2e sér.,* 4: 177–202.

LOEBLICH, A. L. and TAPPAN, H., 1961. Suprageneric classification of the Rhizopodea. *J. Paleontol.,* 35: 245–330.

MARIE, P., 1940. A propos des foraminifères d'un sable de plage provenant de Tahiti. *Bull. du Musée 2e sér.,* 12, 6.

MARIE, P., 1958. Peneroplidae du Crétacé supérieur a faciès récifal. 1. A propos des genres *Broeckina* et *Praesorites* et sur le nouveau genre *Vandenbroekina. Rev. Micropaleontol.,* 1 : 125–139.

MIOHELIN, H., 1846. *Iconographie zoophytologique.* P. Bertrand, Paris, 21–26 : 222–230.

MONTFORT, D., 1808. *Conchyliologie systématique et Classification méthodique des Coquilles;* etc. F. Schoell, Paris, 410 pp.

MUNIER-CHALMAS, E., 1882a (for 1881–1882). Des genres *Renulites, Broeckina, Archiacina. Bull. Soc. géol. France, 3e sér.,* 10: 470–471.

MUNIER-CHALMAS, E., 1882b (for 1881–1882). Du genre *Lacazina. Bull. Soc. géol. France, 3e sér.,* 10: 471–472.

MUNIER-CHALMAS, E., 1902. Sur les Foraminifères rapportés au groupe des *Orbitolites. Bull. Soc. géol. France, 4e sér.,* 2: 351–354.

MUNIER-CHALMAS, E. and SCHLUMBERGER, C., 1885 (for 1884–1885). Note sur les Miliolidées trematophorées. *Bull. Soc. géol. France, 3e sér.,* 13: 273–323.

NUTTALL, W. L. F., 1925. The stratigraphy of the Laki Series (Lower Eocene) of parts of Sind and Baluchistan (India); with a description of the larger Foraminifera contained in those beds. *Quart. J. Geol. Soc. London,* 81: 417–453.

PALMER, D. K., 1934. Some large fossil foraminifera from Cuba. *Mem. Soc. Cubana Hist. Nat.,* 8: 235–264.

PARKER, W. K. and JONES, T. R., 1861. On the nomenclature of the Foraminifera. Pt. VI. *Alveolina. Ann. Mag. Nat. Hist., London,* Ser. 3, 8 : 161–168.

PARKER, W. K. and JONES, T. R., 1865. *Ann . Mag. Nat. Hist., London,* Ser. 3, 16 : 35.

PARKINSON, J., 1811. *Organic Remains of a former World.* 3, Sherwood, Neely and Jones, London, 455 pp.

POKORNY, V., 1958. *Grundzüge der zoologischen Mikropaläontologie,* 1, VEB Deutscher Verlag der Wissenschaften, Berlin, 582 pp.

QUOY, J. R. C. and GAYMARD, J. T. Mollusques, vers et zoophytes. In: DE BLAINVILLE, H. M. D., 1830. *Dictionnaire des Sciences Naturelles, Paris*, 60: 377.

RAUZER-CHERNOUSOVA, D. M. and FURSENKO, A. V., 1959. *Osnovy palaeontologii.* pt. 1. *General part and Protozoa.* Akad. Nauk. S.S.S.R., Moscow. 482 pp.

REICHEL, M., 1933. Sur une Alvéoline cénomanienne du bassin de Beausset. *Eclogae Geol. Helv.*, 26: 269–280.

REICHEL, M., 1936–1937. Étude sur les Alvéolines. *Mém. Soc. paléontol. Suisse*, 57–59: 1–147.

REICHEL, M., 1941. Sur un nouveau genre d'Alvéolines du Crétacé supérieur. *Eclogae Geol. Helv.*, 34: 254–260.

REICHEL, M., 1947. *Multispirina iranensis* nov. gen., nov. sp. *Mém. Soc. paléontol. Suisse*, 65: 1–13.

REICHEL, M., 1952 (for 1951). *Fusarchaias bermudezi* nov. gen., nov. sp., pénéroplidé alvéoliniforme de l'Oligo–Miocène de Cuba. *Eclogae Geol. Helv.*, 44: 458–464.

RENZ, H. H., 1948. Stratigraphy and fauna of the Agua Salada group, State of Falcón, Venezuela. *Mem. Geol. Soc. Am.*, 32: 219 pp.

REUSS, A. E., 1860. Ueber die Foraminiferen aus der Familie der Peneropliden. *K.Böhm. Ges. Wiss., Prag, Math. Naturwiss. Cl. Sitzberichte Prag*: 68–74.

RHUMBLER, L., 1911. Die Foraminiferen (Thalamophoren) der Plankton-Expedition; Erster Teil: Die allgemeinen Organisationsverhältnisse der Foraminiferen. *Plankton-Exped. Humboldt-Stiftung, Ergeb., Kiel und Leipzig*, 3: 1–331.

RICHARZ, P. S., 1909. Der geologische Bau von Kaiser Wilhelms-Land nach dem heutigen Stand unseres Wissens. In: Geologische Mitteilungen aus dem Indo-Australischen Archipel. *Neues Jahrb. Min. Geol. Palaeontol.*, 29: 406–536.

RUTTEN, L., 1913. Studien über Foraminiferen aus Ost-Asien: 2. Eine neue *Alveolinella* von Ost-Borneo. *Samml. Geol. Reichsmuseums, Leiden, Ser.* 1, 9: 219–224.

SACCO, F., 1922. Sul gigantismo di alcune forme eoceniche dell'Istria. *Rev. accad. Sci., Torino*, 57: 351–357.

SCHLUMBERGER, C., 1898. Note sur le genre *Meandropsina* MUN.-CHALM., nov. gen. *Bull. Soc. géol. France, 3e sér.*, 26: 336–339.

SIGAL, J., 1952 Ordre des Foraminifera. In: PIVETEAU, J. *Traité de Paléontologie. Masson et Cie*, Paris, I : 133–301.

SILVESTRI, A., 1920. Fossili rari o nuovi in formazioni del Paleogene. *Boll. soc. geol. ital.*, 39: 57–80.

SILVESTRI, A., 1928. Intorno all' *Alveolina melo* D'ORBIGNY (1846). *Riv. ital. paleontol.*, 34: 17–37.

SILVESTRI, A., 1937. Foramini feridell' Oligocene e del Miocene della Somalia. Paleontologia della Somalia: V. Fossili dell' Oligocene e del Miocene. *Palaeontografica ital.*, 32 (suppl. 2) : 45–264.

SILVESTRI, A., 1939. Foraminiferi dell' Eocene della Somalia. Parte II. Paleontologia della Somalia: IV. Fossili del' Eocene. *Palaeontografica ital.*, 32 (suppl. 4): 1–102.

SILVESTRI, A., 1940 (for 1939). Illustrazione di specie caratteristica del Cretaceo superiore. *Boll. soc. geol. ital.*, 58: 225–234.

SMOUT, A. H. and EAMES, F. E., 1958. The genus *Archaias* (Foraminifera) and its stratigraphical distribution. *Palaeontology*, I: 207–225.

STACHE, G., 1880. Die Liburnische Stufe. *Abhandl. Geol. Reichsanstalt*, 1880: 195–209.

STACHE, G., 1889. Die Liburnische Stufe und deren Grenz-Horizonte, eine studie über die Schichtenfolgen der Cretacisch-Eocänen oder Protocänen Landbildungsperioden im Bereiche der Küstenländer von Oesterreich-Ungarn, *Abhandl. Geol. Reichsanstalt*, 13: 1–170.

STACHE, G., 1912. Ueber *Rhipidionina* ST. und *Rhapydionina* ST. *Jahrb., Geol. Reichsanstalt*, 62: 659–680.

STEINMANN, G., 1880. Mikroscopische Thierreste aus dem deutschen Kohlenkalk (Foraminiferen und Spongien). *Z. Deut. Geol. Ges.*, 32 : 394–400.

THALMANN, H. E., 1932. Nomenclator (Um- und Neubenennungen) zu den Tafeln 1 bis 115 in H. B. BRADY's Werk über die Foraminiferen der Challenger-Expedition, London, 1884. *Eclogae. Geol. Helv.*, 25: 293–312.

VAN DEN BOLD, W. A., 1946. *Contribution to the Study of Ostracoda, with special Reference to the Tertiary and Cretaceous Microfauna of the Caribbean Region.* Thesis Univ. Utrecht, 167 pp.

VAN WESSEM, A., 1943. *Geology and Paleontology of central Camagüey, Cuba.* Thesis Univ. Utrecht, 91 pp.

VERBEEK, R. D. M. and FENNEMA, R., 1896. *Description géologique de Java et Madoura.* J. G. Stemler Cz. Amsterdam, 2: 925–1183.

VON FICHTEL, L. and MOLL, J. P. C., 1798 (1803 reprint). *Testacea microscopica aliaque minuta ex generibus Argonauta et Nautilus ad naturam delineata et descripta*. Camesina Wien, 124 pp.

WEAVER, T., 1841. On the composition of chalk rocks and chalk marl by invisible organic bodies: from the observations of Dr. EHRENBERG. *Ann. Mag. Nat. Hist., London*, 7: 296–315, 374–398

WILLIAMSON, W. C., 1851. On the minute structure of the calcareous shells of some recent species of Foraminifera. *Trans. Microscop. Soc.*, 3: 105–128.

YABE, H. ann HANZAWA, S., 1929. Tertiary foraminiferous rocks of the Philippines. *Sci. Repts. Tôhoku Imp. Univ., Ser. 2 (Geol.)*, XI: 137–190.

ZITTEL, K. A., 1876. *Grundzüge der Paläontologie*. R. Oldenbourg, München – Leipzig, I: 765 pp.

PLATE I

Pseudedomia multistriata HENSON 1948.

1. Holotype: form B; × 41; nearly equatorial section (after HENSON, 1948); specimen P. 35961. Maastrichtian, Jebel Dukhan, Quatar. Reproduced by permission of the British Museum (Natural History).

2. Topotype: form A; × 20; a.lateral; b. edge view; specimen P. 42638.

3. Form A; × 20; axial section; specimen P. 42640; Maastrichtian, Ratawi, South Iraq.

4. Topotype: form A; × 20; specimen P. 42641; oblique section.

5. Form A; × 20; oblique section; specimen P. 42639; Maastrichtian, Ratawi, South Iraq.

6. Reconstruction of the appearance of the tangential section through the top edge of the holotype (*cf.* HENSON, 1948, pl. XI, fig. 2). Little reliance can be placed on this drawing for the original section is very obscure.

PLATE I

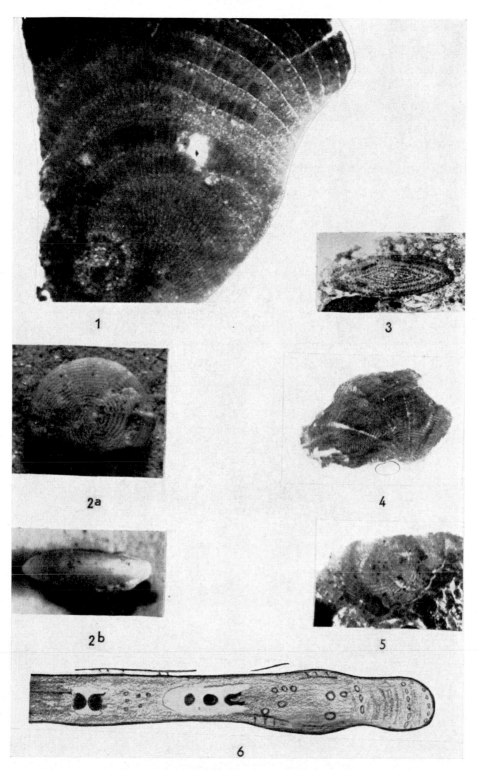

1

2a

2b

3

4

5

6

PLATE II

Pseudedomia globularis nov.sp.
   All specimens are from the Bekhme Limestone, of Campanian age, near Shiranish Nasara, North Iraq.

1–6. Form A, nearly equatorial sections. No. 4 and 5 show an increase of whorl height that is very marked in the last whorl; × 15. No. 5 holotype; specimen P. 42643.

7. Form B, nearly equatorial section; × 15.

8–12. Random sections through the globular early part of the test; × 15.

13–15. Random sections showing the transition from the globular stage to the terminal flange, × 15.

16–18. Specimens in rock sections; British Random sections through the terminal flange; × 10. Museum (Nat. Hist.) specimens P. 42642–6.

   Note that most specimens show the preseptal canal clearly and the buttresses can be seen in No. 5, 9, 11, 12, 16, 18. No. 17 shows that the chambers of the terminal flange are high and recurved. No. 18 is an almost axial section through the terminal flange, the direction of growth being to the left. None of these specimens proves that the terminal stage remains involute; this remains a matter of inference.

PLATE II

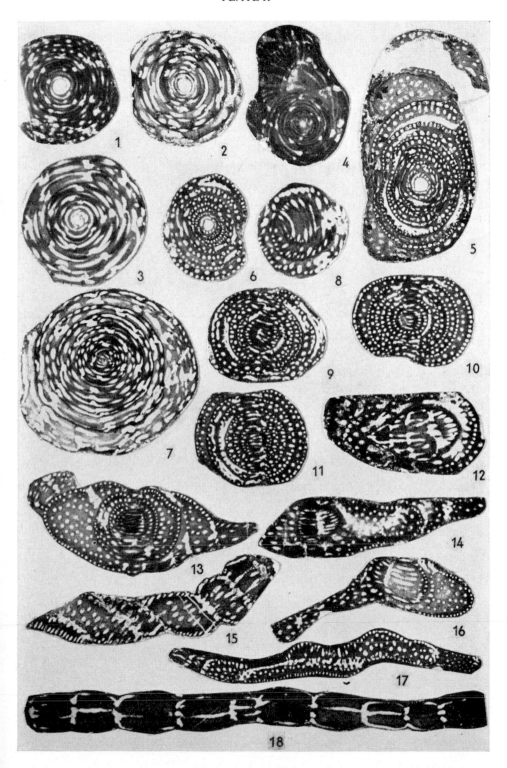

PLATE III

1–3. *Orbitolinella depressa* HENSON 1948.

All specimens are topotypes from Jebel Dukhan, Qatar Peninsula, Arabia; found in limestones that are probably of Cenomanian age; × 50. Specimens are deposited in the collections of the Iraq Petroleum Company Ltd., London.

PLATE III

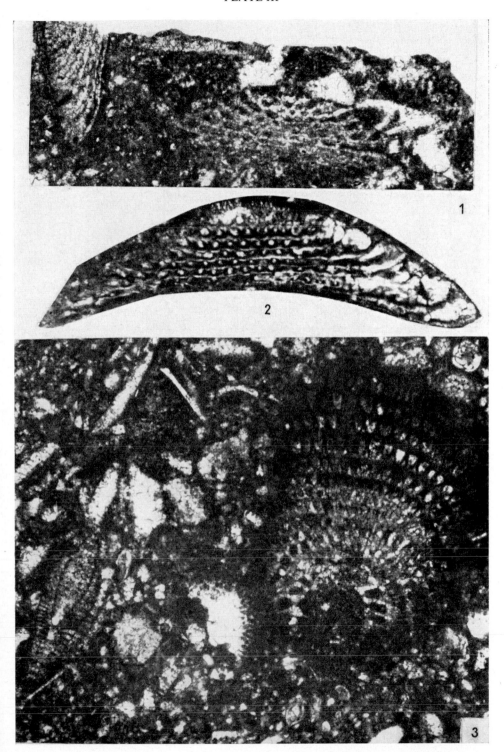

PLATE IV

1, 2. *Orbitolinella depressa* HENSON 1948.
Further random sections of topotypes from Jebel Dukhan, Qatar Peninsula, Arabia; probably Cenomanian; × 50.

3, 4. *"Orbitolites" orbiculus* (FORSKÅL 1775). Lateral and edge views; Gulf of Aqaba, Red Sea; Recent; × 35. British Museum Specimen 1961.11.10.10; Neotype of *Nautilus orbiculus* Forskål, 1775.

5, 6. *"Orbitolites" marginalis* (LAMARCK 1816). Lateral and edge views; shore near Priola, Sicily; Recent; × 50. British Museum Specimen 1961.11.10.9; Neotype of *Orbulites marginalis* LAMARCK 1816.

PLATE IV

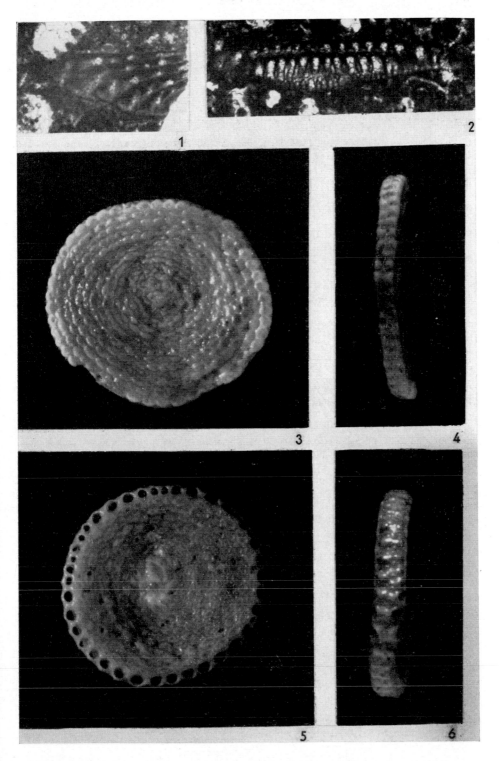

PLATE IV

1, 2. *Orbitolites carpenteri* nov. sp. Holotype, British Museum (Nat. Hist.); specimen 1961.11.10.7, selected from specimens determined as "*Orbitolites marginalis* LAMARCK" by CARPENTER (1883).

1. Lateral view; x 6.4.

2. Marginal view, showing a single row of apertures; x 12.8.

3, 4. *Orbitolites duplex* CARPENTER 1883. Lectotype, British Museum (Nat. Hist.); specimen 1961. 11.10.1, selected from CARPENTER's syntypes.

3. Lateral view; x 4.5.

4. Marginal view, showing a double row of apertures; x 10.

5. *Orbitolites duplex* CARPENTER 1883. Paratype, British Museum (Nat. Hist.); specimen 1961. 11.10.3; one of CARPENTER's syntypes. Equatorial section of the megalospheric nucleoconch; x 96.

6, 7. "*Orbitolites (Marginopora) vertebralis* (QUOY and GAYMARD in BLAINVILLE 1830). Neotype of *Marginopora vertebralis* QUOY and GAYMARD in BLAINVILLE 1830. British Museum (Nat. Hist.); specimen 1961.11.10.8, selected from specimens determined as "*Orbitolites complanata* LAMARCK" by CARPENTER (1883).

6. Lateral view; x 6.4.

7. Marginal view showing a broad band of randomly arranged apertures; x 12.8.

8. *Orbitolites duplex* CARPENTER 1883. Paratype, British Museum (Nat. Hist.); specimen 1961. 11.10.2, one of CARPENTER's syntypes. Equatorial section; x 4.5.

9. "*Orbitolites*" (*Marginopora*) *vertebralis* QUOY and GAYMARD var. *plicata* DANA 1848. Paratype, British Museum (Nat. Hist.); specimen ZF. 2038, one of BRADY's syntypes of *Orbitolites laciniatus* BRADY 1881. Vertical section showing doubling of the margin; x 4.5.

All the figures on this plate are published by permission of the British Museum (Natural History) and are taken from photographs made by the staff of specimens in the W. B. CARPENTER and H. B. BRADY Collections. All specimens were found in Challenger samples at Station no. 172 and were probably living at the time of collection.

PLATE V

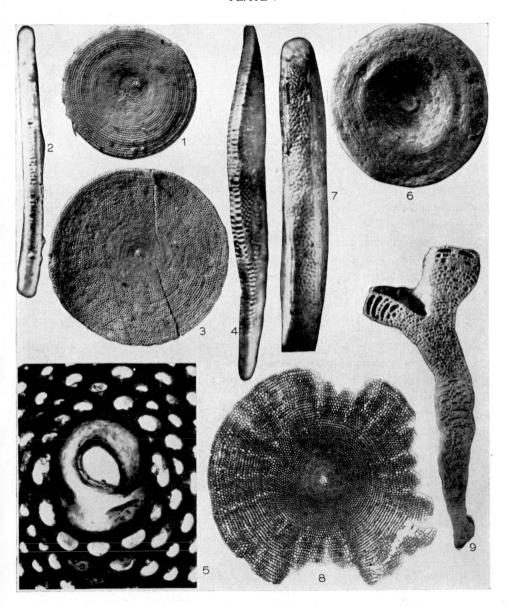

ÜBER EINIGE ENTWICKLUNGSREIHEN VON NUMMULITES UND ASSILINA UND IHRE STRATIGRAPHISCHE BEDEUTUNG

HANS SCHAUB

Naturhistorisches Museum, Basel (Schweiz)

In den letzten Jahrzehnten haben sich Foraminiferen immer mehr als zuverlässige Instrumente für eine Feinstratigraphie erwiesen, vor allem dann, wenn sie als Glieder von Entwicklungsreihen mit erkennbaren Entwicklungstendenzen aufgefasst werden können. Die Versuche zur exakten Formulierung der Gesetzmässigkeiten bei der Phylogenese sind zuerst an Grossforaminiferen angestellt worden. Einen Anstoss zur Anwendung der morphogenetischen Methode bei Grossforaminiferen hat VAN DER VLERK (1922 und 1923) gegeben. Ausgearbeitet wurde die morphogenetische Methode durch TAN SIN HOK (1932–1939). Er und seine Nachfolger haben in ausgezeichneten Arbeiten gezeigt, wie bei verschiedenen Grossforaminiferen von orbitoidalem Bauplan sich im Laufe der Zeit gleichartige, zahlenmässig fassbare, gesetzmässige Veränderungen einstellen, sodass in vielen Fällen das innerhalb einer Entwicklungsreihe erreichte Stadium als Mass für das geologische Alter dienen kann. THALMANN hat 1938 in seinem Aufsatz über "Wert und Bedeutung morphogenetischer Untersuchungen an Grossforaminiferen für die Stratigraphie" sehr eindringlich die Bedeutung der Methode dargelegt und die Folgerungen für eine zuverlässige Anwendung formuliert:

"Der moderne Paläontologe wird sich allmählich von den Fesseln einer nur rein deskriptiv orientierten Systematik befreien müssen, liegt doch das Ziel der Paläontologen nicht nur im Aufstellen und Beschreiben neuer systematischer Einheiten, sondern im Auffinden, und Interpretieren von Entwicklungsgesetzen, im Aufdecken von inneren Zusammenhängen, im völligen Entziffern des Wesens fossiler Dokumente." . . . "Je ausgedehnter und eingehender weitere Grossforaminiferenfaunen von zusammenhängenden, möglichst ungestörten Profilen auf morphogenetischer Grundlage analysiert und gedeutet werden, desto eindeutiger wird die Chronologie der Schichtserien bestimmt werden können, desto sicherer und einwandfreier, weil objektiver, das Fundament zu einer "natürlichen Stratigraphie" des Tertiärs und der Oberkreide (und aller übrigen marinen Ablagerungen) geschaffen werden. Dann lassen sich ohne Schwierigkeit die in derartig chronologisch fixierten Schichten vorkommenden Kleinforaminiferen-Assoziationen genauer studieren und analysieren. Dies wird zu einer Korrelation der neritisch-bathyalen mit den grossforaminiferenführenden litoral-neritischen Sedimenten führen, dem Haupt- und Endziel der Foraminiferen-Stratigraphie".

Die Ausführungen von THALMANN (1938) gelten sinngemäss für die ganze Paläontologie und für alle Schichten mit Fossilien; doch sind die Grossforaminiferen besonders geeignete Hilfsmittel für die exakte Chronologie des Tertiärs. Einerseits, weil die zuverlässigsten Leitfossilien des Mesozoikums, die Ammoniten, fehlen; anderseits weil sich die Grossforaminiferen-Schalen besonders gut für das Studium ontogenetischer, phylogenetischer und feinstratigraphischer Probleme darbieten: Vom Körper einer Foraminifere bleibt ja, abgesehen von den Zellkernen, fossil fast alles erhalten, was auch beim lebenden Tier morphologisch fassbar war. An der leeren Schale kann also die ganze morphologische Ontogenese rekonstruiert werden. Zudem sind viele Grossforaminiferen in einer intensiven Entwicklung begriffen.

Die klassischen Objekte der morphogenetischen Methode sind Grossforaminiferen, bei welchen die megalosphärische Generation darauf tendiert, im Laufe der Ontogenese zu einem radiär-symmetrischen Bau und zur zyklischen Anordnung der Zuwachsstreifen überzugehen. Die Endform wird — im Laufe der Entwicklungsdauer einer Reihe — in einem immer früheren Stadium der Ontogenese erreicht (Acceleration). Als geeignet für solche Untersuchungen erwiesen sich bisher neben den Kreide-Orbitoiden die Lepidocycliniden, die Miogypsiniden und auch die zu den Nummulitiden gehörenden Cycloclypeen. Doch wurden in den meisten Fällen fast nur megalosphärische Exemplare in ihrer Morphogenese dargestellt. Die letzten Bearbeiter warnen immer wieder vor einer voreiligen Verallgemeinerung der "Gesetze" (so DROOGER, 1956, in einer ausgezeichneten Zusammenfassung und VAN DER VLERK, 1959), dann, wenn die zeitliche Folge nicht durch kontinuierliche Profile belegt ist.

Sind Grossforaminiferen von nicht-orbitoidalem Bauplan, also z.B. die bis zum Endstadium spiralig bleibenden Nummulitidae und die Alveolinen des Alttertiärs entsprechenden morphogenetischen Untersuchungen auch zugänglich? Diese Frage ist darum besonders wichtig, weil sich solche Formen massenhaft in sehr reichen Faunen, manchmal gesteinsbildend, in oft zusammenhängenden Profilen im Tethys-Gebiet und zum Teil auch in den Typlokalitäten der Stufen finden. Im folgenden greifen wir einige Ergebnisse unserer Untersuchungen an den Genera *Nummulites* und *Assilina* heraus und versuchen daran die Frage der Gesetzmässigkeiten in der Entwicklung und ihre stratigraphische Anwendung zu skizzieren.

In zahlreichen Profilen des Tethys-Gebietes (inklusive Alpen) untersuchten wir Faunen mit bekannter zeitlicher Aufeinanderfolge. Das erforderte eine sehr umfangreiche, aber notwendige empirische Vorarbeit.

Glücklicherweise erwies sich das erste, sehr genau untersuchte Profil in der Grossen Schlieren (Kanton Obwalden, nördliche Schweizeralpen) als kontinuierlich aufgeschlossene "Série compréhensive" von der Obersten Kreide bis ins Obere Cuisien mit einer vollkommen gesicherten Sukzession von paleocänen und untereocänen Nummuliten und Assilinen (SCHAUB, 1951). Darin konnte das erste Auftreten und die Entfaltung der wichtigsten Entwicklungsreihen der Nummuliten und der Assilinen bis zur Cuisien–Lutétien–Grenze verfolgt werden. In sehr zahlreichen weiteren Profilen und Einzellokalitäten von den Pyrenäen bis nach Anatolien, Ägypten und Indien liessen sich dann die paleocänen und untereocänen Faunen korrelieren und die mittel- und obereocänen Faunen anschliessen. Im Zusammenhang mit unserer Arbeit an einer neuen Monographie der Nummuliten und Assilinen[1] haben wir uns zunächst vor

[1] Unterstützt vom Schweizerischen Nationalfonds zur Förderung der wissenschaftlichen Forschung.

allem mit den Gruppen befasst, die im Unter– und Mitteleocän zu bedeutender Grösse aufblühen und im oberen Mitteleocän plötzlich erlöschen.

Zunächst waren die Art-Definitionen zu revidieren. Dann konnte die Aufeinanderfolge der Arten festgestellt werden. Nachdem die für die Gruppenzugehörigkeit entscheidenden Merkmale erkannt waren, zeigte sich, dass sich die Arten einer Gruppe zu morphologischen Reihen zusammenstellen lassen. Diese morphologischen Reihen zeigen so eindeutig gesetzmässige, allmähliche Formveränderungen im Laufe der Zeit, dass wir sie als Evolutionsreihen zu deuten haben.

Wir müssen auf diese Frage zurückkommen, da neuere, vor allem französische Publikationen die evolutiv bedingte Gesetzmässigkeit dieser Formveränderung in Frage stellen. Ihre stratigraphische Bedeutung wird als reine Hypothese abgetan. Andere führen die Verschiedenheit der Formen (Dimensionen, Megalosphäre, Kammerformen, Windungsweite) zurück auf oekologische Einflüsse und nicht auf verschiedenes Alter oder auf die Zugehörigkeit zu verschiedenen Entwicklungsreihen[1]. Allerdings müssen auch wir zahlreiche Darstellungen der "Evolution" der Nummuliten — ohne genaue Fassung der Arten und ohne Abklärung der stratigraphischen Stellung — als hypothetische Konstruktionen ansehen. Darauf darf sich natürlich keine Stratigraphie aufbauen.

Bei Beginn unserer Arbeit an den Nummuliten (vor über 20 Jahren) konnten wir uns hingegen auf die Publikationen unseres verehrten Kollegen W. LEUPOLD stützen. Seine Arbeiten von 1937, 1938 und 1942 mit guten Darstellungen des zentral- und ostschweizerischen Nummulitikums stützten sich auf gute Kenntnisse der Nummuliten, gegründet auf die Revision der Arten und ihrer Typlokalitäten, und auf eine Neuuntersuchung der Profile des schweizerischen alpinen Nummulitikums. 1946 fasste LEUPOLD seine Ergebnisse in einem Vortrag vor der Schweizerischen Geologischen Gesellschaft zusammen. Leider wurde diese Zusammenfassung nie publiziert. Damals waren unsere Untersuchungen an den Schlierenflysch–Nummuliten im wesentlichen abgeschlossen, und wir konnten feststellen, dass ihre Resultate in vielen Punkten mit den Ergebnissen LEUPOLDS übereinstimmten. Einige Teile der Ergebnisse LEUPOLDS finden sich in den Arbeiten seiner Schüler und Mitarbeiter (SCHUMACHER, 1948, 1949; RUEFLI, 1959; STYGER, 1961). Wir selber verdanken W. LEUPOLD sehr wesentliche Anregungen für eine Weiterarbeit an den Nummuliten und ihrer Stratigraphie.

EVOLUTIONSREIHEN BEI NUMMULITEN

Wir können heute einen grossen Teil der Nummuliten-Arten — wenn auch bei weitem noch nicht alle — zu Gruppen zusammenfassen. Das ist vor allem dort möglich, wo

---

[1] Nach eigenen Beobachtungen bewirken die oekologischen Bedingungen die Auslese, und nicht die Entstehung (*ad hoc*) gewisser Arten. So bleibt *N. burdigalensis* in sandig-tonigem Gestein und in kalkigerem milieu trotz gewisser Verschiedenheiten (z.B. Wanddicke) doch *N. burdigalensis*. Zur gleichen Auffassung ist auch HOTTINGER (1960) bei der Bearbeitung der Alveolinen gekommen.

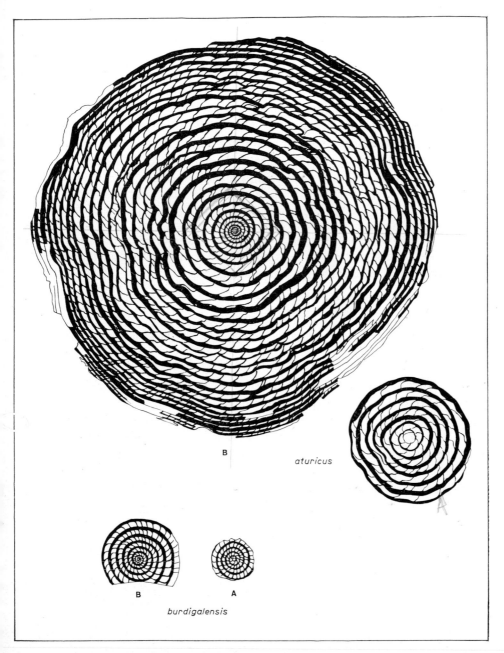

Fig. 1. *Nummulites aturicus* und *N. burdigalensis*, als Vergleich einer evoluierten mit einer primitiven Nummuliten-Art. Erklärung im Text, p. 286. 4 ×.

das "Zwischengerüst", d.h. die Schalenelemente zwischen den aufeinanderfolgenden Schalenumgängen, besonders differenziert ist, durch die besondere Form der Wände und durch die Bildung von Pfeilern. Wir haben (SCHAUB, 1951, p. 91) gezeigt, dass sich die Gruppen *Nummilites partschi–gizehensis, burdigalensis–perforatus* und *pustulosus* durch die Anordnung der Pfeiler definieren lassen. Diesen drei Gruppen können wir die ebenfalls durch das Zwischengerüst definieten Gruppen des *Nummulites planulatus–brongniarti* und des *N. fabianii* anschliessen. An der besonderen Ausbildung der Spiralen und der Septen — erst im Äequatorialschnitt sichtbar — erkennt man die Glieder der heterogenen *irregularis–distans*-Gruppe und der *discorbinus*-Gruppe. Alle diese Gruppen enthalten eine oder mehrere morphologische Reihen, die sich über mehrere Stufen hinweg mit gesetzmässigen Veränderungen verfolgen lassen, und die als Evolutionsreihen zu deuten sind. Als Beispiele seien hier die Gruppe *Nummulites burdigalensis–perforatus* und die Assilinen dargestellt.

Die burdigalensis–perforatus-Gruppe

Die Gruppenzugehörigkeit ergibt sich aus der Struktur der Oberfläche und des Zwischengerüstes, wie auch des Axialschnittes (linsenförmige Gestalt und besondere Art der Pfeilerbildung), die hier alle nicht dargestellt werden.

Bemerkenswerterweise setzt die Pfeilerbildung bei dieser Gruppe ungefähr zur gleichen Zeit ein wie bei den anderen, grossen gepfeilerten Gruppen (*planulatus-brongniarti* und *partschi–gizehensis*), nämlich im Unteren Cuisien (Zone des *N. planulatus*, der *A. placentula* und der *Alveolina oblonga*). Wir können wohl den Anfang der Pfeilerbildung als Beginn der Entfaltung dieser grossen Nummuliten ansehen. Doch entstehen in der *distans–irregularis*-Gruppe Formen ohne oder fast ohne Pfeiler, die zu den grössten überhaupt bekannten Nummuliten führen (*N. millecaput*).

Zum Studium von gesetzmässigen Veränderungen im Laufe der Zeit eignen sich Äquatorialschnitte recht gut, weshalb wir hier Schnittbilder typischer Einzelexemplare der wichtigsten Arten nebeneinander in zweifacher Vergrösserung abbilden (Fig. 2 und 3). Zur vollständigen Kenntnis einer Nummulitenart sind beide Generationen notwendig, die kleinere A-Form (megalosphärisch, Gamont) und die grössere B-Form (mikrosphärisch, Agamont oder Schizont), weshalb wir beide Generationen nebeneinander darstellen. Zunächst betrachten wir aber einen frühen und einen späten Vertreter der Gruppe in etwas stärkerer (4-facher) Vergrösserung.

Nummulites burdigalensis und N. aturicus (Fig. 1)

Am auffälligsten unterscheiden sich die beiden Arten in den Dimensionen:

	Radius B-Form	Radius A-Form
N. aturicus	14 mm	4,5 mm
N. burdigalensis	3 mm	1,5 mm

und in der Spirale:

	B-Form: Windungen	A-Form: Windungen	Megalosphäre
N. aturicus	42	$6^1/_2$	0,8 mm
N. burdigalensis	8	$4^1/_2$	0,2 mm

Halten wir fest: Die B-Formen der beiden Arten unterscheiden sich sehr deutlich in der Zahl der Windungen. Bei den A-Formen hingegen sind die Windungszahlen viel näher beieinander. Der starke Grössenunterschied zwischen den beiden A-Formen beruht vielmehr auf der viel grösseren Embryonalkammer und der weiteren Spirale von *N. aturicus* als auf der Zahl der Windungen.

Spirale und Kammern der B-Formen. Die Spirale von *burdigalensis* nimmt langsam und gleichmässig an Weite zu. Die Kammern sind ebenfalls regelmässig, gleichartig, ungefähr isometrisch (gleich hoch wie lang). Die Kammerwände sind alle leicht geneigt, schwach gebogen. Die *aturicus*-Spirale ist komplizierter gebaut. Verfolgen wir sie vom Zentrum bis zur Peripherie, also von den ersten bis zu den letzten Windungen, so können wir drei Abschnitte auseinanderhalten[1].

Der innerste Abschnitt ist gekennzeichnet durch gleichmässig anwachsende Spirale, isometrische, regelmässige Kammern, also durch die Merkmale der *burdigalensis*-Spirale. Dieser innerste Abschnitt umfasst etwa 1/6 des Radius. Er ist kleiner als die ausgewachsene *burdigalensis*-Spirale.

Der zweite Abschnitt umfasst beim abgebildeten Exemplar etwa 3/6 des Radius. Hier ist die Spirale weit, der Dorsalstrang ziemlich dick und unregelmässig. Auch die Kammern werden unregelmässiger. Die Septen verlieren ihre steife, konstante Form und werden variabel, meist stärker geneigt, einfach oder wellig verbogen. Die im zweiten Abschnitt vorherrschende Kammerform betrachten wir als art-typisch. In diesem Abschnitt treten Windungsverdoppelungen auf, im abgebildeten Exemplar deren vier. Das heisst also, dass nach der vierten Verdoppelung fünf Dorsalstränge parallel neben einander wachsen und die Spirale bilden (*cf.* SMOUT, 1945).

Der dritte, äusserste Abschnitt, etwa 2/6 des Radius umfassend, zeigt eine deutliche Verengerung der Spirale — oder in diesem Falle: der fünf Spiralen. Die Kammern werden gleichmässiger, sehr niedrig und mindestens doppelt so lang wie hoch.

Spirale und Kammern der A-Formen. N. burdigalensis: kleine Megalosphäre; die zweite Kammer nur wenig kleiner, sodass die erste und die zweite Kammer eine 8-Figur bilden. Spiralen- und Kammertyp wie bei der B-Form, also langsam und gleichmässig anwachsende Windungen, regelmässige, ungefähr isometrische Kammern, Septen steif und wenig geneigt.

N. aturicus: grosse Megalosphäre in der Form einer gegen die zweite Kammer abgeplatteten Kugel, die zweite Kammer ist niedrig, nur 1/3 bis 1/4 so hoch wie die erste Kammer. Schon in der ersten Hälfte der ersten Windungen wird die endgültige Windungshöhe und die art-typische Kammerform erreicht. Die Windungshöhe und die art-typische Kammerform werden meist bis zur Peripherie beibehalten.

Halten wir das Wichtigste fest: Die *burdigalensis*-Spirale zeigt in der B- und A-Form einen einfachen Aufbau, den wir als primitiv bezeichnen. Die *aturicus*-Spirale der B-Form beginnt mit einem primitiven Abschnitt, dann folgt der grösste, mittlere, weitspiralige Abschnitt mit der "art-typischen" Kammerform und mit Windungsverdoppelungen, dann der Endabschnitt, mit enger Spirale und langen Kammern. Die *aturicus* A-Form enthält demgegenüber eine einfache Spirale. Der

---

[1] Diese Unterteilung der Spiralen grosser B-Formen von Nummuliten hat auch ROZLOZSNIK (1929) dargestellt.

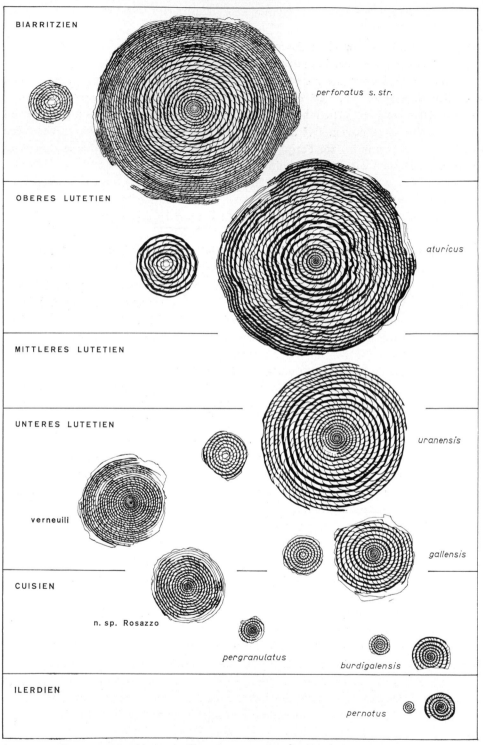

Fig. 2. Äquatorialschnitte der *perforatus*-Gruppe, *aturicus*-Ast. Erklärung im Text, p. 290.

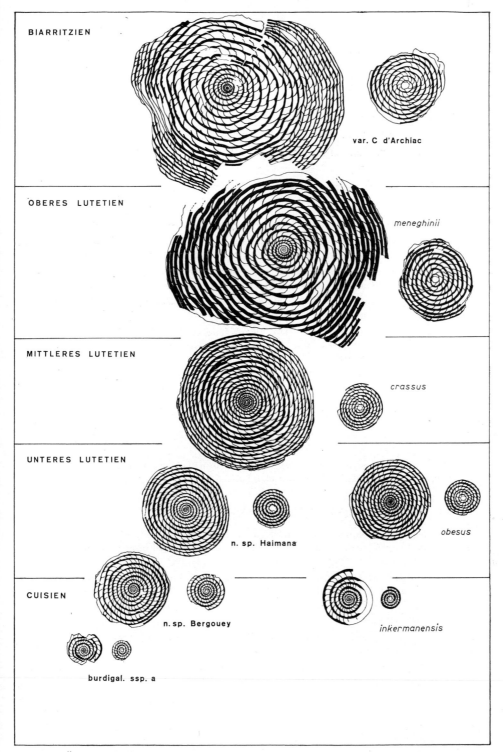

Fig. 3. Äquatorialschnitte der *perforatus*-Gruppe, *meneghinii*-Ast. Erklärung im Text, p. 290.

primitive Abschnitt fehlt. Die grosse Megalosphäre bezeichnet auch schon den Beginn der weiten art-typischen Spirale. Auch der enge Endabschnitt fehlt bei der A-Form oder ist höchstens im letzten 1/2 Umgang leicht angedeutet.

Evolutionsreihen der perforatus-Gruppe

In den Fig. 2 und 3 haben wir die Äquatorialschnitte von 17 typischen Arten der *perforatus*-Gruppe zu Reihen zusammengestellt.

Auf Fig. 2 werden dargestellt (2-fach vergrössert):

Nummulites pernotus SCHAUB, 1951. Ilerdien im Profil der Grossen Schlieren. Schichtnummer S 474 (SCHAUB, 1951). NHM Basel Nr. C 3177 (B-Form, Holotypus) und C 3191 (A-Form).

Nummulites burdigalensis DE LA HARPE, 1926. Unteres Cuisien von Gan (N gare), Basses Pyrénées. NHM Basel Nr. C 3077 (B-Form) und C 3081 (A-Form). In Fig.1: 4 ×; in Fig.2: 2 × vergrössert.

Nummulites gallensis HEIM, 1908. Unterstes Lutétien von Dürrenbach, Toggenburg, St. Gallen (Typlokalität). NHM Basel Nr. C 4334 (B-Form) und C 4335 (A-Form).

Nummulites uranensis (DE LA HARPE, 1883). Unteres Lutétien von Sisikon, Uri (Typlokalität). NHM Basel Nr. C 4340 (B-Form) und C 4341 (A-Form).

Nummulites aturicus JOLY und LEYMERIE, 1848. Oberes Lutétien, Fontaine de la Médaille bei Montfort, Landes (Typlokalität). NHM Basel Nr. C 4344 (B-Form) und C 4345 (A-Form). In Fig.1: 4 ×; in Fig.2: 2 × vergrössert).

Nummulites perforatus (MONTFORT, 1808). Biarritzien (Oberes Mittel-Eocän) von Klausenbug (Cluj), Rumänien (Typlokalität). NHM Basel Nr. C 4348 (B-Form) und C 4349 (A-Form).

Nummulites burdigalensis pergranulatus SCHAUB, 1951. Aus dem oberen Schlierensandstein von Lohalp, Mittleres Cuisien. NHM Basel Nr. C 3367 (B-Form, Holotyp).

Nummulites n.sp. Cuisien–Lutétien Grenze. Rosazzo (Prov. Udine, Italien). NHM Basel Nr. C 4331 (B-Form).

Nummulites verneuili D'ARCHIAC und HAIME, 1853. B-Form. Lutétien von Catalonien. Sammlung d'Archiac, Musée National d'Histoire naturelle, Paris.

Auf Fig. 3 werden dargestellt (2-fach vergrössert):

Nummulites "*burdigalensis* ssp. a (Uebergangsform zu *N. inkermanensis*)" (SCHAUB, 1951). Mittleres Cuisien im Profil der Grossen Schlieren. NHM Basel Nr. C 3376 (B-Form, aus Schicht Nr. S 703), und C 3299 (A-Form, Bach bei Rossboden).

Nummulites inkermanensis SCHAUB, 1951. Oberes Cuisien von Inkerman (Krim). B-Form (Holotyp) nach ROZLOZSNIK (1929, T. 7, Fig. 4). A-Form nach NEMKOV und BARCHATOVA (1961, T. 7, Fig. 16).

Nummulites n.sp., aff. *N. gallensis*. Oberes Cuisien von Bergouey (Chalosse, Dép. Landes). NHM Basel Nr. C 4332 (B-Form) und C 4333 (A-Form).

Nummulites n.sp., aff. *N. obesus*. Unteres Lutétien von Haimana, Anatolien. NHM Basel Nr. C 4336 (B-Form) und C 4337 (A-Form).

Nummulites obesus D'ARCHIAC und HAIME, 1853. Unteres Lutétien von Urcuit, Adour. NHM Basel Nr. C 4338 (B-Form) und C 4339 (A-Form).

Nummulites crassus BOUBÉE, 1834. Mittleres Lutétien der Chalosse (Landes). NHM Basel Nr. C 4342 (B-Form von Nousse) und C 4343 (A-Form von Bastennes, Typlokalität).

Nummulites meneghinii D'ARCHIAC und HAIME, 1853. Oberes Lutétien von San Domino, Isole Tremiti (Typlokalität). NHM Basel Nr. C 4346 (B-Form) und C 4347 (A-Form).

Nummulites "*perforatus* var. C" D'ARCHIAC und HAIME, 1853. Biarritzien von Calders, Catalonien. NHM Basel Nr. 4350 (B-Form) und C 4351 (A-Form).

In allen Fällen (mit Ausnahme von *N. verneuili*) handelt es sich um Arten mit bekannter stratigraphischer Stellung. Versuchsweise stellen wir die Formen in drei bis vier Reihen ("Ästen des *perforatus*-Phylums") zusammen. Als gemeinsame Wurzel ist *N. burdigalensis* anzusehen. Wir haben 1951 gezeigt, dass *N. burdigalensis* aus *N. pernotus* des Mittleren bis Oberen Ilerdien, und *N. pernotus* aus dem kleinen *N. solitarius* des Unteren Ilerdien hervorgeht. In der Hauptreihe, die zu *N. perforatus* führt, sehen wir bei *N. gallensis* des Untersten Lutétien immer noch primitive Spiralen und Kammerformen. Es ist nur eine Grössenzunahme — auch der Megalosphäre — und eine Zunahme der Windungszahl erfolgt. Zwischen *burdigalensis* und *gallensis* sind aus kontinuierlichen Profilen Übergangsformen bekannt (z.B. "ssp. b" in SCHAUB, 1951). Es ist möglich, dass die Art von Bergouey (Fig. 3) auch zu solchen Uebergangsformen gehört. Beim *N. uranensis* des höheren Unterlutétien haben die Dimensionen weiter zugenommen. In der Spirale der B-Form zeigt sich eine erste Andeutung der Unterteilung in Abschnitte. Die n o v a s p e c i e s von Haimana, die im Profil von Haimana kontinuierlich aus *N. burdigalensis* hervorgeht, ist vielleicht als Zwischenform zwischen *gallensis* und *uranensis* zu betrachten. Sie steht anderseits auch *N. obesus*[1] aus dem Unteren Lutétien des Adour-Gebietes recht nahe. *N. obesus* besitzt noch nicht die Dimensionen, auch nicht die Anfänge der dreiteiligen Spirale von *uranensis*, doch schon deutlich längere Kammern.

N. crassus des Mittleren Lutétien kann sowohl als Weiterentwicklung von *N. obesus* aufgefasst werden, wie auch als Form, die von *N. uranensis* zu *N. aturicus* überleitet. Bei ihm ist die Gliederung der Spirale in Abschnitte etwas deutlicher als bei *N. uranensis*. Es treten auch — relativ selten — Windungsverdoppelungen ein. Wegen der Dicke des Dorsalstranges (im Gegensatz zur zierlicheren Spirale von *N. uranensis*) haben wir *N. crassus* einstweilen zum *meneghinii* Ast (Fig. 3) gestellt. Es ist aber möglich, dass die Trennung der Äste des *N. aturicus* und des *N. meneghinii* erst im Mittleren Lutétien erfolgt ist, und dass also *N. crassus* noch zum gemeinsamen Stamm gehört.

Im Oberen Lutétien sind der schon skizzierte *N. aturicus* und *N. meneghinii* D'ARCHIAC und HAIME (synonym *N. renevieri* DE LA HARPE) mit seiner viel plumperen Spirale deutlich unterscheidbar. *N. meneghinii* hat fast keine Windungsverdoppelungen, viel weniger als *N. aturicus*. Das gleiche gilt für die sehr charakteristische Art, die D'ARCHIAC als "var. C" des *N. perforatus* bezeichnet hat, und die wir aus dem nordspanischen Biarritzien kennen. Vielleicht ist das Fehlen der Windungsverdoppelungen der Grund, weshalb "var. C" bis zum Rande eine grössere Spiralenweite behält als *aturicus* und *perforatus*. Trotzdem ist auch bei der "var. C" die Dreiteiligkeit der Spirale sehr ausgeprägt. Die Ähnlichkeit des innersten, primitiven Spiralenabschnittes mit *N. burdigalensis* ssp. a ist deutlich.

N. perforatus, die engspiralige — wir möchten sagen: typische — Endform des *aturicus*-Astes aus dem Biarritzien (Oberstes Mittel-Eocän) des Tethys-Gebietes von

---

[1] *N. obesus* in DE LA HARPE (1883) von Ägypten ist nicht mit *N. obesus* D'ARCHIAC et HAIME, 1853 identisch. Die ägyptische Form ist daher als *Nummulites obsoletus* (DE LA HARPE, 1883) zu bezeichnen.

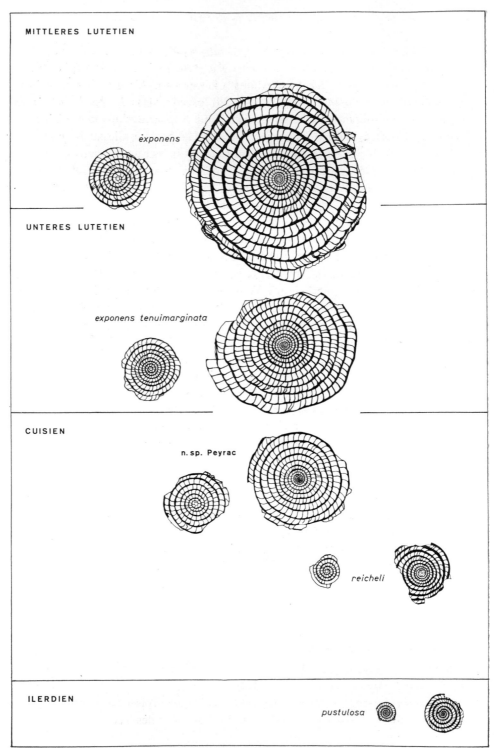

MITTLERES LUTETIEN

exponens

UNTERES LUTETIEN

exponens tenuimarginata

CUISIEN

n. sp. Peyrac

reicheli

ILERDIEN

pustulosa

Fig. 4. Äquatorialschnitte der Reihe der *Assilina exponens*. Erklärung im Text, p. 294.

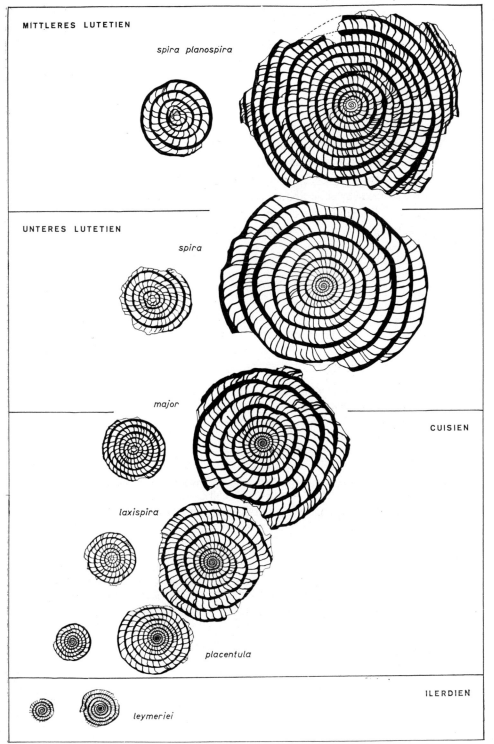

MITTLERES LUTETIEN

spira planospira

UNTERES LUTETIEN

spira

major

CUISIEN

laxispira

placentula

ILERDIEN

leymeriei

Fig. 5. Äquatorialschnitte der Reihe der *Assilina spira*. Erklärung im Text, p. 294.

Spanien, Südfrankreich, aus den Alpen und aus den schönen Profilen des Vicentins, aus den Karpaten und aus Transylvanien, vielleicht auch aus Indien — zeigt am schönsten die Weiterentwicklung der Spiralenmerkmale, die wir bei *N. aturicus* dargestellt haben: Der Endabschnitt mit den engen Windungen und relativ langen Kammern ist hier auf Kosten des zweiten Abschnittes grösser geworden. Auch hier treten, vor allem beim Übergang vom zweiten zum dritten Abschnitt, Windungsverdoppelungen auf. Die Windungen des dritten Abschnittes werden hier sehr eng, was äusserlich häufig (beim hier dargestellten Exemplar nicht) mit dem Übergang zu einer fast kugeligen Form verbunden ist. Daneben gibt es merkwürdigerweise einen Ast, der schon im Oberen Cuisien eine sehr enge Spirale bildet, und den wir einstweilen in *N. verneuili* enden lassen. *N. verneuili* ist die einzige Art unserer Zusammenstellung, deren stratigraphische Stellung noch nicht abgeklärt ist, da wir ihre Typlokalität nicht kennen[1]).

ENTWICKLUNGSREIHEN DER ASSILINEN

Im Anschluss an unsere vorläufige Mitteilung (1955) über die Assilinen geben wir eine Darstellung der deutlich hervortretenden Reihen der Assilinen.

In Fig. 4 sind dargestellt (2-fach vergrössert):

Assilina pustulosa DONCIEUX, 1926. Ilerdien von Las Linques West Montbéraud, Haute Garonne (Typlokalität). Coll. H. SCHAUB HG 32. NHM Basel Nr. C 4353 (B-Form) und C 4354 (A-Form).

Assilina reicheli SCHAUB, 1951. Cuisien-Lutétien-Grenze von Queralt, Catalonien. Coll. L. HOTTINGER Quer. 1. NHM Basel Nr. C 4364 (B-Form) und C 4365 (A-Form).

Assilina, n.sp., *exponens*-Vorläufer. Oberes Cuisien von Bergouey, Chalosse, Landes. Coll. H. SCHAUB Ch 146. NHM Basel Nr. C 4366 (B-Form) und C 4367 (A-Form).

Assilina exponens cf. *tenuimarginata* HEIM, 1908. Unteres Lutétien von Donzacq, Chalosse, Landes. Coll. H. SCHAUB NHM Basel Nr. C 4368 (B-Form) und C 4369 (A-Form).

Assilina exponens (SOWERBY, 1840). Unteres Lutétien, Chalosse, Landes, B-Form von Donzacq. Coll. H. SCHAUB NHM Basel Nr. C 4370; A-Form von Gibret, NHM Basel Nr. C 4371.

In Fig. 5 sind dargestellt (2-fach vergrössert):

Assilina leymeriei D'ARCHIAC und HAIME, 1853. Mittleres Ilerdien von St. Laurent-de-la-Cabrerisse, Corbières Aude (Typlokalität). NHM Basel Nr. C 4352 (B-Form) und C 3001 (A-Form).

Assilina placentula DESHAYES, 1838. Unteres Cuisien von Gan (Tuilerie), Basses Pyrénées. NHM Basel Nr. C 4355 (B-Form) und C 4356 (A-Form).

Assilina laxispira (DE LA HARPE, 1926). Cuisien von Bos d'Arros (Typlokalität). NHM Basel Nr. C 4357 (B-Form) und C 4358 (A-Form).

Assilina major (HEIM, 1908). Oberes Cuisien von Bergouey (Chalosse, Landes). NHM Basel Nr. C 4359 (B-Form) und C 4360 (A-Form).

Assilina spira (DE ROISSY, 1805). Unteres Lutétien von San Vicente de la Barquera, Prov. Santander, Spanien. NHM Basel Nr. C 4361 (B-Form) und C 4362 (A-Form).

---

[1] D'ARCHIAC gibt in seiner Sammlung für den Typ nur "Catalogne" an. Die Angabe "Conca de Tremp" in der Monographie beruht wohl auf einer Verwechslung.

Assilina spira planospira (BOUBEE, 1834). Mittleres Lutétien von Bastennes (Arrimblar), Chalosse, Landes (Typlokalität). Coll. H. SCHAUB Ch 119. NHM Basel Nr. C 4363 (B-Form) und C 3023 (A-Form)

Aus einer grösseren Zahl von kleinen primitiven Assilinen-Arten des Ilerdien (Ober-Paleocän), von denen hier zwei abgebildet sind (*Assilina leymeriei s.str. cf.* SCHAUB, 1960, und *Assilina pustulosa*), differenzieren sich im Cuisien die zwei durch die äussere Form und den Axialschnitt deutlich unterscheidbaren Reihen der *A. exponens* (Fig. 4) und der *A. spira* (Fig. 5). Die letzten *A. exponens* kennen wir in der typischen, grossen Ausbildung von der Lutétien-Biarritzien Grenze (Profil von La Mortola). Die letzten *A. spira* erreichen in sehr grossen Exemplaren die Grenze zwischen dem Mittleren und Oberen Lutétien (*A. "gigantea"* DE LA HARPE).

Entwicklungstendenzen bei Assilinen

Die Darstellungen der Fig. 4 und 5 sprechen wohl eine deutliche Sprache: Bei A- und B-Formen werden die Dimensionen grösser. Die A-Formen zeigen auch eine deutliche Grössenzunahme der Megalosphäre. Bei den B-Formen schliesst sich an den engen primitiven Anfangsabschnitt schon sehr bald ein weitspiraliger zweiter Abschnitt an. Das Einsetzen der Windungsverdoppelungen und das Engerwerden der Umgänge bei den B-Formen, also der Beginn eines Endabschnittes, sind hier nicht deutlich erkennbar. Das hängt zum Teil damit zusammen, dass wir die jüngsten Vertreter nicht dargestellt haben. *Assilina spira planospira* des Mittleren Lutétien zeigt immerhin häufige Windungsverdoppelungen. Es scheint, dass sich die *spira*-Reihe noch verzweigt in einen weitspiraligen Ast, der an die abgebildete *A. spira* des Unteren Lutétien anschliesst und bis in das Lutétien aufsteigt, und einen engspiraligen Ast mit zahlreichen Windungsverdoppelungen, der über *spira planospira* zu den grössten uns bisher bekannten Assilinen (Durchmesser 4,8 cm, *A. "gigantea"* DE LA HARPE) führt. An den auf Fig. 4 zuoberst dargestellten Vertreter der *exponens* Reihe wären ebenfalls noch jüngere, grössere Formen mit Windungsverdoppelungen anzuschliessen.

SUMMARY

The spirally coiled Nummulitidae are found to be good markers for detail Paleogene stratigraphy in the Tethys region. Evolutionary trends in A and B forms of *Nummulites* and *Assilina* are established: Increase in size of the test; increase in size of the megalosphere; differentiation of the B form spire into three parts, an inner or primitive part, a middle part with spire and chambers regarded as typical of the species, and a terminal part with narrow spire and long chambers. The spire of the A form is less differentiated than that of the B form. Thus the spire of *Nummulites aturicus* A form has no "primitive part". Phylogenetic and ontogenetic studies in large Foraminifera should therefore be based on megalospheric and microspheric specimens.

LITERATUR

BARKER, R. W. and GRIMSDALE, T. F., 1936. A contribution to the phylogeny of the orbitoidal Foraminifera, with description of new forms from the Eocene of Mexico. *J. Paleontol.*, 10 : 231–247.

BRÖNNIMANN, P., 1940. Ueber die tertiären Orbitoididen und Miogypsiniden von Nordwest-Marokko. *Schweiz. Paläontol. Abhandl.*, 63 : 1–113.

BRÖNNIMANN, P., 1940. Zur Kenntnis des Embryonalapparates von *Discocyclina* s.s. *Eclogae Geol. Helv.*, 33 : 252–274.

BRÖNNIMANN, P., 1945. Zur Frage der verwandtschaftlichen Beziehungen zwischen *Discocyclina* s.s. und *Asterocyclina. Eclogae Geol. Helv.*, 38 : 579–615.

BRÖNNIMANN, P., 1954–1956. Upper Cretaceous orbitoidal Foraminifera from Cuba, I–V. *Contrib. Cushman Found. Foraminiferal Research*, 5 : 55–61, 91–105; 6 : 57–76, 97–104; 7 : 60–66.

D'ARCHIAC, A. et HAIME, E., 1853. *Monographie des Nummulites.* Gide et J.Baudry, Paris, 164 pp.

DE LA HARPE, PH., 1883. Monographie der in Aegypten und der Libyschen Wüste vorkommenden Nummuliten. *Palaeontographica*, 30 : 157–216.

DROOGER, C. W., 1954. *Miogypsina* in northern Italy. *Proc. Koninkl. Ned. Akad. Wetenschap.*, Ser. B, 57 : 227–249.

DROOGER, C. W., 1956. Parallel evolutionary trends in larger Foraminifera. *Proc. Koninkl. Ned. Akad. Wetenschap.*, Ser. B, 59 : 458–469.

HOTTINGER, L., 1960. Recherches sur les Alvéolines du Paléocène et de l'Eocène. *Mém. suisses de Paléontol.*, 75/76: 1–243.

HOTTINGER, L., SCHAUB, H. und VONDERSCHMITT, L., 1957. Zur Stratigraphie des Lutétien im Adour-Becken. *Eclogae Geol. Helv.*, 49 : 453–468.

HOTTINGER, L. und SCHAUB, H., 1960. Zur Stufeneinteilung des Paleocaens und des Eocaens. Einführung der Stufen Ilerdien und Biarritzien. *Eclogae Geol. Helv.*, 53 : 453–479.

LEHMAN, J. P., 1959. A propos de la "loi" de récapitulation. *Bull. Soc. géol. France, 7e sér.*, 1 : 638–640.

LEUPOLD, W., 1937. Zur Stratigraphie der Flyschbildungen zwischen Linth und Rhein. *Eclogae Geol. Helv.*, 30 : 1–23.

LEUPOLD, W., 1938. Die Flyschregion von Ragaz. Bericht über die Exkursion der S.G.G. *Eclogae Geol. Helv.*, 31 : 403–428.

LEUPOLD, W., 1942. Neue Beobachtungen zur Gliederung der alpinen Flyschbildungen zwischen Reuss und Rhein. *Eclogae Geol. Helv.*, 35 : 247–291.

MANGIN, J. PH., 1960. *Le Nummulitique sud-pyrénéen à l'O. de l'Aragon.* Instituto de Estudios pirenaicos (Zaragoza) 619 pp.

NEMKOV, G. I. und BARCHATOWA, N. N., 1961. Nummuliti, Assilini i Operkulini Krima *Isdatelstwo Akad. Nauk. S.S.S.R. Trud. Geol. Mus.*, 5 : 1–124.

RENZ, D. und KÜPPER, H., 1946. Ueber morphogenetische Untersuchungen an Grossforaminiferen. *Eclogae Geol. Helv.*, 39 : 317–342.

ROZLOZSNIK, P., 1926. Einführung in das Studium der Nummulinen und Assilinen. *Mitt. Jahrb. Ungar. Geol. Anstalt*, 26 : 1–154.

RUEFLI, W. H., 1959. *Stratigraphie und Tektonik des eingeschlossenen Glarner Flysches im Weisstannental.* Diss. ETH Zürich, Schmidberger und Müller, Zürich, 194 pp.

SCHAUB, H., 1950. Ueber die Zugehörigkeit der paleocänen und untereocänen Nummuliten zu Entwicklungsreihen. *Eclogae Geol. Helv.*, 43 : 242–245.

SCHAUB, H., 1951. Stratigraphie und Paläontologie des Schlierenflysches mit besonderer Berüchsichtigung der paleocänen und untereocänen Nummuliten und Assilinen. *Schweiz. Paläontol. Abhandl.*, 68 : 1–222.

SCHAUB, H., 1955. Zur Nomenklatur und Stratigraphie der europäischen Assilinen (Vorläufige Mitteilung). *Eclogae Geol. Helv.*, 48 : 409–413.

SCHAUB, H., 1960. Ueber einige Nummuliten und Assilinen der Monographie und der Sammlung d'Archiac. *Eclogae Geol. Helv.*, 53 : 443–451.

SCHAUB, H., 1962. Contribution à la stratigraphie du Nummulitique du Véronais et du Vicentin. *Mem. Soc. Geol. Ital.* 3 : 59–66.

SCHUMACHER, J., 1948. Zur Gliederung des marinen Lutétien und basalen Priabonien der Schweizeralpen. *Eclogae Geol. Helv.*, 41 : 79–88.

SCHUMACHER, J., 1949. Die Flysch- und Parautochthonzone des oberen Engelbergertales (Zentralschweiz). *Mitt. Naturforsch. Ges. Bern, N.F.*, 7 : 1–52.

SMOUT, A. H., 1954. *Lower Tertiary Foraminifera of the Qatar Peninsula.* Publ. British Museum Nat. Hist., London, 90 pp.

STYGER, G. A., 1961. *Bau und Stratigraphie der nordhelvetischen Tertiärbildungen in der Hausstock- und westlichen Kärpfgruppe.* Diss. ETH Zürich, 151 pp.

TAN SIN HOK, 1932. On the genus *Cycloclypeus* Carpenter. *Wetenschap. Mededel. Dienst Mijnbouw Ned. Indië,* 19 : 3–194.

TAN SIN HOK, 1935. Die peri–embryonalen Aequatorialkammern bei einigen Orbitoididen. *De Ingr. in Ned. Indië,* 2, (IV) : 113–126.

TAN SIN HOK, 1936a. Beitrag zur Kenntnis der Lepidocycliniden. *Proc. Koninkl. Ned. Akad. Wetenschap.,* 39 : 3–12.

TAN SIN HOK, 1936b. Zur Kenntnis der Lepidocycliniden. *Natuurk. Tijdschr. Ned. Indië,* 96 : 235–280.

TAN SIN HOK, 1936c. Zur Kenntnis der Miogypsiniden. *De Ingr. in Ned. Indië,* 3 (IV) : 45–61.

TAN SIN HOK, 1937. Weitere Untersuchungen über die Miogypsiniden. *De Ingr. in Ned. Indië,* 4 (IV) : 35–45, 87–111.

TAN SIN HOK, 1939. On *Polylepidina, Orbitocyclina* and *Lepidorbitoides. De Ingenieur in Ned. Indië,* 6 (IV) : 53–84.

THALMANN, H. E., 1938. Mitteilungen über Foraminiferen IV. 17. Wert und Bedeutung morphogenetischer Untersuchungen an Grossforaminiferen für die Stratigraphie. *Eclogae Geol. Helv.,* 31 : 333–337.

VAN DER VLERK, I. M., 1922. Studiën over Nummulinidae en Alveolinidae. *Verhandel. Ned. Geol. Mijnbouwk. Genoot. Ned. en Kol., Geol. Ser.,* 5 : 329–464.

VAN DER VLERK, I. M., 1923. Een nieuwe *Cycloclypeus* soort van Oost-Borneo. *Samml. Geol. Reichs-Museums, Leiden,* 10 : 137–140.

VAN DER VLERK, I. M., 1928. The genus *Lepidocyclina* in the Far East. *Eclogae Geol. Helv.,* 21 : 182–211.

VAN DER VLERK, I. M., 1959a. Modification de l'ontogénèse pendant l'évolution des Lépidocyclines (Foraminifères). *Bull. Soc. géol. France, 7e sér.,* 1 : 669–673.

VAN DER VLERK, I. M., 1959b. Problems and principles of Tertiary and Quaternary stratigraphy. *Quart. J. Geol. Soc. London,* 115 : 49–63.

VEILLON, M. et VIGNEAUX, M., 1961. Les variations des critères de détermination des *Nummulites* en fonction des changements de lithofaciès. *Compt. rend. Acad. Sci.,* 252 : 576–578.

LES ALVÉOLINES PALÉOGÈNES, EXEMPLE D'UN GENRE POLYPHYLÉTIQUE

L. HOTTINGER

Service géologique du Maroc, Rabat (Maroc)

INTRODUCTION

"Les principes essentiels qui guident les paléontologistes dans la reconstruction de la phylogénèse sont les principes de plus grande ressemblance et de succession continue dans le temps. On admet généralement que des formes ont entre elles des liens de parenté quand elles se ressemblent entre-elles beaucoup plus qu'elles ne ressemblent à toutes les autres, et qu'elles forment un groupe homogène, où les différences sont si subtiles qu'un examen superficiel tendrait à faire croire qu'il n'y a qu'une seule espèce; tel est, par exemple, le groupe du *Cerithium tricarinatum* dans l'Eocène du Bassin de Paris. En outre, il est nécessaire, que les formes que l'on fait dériver les unes des autres se succèdent régulièrement et sans intervalle. La continuité dans le temps est encore le meilleur criterium de la réalité des relations génétiques. Plus il y a de lacunes dans une série phylétique, plus la part de l'hypothèse devient considérable et plus les difficultés de reconstruction deviennent grandes" (BOUSSAC, 1910). Ce principe doit nous guider aussi dans les recherches sur la phylogénie des grands foraminifères. La part de l'hypothèse est d'autant plus faible que l'abondance du matériel fossile procure une succession stratigraphique serrée des faunes dont les espèces successives sont liées entre elles par de nombreuses formes de passage. Ces dernières sont le meilleur critère pour établir des liens phylogéniques d'une espèce à la suivante.

Caractères morphologiques

La morphologie réelle d'un individu forme un tout que l'on ne peut que difficilement décrire et comparer avec celle d'un autre individu. Les reproductions en dessin ou photographie permettent de s'approcher le plus de la réalité morphologique.[1] Pour la description comparative le "tout morphologique" est décomposé artificiellement en éléments que nous appelons caractères morphologiques. La "ressemblance" dont parle BOUSSAC doit donc être établie sur l'analyse de l'ensemble des caractères morphologiques. Une hiérarchie préconçue des caractères analysés conduit fatalement à des

---

[1] En micropaléontologie, la comparaison d'un nombre élevé d'individus à la fois est difficile sous la loupe et impossible dans le cas où l'on étudie des coupes orientées sous le microscope. Dans la pratique, l'utilisation systématique des reproductions agrandies à échelle unique s'impose incontestablement.

erreurs. Il est cependant permis de séparer les caractères morphologiques selon leur fonction par rapport au temps écoulé d'un niveau stratigraphique à l'autre. Chez les alvéolines paléogènes, une partie des caractères reste stable, d'autres changent progressivement. Nous considérons ces derniers comme des caractères évolutifs.

L'étude des caractères morphologiques dans des successions faunistiques suffisamment serrées dans le temps sont le seul critère permettant de séparer valablement les caractères stables des caractères changeants. Il est important d'étendre les recherches sur des bassins sédimentaires indépendants pour pouvoir reconstruire une échelle stratigraphique complète. Pour l'étude des grands foraminifères, liés souvent à des faciès particuliers, ce principe s'impose encore davantage. Dans la majorité des cas, ces faciès n'apparaissent que dans un nombre limité d'horizons et les faunes successives d'un seul bassin ne sont pas assez représentatives pour contrôler la totalité des nombreux rameaux phylétiques de certains genres à chaque niveau stratigraphique.

Les alvéolines paléocènes et éocènes montrent avec clarté que, dans les genres polyphylétiques, les caractères morphologiques stables dans des niveaux stratigraphiques successifs, ne sont pas les mêmes dans chaque rameau phylétique, à l'intérieur du genre. Ce sont la combinaison des caractères et leur importance quantitative qui caractérisent le rameau phylétique.

Changeant progressivement, les caractères évolutifs des alvéolines sont également différents selon les rameaux phylétiques. Leurs tendances peuvent être opposées d'un groupe à l'autre. La combinaison des caractères évolutifs, leur tendance et la vitesse avec laquelle les changements évolutifs sont réalisés, caractérisent également le rameau phylétique.

Il y a cependant des caractères évolutifs communs à tous les rameaux phylétiques et caractéristiques du genre ou de la famille. Dans la présente note nous essayerons d'illustrer la nature différente des caractères évolutifs et leur signification stratigraphique à l'aide des alvéolines éocènes et paléocènes.

Espèce et phylum

Les rameaux phylétiques sont composés d'une suite d'unités taxonomiques élémentaires, spécifiques ou infraspécifiques, se succédant dans le temps. Il est important que celles-ci soient désignées par un nom taxonomiquement valable pour pouvoir réutiliser les éléments dans une reconstitution nouvelle d'un rameau phylétique quand de nouveaux matériaux apporteront des connaissances plus approfondies. Par conséquent, la manière de construire un rameau phylétique se trouve influencée par la conception de l'espèce et des unités infraspécifiques. Si les zoologistes et les botanistes conçoivent la délimitation de l'espèce et des sous-espèces en fonction de l'aire de leur répartition géographique, le paléontologiste utilisera de la même manière leur répartition stratigraphique. Avec BOUSSAC (1911) "nos espèces seront étendues au sens très large dans la direction horizontale et au sens étroit du mot dans la direction verticale, de façon à leur donner le maximum de rendement au point de vue stratigraphique, l'utilisation géologique des fossiles restant toujours notre préoccupation dominante".

Nous ne pouvons cependant pas suivre Burma (1948) qui n'aimerait voir dans chaque faune fossile qu'une seule espèce du même genre, par analogie avec la conception des espèces actuelles. D'une part, les thanatocoenoses des populations fossiles peuvent souvent contenir un mélange d'individus provenant de milieux différents (comme dans le cas du Schlierenflysch, Schaub, 1951). D'autre part, les genres comme ceux établis dans la famille des Alveolinidae sont des genres morphologiques groupant plusieurs rameaux phylétiques (Tintant, 1952, 5, p. 61 et Pokorný, 1958, p. 143). Ils sont compris souvent dans une acception plus large que les genres actuels des zoologistes. Il est vrai cependant, que dans les populations fossiles des alvéolines la présence de deux espèces appartenant au même rameau phylétique est rare.

Dans un remarquable travail théorique, Rauzer-Chernousova (1956) préconise l'assimilation du critère zoologique de la répartition géographique en paléontologie. Elle montre avec raison qu'un tel critère ne peut être utilisé que si le matériel est récolté systématiquement sur une très grande étendue. Une difficulté supplémentaire, et non la moindre, réside dans le fait qu'un synchronisme de précision est difficile à établir là où, pour des raisons géographiques, les faunes se spécialisent et ne sont plus comparables à l'ensemble de la succession des faunes, sur laquelle on base la stratigraphie. Tel est le cas des faunes néogènes de la Parathetys, où les corrélations stratigraphiques avec la Thety et l'Atlantique sont l'objet d'interprétations contradictoires.

Si, pour Veillon et Vigneaux (1961) les "critères de détermination" des nummulites varient avec les changements du faciès, ces éléments morphologiques variables ne peuvent être — par définition — des caractères spécifiques. Les matériaux d'alvéolines que j'ai eu sous la main, obligent à conclure que le faciès d'une roche conditionne la composition de la faune d'alvéolines, règle la présence ou l'absence d'une espèce donnée. Les caractères spécifiques d'une espèce d'alvéoline restent les mêmes dans tous les types de roches dans lesquels on la rencontre réellement. Il est vrai cependant que dans les sédiments éocène au moins, les grands foraminifères discoïdaux plats, à test perforé, operculines, discocyclines, nummulites plates, se rencontrent plus souvent dans les terrains détritiques, tandis que les foraminifères globuleux, nummulites épaisses, alvéolines, se trouvent de préférence dans les calcaires plus ou moins purs.

TENDANCES ÉVOLUTIVES RECONNUES DANS LES RAMEAUX PHYLÉTIQUES
DES ALVÉOLINES PALÉOGÈNES

Une vision rapide de l'ensemble des tendances évolutives reconnues dans les nombreux rameaux phylétiques illustrera la complexité du phénomène "évolution"[1]. Une règle évolutive générale, que l'on retrouve dans la plupart des autres familles de grands foraminifères, commande l'augmentation du volume de la mégalosphère et de la taille de la coquille au cours des temps. L'écart morphologique entre les formes A et B

---

[1] Nous nous permettons de renvoyer le lecteur à notre monographie sur les alvéolines paléocènes et éocènes (Hottinger, 1960) où les espèces mentionnées dans la présente note sont abondamment figurées et décrites en détail.

augmente en fonction du volume de la mégalosphère. Dans chaque rameau phylétique l'évolution suit sa voie particulière en nuançant les principes de la règle générale.

Les glomalvéolines

Le premier déploiement des Alvéolinidae du type structural *Alveolina* s.str. se produit au Paléocène moyen, dont les sédiments à faciès alvéolinifère sont conservés surtout sur les deux versants des Pyrénées centrales, mais aussi dans les Cordillières bétiques, en Egypte et plus rarement dans l'Arc alpin. Les faunes d'alvéolines y sont caractérisées par le groupe *A. primaeva*, formes sphériques d'un diamètre de 1 ou 2 mm. Leur bâti relativement grossier est typique. Le proloculus, toujours très petit, est enveloppé par des tours népioniques ("peloton") dont l'enroulement n'est pas fixé selon l'axe de la coquille. Aucun dimorphisme n'a été observé dans ce groupe. Une forme ovale à caractères morphologiques analogues est connue dans un deuxième horizon plus élevé du Paléocène moyen pyrénéen (*A. levis*). C'est la seule forme ovale qui paraît étroitement liée au groupe *A. primaeva* par ses caractères morphologiques et par sa position stratigraphique.

Dans les Pyrénées, à la base du Paléocène supérieur (Ilerdien) on assiste à un renouvellement total des faunes d'alvéolines. Les glomalvéolines à bâti grossier sont remplacées par des formes ovales (*A. lepidula*) ou légèrement fusiformes (*A. subtilis*), dont le bâti est beaucoup plus fin et fragile. Chez l'espèce *A. lepidula*, un dimorphisme peut être démontré qui n'affecte cependant que le stade népionique de la coquille. Des formes de ce type persistent pendant l'Eocène inférieur et moyen, où elles sont accompagnées de formes sphériques (*A. minutula*). On est tenté de rattacher à ce groupe de glomalvéolines *A. boscii* (espèce-type du genre *Alveolina* s. str.) caractérisée par sa structure menue et fragile, sa taille réduite par rapport aux formes contemporaines et par son dimorphisme aussi réduit que celui d'*A. lepidula*.

En Egypte, un horizon à la base de la série éocène du Ouadi Araba m'a fourni une faune dans laquelle coexistent des formes du groupe *primaeva* (*A. dachelensis*) et du groupe *lepidula* (*A. telemetensis*, ovale; *A.* cf. *pilula*, subsphérique). L'espèce du groupe *primaeva* n'est pas liée aux autres par des formes de passage, ce qui oblige à séparer à l'intérieur des glomalvéolines deux groupes distincts qui n'ont pas de relations phylétiques directes.

Au cours du Paléocène moyen (zone à *A. primaeva* et à *A. levis*), la spire de plus en plus lâche, les logettes spacieuses et le nombre progressif de tours provoquent une augmentation graduelle du volume total de la coquille des glomalvéolines du groupe *primaeva*. Un léger allongement n'est réalisé que chez *A. levis*.

A partir du Paléocène supérieur et pendant l'Eocène inférieur et moyen la tendance évolutive des glomalvéolines du groupe *lepidula* conduit à un resserrement progressif de la spire (*A. telemetensis – lepidula – subtilis*). Au Lutétien, les glomalvéolines minuscules, encore mal connues, ont un bâti plus fin, une spire plus serrée que celle d'*A. lepidula*, tandis que *A. boscii*, de taille beaucoup plus grande, représente une tendance opposée.

Le groupe hétérogène et complexe des glomalvéolines réputées "primitives" ne paraît pas représenter la racine de tous les rameaux phylétiques des alvéolines du type structural éocène.

Les flosculines

Plusieurs formes d'alvéolines sphériques, caractérisées par l'épaississement de la couche basale dans la zone équatoriale du test, apparaissent en même temps à la base du Paléocène supérieur (Ilerdien). Il est commode de les désigner globalement par l'ancien nom générique *Flosculina* de SCHWAGER (1883) basé sur ce caractère frappant, quoiqu'il ne me paraisse pas opportun de séparer ces formes des alvéolines à couche basale peu ou non épaissie par une barrière taxonomique. Le caractère de la flosculinisation est en effet commun à plusieurs groupes non apparentés, dont certains sont eux-mêmes hétérogènes. Dès leur apparition, ces groupes se distinguent entre eux par les caractères de leur spire, l'allongement des tours internes et par le mode et le grade de différenciation des stades ontogéniques. L'écart morphologique, généralement peu accusé, des générations micro- et mégalosphériques diffère selon les groupes. Il atteint son maximum dans les formes sphériques de l'Ilerdien moyen à proloculus de grand diamètre, *A. triestina* et *globosa*, et chez la forme allongée du Cuisien, *A. canavarii*.

Après une première floraison pendant le Paléocène supérieur, les nombreux groupes des flosculines sphériques et subsphériques sont relayés, dans le Cuisien méditerranéen, par un groupe unique d'espèces sphériques qui prend sa racine dans des formes de petite taille de l'Ilerdien supérieur (*A. parva*). Il porte le nom d'*A. indicatrix* d'après l'espèce caractéristique et répandue du Cuisien inférieur. Le Lutétien de la Sicile contient une forme géante, légèrement ovale (*A. palermitana*) qui paraît représenter la dernière flosculine de ce groupe. Les espèces sont caractérisées par leur stade juvénile à nombreux tours serrés et se distinguent de toutes les flosculines paléocènes par leur plus grand nombre de loges par tour de spire. Les formes microsphériques, connues dans les espèces cuisiennes seulement, ne s'écartent que de très peu des formes mégalosphériques. Les faunes des Indes, actuellement à l'étude, paraissent contenir un rameau phylétique supplémentaire (*A. globosa* NUTTALL non LEYMERIE, Meting limestone – *A. ovoidea* D'ORBIGNY, Kirthar beds. A rattacher à *A. pisiformis*?).

Au cours de l'évolution, l'accroissement des dimensions de la coquille et l'augmentation graduelle des tours de spire et du nombre des loges par tour se répètent dans tous les groupes. Le stade juvénile, bien délimité, à tours serrés dans les groupes *A. pasticillata* (hétérogène), *A. minervensis* et *A. indicatrix* augmente graduellement le nombre de tours avec l'accroissement du volume de la coquille entière. Dans les groupes à mégalosphère volumineuse et à spire lâche dès les premières loges, ce caractère apparaît dans l'espèce la plus ancienne et reste constant.

Pendant le Paléocène supérieur deux groupes de flosculines allongées (groupes *A. decipiens* et *A. canavarii*) se détachent des formes sphériques. Les formes A du groupe *A. decipiens* sont caractérisées par leur spire serrée dans les deux ou trois premiers tours. Les formes B montrent le même caractère plus accentué: leur stade juvénile compte au moins dix tours serrés. Le groupe peut être suivi jusqu'au Cuisien (*A. sicula*, dont on ne connaît cependant pas la forme B).

A. canavarii est répandue dans le Cuisien méditerranéen mais ses prédécesseurs (*A. laxa*) apparaissent dans l'Ilerdien des Pyrénées et de Trieste. La spire des formes A, lâche dès le premier tour, et la mégalosphère volumineuse sont les caractères frappants de ce groupe. La forme B de l'espèce *canavarii* atteint des dimensions considérables. L'irrégularité de la spire dans les tours flosculinisés, à l'équateur du test, représente le lien commun des deux groupes de flosculines allongées.

On saisit le plus facilement les caractères évolutifs des flosculines allongées dans leur allongement progressif aux dépens de l'épaississement de la couche basale à l'équateur. Comme chez les flosculines sphériques, la taille augmente au cours de l'évolution.

Les alvéolines ovales

Les rameaux phylétiques et les espèces des alvéolines ovales sont les plus difficiles à distinguer. L'allongement et le nombre des loges par tour de spire augmentent graduellement dès la base de l'Ilerdien. Dans les groupes d'*A. subpyrenaica* à couche basale épaissie, l'allongement progressif fait diminuer l'épaississement équatorial de la couche basale des formes mégalosphériques. On ne distingue que difficilement les formes A des espèces de l'Ilerdien moyen (groupe *A. subpyrenaica*) de celles des espèces à couche basale mince (groupe *A. ellipsoidalis*). Les formes microsphériques traduisent mieux les caractères des groupes. Dans tous les groupes elles s'écartent progressivement des formes mégalosphériques par la modification accélérée des caractères évolutifs, allongement et taille.

L'allongement progressif au cours des temps n'est pas partagé par le groupe hétérogène d'*A. elliptica*. Il comprend des formes ilerdiennes comme *A. aragonensis*, cuisiennes (*A. fornasinii*, *A.* aff. *minuta*) et lutétiennes (*A. stercus-muris*, *A. elliptica*). Les formes microsphériques, extrêmement rares, sont inconnues dans la plupart des espèces. La génération mégalosphérique montre un épaississement axial et équatorial de la couche basale dans les tours internes dont la variabilité individuelle est beaucoup plus accentuée que dans les autres groupes. Dans sa thèse, BAKX (1932) a décrit avec beaucoup de précision ce phénomène chez les espèces ovales des Iles de la Sonde, par exemple chez *A. javana*, apparentée à *A. elliptica*. On a voulu à tort généraliser ce phénomène. Il est caractéristique pour un nombre restreint d'espèces particulières.

Les tendances évolutives de ce groupe se réduisent à un accroissement progressif de la taille, réalisé par un nombre de tours à caractères adultes toujours croissant et par l'accroissement graduel du calibre des cavités du test. La variabilité de la flosculinisation est plus accusée dans les espèces lutétiennes de grande taille que dans les formes de dimensions modestes du Paléocène supérieur.

Dans les espèces ovales du groupe d'*A. elliptica*, *A. aragonensis*, *A. fornasinii*, on constate des tendances évolutives diamétralement opposées à celles des glomalvéolines *A. telemetensis* – *A. lepidula* – *A. subtilis*. Les premières accroissent le calibre des cavités du test, le pas de la spire augmente, tandis que les dernières multiplient leurs logettes en diminuant le calibre et en resserrant la spire à l'équateur.

Les alvéolines allongées fuselées

Avec l'Eocène inférieur, pour la troisième fois dans l'histoire de la famille des Alveolinidae, des éléments structuraux supplémentaires apparaissent dans la région polaire des formes allongées de grande taille. Les formes microsphériques des alvéolines fuselées du Cuisien (*A. distefanoi, A. cremae*) montrent les premières un développement considérable des logettes supplémentaires dans la couche basale des tours adultes. Les formes mégalosphériques en sont dépourvues à l'exception des représentants ultimes du groupe (*A. pinguis, A.* aff. *levantina*). Dans les deux générations, les tours internes sont peu allongés, subsphériques. Nombreux dans les espèces du Cuisien, ils sont réduits peu à peu au cours du Lutétien, tendance opposée à celle des flosculines du groupe d'*A. indicatrix*. L'allongement des alvéolines fuselées microsphériques progresse plus rapidement que celui des formes mégalosphériques. L'écartement des générations atteint les valeurs extrêmes observées dans ce genre, avec *A.* aff. *levantina*, dernière espèce attachée à ce groupe (Fig. 1).

Les alvéolines allongées cylindriques

Les alvéolines cylindriques se distinguent des espèces fuselées par leurs premiers tours allongés dans les formes A, leur petit nombre de tours sphériques dans les formes B. Elles ne sont connues que depuis le Cuisien supérieur (*A. violae*) et possèdent dès leur apparition des logettes supplémentaires dans les deux générations.

Leur caractère évolutif saillant est la progression de l'allongement. Il fournit l'exemple le plus clair et le plus facilement mesurable d'une évolution orthogénétique chez les alvéolines. Il est cependant nuancé selon des règles particulières, propres au groupe. La progression de l'allongement est plus accentuée chez les espèces cylindriques à spire serrée (groupe *A. munieri*) que celle des espèces à spire lâche (groupe *A. gigantea*). L'accroissement de l'écart morphologique entre les générations est plus rapide chez les espèces fuselées que celui des alvéolines allongées cylindriques (Fig. 1).

Les alvéolines du Biarritzien

Dans les couches à *Nummulites brongniarti*, trois espèces répandues d'Alvéolinidae allongées représentent une dernière floraison du genre qui disparaîtra dans le niveau stratigraphique suivant. Les trois espèces ne sont pas liées par des formes de transition aux rameaux phylétiques lutétiens. Elles en sont séparées par l'horizon stratigraphique précédant à *Nummulites aturicus* dont on ne connaît encore aucune alvéoline. Par sa morphologie, *A. fusiformis* du Biarritzien se rapproche des alvéolines fuselées. *A. elongata*, espèce cylindrique à spire lâche, est voisine des espèces du groupe d'*A. gigantea*, tandis que *A. fragilis* est caractérisée par une spire serrée comme les espèces du groupe *A. munieri*.

Il est permis de comparer ces espèces tardives avec les espèces antérieures, à morphologie analogue: *A. fusiformis* se distingue des formes fuselées du Lutétien par l'allongement plus accusé des formes A dont la mégalosphère reste cependant deux à trois fois plus petite. Les formes B sont moins allongées et l'écart entre les générations reste donc moins important que chez les alvéolines du groupe *A. levantina*. *A. elongata*, dont on ne connaît que la forme mégalosphérique, est beaucoup plus allongée qu'*A. gigantea* du Lutétien. Ses tours adultes sont irréguliers, la surface du test rugueuse, mais le proloculus est moins volumineux. *A. fragilis*, à proloculus très grand et un peu allongé, possède une spire très serrée mais elle est nettement moins allongée que les formes lutétiennes du groupe *A. munieri*. La surface du test microsphérique est plus rugueuse, les tours plus irréguliers.

Par rapport aux formes lutétiennes les plus évoluées, les alvéolines du Biarritzien présentent à la fois des caractères "plus avancés" et "retardés" qui ne sont pas les mêmes dans les trois espèces. On ne pourra qualifier les caractères "retardés" de décadents que lorsqu'il sera prouvé, par des formes de passage, que les espèces biarritziennes appartiennent réellement aux rameaux phylétiques des grandes alvéolines allongées du Lutétien.

MODIFICATIONS DE LA STRUCTURE

Au sein du genre *Alveolina* s.str., défini si soigneusement par REICHEL (1937), le plan du bâti est le même dans tous les rameaux phylétiques (Fig. 2): alternance des cloisonnettes, présence d'un canal pré- et postseptal, ouvertures alternantes en deux rangées. Ces dispositions particulières distinguent le genre *Alveolina* s.str. des genres voisins du Crétacé et du Néogène.

On distingue cependant trois modifications importantes dans les alvéolines éocènes (Fig. 2): (*1*) Le pelotonnement des premiers tours peut être abandonné par les formes mégalosphériques. (*2*) La couche basale peut s'épaissir dans toute la largeur de la loge (type des "flosculines") ou dans la partie polaire seulement (alvéolines ovales ou allongées, cylindriques et fuselées). (*3*) Des logettes supplémentaires apparaissent dans la couche basale. Ces modifications se suivent dans le temps et peuvent être considérées comme caractères évolutifs.

Les modifications évolutives de la structure sont réalisées à un moment précis de l'histoire particulière d'un rameau phylétique donné. L'apparition "soudaine" des nouveaux caractères paraît liée aux progrès réalisés graduellement par d'autres caractères évolutifs: (*1*) REICHEL a montré dès 1937, que le pelotonnement des premiers tours chez les alvéolines éocènes est abandonné, dès que le diamètre du proloculus dépasse une limite située autour des 100 μ. L'abandon du pelotonnement se répète dans chaque rameau phylétique au fur et à mesure que le diamètre critique des mégalosphères est dépassé au cours de l'évolution (HOTTINGER, 1960, fig. 27). Le pelotonnement n'est jamais abandonné par les formes microsphériques, où le diamètre de la microsphère reste toujours très petit (10 – 40 μ). (*2*) L'épaississement de la couche basale du

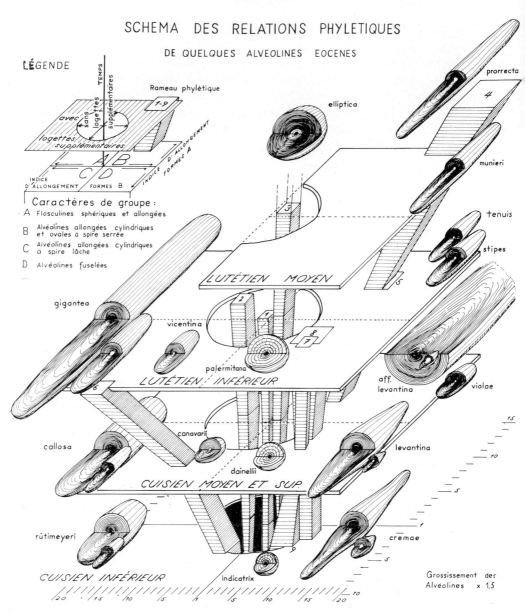

Fig. 1. Pour représenter les relations phylétiques complexes des alvéolines éocènes, une construction dans l'espace permet de réunir dans un seul schéma: (*1*) le temps, (*2*) les caractères morphologiques stables, les plus importants des groupes, (*3*) les rameaux phylétiques, (*4*) l'évolution de l'allongement axial du test en fonction du temps et (*5*) l'acquisition des logettes supplémentaires en fonction de l'allongement et du temps. Ce schéma simplifie, sous forme d'un modèle, les relations mathématiques complexes qui découlent des mesures biométriques des tests des alvéolines éocènes.

(*1*) Les niveaux stratigraphiques successifs sont symbolisés par des plans horizontaux. Les niveaux moyen et supérieur du Cuisien sont réunis dans un seul horizon. *A. dainellii* et *A. canavarii* de grande taille caractérisent le Cuisien moyen; leurs successeurs au Cuisien supérieur sont inconnus. *A. violae* caractérise le Cuisien supérieur tandis que la répartition stratigraphique des espèces *A. levantina* et *A. callosa* dans le Cuisien moyen et supérieur est incertaine.

(2) Dans notre schéma, les alvéolines de l'Eocène sont divisées en quatre groupes morphologiques A-D dont chacun occupe un quadrant du système des coordonnées horizontales. Le quadrant A groupe les formes sphériques et allongées à tours flosculinisés. Le groupe B comprend les alvéolines très allongées à spire serrée et les formes ovales du groupe *A. elliptica* à tours adultes serrés avec une flosculinisation individuelle très variable dans les tours internes. Le groupe C comprend les Alvéolines éocènes, allongées, cylindriques, à spire lâche et le quadrant D est occupé par quelques espèces des alvéolines fusiformes.

(3) Les rameaux phylétiques numérotés de 1–9 ne comprennent pas la totalité des espèces éocènes connues. Le rameau 1 groupe les flosculines sphériques et subsphériques *A. indicatrix* (Cuisien inférieur), *A. dainellii* (Cuisien moyen) et *A. palermitana* (Lutétien inférieur), le rameau 2 les variétés de l'espèce *A. canavarii* du Cuisien et *A. vicentina* du Lutétien inférieur. Le rameau 3 symbolise schématiquement les tendances évolutives de tout un ensemble encore mal connu d'espèces elliptiques. Les valeurs d'allongement indiquées pour le Cuisien correspondent à celles trouvées chez *A.* aff. *minuta*, pour le Lutétien à *A. stercus-muris*. La position stratigraphique d'*A. elliptica* type n'est pas connue avec précision. Aux Indes, elle accompagne *Nummulites obtusus* (échantillon type de cette nummulite dans la collection d'Archiac).

Le rameau phylétique 4 symbolise la succession des espèces lutétiennes *A. tenuis*, *A. munieri* et *A. prorrecta*, dont les formes B, très allongées, ne sont pas figurées, car elles auraient gêné la composition du tableau par leur taille énorme. *A. prorrecta* caractérise en Aquitaine un niveau particulier du Lutétien moyen à *Assilina spira planospira*, *Nummulites millecaput* type et *Nummulites crassus* type. Ce niveau est plus élevé que celui d'*A. munieri* (HOTTINGER et al., 1956). Les espèces *A. violae* et *A. stipes* ne paraissent pas représenter les prédécesseurs directs du groupe d'*A. munieri*. Un hiatus morphologique les sépare, *A. stipes* (rameau 5) ayant une spire plus lâche et un bâti plus grossier qu'*A. tenuis*. Le groupe d'*A. gigantea* (rameau 6) débute au Cuisien inférieur avec *A. rütimeyeri*, suivi d'*A. callosa* et d'*A. gigantea*. La forme B figurée pour *A. gigantea* est un individu de petite taille et représente le minimum observé. Les trois rameaux phylétiques 7–9 ne symbolisent que schématiquement les relations phylétiques plus complexes des alvéolines fuselées: les valeurs indiquées par le quadrilatère 7 représentent celles trouvées chez *A. frumentiformis*. Cette espèce pourrait dériver des *A. schwageri-distefanoi* dont les valeurs figurent sous 9 au plan du Cuisien inférieur. *A. cremae* paraît se raccorder étroitement à *A.* aff. *levantina* (rameau 8) tandis que *A. levantina* type du Cuisien moyen et supérieur ne peut être rattachée à ce rameau provisoirement. Des recherches étendues sont nécessaires pour éclaircir le détail des relations phylétiques des alvéolines fuselées.

(4) L'indice d'allongement des espèces (rapport diamètre axial: diamètre équatorial du test adulte) est symbolisé par la position des quadrilatères — résultant de l'intersection des rameaux phylétiques avec les plans horizontaux — par rapport à l'échelle indiquée sur le plan le plus bas. La longueur des quadrilatères (distance côté avant – côté arrière) indique la variabilité spécifique de l'indice d'allongement des formes A, la largeur: celle des formes B. La variabilité augmente au cours du temps, le plus nettement dans les rameaux phylétiques des alvéolines allongées. En fonction du temps, les rameaux phylétiques s'écartent progressivement de l'axe du schéma, dans la mesure où l'allongement des deux générations A et B augmente. La vitesse avec laquelle l'allongement progresse, est variable selon le rameau phylétique et se lit facilement dans l'inclinaison des rameaux phylétiques par rapport à la verticale.

(5) Dans les plans horizontaux successifs, les périphéries des surfaces découpées indiquent la limite entre les espèces avec et sans logettes supplémentaires dans la couche basale du test, en fonction de l'allongement et du temps. Les espèces simples, dépourvues de logettes supplémentaires, se placent à l'intérieur d'une surface que l'on peut limiter par un contour à peu près circulaire. Le rayon du cercle correspond à un indice d'allongement approximatif de six à huit. Cette valeur dépassée, les logettes supplémentaires apparaissent dans la couche basale. Beaucoup d'espèces d'alvéolines fuselées se placent à cheval sur cette limite, ce qui correspond bien à leur caractère particulier; les formes B plus allongées ayant des logettes supplémentaires, les formes A étant simples. L'acquisition des logettes supplémentaires s'effectue dans chaque rameau phylétique au moment où la valeur critique de l'indice d'allongement est dépassée au cours de l'évolution.

Pour conserver une présentation cohérente du schéma, j'ai extrapolé — d'après la taille de la mégalosphère et les caractères des formes apparentées — les valeurs de l'allongement des formes B dans les espèces suivantes: *A.* aff. *minuta*, *A. stercus-muris*, *A. elliptica*, *A. vicentina*, *A. tenuis*, *A. prorrecta*, où elles ne sont que peu connues.

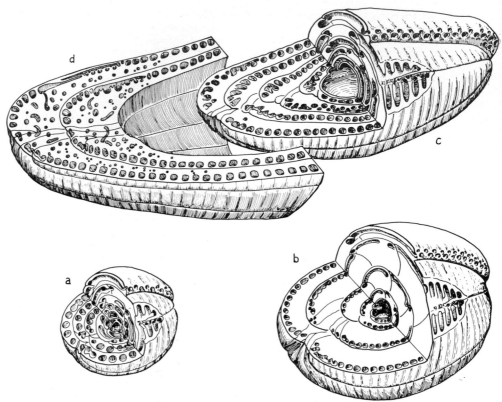

Fig. 2. Les caractères structuraux des alvéolines paléogènes, d'après REICHEL (1937).
   a. Glomalvéoline: l'enroulement des premiers tours n'est pas fixé selon l'axe des tours adultes.
b. Flosculine: la couche basale est épaissie dans la région équatoriale du test. c. Alvéoline simple.
Type structural des alvéolines ovales, elliptiques et fuselées, peu allongées. d. Tours décortiqués
externes à logettes supplémentaires dans la couche basale de la région polaire. Type structural des
alvéolines allongées fusiformes et cylindriques.
   Dans les coupes tangentielles en particulier, on se rend facilement compte des éléments structuraux
communs, caractéristiques du genre *Alveolina* s.str.: alternance des cloisonettes, présence d'un canal
préseptal et postseptal, deux rangées d'ouvertures.

type flosculine et des alvéolines allongées apparaît à la fois dans plusieurs rameaux
phylétiques à la base de l'Ilerdien. L'apparition semble liée à un nombre minimum de
tours dans la coquille adulte (12 – 15). Les formes, dont le nombre spécifique de tours
est en-dessous de ce seuil, ne différencient pas leur spire et gardent un test à peu près
globuleux. (*3*) Dans les alvéolines allongées, les logettes supplémentaires apparaissent
dans la couche basale de la région polaire, dès que l'indice d'allongement critique —
environ 6–8 — est dépassé (Fig. 1). Dans plusieurs espèces, elles apparaissent dans
les formes B, dont l'indice d'allongement est supérieur à la valeur critique, tandis que
les formes A, beaucoup plus courtes, en sont dépourvues.
   Les valeurs du diamètre de la mégalosphère, de l'indice d'allongement et du nombre
des tours, que nous avons appelées critiques pour l'acquisition des nouveaux caractères structuraux, varient dans les limites de la variation spécifique de tous les caractères

morphologiques. Dans l'état actuel de nos connaissances, l'apparition des nouveaux caractères paraît obligatoire dès que les valeurs critiques sont dépassées. Dans chaque rameau phylétique, les modifications structurales sont effectuées séparément selon la voie d'évolution particulière du rameau.

Chez les Alveolinidae des genres voisins, on observe des tendances d'évolution analogues. Si, pour l'ensemble de la famille, les règles de l'abandon du pelotonnement, de l'acquisition de logettes supplémentaires et de la différenciation de la couche basale — dans la direction axiale au moins — restent valables, les seuils ne sont plus les mêmes. Chez les préalvéolines du Cénomano–Turonien par exemple, le pelotonnement des premiers tours est abandonné et les logettes supplémentaires sont acquises avec des valeurs critiques beaucoup plus basses, "précoces" au sens évolutif.

SIGNIFICATION STRATIGRAPHIQUE DES CARACTÈRES ÉVOLUTIFS

En suivant les espèces successives et liées par des formes de transition, l'évolution observée dans les rameaux phylétiques se traduit par un ensemble de caractères évolutifs, particulier et typique pour chaque rameau. Les modifications qualitatives et quantitatives des ensembles de caractères permettent de bâtir une échelle stratigraphique très serrée. Les rameaux phylétiques parallèles d'un même genre se contrôlent les uns les autres, ce qui permet d'intégrer dans l'échelle stratigraphique des couches à faciès particuliers, dépourvues d'autres genres caractéristiques.

La méthode phylogénétique est encore le moyen le plus adéquat de s'approcher du but stratigraphique, l'établissement d'une échelle chronologique universelle, dont les éléments seraient délimités par des lignes isochrones (HUPÉ, 1960; SIGAL, 1961).

Dans un genre polyphylétique, le caractère évolutif — à lui seul — n'a aucune valeur comme critère stratigraphique: dans un rameau phylétique d'alvéolines (fig. 1) un indice d'allongement "x" est atteint dans un autre niveau stratigraphique que le même indice "x" d'un rameau phylétique parallèle. Par contre, l'indice d'allongement "x" observé dans un spécimen à caractères morphologiques déterminés se trouve lié à son rameau phylétique et peut servir comme critère stratigraphique. Autrement dit, un caractère évolutif, et en particulier les éléments structuraux acquis au cours de l'évolution, n'ont de valeur stratigraphique que dans le cadre d'une détermination spécifique rigoureuse et complète, avec tout le travail et les connaissances que nécessite une telle détermination. C'est là une des sources d'erreur les plus importantes dans l'utilisation stratigraphique des caractères évolutifs et c'est avec raison que l'utilisation imprudente de caractères "primitifs" et "évolués" est souvent critiquée.

LES CATÉGORIES ÉVOLUTIVES DE SEWERTZOFF

Dans son livre excellent sur la micropaléontologie POKORNÝ (1958, 1, p. 147) essaye de caractériser l'évolution des foraminifères avec les catégories évolutives de SEWERT-

ZOFF. Il constate avec raison, que ces catégories, créées pour caractériser les êtres multi-cellulaires, ne sauraient constituer que des analogies formelles par rapport à celles utilisables chez les foraminifères unicellulaires et introduit les termes pseudoanabolie pour des caractères évolutifs apparaissant à la fin de la croissance du test d'un foraminifère, pseudodéviation pour ceux caractérisant des stades intermédiaires de la croissance et pseudoarchallaxis pour des caractères surgissant dès le commencement de l'ontogénèse. Les exemples donnés sont choisis parmi les foraminifères de petite taille, où l'on n'observe qu'un nombre restreint de caractères évolutifs. Ces catégories sont-elles applicables aux alvéolines éocènes ?

L'abandon du pelotonnement peut être compris comme pseudoanabolie, l'enroulement selon l'axe définitif progressant vers le centre et éliminant les caractères embryonnaires (accélération). L'épaississement de la couche basale se produit selon le mode de la pseudoarchallaxis (flosculines du groupe *globosa*, *canavarii*, alvéolines allongées cylindriques) ou de la pseudodéviation (flosculines des groupes *A. pasticillata*, *A. indicatrix*, *A. elliptica*). Au cours de l'évolution, les logettes supplémentaires apparaissent d'abord dans les tours les plus allongés et progressent avec l'épaississement de la couche basale vers le centre et vers les tours externes, ce qui correspond à une catégorie intermédiaire entre la pseudoanabolie et la pseudodéviation.

Chez les alvéolines, l'évolution des caractères appartenant à des catégories différentes s'inscrit dans un cadre homogène et cohérent et paraît régie par les mêmes règles. L'application des catégories de SEWERTZOFF est sans doute artificielle.

LA SURFACE DE L'ENDOPLASME

En observant l'accroissement du volume du test et la multiplication progressive des cavités se répéter au cours de l'évolution, on peut se demander s'il existe des rapports entre la croissance de la surface de la sarcode et l'augmentation du volume total du test, et quelle serait la nature de ces rapports ("surface/volume ratio" selon BRÖNNIMANN et BROWN, 1955, p. 517). L'on sait que quantité de réactions biochimiques complexes sont liées à des phénomènes physicochimiques propres à la surface d'un corps et l'on serait tenté de voir dans l'augmentation de la surface du corps endoplasmique un moteur physiologique, une cause interne de la formation des structures toujours plus complexes chez les foraminifères.

Les nombreux exemplaires regénérés, surtout chez les formes microsphériques allongées de grande taille, enseignent que l'animal continuait à vivre s'il était amputé de plus de la moitié de sa coquille. Après l'accident, un premier tour nouveau recouvrit la spire découverte et les proportions spécifiques furent atteintes par une croissance accélérée. La surface totale de la sarcode n'est pas reconstituée du fait que la couche basale est plus épaisse pendant la croissance régénératrice et que les proportions spécifiques des cavités du test ne sont pas abandonnées.

Dans les nombreuses coquilles jumelées d'alvéolines, deux jeunes individus mégalosphériques se joignent pour former ensemble une coquille adulte. Dès le premier tour commun, les dimensions spécifiques des cavités sont respectées, malgré la proportion différente des surfaces par rapport au volume de la coquille à ce stade ontogénique. Plus tard, l'animal adulte atteint une taille un peu plus grande que l'exige la norme spécifique en conservant la texture caractéristique des logettes et des canaux.

Au cours de l'évolution, la surface totale du corps endoplasmique et le volume total de la coquille augmentent plus ou moins vite. Leurs rapports peuvent s'exprimer par un indice "Is" dont la formule doit tenir compte du fait que l'on compare l'accroissement d'une surface à celui d'un volume:

$$Is = \frac{\sqrt{\text{surface de l'endoplasme (mesurée en mm}^2)}}{\sqrt[3]{\text{volume du test adulte (mesuré en mm}^3)}}$$

Nous avons choisi des représentants caractéristiques des quatre groupes illustrant le plus clairement les tendances évolutives divergeantes: les glomalvéolines, les flosculines sphériques du groupe *A. indicatrix*, les alvéolines ovales du groupe d'*A. elliptica* et le groupe des *A. munieri* allongées, cylindriques, à logettes supplémentaires (Fig. 3).

Les valeurs de la surface de l'endoplasme se basent sur la coupe axiale de la coquille[1]. Elles ne peuvent être que des approximations relativement grossières. Les inexactitudes découlant des méthodes de mesure sont dans la plus grande partie systématiques et permettent de comparer les valeurs obtenues. Etant beaucoup plus importante, la variation spécifique affecte surtout les tours externes du test, abritant une grande partie de l'endoplasme total. Les variations dans les tours externes se répercutent ainsi sur la valeur totale de la surface dans une proportion plus forte qu'elles ne s'expriment dans la morphologie.

Au cours de l'évolution, les valeurs du rapport "Is" diminuent dans les coquilles sphériques et ovales et elles restent plus ou moins stationnaires pour les glomalvéolines, à l'exception d'*A. boscii*, où l'indice augmente par rapport aux espèces de petite taille. Les valeurs du rapport "Is" changent dans des voies relativement étroites, caractéristiques pour chaque groupe. Les indices les plus élévés sont atteints chez les espèces ovales du groupe d'*A. elliptica*.

Les observations sur les spécimens régénérés et jumelés et les mesures approximatives rapportées suggèrent que les valeurs du rapport entre la surface de la sarcode et le volume du test sont liées aux rameaux phylétiques et modifiées au cours de l'évolution selon la modification morphologique. Elles doivent être réglées par les mêmes lois qui régissent la sécrétion du test et qui lui donnent sa morphologie caractéristique. Elles ne peuvent pas être une cause directe de la complexité structurale croissante et de l'allongement évolutif des alvéolines.

---

[1] Quelques valeurs approximatives de la surface endoplasmique (formes mégalosphériques): *A. elliptica*: 930 cm²; *A. prorrecta*: 620 cm²; *A. palermitana*: 85 cm²; *A. (Glomalveolina) minutula*: 15 cm². La surface endoplasmique des formes microsphériques de grande taille doit dépasser 1 m²!

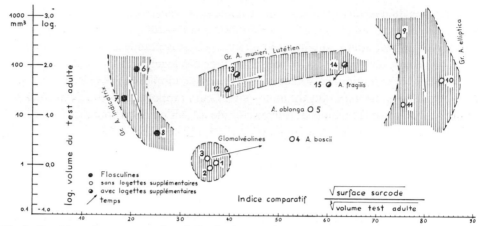

Fig. 3. Graphique du rapport surface de l'endoplasme/volume total de la coquille pour des représentants mégalosphériques caractéristiques des espèces d'*Alveolina*: (1) *A.(Glomalveolina)primaeva*, Paléocène moyen; (2) *A.(Glomalveolina)lepidula*, Paléocène supérieur; (3) *A.(Glomalveolina) minutula*, Eocène inférieur; (4) *A. boscii*, Eocène moyen; (5) *A. oblonga*, Eocène inférieur.

Flosculines sphériques: (6) *A. palermitana*, Lutétien; (7) *A. indicatrix*, Cuisien; (8) *A. parva*, Ilerdien supérieur à Cuisien inférieur.

Alvéolines ovales: (9) *A. elliptica*, Lutétien moyen; (10) *A. stercus-muris*, Lutétien inférieur; (11) *A.* aff. *minuta*, Cuisien inférieur.

Alvéolines allongées cylindriques: (12) *A. tenuis*, Lutétien inférieur; (13) *A. munieri*, Lutétien moyen; (14) *A. prorrecta*, Lutétien moyen, niveau supérieur; (15) *A. fragilis*, Biarritzien.

Dans la verticale, les valeurs logarithmiques du volume total de la coquille adulte. Dans l'horizontale les valeurs du rapport comparatif surface de la sarcode/volume du test. Les surfaces sont mesurées en millimètres carrés, les volumes en millimètres cubes.

A noter les tendances évolutives et les valeurs absolues nettement séparées selon le type morphologique du test déterminant la construction des rameaux phylétiques: glomalvéolines, flosculines, alvéolines ovales et alvéolines allongées à logettes supplémentaires.

Les valeurs d'*A. fragilis* du Biarritzien (15) apparaissent "retardées" par rapport à *A. prorrecta* du Lutétien moyen (14). *A. oblonga* du Cuisien (15) apparaît éloignée du groupe hétérogène d'*A. elliptica*, dans lequel *A.* aff. *minuta* (11) représente mieux la racine cuisienne de la lignée neuf à onze qu'*A. oblonga*. C'est la raison pour laquelle nous n'avons pas figuré cette espèce si répandue du Cuisien dans le schéma des relations phylétiques des Alveolinidae éocènes (Fig. 1).

Malgré la présence des logettes supplémentaires dans la couche basale, les alvéolines allongées du groupe d'*A. munieri* ne fournissent pas de valeurs extrêmes de la surface relative endoplasmique. Elles sont réalisées dans les alvéolines ovales à nombreux tours serrés et à bâti relativement grossier du groupe d'*A. elliptica*. Ce type morphologique est réalisé depuis la base du Paléocène supérieur (*A. ellipsoidalis*) et caractérise plusieurs rameaux phylétiques "conservateurs".

CONCLUSION

S'il est permis d'ajouter une conclusion d'après les observations rapportées dans la présente note, celle-ci ne peut être valable que pour le genre *Alveolina* s.str. Des allures et tendances évolutives similaires dans d'autres groupes de grands foraminifères ne peuvent être qu'une analogie, par le fait même qu'il s'agit de formes d'un bâti morphologique totalement différent. Il me paraît difficilement admissible de voir des mêmes lois régir l'évolution des formes sans relations phylétiques, même si l'évolution de celles-ci montre des analogies frappantes.

Chez les alvéolines du type éocène, les tendances évolutives paraissent s'inscrire dans un cadre caractéristique du genre. S'il m'est permis d'utiliser un modèle, on dirait qu'il existe un plan générique, qui tient à la disposition de chaque rameau phylétique un nombre déterminé d'éléments morphologiques à faire évoluer. Chaque rameau en utilise un certain nombre dès son apparition, qu'il garde et qu'il modifie, dans la voie choisie. Il n'y a ni retour ni changement de caractères évolutifs: Des alvéolines allongées ne peuvent dériver d'une flosculine sphérique. Toutes les combinaisons possibles des caractères évolutifs sont réalisées, certaines d'entre elles sont utilisées deux fois de suite. Des règles et des limites, caractéristiques du genre, régissent le déploiement des rameaux phylétiques et prescrivent les voies d'évolution pour un choix de caractères évolutifs.

Les caractères évolutifs et les règles de leur modification dans le temps caractérisent les espèces et les genres dans le même rang que les caractères morphologiques stables. Elles font partie de la morphologie intégrale de l'individu et doivent être ancrées dans la somme héréditaire du genre, même si la morphologie phénotypique de l'individu ne contient qu'une seule variante de toutes les formes potentiellement réalisables.

REMERCIEMENT

Il m'est agréable de remercier ici M. M. DIOURI, Directeur du Service géologique du Maroc et M. G. CHOUBERT, chef du Service de la carte géologique, pour la compréhension et l'intérêt dont ils ont fait preuve à l'égard d'études théoriques, en me laissant toute liberté de les poursuivre.

SUMMARY

Evolution in the Eocene genus *Alveolina* s.str. is found to be polyphyletic and very complex. Each phylum has its own particular history, the evolutionary trends being partly parallel, partly divergent. Modifications of structure take place separately in each phylum, when gradual changes in size and shape reach a clearly determined level. The surface/volume ratio develops in opposite directions: the ratio values rise in long, cylindrical alveolines with supplementary chamberlets, and fall in globular flosculines and elliptical forms with tightly wound spires, in which the absolute values are highest. Modifications of shape, size and structure in time are presumed to be an integral part of the genotypic morphology. In the case of one particular phylum, these modifications are only of a phenotypic nature.

BIBLIOGRAPHIE

BAKX, L. A. J., 1932. De genera *Fasciolites* en *Neoalveolina* in het Indo–Pacifische gebied. *Verhandel. Ned. Geol. Mijnbouw. Genoot. Ned. en Kol.*, 9: 205–266.

BOUSSAC, J., 1910. Du rôle de l'hypothèse en paléontologie stratigraphique. *Rev. sci.*, 48: 6–14.

BOUSSAC, J., 1911. Études paléontologiques sur le Nummulitique alpin. *Mém. Carte géol. France*, 437 pp.

BRÖNNIMANN, P. and BROWN, N. K., 1955. Taxonomy of the Globotruncanidae. *Eclogae Geol. Helv.*, 48: 503–561.

BURMA, B. H., 1948. Studies in quantitative Paleontology. *J. Paleontol.*, 22: 725–761.

HOTTINGER, L., 1960. Recherches sur les Alvéolines paléocènes et éocènes. *Mém. Suisses paléontol.*, 75/76: 1 – 243.

HOTTINGER, L., SCHAUB, H. und VONDERSCHMITT, L., 1956. Zur Stratigraphie des Lutétien im Adour-Becken. *Eclogae Geol. Helv.*, 49: 453–468.

HUPÉ, P., 1960. Les zones stratigraphiques. *Bull. Serv. inf. géol. Bur.rech. géol. min., Paris*, 49: 1–20.

POKORNY, V., 1958. *Grundzüge der zoologischen Mikropaläontologie.* VEB Deutscher Verlag der Wissenschaften, Berlin, 1, 582 pp.

RAUZER-CHERNOUSOVA, D. M., 1956. Les unités taxonomiques élémentaires dans la systématique des foraminifères. *Voprosy Micropaleontol. S.S.S.R. (traduction B.R.G.M.)*, 1615: 5–22.

REICHEL, M., 1937. Étude sur les Alvéolines. *Mém. Suisses paléontol.*, 57 et 59: 1–147.

SCHAUB, H., 1951. Stratigraphie und Paläontologie des Schlierenflysches. *Mém. Suisses paléontol.*, 68: 1–222.

SCHWAGER, C., 1883. Die Foraminiferen aus den Eocaenablagerungen der libyschen Wüste und Aegyptens. *Palaeontographica*, 30: 81–153.

SIGAL, J., 1961. Existe-t-il plusieurs stratigraphies? *Bull. Serv. inf. géol. Bur. rech. géol. min.*, 51: 1–5.

TINTANT, H., 1952. Principes de la Systématique. In: J. PIVETEAU, *Traité de Paléontologie*, Masson et Cie, Paris, 1: 41–67.

VEILLON, M. et VIGNEAUX, M., 1961. Les variations des critères de détermination des Nummulites en fonction des changements de lithofaciès. *Compt. rend. Acad. Sci.*, 252: 576–578.

EVOLUTIONARY TRENDS IN THE MIOGYPSINIDAE

C. W. DROOGER

Geological Institute, State University of Utrecht, Utrecht (The Netherlands)

INTRODUCTION

The foraminiferal family Miogypsinidae arose in Oligocene time from some trochoid, simple-spiralled ancestor which resembled *"Rotalia" mexicana* NUTTALL. The possession of equatorial chambers not radially arranged around the remainder of the *Rotalia* stage enables the family to be morphologically distinguished from the ancestral group as well as from all other orbitoidal Foraminifera. During the Late Oligocene, and until the moment of extinction well up in the Miocene, the Miogypsinidae underwent a rapid and varied evolution in many of the shallow and warm marine environments all over the world.

Throughout the last twenty-five years our knowledge of the family has been steadily increasing. As a result, a fairly good picture can be obtained of the general pattern of evolution, though much work remains to be done, both in exploring the group in several new regions and in considerably deepening the research in better-known areas.

The evolutionary trends at various places on the globe show distinct parallelism between the developing groups. The directions may be seen as adaptive, most of them in connection with a general trend towards greater radial symmetry of the test of the organism which probably had some functional advantage. Similar trends are known to have occurred in many other groups of orbitoidal Foraminifera (DROOGER, 1956b).

In giving a summary of our present knowledge, a summary which will not be free from a certain amount of bias, an endeavour will first be made to analyse the development of the separate morphological features.

Nearly all research thus far has been concerned with the individuals of the macrospheric generation.

NEPIONIC CHAMBERS

With regard to the changes in the macrospheric generation we may start with the characteristics that most clearly show the adaptive trends. Since the remarkable advance made by TAN SIN HOK (1936, 1937), it is known that the nepionic part of the test manifestly shows the evolution pattern.

In the oldest forms the later chambers of the simple, trochoid *Rotalia* spiral developed a distal stolon, which inaugurated formation of (equatorial) chambers in a different direction. As a result, the *Rotalia* spiral came to an end, and further growth of the individual was concentrated in the sector of the equatorial chambers (TAN's *complanata* type, see Fig. 1). In the course of evolution the acquisition of a distal stolon and, correspondingly, the onset of growth of equatorial chambers shifted to earlier chambers of the original *Rotalia* spiral. Consequently this nepionic spiral became increasingly shortened, while it also lost its trochoid character (*borneensis* type). This shortening during geological time is one of the most convincing examples of TAN SIN HOK's "principle" of nepionic acceleration.

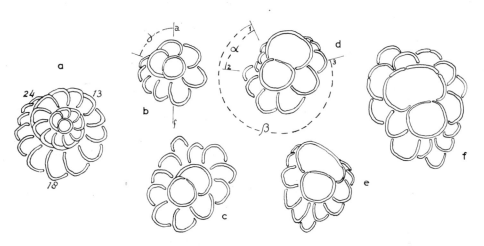

Fig. 1. Schematic drawings of types of nepionic arrangement (mainly after TAN SIN HOK, 1936). Stolons other than basal have been ignored in the figures. a. *complanata*. b. *borneensis*. c. *ecuadorensis*. d. *bifida*. e. *indonesiensis*. f. *excentrica* types. In Fig. 1a the derivation of X (= 24), Y (= 13) and Z (= 18) has been indicated. Fig. 1b shows the position of the apical-frontal line (a–f) and the angle γ. In the *bifida* and *indonesiensis* types, only the protoconchal nepionic spirals have to be taken into consideration. Their measurement by means of the arc lengths α (from 1 to 2) and β (from 1 to 3) is shown in Fig. 1d.

As soon as possession of the second stolon reached the third chamber (the first principal auxiliary chamber), the protoplasm formed a second nepionic spiral, in opposite direction alongside the deuteroconch (*ecuadorensis* type). The next step gave two stolons in the deuteroconch, with two principal auxiliary chambers, and the possibility of four nepionic spirals. In course of time both the principal auxiliary chambers and the spirals originating from them underwent a change in size from grossly unequal (*bifida* type) to equal, and bilateral symmetry of the initial stages consequently resulted (*indonesiensis* type).

The following phase of the evolution, known from unrelated groups, would have been development of more than two stolons from the embryonic apparatus originating more than two auxiliary chambers. This stage (*excentrica* type) was hardly achieved by the Miogypsinidae; general extinction occurred approximately at this level of development.

These arrangements of the nepionic part of the test have been used as the main feature for specific separation. For the older group the number of spiral chambers (X) offers a possibility of classification, by applying the mean value of this characteristic per sample (M_X). As soon as individuals with two principal auxiliary chambers begin to dominate the samples we use the degree of symmetry of both protoconchal nepionic spirals (200 α/β, see Fig. 1d), the mean values of which are expressed on a scale from 0 (absence of the second principal auxiliary chamber) to 100 (protoconchal spirals of the same length). Beyond the subdivision of the M_{200} α/β scale there has thus far been no need of a method for subdividing still more highly developed populations. But a single example is known in which probably over fifty per cent of the individuals possess more than two auxiliary chambers (*M.excentrica*).

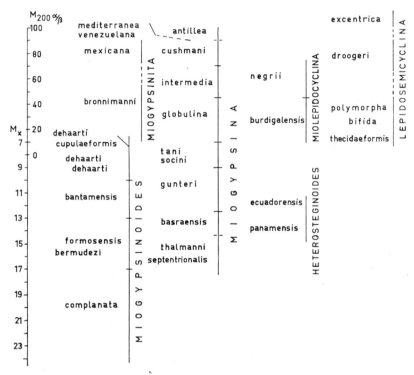

Fig. 2. Specific classification of the Miogypsinidae on the basis of the M_X and M_{200} α/β scales, and the grouping of the species into the six subgenera of the single genus *Miogypsina*. Since features other than the degree of nepionic development are sometimes just as important, the place of some of the species against this background is fairly arbitrary. Some specific names (*formosensis, bantamensis*) have been chosen on the basis of rather poor original descriptions. Relationships between the species are not given (see Fig. 25).

The species recognized according to these scales are shown in Fig. 2. For the main *Miogypsinoides – Miogypsina* line, some ten species are sufficient. All others are based on combinations of the degree of nepionic development with some other feature.

The nepionic acceleration from beginning to end, which underlies the above classification, of course needs stratigraphic confirmation, to prove the evolutionary trend of the features M_X and M_{200} α/β.

In broad outline it is certainly correct. The *M.complanata* group mainly characterizes the Late Oligocene, while *M.cushmani*, for instance, is found well above the base of the Miocene. At present we even have at our disposal many examples which confirm nepionic acceleration in detail, in sets of *Miogypsina*-bearing samples with clear stratigraphic interrelation, either from well-exposed sections or from borings (France, Italy, Gulf Coast, Egypt, etc.). This is particularly true of the M_{200} α/β group and of the younger M_X group. For the former, evidence can also be found in Fig. 3. If it is borne in mind that the faunal elements in these deposits of the Aquitaine basin have

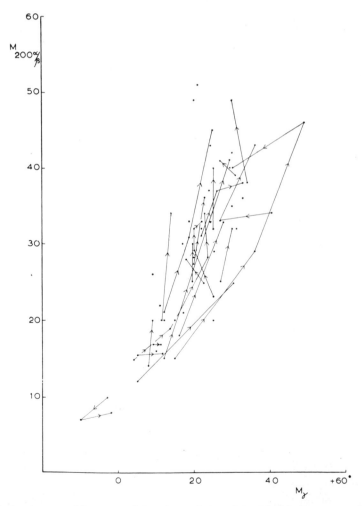

Fig. 3. Relation between M_{200} α/β and $M\gamma$ for samples of the *M.globulina* group of the Aquitaine basin. Points referring to samples whose stratigraphic interrelation was visible in the field have been connected. The arrows point towards the higher samples.

been frequently displaced, and also that the standard errors of the means are sometimes considerable, it follows that the general picture of this figure gives definite proof
of the validity of nepionic acceleration.

It is remarkable that such proof is much less clear in the case of the long-spiralled M_X
group, which is the oldest. Thus far, stratigraphic sections with representatives of
these species have hardly been investigated in detail. It would appear however, that on
the less exact basis of circumstantial evidence, nepionic acceleration seems to be valid
for this group as well. There are also a number of confirmatory data, mainly from
borings, from the Western Pacific area (TAN SIN HOK, 1936, 1937 a, b; HANZAWA,
1940, 1957; COLE, 1954, 1957 a, b). Nevertheless, it might be possible that the trend
towards reduction of the total number of spiral chambers in this oldest group was less
rigorous.

One might therefore suggest that the number of operculinid chambers (Y) — those

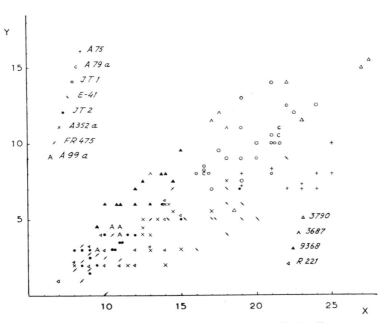

Fig. 4.   Relation between X and Y in samples from America and the Mediterranean region.
A 75   : *M.complanata*, Escornebéou, southwestern France.
A 79a :   —   , Saint-Etienne-d'Orthe, southwestern France.
JT 1   :   —   , Villa Giuseppina, northern Italy.
A 352a : *M.formosensis-bantamensis*, Christus, southwestern France.
JT 2   :   —   *bantamensis*, Bric del Duca, northern Italy.
A 99a :   —   , Abesse, southwestern France.
FR 475 : *M.bantamensis-dehaarti*, Sausset, southern France.
E-41   : *M.septentrionalis*, Novaj, near Eger, Hungary.
3790   : *M.complanata*, Roussillac well, Trinidad.
3687   : *M.bermudezi*, Baños well, Cuba.
9368   : *M.* cf. *bermudezi*, Southern Nat. Gas, Bernard well 1, La., U.S.A.
R 221   : *M.gunteri*, Huacapuy, Peru.

without a second stolon — is a more essential character, since it is more fundamentally connected with the theory of nepionic acceleration, whereas X also includes the later spiral chambers, the number of which may be thought to vary more irregularly.

This feature Y has hardly been used so far, mainly because it has certain disadvantages. In the first place, it covers a shorter numerical range than X. But the main reason is that the end of the Y-spiral is very difficult to ascertain, because distal stolons are often invisible. It is therefore hard to decide which is the last operculinid chamber, and hence, where growth in a different direction actually started (first equatorial chamber). This question has the following background. We know that in individuals of many *Rotalia* species, especially in the thick-walled ones, peripheral cavities were formed in between the lamellae and mainly at places where two successive chambers meet. Such cavities can certainly not be referred to as equatorial chambers. The same complication occurs in the early miogypsinids. Consequently, if stolons cannot be observed, it is impossible to distinguish such cavities from real equatorial chambers. Differences in size can probably not be used, since it has frequently been noticed that cavities of considerable size, or small equatorial chambers without further issue, occur along the apical border of the spiral, *i.e.*, in an ontogenetic stage much earlier, than the beginning of genuine equatorial growth.

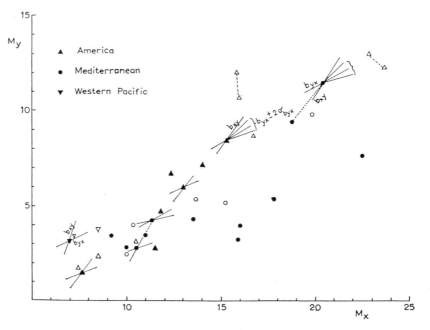

Fig. 5. Relation between M_X and M_Y in a number of samples. White symbols are based on less than 10 specimens, dark ones on 10 or more. For some of the samples both regression coefficients have been given, and for two of them the corresponding standard error. In the case of some of the samples two independent sets of counts were available which had been made with an interval of several years between them. The bulk of the specimens was the same both times. For four samples with notable differences, the two means have been entered, connected by a broken line. For the sample with the greatest shift, the discrepancy is mainly due to a considerable difference in the number of observations.

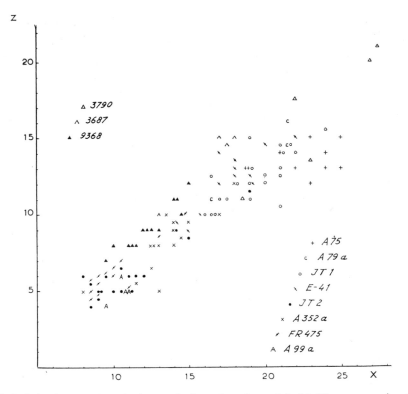

Fig. 6. Relation between X and Z in samples from America and the Mediterranean region. See Fig. 4 for explanation of the sample numbers.

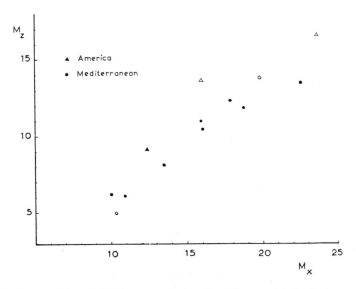

Fig. 7. Relation between M_x and M_z in some samples. Closed/open symbols refer to means based on 10 or more/less than 10 individuals, respectively.

The difficulty in determining the factor Y is clearly shown in Fig. 5 in respect of the samples of which a double set of counts was available. The results give grounds for suspecting whether the wide scatter of $M_X.M_Y$ values in this figure cannot be equally due to such differences of observation. In actual fact the four deviating points in the lower right part were computed at much later dates than the others. Owing to all these evaluation difficulties (in respect of only one investigator, be it noted), Y is considered not to be a better factor than X, pending further research.

The scatter diagrams of Fig. 4 and 5 show that correlation between X and Y, and between M_X and M_Y, is certainly present. As may be seen from the regression coefficients, we had better refrain from drawing too far-reaching conclusions based on differences in correlation coefficients and on regression lines.

Instead of Y, one might suggest for the long-spiralled forms the use of the spiral length up to the biggest chamber, the factor Z (Fig. 1a). Theoretically, the spiral chambers should begin decreasing in relative size as soon as protoplasm starts to "flow off" through distal stolons. But in practice, this Z does not allow of accurate observations, either. The chamber size, as estimated in the sections, very often changes gradually so that the decision about the largest chamber becomes a guess. Nevertheless, the estimates appear to be fairly well correlated with X. (Fig. 6, 7).

As regards the correlations between X and Z (Fig. 6) and between M_X and M_Z (Fig. 7), one gets the impression that the observations of Z are less disputable than those of Y.

As might be expected, on the whole X, Y and Z appear to follow the same trend of reduction. Their value will have to be carefully checked as soon as stratigraphic sections with reliable relations between samples containing *Miogypsinoides* individuals become available. Their combinations may offer future possibilities of distinguishing regional trends, as has been done already in giving a morphological basis to the separation of *M.thalmanni* and *M.septentrionalis* (DROOGER, 1960).

Another measurable feature of the nepionic (and embryonic) stage is the factor γ, the angle between the apical–frontal line of the test and the line connecting the centres of the two embryonic chambers (Fig. 1, 8). Individual values are rather inaccurate,

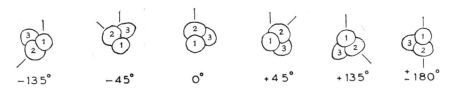

Fig. 8. Schematic drawing, showing the way of measuring γ, the angle between the apical–frontal line and the line connecting the centres of both embryonic chambers. The 0-point of the scale was chosen at the level of beginning development of the second principal auxiliary chamber which, in the *Miogypsina* s.str. series, is approximately between *M.tani* and *M.globulina*. For the earlier species, in order to achieve correct statistical means, it is necessary to continue the scale in a negative sense beyond $-180°$. For instance, in Fig. 1a, γ would be $-410°$. 1 = protoconch, 2 = deuteroconch, 3 = first principal auxiliary chamber. The apical-frontal line is vertical, with the apex at the top.

because of the frequently inexact position of the apical-frontal line. The values range from −550° to + 180°; the frequency distributions per sample may be considered as normal, though platykurtic; the known means range from about −440° to about + 90°.

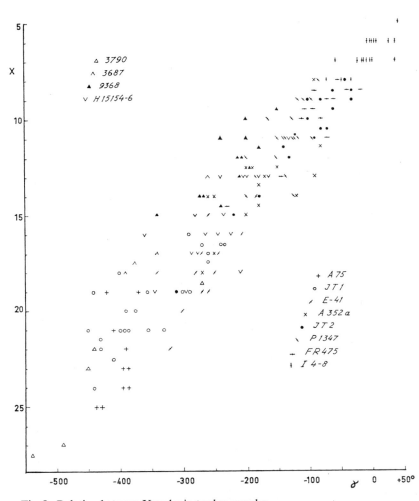

Fig. 9. Relation between X and γ in twelve samples.

A 75	:	*M.complanata*, Escornebéou, southwestern France.
JT 1	:	— , Villa Giuseppina, northern Italy.
A 352a	:	*M.formosensis-bantamensis*, Christus, southwestern France.
JT 2	:	*M.bantamensis*, Bric del Duca, northern Italy.
P 1347	:	— , Gebel Gharra, Egypt (after SOUAYA, 1961).
FR 475	:	*M.bantamensis-dehaarti*, Sausset, southern France.
E-41	:	*M.septentrionalis*, Novaj, near Eger, Hungary.
I 4-8	:	*M.tani-globulina*, Inharrime wells 4 and 8, Mozambique.
3790	:	*M.complanata*, Roussillac well, Trinidad.
3687	:	*M.bermudezi*, Baños well, Cuba.
9368	:	*M.* cf. *bermudezi*, Southern Nat. Gas, Bernard well 1, La., U.S.A.
H 15154-6	:	*M.thalmanni*, Baitao, Dominican Republic.

Since, in the older species, the sector of growth of the equatorial chambers is concentrated along the later part of the spiral, the length of this spiral is connected with the γ values (Fig. 9). As regards the relation between the means of X and γ, we see that there is a very good correlation (Fig. 10).

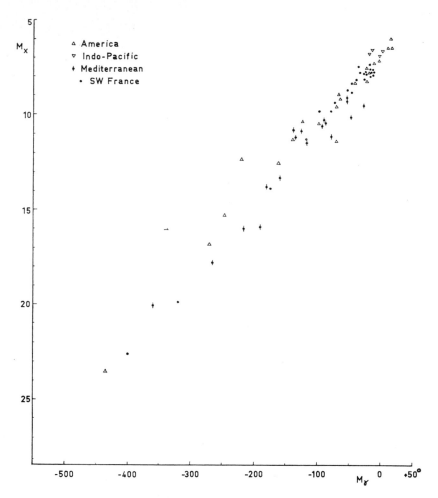

Fig. 10. Relation between M_X and $M\gamma$ in a number of samples.

In the case of the younger Miogypsinidae, the relation between 200 α/β and γ, and between their means, and hence also the evolutionary trend of γ, becomes less rigorous (Fig. 11, 12). For the early part of the group, correlation is still fair, though the details in Fig. 3 show some more deviations in the increase of $M\gamma$ than in that of $M_{200 \ \alpha/\beta}$. The differences in variability of these two features would become still more distinct if the standard errors of the means would be involved in evaluation of the changes in this diagram.

It is understandable that the evolutionary value of γ diminishes in this group, since the shortening of the primary spiral becomes fainter and is counterbalanced by the development of the second protoconchal spiral. Theoretically, one would expect that the γ values would again decrease to about 0 on approaching the complete symmetry of both protoconchal spirals, as such a position would be in accordance with the

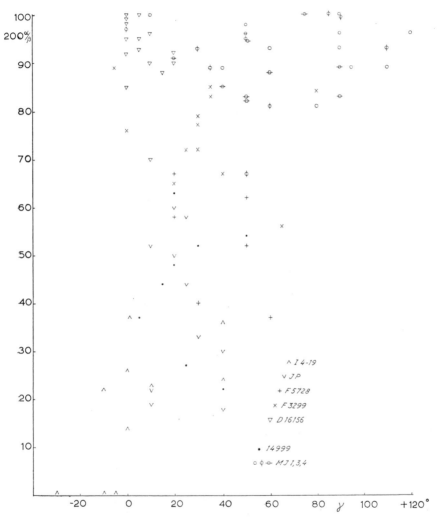

Fig. 11. Relation between 200 α/β and γ in a number of widely scattered samples of the Eastern Hemisphere.

I 4-19	:	*M.tani-globulina*, Inharrime well 4, core 19, Mozambique.
JP	:	*M.globulina*, Syukunohora, Japan.
F 5728	:	*M.intermedia*, Pakaurangi Point, New Zealand.
F 3299	:	*M.cushmani*, Island Creek, New Zealand.
D 16156	:	*M.antillea*, Wai Papan, southern Sumatra.
14999	:	*M.globulina-intermedia*, Epirus, Greece.
MJ 4	:	*M.cushmani-mediterranea*, Merguelida, Majorca.
MJ 1	:	*M.mediterranea*, Santa Margarita, Majorca.
MJ 3	:	*M.mediterranea*, Merguelida, Majorca.

direction of maximum equatorial growth. Such a trend is actually present in the group in which the early stages occupy a perfectly peripheral position (*M.antillea*). However, in the later species with slight centripetal trends (*M.mediterranea, M.mexicana, M.venezuelana*), the angle γ tends to increase. Equatorial chambers growing also in apical direction, a position of the embryonic chambers more or less at right angles to

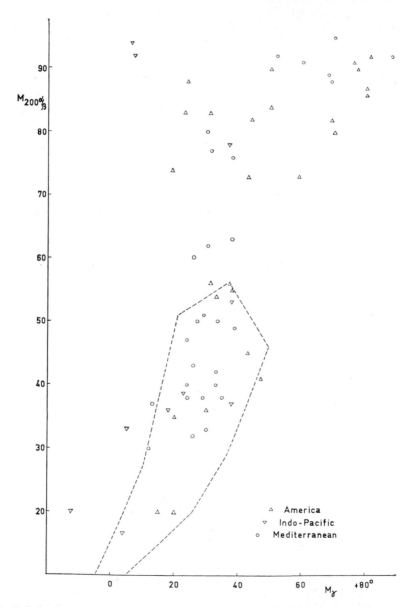

Fig. 12. Relation between M_{200} α/β and M_γ in a number of samples from the three major regions. For the Mediterranean region only the points outside SW. France have been entered. For the latter area the outline of the scatter (of Fig. 3) is indicated by a broken line.

the apical–frontal line, was evidently more favourable. These two trends account for the enormous scatter among the youngest species in Fig. 12.

EMBRYONIC CHAMBERS

The embryonic stage, consisting of the first two chambers, protoconch (I) and deutero-conch (II), is also known to show evolutionary trends, which, however, do not allow of much diversity.

First, there is the general rule that the embryonic chambers become of greater abso-lute size during evolution. Increase in volume of the early chambers is a general trend in the development of smaller taxonomic units in the Foraminifera. Cosijn (1942)

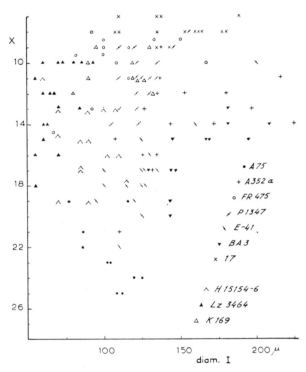

Fig. 13. Relation between the diameter of the protoconch and X in some samples from America and the Mediterranean region.

H 15154-6 :	*M.thalmanni*, Baitao, Dominican Republic.
Lz 3464 :	*M.basraensis*, Kapur Quarry, Trinidad.
K 169 :	*M.gunteri*, Falcón, Venezuela.
A 75 :	*M.complanata*, Escornebéou, southwestern France.
A 352a :	*M.formosensis-bantamensis*, Christus, southwestern France.
P 1347 :	*M.bantamensis*, Gebel Gharra, Egypt (after Souaya, 1961).
FR 475 :	*M.bantamensis-dehaarti*, Sausset, southern France.
E-41 :	*M.septentrionalis*, Novaj, near Eger, Hungary.
BA 3 :	— , Astrup, Germany.
17 :	*M.tani*, Lariey, southwestern France.

argued for some foraminiferal groups that there would be a period of increase followed by one of decrease in this feature. However, the data he gives for *M.complanata*

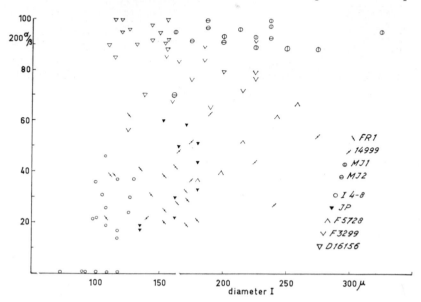

Fig. 14. Relation between the diameter of the protoconch and 200 α/β in some samples from the Mediterranean and the Indo-Pacific.

FR 1   : *M.globulina*, Gamachot, southwestern France.
14999 : *M.globulina-intermedia*, Epirus, Greece.
MJ 1   : *M.mediterranea*, Santa Margarita, Majorca.
MJ 2   : *M.mediterranea*, Merguelida, Majorca.
I 4-8   : *M.tani-globulina*, Inharrime wells, Mozambique.
JP   : *M.globulina*, Syukunohora, Japan.
F 5728 : *M.intermedia*, Pakaurangi Point, New Zealand.
F 3299 : *M.cushmani*, Island Creek, New Zealand.
D 16156 : *M.antillea*, Wai Papan, southern Sumatra.

from Puente Viejo in southern Spain are not convincing, since his samples had been taken from a series of turbidites in between *Globigerina* marls, and definitely contain largely derived and mixed assemblages (DROOGER, 1956a).

Fig. 15 shows that there is a general tendency for the mean protoconch diameter (M^I) to increase with evolution, expressed by the M_X and M_{200} α/β scales, but the scatter appears to be very wide. A similar scatter is obtained if the individuals of a number of samples are plotted (Fig. 13, 14), though the frequency distribution of the diameter of the protoconch may be fairly narrow in a single sample. SOUAYA (1961) therefore concluded that M_I might be an important taxonomic feature, which, in our opinion, must be doubted. M_I appears to show many divergencies from the rule of general increase, both in well-known stratigraphic sections and on a wider geographic scale. Apart from some genetic control, environment probably acted in some way as a modifier of these dimensions, as it is known to act in many organisms.

The poor correlation in the samples between the diameter of the protoconch and the angle γ is shown in Fig. 16. The peculiar shape of the total scatter is accidental, due to the selection of the samples. The picture would change substantially if we had included, for instance, some samples of the *M.gunteri–tani* group of southwestern France (DROOGER, 1955a).

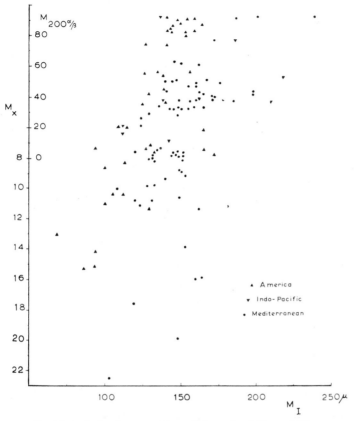

Fig. 15. Relation between M_I and the scale of M_x and M_{200} α/β.

SOUAYA (1961) elaborated the relation between various dimensions of the embryonic and nepionic parts of the test for material from Egypt. He shows the (often significant) positive correlation between D_I (diameter protoconch), D_{II} (diameter deuteroconch), ε (distance between the apex and the centre of the protoconch), $L_{I + II}$ (length I + II, measured along the line connecting the centres of both chambers) and $L_e \times W_e$, *i.e.*, length × width of the embryonic–nepionic stage as a measure of its surface in horizontal section (Fig. 17). Although no further research has yet been done, and much more material will be needed, it may be concluded that the proportions of the linear dimensions of the early stages remained about the same in every population during the ontogeny of the individuals. Such a constancy within certain limits is not surprising. During evolution, differences in regressions between groups of samples may be expected.

One distinct change in proportions from the beginning to the end of the evolution
of the Miogypsinidae is well known. Observation of the successive early chambers of
M.complanata or *M. bermudezi* for instance, shows that there seems to be a gradual
increase in chamber dimensions in section, as if there were an exponential relation

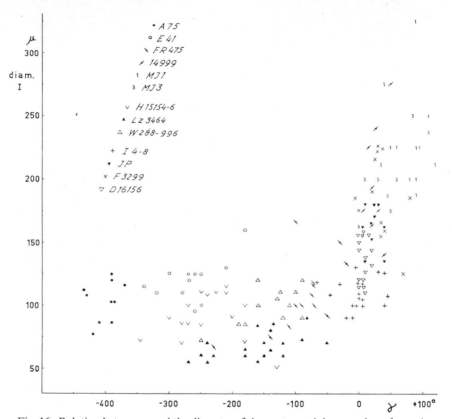

Fig. 16. Relation between γ and the diameter of the protoconch in a number of samples.

A 75	:	*M.complanata*, Escornebéou, southwestern France.
E-41	:	*M.septentrionalis*, Novaj, near Eger, Hungary.
FR 475	:	*M.bantamensis-dehaarti*, Sausset, southern France.
14999	:	*M.globulina-intermedia*, Epirus, Greece.
MJ 1	:	*M.mediterranea*, Santa Margarita, Majorca.
MJ 3	:	*M.mediterranea*, Merguelida, Majorca.
H 15154-6	:	*M.thalmanni*, Baitao, Dominican Republic.
Lz 3464	:	*M.basraensis*, Kapur Quarry, Trinidad.
W 288-996	:	*M.gunteri*, Well 288, Port St. Joe, Florida, U.S.A.
I 4-8	:	*M.tani-globulina*, Inharrime wells 4 and 8, Mozambique.
JP	:	*M.globulina*, Syukunohora, Japan.
F 3299	:	*M.cushmani*, Island Creek, New Zealand.
D 16156	:	*M.antillea*, Wai Papan, southern Sumatra.

for size which is probably connected with a similar relation in the increase of the protoplasm volume of the individual. Obviously, this trend becomes hard to trace as soon
as protoplasm begins to "escape" through distal stolons to form equatorial chambers.

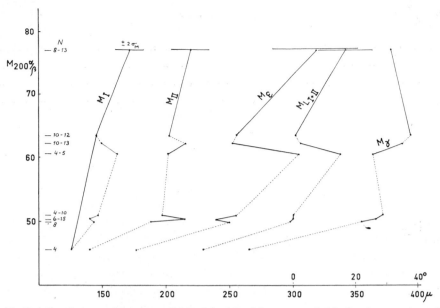

Fig. 17. Relation between $M_{200\ \alpha/\beta}$ and M_I, M_{II}, M_ε, $M_{L_{I\ +\ II}}$ and $M\gamma$ for the samples of the *Miogypsina intermedia* group of Egypt (after SOUAYA, 1961). The samples have been arranged according to their $M_{200\ \alpha/\beta}$ values. Points referring to samples of one stratigraphic section have been connected by full-drawn lines, the others by broken lines. The lowermost sample comes from the same section as the uppermost two. The numbers of individuals (N) on which the means have been based are given, as well as the range of the standard error by means of $\pm\ 2\ \sigma_M$ for the uppermost sample.

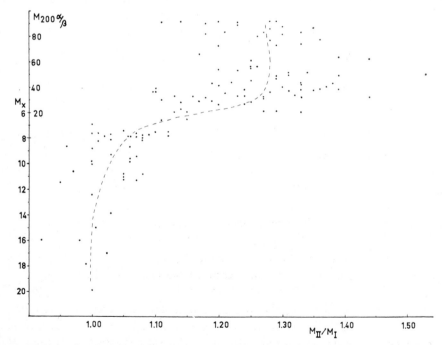

ig. 18. Relation between M_{II}/M_I and the scale of M_X and $M_{200\ \alpha/\beta}$ for samples from all three major regions. Rough M_{II}/M_I averages at successive levels of nepionic development have been indicated by a broken line.

With the reduction of the primary spiral in course of time, this probably exponential relation becomes less apparent, the more so as lateral chambers were formed as well.

It is strange to note, if the mean larger diameters of II and I, are plotted as a rough measure of size against the M_x–M_{200} α/β scale for samples of the successive species (Fig. 18), that there is a fairly abrupt increase in proportion, which more or less coincides with the incipient development of the second principal auxiliary chamber. This proportion subsequently remained constant between very wide limits. Did, at this level, a fundamental change of the exponential function of chamber growth take place? If we estimate the volume of both principal auxiliary chambers, and consider it to be the next budding step in ontogeny, this is certainly not the case, because then the volume would be much too small. Or would already at this early stage formation of lateral chambers have begun? This also seems unlikely if one pays attention to the juvenile individuals of *M.bronnimanni* and *M.globulina*, described from Central America (DROOGER, 1952, 1957), which lack lateral chambers but show the same divergency. For some unknown reason (a planktonic stage?) the embryonic chambers became suddenly more distinct as a separate phase in ontogeny.

The change in the shape of the deuteroconch, from wide comma- to kidney-shaped in section, which is roughly correlated with this increase in relative size, is easier to understand, because it is related to the acquisition of the second stolon, and probably gave a better radial symmetry to the total of embryonic and auxiliary chambers.

As far as our numerous measurements would indicate, there is no notable change observable during evolution in the degree to which the protoconch is embraced by the deuteroconch as seen in section. Such a change is of great importance in other groups, as has been shown by VAN DER VLERK (1959) for the Lepidocyclinidae.

EQUATORIAL CHAMBERS

There are very few exact data on the equatorial chambers of the Miogypsinidae, though definite changes occurred in them in the course of evolution. One of the main reasons is that there is such considerable differentiation in the course of ontogeny; furthermore, it is very difficult to state the changes in more than vague, qualitative terms. There is a tendency for newly acquired characteristics of the equatorial chambers to shift from later to earlier ontogenetic stages in the course of evolution. Consequently, observations strongly depend on the ultimate size of the individuals. Since this size again mainly depends on environment and on geological phenomena which had an effect during life or after death, comparable data are sometimes difficult to obtain.

No attempt is made here to give numerical data. It can, however, be stated that one trend is that of a general increase in the total number of equatorial chambers from the early species to the later ones. Correspondingly, there is a decrease in volume of the individual chambers, as there is a decrease in the height of the median layer. There is no good reason to think that the ontogenetic rate of increase of chamber volume changed much in the course of phylogeny. If so, it must be very irregular, as the size of the equatorial chambers is known to depend considerably on environmental influences during life.

More has been written about the change in shape of the equatorial chambers, in

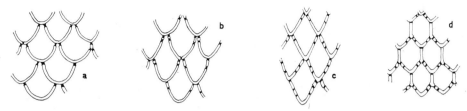

Fig. 19. Schematic drawings of equatorial chambers and their stolon arrangements (mainly after TAN SIN HOK, 1936; and BRÖNNIMANN, 1940). *a.* Arcuate chambers with single basal-stolon system; *b.* Ogival with double system; *c.* Rhombic with double and triple systems; *d.* Hexagonal with double system and annular stolons; Occasional annular and radial stolons occur in the other types as well.

ontogeny and in phylogeny (Fig. 19), which change in general goes from open arcuate to rhombic. TAN SIN HOK (1936) and BRÖNNIMANN (1940) also showed that there is a corresponding change in the stolon systems of the equatorial chambers. Later authors generally neglected this feature, regarding it as being more of academic than of practical value. As a whole, the changes in the stolon systems seem to lead to easier communication between the adjacent chambers. It has been argued that the change in shape of the chambers tends to increase their relative length.

Thus far, these features of the equatorial chambers have not lent themselves for the purpose of refining the subdivision of the Miogypsinidae. One exception must be made. In the western Pacific region, and at least as far west as India, a group of species (*Lepidosemicyclina*) has been found in which, during ontogeny, the equatorial chambers rapidly attain hexagonal shape. Chambers of somewhat hexagonal shape frequently occur towards the frontal margin in larger specimens of younger species all over the world. In *Lepidosemicyclina*, however, the trend is very strong, and in some species the chambers even become very soon of elongate-hexagonal shape. This trend can certainly not be explained as leading towards greater radial symmetry. It tends to lengthen the test, often more strongly so at some places only, which results in a strongly indented frontal margin (*M.bifida*). The group seems to be rather complicated because the degree of nepionic development and the trend towards more elongate equatorial chambers are not clearly correlated.

Better known are the trends relating to the position of the embryonic–nepionic stage within the equatorial layer. In primitive *Miogypsinoides*, the initial stages are strictly peripheral and this remains the case throughout the development of the main *Miogypsinoides-Miogypsina* s.str. stem. However, at different levels of nepionic development local stocks of this main lineage independently gave rise to side lines in which the early stages shifted to a more central position (Fig. 20).

A nearly radial development was obtained in the north Italian lineage from *M. gunteri*, via *M.socini* and *M.burdigalensis*, to *M.negrii* (subgenus *Miolepidocyclina*), in which the microspheric individuals of the later species also show this centripetal trend.

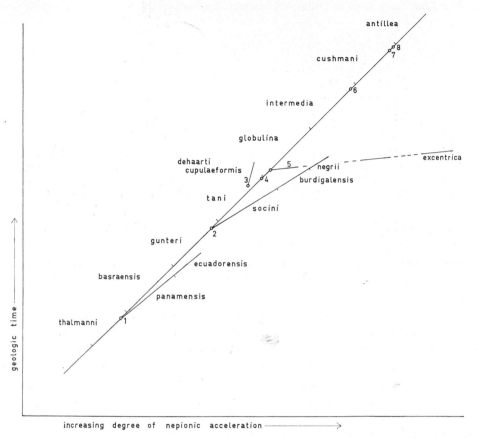

Fig. 20. Starting points from the main lineage of groups with centripetal trends. The main *Miogypsina* s.str. lineage is given as a straight reference line in the relation between the rate of nepionic acceleration and geological time.
1. *Heterosteginoides* lineage.
2. *Miolepidocyclina* lineage.
3. *Miogypsina dehaarti cupulaeformis*, starting from the parallel *Miogypsinoides* stock.
4. *Miogypsina bronnimanni*.
5. *Lepidosemicyclina* group.
6. *Miogypsina mexicana*.
7. *Miogypsina venezuelana*.
8. *Miogypsina mediterranea*.

Unfortunately the microspheric generation is unknown in the lineage of the American species from *M.thalmanni* to *M.panamensis* and *M.ecuadorensis* (subgenus *Heterosteginoides*), the last of which species also shows a considerable degree of centripetal displacement of the early stages in the macrospheric individuals.

Separate and less successful developments in this direction are those of *M.bronni-*

manni, *M.mexicana* and *M.venezuelana* in America (subgenus *Miogypsinita*); that of *M.mediterranea* in the Mediterranean region; and that of *M.excentrica* of the Indonesian *Lepidosemicyclina* group. The centripetal shift in these species is never great, and in the case of some of them it is known that the microspheric individuals did not follow the trend.

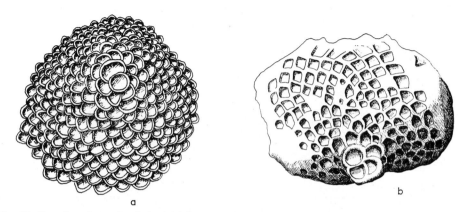

Fig. 21. Centripetal trends of the initial stages: a. in a flat median layer (*M.burdigalensis*); b. in a conical median layer (*M.dehaarti cupulaeformis*).

Thus far, all centripetal shifts occurred in a relatively flat median layer. This is not the case in the peculiar trend of the later *Miogypsinoides* stock of the western Pacific. At least part of the individuals of these populations show extension of the median layer in anti-frontal direction, while at the same time the median layer, as well as the test, acquire the shape of an oblique low cone with the early stages protruding at the apex (Fig. 21). Since in the samples containing *M.dehaarti cupulaeformis* flat types occur as well, the subgenus *Conomiogypsinoides* has a poor basis.

All these independent developments clearly fit in with the general evolutionary trend towards greater radial symmetry. No exact measurements have ever been made. For Egyptian material of *Miogypsina* with peripheral initial stages, SOUAYA (1961) measured a degree of relative excentricity of the protoconch by means of ε, the distance between the centre of this chamber and the apex. As might be expected for these samples, ε was found to be positively correlated with the other dimensions of the embryonic nepionic stage (see Fig. 17). Such measurements have not been made for species with distinct centripetal trends. Their value may be dubious, as they will depend largely on the degree of development of the median layer of the individual, *i.e.*, on the size of the test. It seems that an estimate of the relative position, proportionate to the diameter of the test, cannot be much exceeded in accuracy.

The example of the *Miolepidocyclina* series of northern Italy (Fig. 22) makes it clear that, in this case at any rate, the centripetal trend was not gradual. In the intermediate group the position of the early stages was found to be very different in the individuals of each sample, varying from peripheral to subcentral.

WALL STRUCTURES

Just as in the ancestral Rotaliidae, the wall structure of the Miogypsinidae is primarily lamellar, owing to the addition of a thin layer all over the test at each step of
chamber formation. The sidewalls of the test may become very thick in *Miogypsinoides*
individuals which still lack lateral chambers. Lamellar, horizontal structures are sometimes very predominant, as for instance in *M.dehaarti* (VAN DER VLERK, 1924).

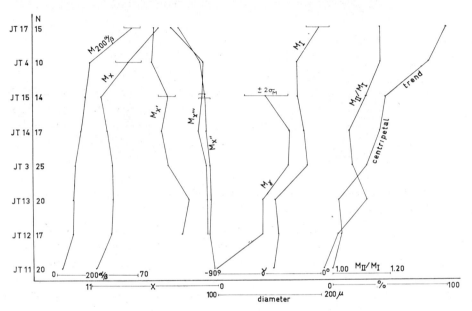

Fig. 22. Development of several characteristics, expressed by their means in the series *Miogypsina
gunteri* (JT 11) – *M.socini* (JT 12, 13) – *M.socini-burdigalensis* (JT 3, 14, 15) – *M.burdigalensis* –
M.negrii (JT 17) from the hills of Turin, northern Italy. The samples have been placed in correct stratigraphic order, but at equal distances which bear no relation to the real stratigraphic intervals. All
four nepionic spirals are given; those from the first principal auxiliary chamber are X and X', those
from the second X" and X'''. X and X" are the protoconchal spirals. The degree of centripetal shift is
expressed as the percentage of the total number of specimens per sample, formed by the individuals
showing this trend. Standard errors, by means of ± 2σ$_M$, have been entered at some places, as well as
the number of individuals per sample (N) on which the means were based.

Increased thickening of the sidewalls was formerly considered to be an evolutionary
trend (DROOGER, 1951). The thin-walled *M.bermudezi* was thought to be a very primitive species, ancestral to the thick-walled *M.complatana* group. In the meantime, some
examples have been found of undoubtedly much more highly developed populations,
even of *Miogypsina* s.str. (AKERS and DROOGER, 1957), in which the individuals have
very thin outer walls. This shows that other factors, probably including environmental
ones, were at least as important to the degree of development of this character as
closeness in time to the *Rotalia* ancestor. The validity of thickening of the sidewalls as
a rigorous evolutionary trend must now be doubted.

Another trend in the development of the sidewalls is the acquisition of a system of lateral chambers on either side of the median layer, which trend is also known from several other, unrelated, groups of orbitoidal Foraminifera. Why such lateral chambers develop in so many groups is not very clear. GRIMSDALE (1959) advanced the hypothesis that the commensal Algae were stored in these lateral systems. The idea of a more highly organized "agriculture" certainly appeals to our imagination, but proof is still entirely lacking.

In the thick sidewalls of already all *Miogypsinoides* species, cavities may occur in between the lamellae, preferably at places where the latter are not straight, such as for instance over the septa. They may partly be enlarged portions of vertical canals. In early *Miogypsina* s.str. species, lateral chambers develop all over the median layer. They are few in number, of different size and shape, irregularly arranged, and commonly with convex outer walls. During further development of the group there is a general increase in number, the chambers become more equal in size and shape, their arrangement changes from irregularly imbricate towards a placement in columns and layers, while the roofs of the individual chambers become flatter and often relatively thinner. These trends are not very rigorous; there is considerable variation at each level of nepionic development.

The transition from thick sidewalls to the systems of lateral chambers has been used for the taxonomic differentiation between the subgenera *Miogypsinoides* and *Miogypsina*. This change is but moderately correlated with the degree of nepionic development. Taking the latter as a basis, the initial development of lateral chambers occurred at different levels (Fig. 25). In America it happened early, *M.thalmanni* being the first species of *Miogypsina* s.str.; in the western Pacific very late, at least not before populations of a nepionic level comparable to that of *M.tani*. In the Mediterranean area *M.gunteri* was usually the first *Miogypsina* species (southwestern France, northern Italy), but even in such a restricted area as the western Mediterranean several deviations can be shown to exist already. In Morocco a more primitive *Miogypsina* species, *M.basraensis*, has been found, while the northern offshoot of *M.septentrionalis* (Germany, Hungary) is still more primitive. But also samples of the degree of nepionic development of *M.gunteri*, but without distinct lateral chambers, are known from Provence, not far away from the good populations of *M.gunteri* proper in northern Italy.

Apart from the general trends of sidewall development outlined above, the details seem to be poorly correlated with the nepionic development. The fact, for instance, that some populations of *M. globulina* of the Gulf Coast (AKERS and DROOGER, 1957) practically lack lateral chambers, again leads to the conclusion that environment, and probably haphazard genetic factors in local stocks, greatly influenced the character of the sidewalls.

Another feature of sidewall development is the pillars and their ends on the surface, the pustules. In primitive *Miogypsinoides* the pillars are formed especially over the horizontal walls of the median chambers by greater thicknesses of the lamellae. With continued thickening of the sidewalls they tend to split up, and they also begin to develop over the septa, preferably at places where three septa meet. In species with lateral chambers, pillars of a new type are commonly formed at the junction points of adjoining lateral chambers, to the accompaniment of more or less columnar arrangements of the latter. Occasionally pillars seem to be strengthened columns of such chambers.

Throughout the course of evolution there is a distinct change in type of the pillars, from inflational and even incised towards mainly interstitial. This change is clearly connected with the acquisition of lateral chambers.

The degree of development of pillars is considered to be highly dependent on environment. In *Miogypsina* samples from southwestern France it was found, for instance (DROOGER, 1955a), that the individuals of *M.globulina* from more turbulent water had developed much stronger pillars than the contemporaneous specimens of the same species in quieter water. Strengthening of the test against abrasion is evidently the main function of pillars, and in that connection their size in particular, greatly depended on external influences.

Not much is known about the canals of the Miogypsinidae. The rotaliid spiral system and the connecting intraseptal spaces are most distinct in early *Miogypsinoides*. No doubt there is a general tendency for these systems to become narrow and obscure in younger species. In between the later chambers of the individuals, the intraseptal spaces seem to become narrowed down to canals near the side walls. Nevertheless, there appear to be considerable deviations from the general trend.

Interesting observations were made on the fairly highly developed *Miogypsinoides* individuals, of the level of nepionic development of *M.bantamensis-dehaarti*, from Abesse, southwestern France. They show very wide intraseptal spaces, which possibly indicate vigorous streaming of protoplasm. This idea would be corroborated by the fact that the surface ornamentation shows feather-like structures along the sutures, of the same type as known from other groups of the Rotaliidea. In the nearby locality Estoti the same external type was encountered, but there it intergrades with a more normal pustulate type. Possibly we again have to do with some response to environment.

THE TEST

The external features of the Miogypsinidae cannot be expected to show much indication of evolutionary trends.

Increase in absolute size during evolution holds good in only a very vague sense. Environmental and posthumous geological factors seriously hamper research in this direction. In the case of several samples, the size of the test was shown not to be correlated with the main nepionic features (DROOGER, 1952).

In southwestern France relative thickness was found to be highly dependent on outside influences (DROOGER et al., 1955a). Specimens from turbulent water, which had evidently been rolled about during life, appeared to have developed, in addition to stouter pillars, relatively much thicker tests than individuals of the same species from quieter water. The two groups could be shown to be approximately identical in their main internal features. Mixtures of both external types in a single sample occur frequently, often with intermediates that are less abundant. Such mixtures may lead to the false assumption that two different species are present, whereas sedimentary phenomena may easily account for the mixture. The different types are not necessarily of the same age; the rolled and transported specimens may be somewhat older (see also MOHAN, 1958). If there is no considerable difference in age, internal morphological differences between the two groups will be difficult to detect.

Nevertheless, relative thickness of the test may partly be genetically fixed. For instance, representatives of the *M.globulina* group of northern Italy (DROOGER, 1954a, 1959b), were found to be thicker on the average than their counterparts with corresponding diameter in the Aquitaine basin (DROOGER, 1955a), though the ranges of variation show a wide overlap.

It might be imagined that the shape of the test in lateral view changed in the course of evolution. Actually the original fan shape became more circular, owing to growth along a greater sector of the circumference, in some of the groups with centripetal shift of the early stages (*Miolepidocyclina* and *Heterosteginoides*). However, in other groups with this trend the shape of the test did not notably change. On the other hand, we find that at all levels of the *Miogypsina* s. str. series fan-shaped and more circular forms dominate the samples, seemingly without following a general rule. In younger *Miogypsina* species the incomplete encircling of the embryonic stage is frequently expressed in the populations by specimens which are strongly pointed at their initial ends. Another frequently observed tendency in younger species, to develop an indented or undulated frontal margin, may be seen as a trend towards attainment of a longer active front for the protoplasm.

THE MICROSPHERIC GENERATION

Generally microspheric specimens are relatively scarce in the samples; in many they were not found at all.

In the younger species the microspheric individuals are usually characterized by greater size. Proportional differences in the relative numbers of microspheric individuals may therefore have been influenced by sorting phenomena.

It is worth mentioning that the relative amount seems to be greatest in some populations of the Oligocene *Miogypsinoides* group. For instance, in sample A 75 from Escornebéou, southwestern France, about half the number of sectioned individuals of *M.complanata* appeared to be microspheric. This high relative frequency cannot be accidental. Another remarkable fact about this sample is that the microspheric and macrospheric specimens do not differ notably in size of the test.

From this insufficient number of data it is impossible to decide whether the suggested decrease in relative proportion of the microspheric specimens and a differentiation in size have to be regarded as evolutionary trends among the Miogypsinidae. Again, local environmental factors may also have had some influence.

As far as is known the nepionic part of the test is always single-spiralled. Our relatively few data (Fig. 23) on the length of this spiral suggest that nepionic acceleration
is also valid for the representatives of the microspheric generation. Whether the wide
scatter in the diagram is of any significance cannot yet be decided.

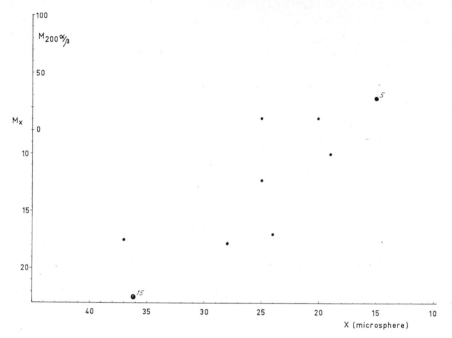

Fig. 23. Scattered data on the relation between the total number of spiral chambers in microspheric
individuals and the M_X or M_{200} α/β values of the accompanying macrospheres. Mean values of X
(microsphere) are accompanied by the number of specimens on which these means were based. The
other data refer to single observations.

COMBINATIONS OF TRENDS

On reviewing the many trends enumerated it is obvious that there are considerable
differences in rigour, as well as in the degree by which their effect may be masked by
external influences. Other factors in their evaluation are the accuracy and bias of the
observations and, to a minor extent, the possibility of expressing them in exact terms.

Many of the correlations and combinations of features have been discussed in the
preceding chapters. Some of the trends are clearly interdependent; others are so in a
more general way.

On examination of all available features, some difference in regression or combination can easily be found between nearly any two samples. Hence, it would be easy to
prove that any two samples were not fully identical. This commonplace is worth
remembering in considering the differences observed.

The practical point in such considerations is that of classification and nomenclature. Overburdening of systematics by numerous specific names in order to express all kinds of minor morphological differences certainly is a danger that would hinder treatment of the group.

The theoretical point is that we must guess at much of the genetic background. The adaptive character of the major changes caused parallel developments which, in our relatively simple organisms, make it very difficult to decide on genetic connections or isolation when we find morphologically very similar stocks at great distances from one another, such as, for instance, those of the three major regions treated here.

Certain side lines can be traced by special combinations of morphological features. Their genetic isolation from the main group can easily be proved (*Miolepidocyclina*, *Heterosteginoides*) because the species have been found together with members of this main lineage, without any intergradation being present in the samples. The same is true for some species of the *Lepidosemicyclina* group (*M.excentrica, M.droogeri*), but for other populations hybridization with *Miogypsina* s.str. may have taken place.

Much more difficult are the relations within the main lineage, the *Miogypsinoides–Miogypsina* series, with its world-wide distribution.

It is apparent that the data in our scatter diagrams are insufficient to justify the conclusion that we are dealing with parallel evolution of genetically isolated stocks in the three major regions of the world. The opposite cannot be proved either. There is always considerable overlap in the feature combinations of the samples from different regions. Moreover, the scatter is generally as wide for the samples of one area, in the case of which there is less doubt about the relationships, as it is for all the data together.

Some deviations are indicated, such as, for instance those of the few data in the combinations of M_X with M_Y, M_Z and $M\gamma$, which suggest that the group of spiralled miogypsinids from America could partly be somewhat different from the mass of European equivalents. These points refer to *M.bermudezi* and *M.thalmanni*, which had already been separated for other reasons. Fig. 15 clearly suggests that the American miogypsinids have, on the average, smaller protoconches than their Mediterranean counterparts.

Such differences cannot be due to environment alone. Genetic differences probably existed, but it must be considered likely that they were also present within each of the major regions, between population groups of its various smaller areas.

The differences observed in respect of the main stock can, in our opinion, be well explained by restricted genetic connections throughout time between imperfectly isolated population groups. As will be argued below, the degree of genetic exchange would certainly not have been constant all the time. Short-time isolations of local groups did occur to judge from the various side lines.

A related problem is that of the origin of the family, either polyphyletic or monophyletic. A polyphyletic origin at about the same moment at widely separated places on the globe is only feasible if we grant to some *Rotalia* ancestor, with probably the same restrictions inherent in a benthonic, shallow-water life, means of world-wide dispersal which were denied to the miogypsinids. Such a hypothesis only amounts to a shifting of the difficulties; it does not solve them.

We prefer to assume a monophyletic origin, and not only for theoretical reasons. It has been frequently noticed that primitive *Miogypsinoides (M.complanata)* is often accompanied by *Rotalia* specimens with very similar ornamentation which could easily be mistaken for juvenile miogypsinids (DROOGER, 1954a, 1959a). This association is very common in the Mediterranean area, and we believe it to occur in the western Pacific region as well (COLE, 1954, *M.grandipustula* p.p.).

In order to check the relationships, we analyzed a sample from southwestern France, containing both types (Fig. 24). The four clusters in the diagram show the presence

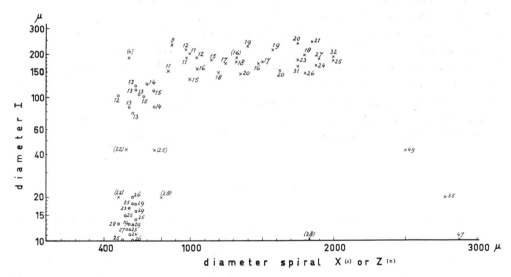

Fig. 24. Scatter diagram of the relation between the diameter of the protoconch (logarithmic) and the diameter of the spiral in specimens of *Miogypsina complanata* (o) and *Rotalia* sp. (x), both from sample A 75, Escornebéou, southwestern France. For the *Rotalia* individuals, the complete spiral (X) has been taken into account; for the *Miogypsina* specimens, the spiral up to the biggest chamber (Z). These numbers have been entered in italics for each specimen. Numbers between brackets for some of the *Rotalia* individuals refer to measurements in earlier parts of more complete specimens entered farther to the right side of the diagram.

of two distinct species, each represented by micro- and macrospheric individuals. Although juvenile stages, especially of microspheric specimens, are fairly close in both species, the later development of a rapidly disappearing main spiral together with formation of a considerable number of equatorial chambers in the miogypsinids, and the continuous growth of the spiral without such development in the rotaliids, distinguish both species. If these species were akin, the relationship would already be very remote. The few measurable data obtainable from COLE's photos from the western Pacific (Bikini, 1954; Eniwetok, 1957a) suggest a similar, possibly closer, relationship.

These observations certainly do not support the assumption of a polyphyletic origin of the family. A monophyletic rise, with a subsequent rapid distribution of the early species *M.complanata* all over the world, is thought to be more likely.

In the later development we see considerable diversity. Several side lines formed, but the main stock probably kept in contact all over the world. It is remarkable that *M.globulina* afterwards became the most widespread of all the species, often appearing at the base of local transgressive sequences. Connections of transgressive character possibly enabled this species to restore much of the partly lost genetic homogeneity. In the evolution of the last Miogypsinidae, some regional variation reappeared.

This theory, that the representatives of the main lineage belonged to a single genetic stock throughout and everywhere, cannot be proved, but it is certainly not contradicted by our present data. In consequence it is considered inadvisable to give too much weight on the taxonomic level to most of the differences of correlation and regression observed until now. UJIIÉ and OSHIMA's idea of evolutionary lines (1960), forwarded as a linear relation between three parameters, though like the triangular diagram (DROOGER, 1955a), useful for the purpose of visualizing close relationships, is also of doubtful value in disentangling evolution patterns. One objection to it is that such lines would be difficult to compare, for instance because of the equal statistical treatment of at least three characters of different evolutionary and taxonomic value.

CLASSIFICATION

It will be understood that the basis of our specific classification is to be found in the former populations, as reflected by the samples. Hence, each sample is thought to contain individuals of a single homogeneous population, unless discontinuities can be found in the distribution patterns of the measured characters, at least in those which best show the evolutionary trends.

In practice the features relating to arrangement of the nepionic stage have appeared to be most reliable, showing the adaptive trends most clearly, while they were evidently hardly, if at all, influenced by external factors. In order to distinguish various lineages or separate groups of subgeneric rank, use has been made of the absence (*Miogypsinoides*) or presence (*Miogypsina*) of systems of lateral chambers in the main group with the early stages in peripheral position, and furthermore of the centripetal trends of the initial stages (*Miolepidocyclina, Heterosteginoides, Miogypsinita, Conomiogypsinoides*?) and the predominantly hexagonal shape of the equatorial chambers (*Lepidosemicyclina*).

Mixtures of specimens from different populations through sedimentary phenomena are fairly common. If they involve individuals of considerably different time levels, this readily appears from the distribution patterns of the internal features. If the age differences are not so great, the sample may often appear homogeneous, and there will be but a slight chance of splitting it in a reliable way. Another type of association may be caused by mixtures of individuals from somewhat different habitats, mostly from shallow and deeper environments. This is generally not reflected in the main internal features, but it may be found in the external characteristics that had been influenced by the surroundings. This differentation may go so far that two external types occur without clear intergradation.

Splitting of samples into closely similar species on the basis of insufficiently stated differences in features of low taxonomic rank, such as external characters of the test, are still common in the recent literature (see for instance, KÜPPER, 1960). Many difficulties seem to exist in accepting a population as homogeneous if it exhibits incipient development of a second principal auxiliary chamber, occurring only in part of the individuals. An example of this, acknowledged as such by the authors, is given by UJIIÉ and OSHIMA (1960).

Other classifications of typological character do exist. HANZAWA's (1957) pronounced splitting of *Miogypsinoides* into species, based on the ordinal number of the nepionic chamber at the apex of the test (a feature correlated with our γ), completely disregards the existing variation in every sample. COLE's most recent classification (COLE, 1957b) of the American Miogypsinidae is also typological. Although this author recognizes only five fairly wide species, they are based on types, since he does not hesitate to split populations at the borderlines of his species.

REGIONAL PATTERNS

Outlines of the evolutionary series in the three major regions cannot be other than tentative (Fig. 25), since new data coming to the fore make it constantly necessary to modify previous ideas.

Mediterranean region

The entire sequence of *Miogypsinoides* and *Miogypsina* species is known from this area and more than one point of transition exists between the two subgenera. Only the final member of the lineage shows a deviating character in a slight centripetal trend and a very high M_γ value (*M.mediterranea*). The most important offshoot is the *Miolepidocyclina* lineage, which originated in northern Italy. Before extinction, one of its members, *M.burdigalensis*, spread over at least the western part of the Mediterranean area, where it is known to occur in the Aquitaine basin, Morocco and Cameroon. An early side branch is that of *M.septentrionalis*, in Central Europe, which shows very early development of lateral chambers.

The presence of *Miogypsina* species in typical deposits of Chattian, Aquitanian and Burdigalian age is of great importance for stratigraphic correlations. The wide distribution of the early Burdigalian species, *M.globulina* and *M.burdigalensis*, as far south as Cameroon and on the other side of Africa down to Portuguese East Africa, is probably due to a fairly general transgressive phase. The reported coexistencies of one of these species with *Miogypsinoides* of about the degree of development of *M.bantamensis* in Egypt (SOUAYA, 1961) and in Cameroon (KÜPPER, 1960) may be due to mixtu-

res with extra-Mediterranean stocks of this subgenus with slower nepionic acceleration.

Another remarkable feature of the distribution of the younger species is that
practically everywhere in Europe the main lineage stops with *M.intermedia* — southwestern France, northern Italy, Austria (PAPP, 1960)—whereas the younger species have
been found only further south, mainly in North Africa. Whether this was due to an
unfavourable climatic influence can only be suggested.

America

In the Western hemisphere, the entire series of species of the main lineage is also represented, from *M.complatana* up to *M.antillea*. Whether the Miogypsinidae originated
in America, as has long been suggested (DROOGER, 1951), is again an undecided question.
The position of *M.bermudezi* is not clear. Apart from its very thin sidewalls it seems to
have somewhat deviating features in its spiral part, such as the high Y and Z values as
compared to the corresponding X values. The position of the species, as given in Fig.
25, is entirely hypothetical. Better stratigraphic information on the early species may
solve this problem.

The change from *Miogypsinoides* to *Miogypsina* took place at a very early level of
nepionic development (*M.thalmanni*). The main older side line is that of *M.pana-
mensis* and *M.ecuadorensis*, the occurrences of which are mainly found along the west
coast. The younger Miogypsinidae show several offshoots with some centripetal tendency. They may be partly related. It is not known whether they achieved genetic
isolation from the main group.

Indo-Pacific region

Since the papers of TAN SIN HOK, not very much has been added to our knowledge,
as authors on this region generally advocate a typological approach in their descriptions, which seriously hampers estimation of the populations.

M.complatana occurs in the area and it was followed by a very long suite of *Miogypsinoides* species. The end, with *M.dehaarti* and its conical variants, was probably contemporaneous in places with early *Miogypsina*, which started at about the level of
M.tani. From about *M.globulina*, which is again widespread, from Portuguese East
Africa and India to Japan and New Zealand, arose the remarkable group of *Lepidosemicyclina*; the complicated relationships between its members still remain to be
disentangled. This side line(s) probably soon became extinct, while the main line continued up to the level of *M.antillea*. Whether and how much hybridization took place
between local stocks of both groups is still obscure. It seems reasonable to assume
that it did occur, bearing in mind the fact that many of the younger *Miogypsina* s.str.
populations of this region show tendencies towards formation of somewhat hexagonal
chambers, more strongly so than the corresponding forms or America and the Mediterranean area. Some of the *Lepidosemicyclina* species did, however, attain genetic
isolation.

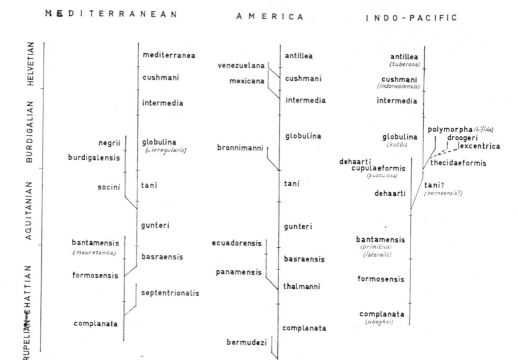

Fig. 25. Tentative relationships of the *Miogypsina* species in the three main regions investigated. In the case of the Mediterranean the chronostratigraphic scale has been placed alongside. Some names frequently used in the literature have been added in italics.

RATE OF NEPIONIC ACCELERATION

One important problem remains to be discussed. From a theoretical point of view, but also because of the stratigraphic correlation possibilities, it would be interesting to know more about the speed of the main evolutionary factor, the nepionic acceleration. This acceleration is considered to be the most rigorous trend, but it has a general, adaptive character. Therefore it is quite imaginable that its speed is not the same in, for instance, remote population groups of the main *Miogypsina* lineage.

Regarding the side lines, information can be obtained if we take this main *Miogypsina* lineage as a basis of reference (Fig. 20). Against this background we see that nepionic acceleration was relatively faster in the *Miolepidocyclina* line of northern Italy, where its last species (*M.negrii*) is much more highly developed in this respect than the *M.globulina* populations, which replaced it in higher levels of the same stratigraphic section.

As regards the American *Heterosteginoides* lineage, the situation is less distinct. The development of the second principal auxiliary chamber and its spirals in *M.ecuadorensis* of Peru (DROOGER, 1953a) is hardly higher than it is in the accompanying *M. gunteri* of the main line. The great length of the primary spiral of *M. ecuadorensis* may be considered of less importance here because of the special position it occupies in the median layer.

For the species of the *Lepidosemicyclina* group a relatively more rapid nepionic acceleration may also hold good, if it is noted that *M.excentrica* of Madura (TAN SIN HOK, 1937b) and *M.droogeri* of India (MOHAN, 1958) have been reported together with species of a distinctly lower degree of nepionic development, *i.e.*, of the level of *M.globulina*. The relative lengthening of the equatorial chambers in this group is evidently a less rigorous trend. The maximum is attained already in *M.polymorpha* and *M.bifida*, at a fairly low level of nepionic development, whereas *M.excentrica* and *M.droogeri*, of higher nepionic development, are less advanced as regards the lengthening of the equatorial chambers.

Less distinct is the frequently reported coexistence of representatives of *Miogypsinoides* and *Miogypsina* s.str. (or *Miolepidocyclina*), which would imply some kind of relative nepionic retardation in the former group. Some could be shown as probably due to reworking (DROOGER, 1954b), others to misidentifications. Recently, two more examples were published: from Cameroon (KÜPPER, 1960) and from Egypt (SOUAYA, 1961). The geological-stratigraphic background of these occurrences is not fully clear, and hence reworking phenomena cannot be completely excluded. However, it must be considered quite likely that local stocks of *Miogypsinoides* evolved more slowly than elsewhere, and became genetically distinct before mixing again with more highly developed populations of the main or side lines. The often recorded coexistence of *M.dehaarti* and *M.globulina* or (and) *M.thecidaeformis* in the western Pacific area is another example of this kind.

These data clearly show that nepionic acceleration was or could be different in the side lines or in local tribes of the main lineage. It is much more difficult to prove that it was constant or variable in our reference series, the general, main *Miogypsina* lineage. Here we should need circumstantial evidence from unrelated groups, and unfortunately no other contemporaneous groups which show equally fast and well-known developments have yet been investigated.

At the moment it looks likely that the "*Nephrolepidina*" lineage of the Lepidocyclinidae evolved more slowly in its measurable characters than the Miogypsinidae did. In the European–Mediterranean region *Lepidocyclina morgani* has thus far invariably been found together with representatives of the *Miogypsinoides* group. The more highly developed *L.tournoueri* occurs in northern Italy together with the younger *M.globulina*. If we now consider the representatives of *Nephrolepidina* to belong to one group with the same adaptive trend all over the world (which is still open to doubt, see VAN DER VLERK, 1959), it is worth while to draw attention to some scattered data. In Borneo, *M.thecidaeformis*, comparable to *M.globulina* in nepionic development, was found together with representatives of *Nephrolepidina*, which were not identical with *L.tournoueri*, but were approximately of the same level of embryonic–nepionic development. In New Zealand an ill-preserved *M.tani* sample is accompanied by Nephrolepidinae intermediate between *L.morgani* and *L.tournoueri*, which would fit in perfectly with European standards.

These cross checks constitute no more than a very modest beginning, but they may indicate that the nepionic acceleration in the main *Miogypsina* stock did not show very wide divergencies when seen in the context of worldwide distribution.

This would also follow from the Middle Miocene datum plane provided by the rise of the planktonic genus *Orbulina*. In the Mediterranean area, in America and in the western Pacific region, all our verified data point to the appearance of *Orbulina*, after the extinction of the last Miogypsinidae, but the lapse of time in between does not seem very great. However, strong deviations from this have been reported in the literature. For instance, GORDON (1959, 1961) reports *M. complanata* as ranging well above the *Orbulina* limit in Puerto Rico. If this is true interest in the Miogypsinidae for worldwide stratigraphic correlations would decline immediately.

All this does not imply that a rigidly constant rate of nepionic development in the main group existed all over the world, but no serious discrepancies have appeared as yet. This in turn favours the idea of continuous genetic connections. Widening the field of possibilities for cross checks on the evolutionary series will be one of the most interesting tasks of the near future, from both the paleontological and stratigraphical points of view.

SUMMARY

Variation in the interplay of genetic and environmental factors is thought to have caused the complex pattern of evolutionary trends in the Miogypsinidae. In order to ascertain these trends and the nature of their controls, it is necessary to start by examining death assemblages with factual stratigraphic interrelation.

It then appears that nearly all morphological characteristics changed in the course of time. In the case of some of these characteristics, especially those of the nepionic configuration, the trends appear to be well correlated with time; they were probably adaptive in a general way *with but* minor influences from environmental differentiation. Other characteristics, such as those based on the absolute size of certain features, appear to be less rigorous, evidently depending to a considerable degree on haphazard influences.

Analysis of the characteristics and of their interrelations brings out their respective values for disentangling the evolutionary history of the group.

REFERENCES

AKERS, W. H. and DROOGER, C. W., 1957. Miogypsinids, planktonic Foraminifera, and Gulf Coast Oligocene-Miocene correlations. *Bull. Am. Ass. Petr. Geologists*, 41: 656–678.

BRÖNNIMANN, P., 1940. Über die tertiären Orbitoididen und die Miogypsiniden von Nordwest-Marokko. *Schweiz. Paleontol. Abhandl.*, 63 : 1–113.

COLE, W. S., 1954. Larger Foraminifera and smaller diagnostic Foraminifera from Bikini drill holes. *U.S. Geol. Surv, Profess. Papers*, 260–O : 569–608.

COLE, W. S., 1957a. Larger Foraminifera from Eniwetok Atoll drill holes. *U.S. Geol. Survey, Prof. Paper*, 260–V : 743–784.

COLE, W. S., 1957b. Late Oligocene larger Foraminifera from Barro Colorado Island, Panama Canal Zone. *Bull. Am. Paleontol.*, 37 (163) : 313–339.

COSIJN, A. J., 1942. On the phylogeny of the embryonic apparatus of some Foraminifera. *Leidsche Geol. Mededel.*, 13 : 140–171.

DROOGER, C. W., 1951. Notes on some representatives of *Miogypsinella. Proc. Koninkl. Ned. Akad. Wetenschap., Ser. B*, 54 : 357–365.

DROOGER, C. W., 1952. *Study of American Miogypsinidae.* Thesis, Univ. of Utrecht, 80 pp.

DROOGER, C. W., 1953a. Two species of *Miogypsina* from Southern Perú. *Boll. Spc. Geol. Perú*, 26 : 9–16.

DROOGER, C. W., 1953b. Some Indonesian Miogypsinae. *Proc. Koninkl. Ned. Akad. Wetenschap., Ser. B*, 56 : 104–123.

DROOGER, C. W., 1954a. *Miogypsina* in Northern Italy. *Proc. Koninkl. Ned. Akad. Wetenschap., Ser. B*, 57 : 227–249.

DROOGER, C. W., 1954b. *Miogypsina* in Northwestern Morocco. *Proc. Koninkl. Ned. Akad. Wetenschap., Ser. B*, 57 : 580–591.

DROOGER, C. W., KAASSCHIETER, J. P. H. and KEY, A. J., 1955a. The microfauna of the Aquitanian–Burdigalian of Southwestern France. *Verhandel. Koninkl. Ned. Akad. Wetenschap., afdel. Nat., Ser.* 1, 21 (2) : 5–108.

DROOGER, C. W., 1955b. Remarks on *Cycloclypeus. Proc. Koninkl. Ned. Akad. Wetenschap., Ser. B*, 58 : 415–433.

DROOGER, C. W., 1956a. *Miogypsina* at Puente Viejo, Spain. *Proc. Koninkl. Ned. Akad. Wetenschap., Ser. B*, 59 : 68–72.

DROOGER, C. W., 1956b. Parallel evolutionary trends in larger Foraminifera. *Proc. Koninkl. Ned. Akad. Wetenschap., Ser. B*, 59 : 458–469.

DROOGER, C. W. and MAGNÉ, J., 1959a. Miogypsinids and planktonic Foraminifera of the Algerian Oligocene and Miocene. *Micropaleontol.*, 5 : 273–284.

DROOGER, C. W. and SOCIN, C., 1959b. Miocene Foraminifera from Rosignano, Northern Italy. *Micropaleontol.*, 5 : 415–426.

DROOGER, C. W., 1960. *Miogypsina* in Northwestern Germany. *Proc. Koninkl. Ned. Akad. Wetenschap., Ser. B*, 63 : 38–50.

DROOGER, C. W., 1961. *Miogypsina* in Hungary. *Proc. Koninkl. Ned. Akad. Wetenschap., Ser. B*, 64 : 417–427.

GORDON, W. A., 1959. The age of the Middle Tertiary rocks of Northwestern Puerto Rico. *Trans. Sec. Caribbean Geol. Conf.*, pp. 87–90.

GORDON, W. A., 1961. Foraminifera from the 4CPR oil test well near Arecibo, Puerto Rico. *Publ. Puerto Rico Mining Comm.*, pp. 25–40.

GRIMSDALE, T. F., 1959. Evolution in the American Lepidocyclinidae (Cainozoic Foraminifera): an interim review. *Proc. Koninkl. Ned. Akad. Wetenschap., Ser. B.*, 62 : 8–33.

HANZAWA, S., 1940. Micropaleontological studies of drill cores from a deep well in Kita-Daito-Zima (North Borodino Island). *Jub. Publ. Yabe's 60th birthday.*, pp. 755–802.

HANZAWA, S., 1957. Cenozoic Foraminifera of Micronesia. *Geol. Soc. Am., Mem.* 66 : 1–163.

KÜPPER, I., 1960. Miogypsinen aus Britisch West-Afrika (Cameroon). *Sci. Rep. Tohoku Univ., Ser.* 2, *Hanzawa Mem. Vol.*, pp. 56–69.

MOHAN, K., 1958. Miogypsinidae from Western India. *Micropaleontol.*, 4 : 373–390.

PAPP, A., 1960. Das Vorkommen von *Miogypsina* in Mitteleuropa und dessen Bedeutung für die Tertiärstratigraphie. *Mitt. geol. Ges. Wien*, 51 : 219–228.

SOUAYA, F. J., 1961. Contribution to the study of *Miogypsina* s.l. from Egypt. *Proc. Koninkl. Ned. Akad. Wetenschap., Ser. B*, 64 : 665–705.

TAN SIN HOK, 1936. Zur Kenntnis der Miogypsiniden. *De Ingr. in Ned. Indiè*, 3 (IV) 45–61, 84–98, 109–123.

TAN SIN HOK, 1937a. Note on *Miogypsina kotôi* HANZAWA. *De Ingr. in Ned. Indië*, 4 (IV) : 31–32.

TAN SIN HOK, 1937b. Weitere Untersuchungen über die Miogypsiniden. *De Ingr. in Ned. Indië*, 4 (IV) : 35–45, 87–111.

UJIIÉ, H. and OSHIMA, K., 1960. Statistical characters of two *Miogypsina* assemblages from the Mizunami district, Gifu Prefecture. *Sci. Repts. Tokyo Univ. Educ.*, 7 : 105–116.

VAN DER VLERK, I. M., 1924. *Miogypsina dehaartii* nov. spec. de Larat (Moluques). *Eclogae Geol. Helv.*, 18 : 429–432.

VAN DER VLERK, I. M., 1959a. Problems and principles of Tertiary and Quaternary stratigraphy. *Quart. Geol. Soc. London*, 115 : 49–64.

VAN DER VLERK, I. M., 1959b. Modification de l'ontogénèse pendant l'évolution des Lépidocyclines (Foraminifères). *Bull. Soc. géol. France*, 7e sér., 1 : 669–673.

ÜBER DIE ENTWICKLUNG VON HETEROSTEGINEN

A. PAPP

Paläontologisches Institut der Universität Wien, Wien (Österreich)

Bei jedem Versuch, die Entwicklung einer Gruppe von Organismen zu schildern, ist eine Kenntnis der phylogenetisch wichtigen Merkmale erforderlich. Die Auswertung von morphologisch–genetischen Erkenntnissen in der Geochronologie setzt die richtige Reihung der einzelnen Formtypen zueinander voraus. Bei allen Gattungen, die eine monophyletische Entwicklung haben, ist die Beurteilung relativ leicht, sobald der phylogenetische Wert der Merkmale erkannt ist. Bei den Heterosteginen steht die polyphyletische Entwicklung ausser Frage. Es können daher nur sehr eingehende taxonomische Studien die Voraussetzungen für morphologisch–genetische Gruppierungen sein. Bei dem heutigen Stand der Materialkenntnis kann aber nur in wenigen Fällen die Entwicklung einer Linie vollständig belegt werden. Hier liegt noch ein weites Feld der Erkenntnis vor uns.

Die ältesten Heterosteginen sind aus dem Eozän beschrieben. Es handelt sich um Typen, die bereits ein vollentwickeltes System von Sekundärsepten zeigen. Als Beispiel möge *H. helvetica* KAUFMANN aus dem obereozänen Flysch vom Käsboden (Schrattenfluh-Gebiet) angeführt werden, ebenso Heterosteginen aus dem Eozän von Kuba (vgl. Fig. 1a).

Schon im Eozän lassen sich zwei Gehäuseformen auseinanderlegen:
(*1*) Involutiforme Heterosteginen. Gehäuse mit Kalkanlagerungen im Zentrum bzw. in der Umbonalregion. Sie zeigen ein hochentwickeltes System von Sekundärsepten, wobei die Hauptsepten starke Knickungen zeigen können. Derartige Typen sind vom Eozän bis in die Gegenwart bekannt, wobei wir heute annehmen, dass es sich um einen im Eozän entstandenen und bis in die Gegenwart persistierenden Stamm handeln dürfte.

Involutiforme Heterosteginen sind zweifellos die Stammformen der eozänen Vertreter der Gattung *Spiroclypeus* DOUVILLÉ 1905. Aus dem Ober Eozän der Jakobo Formation (Kuba) liegt ein Material vor, wo die juvenilen Gehäuse, wie erwähnt, den Septenbau voll entwickelter Heterosteginen zeigen (Fig. 1a). Im weiteren Wachstum werden auch im zentralen Schalenteil Kalkschichten angelagert, das Gehäuse ist weitgehend involut, zeigt aber keine typischen Lateralkammern wie *Spiroclypeus* (Fig. 1c).

Bei *Spiroclypeus* ist eine starke Biegung der Primärsepten charakteristisch (Fig. 1d). Einen Anklang an die Septenform von *Spiroclypeus* findet man in den äusseren Umgängen der genannten Heterosteginen aus Kuba deutlich ausgeprägt. Jedenfalls

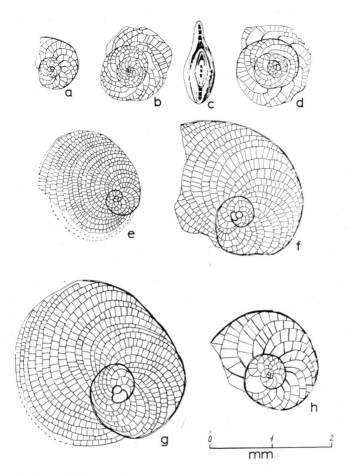

Fig. 1. Medianschnitte von Heterosteginen.

a. *Heterostegina* sp. juveniles Gehäuse einer involutiformen *Heterostegina* mit voll entwickelten Sekundärsepten. Jakobo Formation, Pinar del Rio (Kuba), Ober Eozän.

b. *Heterostegina* aus dem gleichen Vorkommen wie a, mit dem Septenbau von *Spiroclypeus*.

c. wie b, senkrechter Schnitt. Das Gehäuse ist stark involut, zeigt aber keine typischen Lateralkammern.

d. *Spiroclypeus* sp. Ofener Mergel (Ungarn).

e. *Heterostegina praecursor* TAN SIN HOK. Tjimangoe 8. Unter Oligozän (Material aus dem Nachlass von TAN SIN HOK).

f. *Heterostegina* cf. *praecursor* TAN SIN HOK. Ramleh, Palestina M/4313, Unter Oligozän.

g. *Heterostegina* sp. in der Gehäuseform und der Anlage der Septen der *H. praecursor* sehr ähnlich. Kuba, Oriente Prov. Rio Centra maestre, Unter Oligozän.

h. *Heterostegina granulatatesta granulatatesta* PAPP und KÜPPER, Rauchstallbrunngraben, Badener Serie, Wiener Becken, obere Lagenidenzone.

können derartige Vormen zwanglos als Vorformen von *Spiroclypeus* gelten (vgl. Fig. 1b und c).

(2) Planspirale Heterosteginen. Die Gehäuse dieser Gruppe sind im senkrechten Schnitt sehr schmal und zeigen keine lateralen Kalkanlagerungen. Sie sind im Eozän sicher schon vertreten. Auf derartige Formen geht die von TAN SIN HOK (1932)

beschriebene *H. praecursor* zurück (Fig. 1e), bei welcher die Primärsepten schon sehr stark übergreifen. Sie stellen gleichzeitig ein Übergangsstadium zur Gattung *Cycloclypeus* CARPENTER 1856 dar und kommen, im Gegensatz zu den typischen Vertretern der Gattung *Cycloclypeus*, auch noch im Vorderen Orient vor (Fig. 1f). Diesem Niveau scheint im Indo-Malayischen Bereich auch stratigraphische Bedeutung zu zukommen.

Es ist darüber hinaus bemerkenswert, dass im Oligozän von Kuba (Oriente Prov. Rio Contra maestre bei Rancho Bacardi) Heterosteginen vorkommen, die gewisse Anklänge an *H. praecursor* zeigen. Es muss offen bleiben, ob es sich hier um blosse Konvergenzen oder um einen genetischen Zusammenhang handelt (vgl. Fig. 1g).

Die Entwicklungsreihe der *Heterostegina granulatatesta* ist im Neogen Europas relativ gut belegt. Als älteste bisher bekannte Art kann *Heterostegina granulatatesta praeformis* aus Orthez (südwest Frankreich), wahrscheinlich helvetischen Alters, gewertet werden.

Zweifellos jünger ist *Heterostegina granulatatesta granulatatesta* aus der Badener Serie des Wiener Beckens (Fig. 1h).

Die bisher am besten belegte Entwicklungsreihe innerhalb der Heterosteginen ist die Artengruppe der *H. costata–complanata*. Hier kann auch die Beziehung zu der Stammgruppe *Operculina* belegt werden. Es ist bemerkenswert, dass in zahlreichen Fundorten (z. B. St. Paul bei Dax, Vielle bei Dax, Gaillat u.s.w.) *Operculina complanata*, oft in grossen Exemplaren, auftritt (Fig. 2a). In jenen Fundorten, die durch das Vorkommen von *Miogypsina globulina* (= *M. irregularis*) und *M. intermedia* kontrolliert werden konnten, tritt *Heterostegina heterostegina* auf, eine Art, welche an den Primärsepten sehr kurze orimentäre Sekundärsepten zeigt (Fig. 2b). Typische Vertreter von *Operculina complanata* fehlen. Wir sehen darin ein chronologisches Element, welches für die Ablagerungen des Burdigaliums im Mittelmeer-Gebiet bedeutungsvoll ist.

In den Profilen der Colli Torinesi an der Strasse Superga-Baldissero wurden durch DROOGER (1954) von Croce Berton *Miogypsina globulina* bzw. *M. globulina–intermedia* angeführt. Die Heterosteginen zeigen den gleichen Habitus wie jene aus Saucats (Fig. 2c), womit das durch Miogypsinen bewiesene burdigale Alter unterstrichen wird. Croce Berton wird im italienischen Schrifttum als "Elveziano" geführt, und somit auch der locus typicus von *Heterostegina heterostegina*.

Aus dem Schichtenbereich zwischen dem Burdigalium und der Badener Serie im Wiener Becken liegt dem Verfasser leider kein Material von der Artengruppe der *H. costata–complanata* vor. Erst aus der Badener Serie im Wiener Becken (Österreich) ist reiches Material bekannt. Die ältesten Formen stammen hier aus der unteren Lagenidenzone und zeigen eine merklich höhere Entwicklung der Sekundärsepten als bei *H. heterostegina* aus dem Burdigal (Fig. 2d). Wir trennten diese Formen von der typischen *H. heterostegina* aus Croce Berton als *H. heterostegina praecostata* ab. Es folgen in der oberen Lagenidenzone Formen der *H. costata costata* (Fig. 2e) und schliesslich die am höchsten entwickelten Formen der *H. costata politatesta* in der Buliminen – Bolivinen Zone (vgl. Fig. 2f).

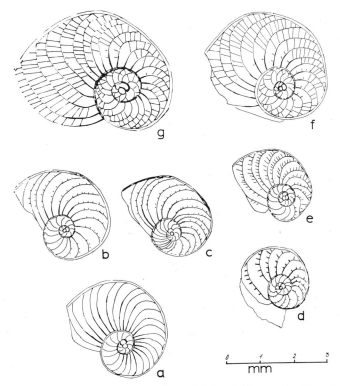

Fig. 2. Medianschnitte von neogenen Heterosteginen der Entwicklungsreihe *H. costata–complanata*.

a. *Operculina complanata* (DEFRANCE). St. Paul de Dax (südwest Frankreich)? Aquitan.

b. *Heterostegina heterostegina heterostegina* (SILVESTRI), Saucats (südwest Frankreich). Burdigal.

c. *Heterostegina heterostegina heterostegina* (SILVESTRI). Croce Berton, Colli Torrinesi (Italien). Burdigal.

d. *Heterostegina heterostegina praecostata* PAPP und KÜPPER. Niederleis, Badener Serie, Wiener Becken, untere Lagenidenzone.

e. *Heterostegina costata costata* (D'ORBIGNY). Vöslau, Badener Serie, Wiener Becken, obere Lagenidenzone.

f. *Heterostegina costata politatesta* PAPP und KÜPPER. Neudorf, Sandberg, Badener Serie, Wiener Becken, Buliminen – Bolivinen Zone.

g. *Heterostegina complanata spiralis* PAPP und KÜPPER-Chania (Kreta), oberes Miozän oder Pliozän.

Es unterliegt keinem Zweifel, dass *H. heterostegina praecostata* als marin- mediterranes Faunenelement an der Basis der Badener Serie mit anderen Faunenelementen (z.B. *Orbulina*) in den Mitteleuropäischen Raum gekommen ist. Die weitere Entwicklung kann, ähnlich anderen Faunenelementen (z.B. Uvigerinen), im mittleren Donaubecken einen gewissen Endemismus gehabt haben. Im Mittelmeerraum wird die Weiterentwicklung von *H. heterostegina* zweifellos in ähnlicher Weise erfolgt sein, nur fehlt ein entsprechendes Belegmaterial. Die Heterosteginen aus dem Formenkreis der *H. complanata* (Fig. 2g) (z.B. *H. complanata spiralis* aus dem Ober Miozän oder Unter Pliozän von Chania, Kreta) steht der Artengruppe der *H. costata* aus dem Wiener Becken nahe, nur ist die Form höher entwickelt.

Neben den genannten Gruppen bzw. Entwicklungsreihen ist jedoch in Mitteleuropa noch mit einer weiteren Reihe zu rechnen, die aber nur bruchstückweise bekannt ist. Ihr gehört eine grosse schmale *Heterostegina* vom Typus der *H. papyracea gigantea* an, deren Vorkommen auch in der Badener Serie erwähnenswert ist.

Nach der hier gegebenen Übersicht sind also mehrere Entwicklungsreihen zu unterscheiden, wobei vorerst sicher nicht allen Möglichkeiten Rechnung getragen werden konnte. Es wurde von dem Gedanken ausgegangen, dass alle Reihen auf Formen der Gattung *Operculina* zurückgehen und im Laufe ihrer Evolution die Sekundärsepten immer konsequenter ausbauen. Demnach wäre die Gattung *Heterostegina*, im heutigen Sinn, polyphyletisch.

Mit der Polyphylie einer Gruppe werden allerdings eine Fülle taxonomischer und nomenklatorischer Fragen aufgeworfen. In diesem Rahmen soll nur zu folgenden Punkten Stellung genommen werden:

(*1*) Bei der Beschreibung einer Art wurde ausser den Innenmerkmalen auch die Gehäuseform und Skulptur herangezogen (vgl. PAPP und KÜPPER, 1954), um in manchen Fällen zusätzliche Merkmale zu bekommen. So haben z.B. die Angehörigen der Artengruppe *H. granulatatesta* gegenüber *H. costata* eine charakteristische Gehäuseform und Skulptur (vgl. PAPP und KÜPPER, 1954, Tafel 22). Die unter Berücksichtigung der äusseren Merkmale angewandte trinäre Nomenklatur ist allerdings schwerfällig und kann in manchen Fällen überflüssig sein. Um hier ein allgemein gültiges Urteil bilden zu können, fehlen jedoch noch die Grundlagen.

(*2*) Für die Trennung der Genera *Heterostegina* und *Operculina* wurde das Vorhandensein von Sekundärsepten herangezogen. Demnach sollten nur jene Arten bei *Operculina* verbleiben, die keinerlei Sekundärsepten haben. Wenn dadurch auch eine unglückliche Wortkombination wie *Heterostegina heterostegina* für eine sehr primitive Art zustande kommt, so wird an dieser Definition wohl festzuhalten sein.

Die Unterscheidung verschiedener Entwicklungsreihen wird in Zukunft den Systematiker bei Auffindung von Formen mit orimentären Sekundärsepten immer wieder vor die Frage stellen, wo die Grenze zwischen *Operculina* und *Heterostegina* zu legen ist. Nach der von uns vorgeschlagenen Definition kann eine klare Trennung erfolgen.

(*3*) Mit der Erkenntnis der Polyphylie einer Gattung tritt die Frage auf, ob hier nicht jede Entwicklungsreihe den Rang einer Untergattung bzw. Gattung erhalten müsste. In dem speziellen Fall der Heterosteginen halten wir diesen Vorgang noch für verfrüht. Das bekannte Material hat noch nicht den Umfang, um hier eine sinnvolle Lösung zu gewährleisten. Immerhin ist der Versuch, einzelne Entwicklungsreihen zu erfassen, der erste Schritt zur Erstellung einer exakteren Systematik.

(*4*) Der stratigraphische Wert einzelner Entwicklungsreihen ist heute unbestritten. Heterosteginen dürften in ihrem Vorkommen stark von ökologischen Faktoren abhängen. Damit wird auch ihr sporadisches Vorkommen verständlich. Es fehlen in vielen Fällen eben die Sedimente ihres Lebensraumes, oder ihrem Vorkommen wurde nicht die entsprechende Aufmerksamkeit gewidmet. In jenen Fällen, wo entsprechendes Material vorhanden ist (z.B. im Neogen, Badener Serie des Wiener Beckens = "Torton") können auch Heterosteginen gute Dienste als Zonen-Leitfossilien leisten.

Als klassisches Beispiel möge die Gattung *Cycloclypeus* erwähnt werden, deren Evolution TAN SIN HOK (1932) an idealem Material schildern konnte.

SUMMARY

The evolution of the tertiary Heterosteginae is polyphyletic. A short sketch is given of the evolutionary lines known at present. Moreover, attention is drawn to the probable worldwide occurrence of forms belonging to the *Heterostegina praecursor* type in a certain interval of the lower Oligocene.

The evolution of *Heterostegina costata* resp. *H. complanata* might be of importance for the zonation of the Neogene in Europe.

Finally, general problems of taxonomy and nomenclature which arise in studying a polyphyletic group are discussed.

LITERATUR

DROOGER, C. W., 1954. *Miogypsina* in Northern Italy. *Proc. Koninkl. Ned. Akad. Wetenschap., Ser. B*, 57 : 227–249.

DROOGER, C. W., KAASSCHIETER, J. P. H. and KEY, A. J., 1955. The microfauna of the Aquitanian – Burdigalian of southwestern France. *Verhandel. Koninkl. Ned. Akad. Wetenschap., Ser. 1*, 21 (2) : 1–136.

PAPP, A. and KÜPPER, K., 1954. The Genus *Heterostegina* in the Upper Tertiary of Europe. *Contrib. Cushman Found. Foraminiferal Research*, 5 : 108–127.

TAN SIN HOK, 1932. On the Genus *Cycloclypeus* CARPENTER Part I and an Appendix on the Heterostegines of Tjimanggoe, S. Bantam, Java. *Wetenschap. Mededeel. Dienst Mijnbouw Ned. Indië*, 19 : 3–194.

PRINTED IN THE NETHERLANDS BY N.V. J. F. DUWAER EN ZN., AMSTERDAM